Petroleum Accounting

Principles, Procedures and Issues

8th Edition

Petroleum Accounting

Principles, Procedures and Issues

8th Edition

John Brady
Partner
PwC

Dennis Jennings
Retired Partner
PwC

Rich Shappard
Partner
PwC

Editor-in-Chief
Leslie Warren
Senior Manager, PwC

Publisher
Professional Development Institute
Denton, Texas

At PwC, our purpose is to build trust in society and solve important problems. PwC is a network of firms in 158 countries with over 250,000 people who are committed to delivering quality in assurance, advisory and tax services. Find out more and tell us what matters to you by visiting us at www.pwc.com/us.

Financial Accounting Standards Board (FASB) *Accounting Standards Codification®* material included in this work is copyrighted by the Financial Accounting Foundation, 401 Merritt 7, Norwalk, CT 06856, and is reproduced with permission. Complete copies of the FASB *Accounting Standards Codification®* are available from the FASB.

This publication is designed to provide accurate and authoritative information and explanation in regard to U.S. petroleum financial accounting principles and practices prior to publication. It is sold with the understanding that the publisher, Professional Development Institute (PDI), is not engaged in rendering legal, accounting, or other professional services. The book is intended to serve neither as professional advice nor conclusive guidance for a particular transaction or financial presentation. If legal, accounting, or other expert assistance is required, the services of a competent professional person should be sought.

Cover photograph by Mikeuk/iStock

International Standard Book Number: 978-0-940966-32-1

Professional Development Institute
University of North Texas
Denton, Texas 76201

Printed in the United States of America

In 1981, this publication appeared under the title *Accounting for Oil & Gas Producing Companies, Part I,* which was followed by Part 2 in 1982 under the same title.

In 1985, the publication appeared as *Petroleum Accounting: Principles, Procedures and Issues.*

In 1990, 1996, 2000, 2007 and 2011 the publication appeared as *Petroleum Accounting: Principles, Procedures, & Issues.*

About the authors

John Brady, CPA, is an Assurance Partner in PricewaterhouseCoopers' (PwC) Energy Practice based in Houston, Texas. Over the course of his career, John has served a wide variety of multinational public and private companies in the oil and gas exploration and production, petroleum refining, oilfield services and energy marketing sectors of the energy industry. He has substantial SEC reporting and technical accounting expertise specific to both independent and integrated oil and gas companies. As one of the firm's oil and gas subject-matter champions, John frequently consults with clients on transactions unique to the industry: joint ventures, production payments, accounting method conversions, business combinations, due diligence matters, capital markets transactions and financial risk management activities. John has also served as the Technical Liaison Partner for the PwC Energy Practice where he was responsible for coordinating the firm's thought leadership and knowledge sharing initiatives. His responsibilities also included monitoring current and emerging issues facing the industry; representing the firm in various industry forums; and providing industry perspective in firm interactions with the accounting and regulatory standard setters. John is a graduate of The University of Texas at Austin and holds CPA licenses in Texas and Oklahoma.

Dennis Jennings, CPA, retired from PwC after a 33 year career where he served as co-chairman of a legacy energy industry practice; assurance partner on large, public company engagements with extensive international operations; global leader of the international energy and mining industry risk management practice; member of the global risk management executive committee; and coordinator of quality control with the Japanese and Mexican firms. After retirement, Dennis was a deputy director with the PCAOB and leader of the southwest region. He was director of energy programs at PDI and director-in-residence of the Institute for Excellence in Corporate Governance at The University of Texas at Dallas (UTD). He taught graduate classes at UTD and the University of North Texas and has been a sought after consultant, author and speaker. He served as president of COPAS of Dallas, chair of the North American Petroleum Accounting Conference, the AICPA/PDI National Oil and Gas Conference, technical editor of the Petroleum Accounting and Financial Management Journal and board member of the Institute of Petroleum Accounting. He is a member of the AICPA and the Texas Society of CPAs and served on the AICPA's Sustainability Joint Task Force with the Canadian Institute of Chartered Accountants. He graduated cum laude from Texas Tech University with a BBA in accounting and was named 1997 Distinguished Accounting Alumnus.

Rich Shappard, CPA, is an Assurance Partner in PwC's Energy Practice in Houston, Texas. He has more than 34 years of experience serving a wide range of public energy companies, including upstream independents, integrated oil and gas companies and multinational drillers. Within PwC, Rich has held a number of leadership positions, including the firm's U.S. Energy Sector Assurance Leader and Greater Houston Market Assurance Leader roles. As a senior partner in the Houston Energy Practice, Rich is a leading contributor to thought leadership and knowledge sharing, and he has extensive SEC accounting and reporting experience and specialized knowledge in the areas of business combinations, income taxes and stock-based compensation. Rich is a graduate of Indiana University with a B.S. in accounting and is a licensed CPA in Texas, Colorado and Missouri. He is also a board member of Interfaith of The Woodlands.

In memorium

As this 8th edition of *Petroleum Accounting: Principles, Procedures and Issues* was in the final stages of preparation and review before publication, Author Emeritus **Dr. Horace Rhea Brock** passed away on October 26, 2019. Horace was a primary author of the first three editions of this publication and worked with Dennis R. Jennings, a now retired PwC partner and primary author and editor of this 8th edition, to transition this important industry publication to PwC beginning with the 4th edition, with a view of ensuring its continuation through future editions for energy industry professionals, academic users and others who work in and serve the energy industry.

During his academic career, Horace was a key professional in contributing to the development of standards for petroleum accounting. He was a founder and director of the University of North Texas' Institute of Petroleum Accounting and was involved with the creation of the Professional Development Institute. He was also active with numerous professional associations in various aspects of the petroleum industry.

The authors recognize his pioneering work in laying the foundation for ongoing development of petroleum accounting and are honored to have carried on what he began by offering current guidance now through this 8th edition. He will be sorely missed, but his contributions will carry on.

Preface

Petroleum Accounting focuses on U.S. financial accounting and reporting for petroleum exploration and production activities. This book describes petroleum activities as well as the numerous accounting principles, practices and procedures employed. *Petroleum Accounting* was written to serve as a college textbook and as a general reference source for petroleum accountants, financial statement auditors and other interested parties. As with any textbook or guidance, the book is neither intended to serve as professional advice nor conclusive guidance for a particular transaction or financial presentation. If legal, accounting or other expert assistance is required, the services of a competent professional should be sought.

This 8th edition is a significant update to the 7th edition text. Since the last edition in 2011, important developments have occurred in the industry and in areas of accounting including:

- The FASB's issuance of standards affecting oil and gas companies on topics such as business combinations, revenue recognition and leasing.

- Significant growth in the domestic production of unconventional oil and gas resources leading to the U.S. being a net exporter of oil and gas.

- Sustained depressed commodity prices since the downturn that started in late-2014, which has changed the landscape for the sector as a whole as it relates to merger, acquisition and divestiture activity, access to capital markets and innovative financing structures.

Authorship

PricewaterhouseCoopers LLP (PwC) is the U.S. member of PricewaterhouseCoopers, an international professional services firm that provides auditing, tax and consulting services to many of the world's leading petroleum exploration and production companies. For this edition, **John Brady, Dennis Jennings** and **Rich Shappard** are the primary authors. They wish to acknowledge and thank Author Emeritus **Dr. Horace R. Brock** for his instrumental role as the primary author of earlier editions. Additionally, they would like to thank PwC Senior Manager **Leslie Warren** for her substantial editing and review contributions and for leading the 8th edition project.

Numerous PwC partners, staff, alumni and industry friends have given their assistance and advice for this book. Their backgrounds span major operational areas of petroleum exploration and production including: senior company management; property acquisition, valuation and sale; geological and geophysical analysis; reservoir petroleum engineering; production engineering; oil and gas processing; oil and gas marketing; international operations; financial reporting; income tax reporting and joint venture accounting.

John Brady	**Dennis Jennings**	**Rich Shappard**
Houston, Texas	Dallas, Texas	Houston, Texas

Contributors

The authors wish to acknowledge and thank the many people who have contributed to the writing and editing of this 8th edition:

PwC Partners and Principals

Seenu Akunuri, MBA, ASA, Assurance Principal, Houston, Texas
Rich Call, CPA, Assurance Partner, Houston, Texas
David Carroway, CPA, Assurance Partner, Houston, Texas
Rowena Cipriano-Reyes, CPA, Assurance Partner, Denver, Colorado
Hilary Clark, CPA, Assurance Partner, Houston, Texas
Maria Collman, CPA, Tax Partner, Houston, Texas
Keith Considine, CPA, Advisory Partner, Houston, Texas
Misael De Paz, CPA, Assurance Partner, Houston, Texas
Joseph P. Dunleavy, CPA, Assurance Partner, Houston, Texas
Kasey Dunn, CPA, Tax Partner, Houston, Texas
Michaela Greenan, MA, Advisory Principal, Houston, Texas
Robert Gruman, Advisory Principal, Houston, Texas
Thomas Hatfield, CPA, Assurance Partner, Houston, Texas
Ryan Hawk, Advisory Principal, Chicago, Illinois
Kevin Heard, Advisory Principal, Houston, Texas
Chelsea Hendrickson, CPA, Assurance Partner, Houston, Texas
Tracy Herrmann, CPA, Assurance Partner, Houston, Texas
Kyle Liner, CPA, Assurance Partner, Dallas, Texas
Marty Makulski, Advisory Principal, Houston, Texas
Ricardo Moreno, CPA, Assurance Partner, Houston, Texas
Reid Morrison, MA, Advisory Principal, Houston, Texas
Charles Munsell IV, CPA, Assurance Partner, Houston, Texas
Michael O'Riordan, CPA, Assurance Partner, Houston, Texas
Douglas Parker, CPA, Assurance Partner, San Francisco, California
Mark Pollock, CPA, Assurance Partner, Houston, Texas
Jodi Probst, CPA, Assurance Partner, Houston, Texas
Nathan Rice, CPA, Assurance Partner, Oklahoma City, Oklahoma
Mike Scheller, Advisory Principal, Denver, Colorado
David Shebay, MS, MBA, Advisory Principal, Houston, Texas
Mark A. Smith, MBA, Advisory Principal, Houston, Texas
Yana Storms, CPA, Assurance Partner, Houston, Texas
Jade Walle, CPA, Assurance Partner, Denver, Colorado
Mark West, CPA, Assurance Partner, San Antonio, Texas
Nicole Wier, CPA, Assurance Partner, San Francisco, California

PwC Staff

Manas Pattanaik, Advisory Managing Director, Houston, Texas
Tim Stuhlreyer, MBA, Assurance Managing Director, Houston, Texas
Hidar Akhras, CPA, Assurance Director, Houston, Texas
Jason Carter, MBA, Advisory Director, Houston, Texas
John Hillhouse, CPA, Assurance Director, Houston, Texas
Daja Jackson, CPA, Assurance Director, Houston, Texas
Will Lopez, CPA, Assurance Director, Houston, Texas
John Ly, CPA, Assurance Director, Houston, Texas
Alex Mayberry, Assurance Director, Denver, Colorado
Umang Patel, CPA, Tax Director, Houston, Texas
Shelley Potter, CPA, Assurance Director, Houston, Texas
Ross Roark, CPA, Assurance Director, Dallas, Texas
Simi Saxena, CPA, Assurance Director, Houston, Texas
Darryl Schwark, CPA, Assurance Director, Houston, Texas
Michael Spaniol, CPA, Assurance Director, San Antonio, Texas
Kelly Tinney, CPA, Assurance Director, Denver, Colorado
Diane Yi, CPA, Assurance Director, Houston, Texas
Kayla Lewis, CPA, Assurance Senior Manager, Denver, Colorado
Leslie Warren, CPA, Assurance Senior Manager, Houston, Texas
Andrew Miller, CPA, Assurance Manager, Houston, Texas
Jenna Allred, CPA, Assurance Senior Associate, Houston, Texas
Alex Yu, CPA, Assurance Senior Associate, Houston, Texas
Jay Zhang, CPA, Assurance Senior Associate, Houston, Texas
Nayab Dhukka, Assurance Associate, Houston, Texas
Yuxi Li, Assurance Associate, Austin, Texas
Kateryna Kruk, Assurance Associate, Houston, Texas
Jesse Hellman, Assurance Associate, Houston, Texas
Dustynn Smith, Assurance Associate, Houston, Texas

PwC Alumni

Rachel Andries, Houston, Texas
Daniel Cavazos, Houston, Texas
Craig Friou, Houston, Texas
Jim Harris, Houston, Texas
Ross Hovde, Houston, Texas
Ryan McKenny, Houston, Texas
Nicole Nahlous, Houston, Texas

Cover Design

Chris Tepler, Senior Manager, Minneapolis, Minnesota

Document Development Center

Smarajit Ghosh, Team Lead
Prabhakar Acharya, Designer
Suman V S, Designer

Copy Editors

Paule Hewlett, Houston, Texas
Denise Zwicker, Houston, Texas

Photographs and Exhibits

Cover photograph by Mikeuk/iStock

Special thanks to **Petroleum Extension (PETEX®)** at the University of Texas, the **American Association of Petroleum Geologists EXPLORER** publication and **iStock** for providing graphics and photographs used throughout the text.

Table of contents

17. IMPAIRMENT OR DISPOSAL OF LONG-LIVED ASSETS 303

18. FULL COST ACCOUNTING 315

Introduction to the Petroleum Industry

Key concepts

- Chemistry and measurement

- History of the U.S. petroleum industry

- Current state of the industry

The word petroleum refers to the hydrocarbon compounds of crude oil and natural gas that are found in underground geological formations. These reservoirs generally are thousands of feet below the Earth's surface and comprise the remains of ancient marine organisms that lived millions of years ago. Petroleum may also seep to the Earth's surface along fault lines and cracks in rock formations, where it pools as tar, asphalt or bitumen. Its name is derived from the Latin terms *petra* (rock) and *oleum* (oil). In current usage, petroleum refers to both crude oil and natural gas.

Human use of petroleum is as old as recorded history. Ancient cultures used sticky crude oil to bind objects and repel water. Five thousand years ago, Sumerians used asphalt to inlay mosaics in walls and floors. Mesopotamians used bitumen to line water canals, seal joints in wooden boats and build roads. Egyptians greased their chariots with pitch and placed coatings of asphalt on mummies. Chinese were the first to discover underground deposits of oil and gas and transport these hydrocarbons in bamboo pipelines.

Modern uses of petroleum and its by products include:

- Transportation fuels, such as gasoline, diesel fuel, jet fuel and compressed natural gas.

- Heating fuels, such as propane, heating oil and natural gas.

- Electric-generation fuels, such as natural gas and fuel oil.

- Many manufactured products, such as plastics and building materials.

Chemistry and measurement

The various mixtures of hydrocarbons differ in their uses and economic values.

Crude oil refers to unrefined hydrocarbon mixtures produced from underground reservoirs. These mixtures are liquid at normal atmospheric pressure and temperature. Crude oil ranges in color from almost clear to green, amber, brown or black and is classified as light or heavy depending on the mixture's density.

Heavy crude oil has more of the longer, larger hydrocarbon molecules and, therefore, greater density than light crude oil. Heavy crude oil is difficult to produce and transport to market and more expensive to process into valuable products. Heavy crude oils weigh more than other mixtures, but sell for much less.

Natural gas refers to hydrocarbon mixtures that are not liquid, but gaseous at normal atmospheric pressure and temperature. Natural gas is largely methane, which is a clear, odorless hydrocarbon mixture. It has the smallest natural hydrocarbon molecule, consisting of one carbon atom and four hydrogen atoms (CH_4). Natural gas also may contain some of the larger hydrocarbon molecules commonly found in nature:

- Ethane (C_2H_6)

- Propane (C_3H_8)

- Butane (C_4H_{10})

- Natural gasolines (C_5H_{12} to $C_{10}H_{22}$)

Ethane, propane, butane and natural gasolines are called, collectively, natural gas liquids (NGLs). They are valuable feedstocks for petrochemicals. When removed from the natural gas mixture, these larger, heavier molecules liquefy under various combinations of higher pressure and lower temperature. Liquefied petroleum gas (LPG) usually refers to propane and butane, which are stored as liquids, under pressure. LPG is the fuel used in portable gas barbecue grills.

Both crude oil and natural gas may contain contaminants such as sulfur compounds and carbon dioxide (CO_2). These must be substantially removed before marketing. The contaminant hydrogen sulfide (H_2S) is poisonous and, when dissolved in water, corrodes metals. Additionally, some crude oils contain small amounts of metals that must be removed during refining. Crude oil and natural gas containing high levels of sulfur compounds are called sour crude oil and sour gas. Intermediate crude contains lower levels of sulphur compounds than sour crude, and sweet crude oil contains minimal levels of sulfur compounds.

In the U.S., natural gas is measured in two ways. Both are important in petroleum accounting:

- By the amount of energy or heating value when burned, expressed in British thermal units (Btu).

- By volume, expressed in:

    - Mcf (thousand cubic feet)

    - MMcf (million cubic feet)

    - Bcf (billion cubic feet)

    - Tcf (trillion cubic feet)

Gas volumes are measured at a standard pressure and temperature, typically at an atmospheric pressure base of 14.65 to 15.025 pounds per square inch absolute (psia) and a temperature of 60 degrees Fahrenheit (°F).

The ratio of MMBtu (energy) to Mcf (volume) varies from approximately 1-to-1 to 1.3-to-1. The more NGLs in the gas mixture, the higher the ratio, the greater the energy and the richer or wetter the gas.

Wet gas travels through a mechanical separator near the well. Some natural gasolines within the gas condense into liquid, classified as light crude oil and called condensate. To create pipeline-quality natural gas, the wet gas travels from the wellhead by pipeline to a gas processing plant, which removes the bulk of the NGLs. The NGLs are sold to petrochemical plants or refineries. The remaining gas mixture, called residue gas or dry gas, is more than 90 percent methane. This natural gas is burned for home heating, electric generation and industrial uses.

Crude oil is measured in the U.S. by volume expressed in barrels. One barrel (BBL) equals 42 U.S. gallons. However, for comparative purposes, hydrocarbons may be expressed on a barrel of oil equivalent (BOE) basis; gas volumes in Mcf are converted to barrels based on their energy content or sales value. Approximately 5.6 Mcf of dry gas has the same energy content (approximately 5.8 MMBtu) as one average U.S. barrel of oil.

Equivalence can also be expressed based on value. For example, if one Mcf of gas sells for $2 per Mcf when oil is selling for $50 per barrel, then 25 Mcf equates to one barrel of oil. For one million BOE of gas, the corresponding Mcf is shown below for the conversion ratios indicated.

Figure 1-1

Conversion ratios

Conversion basis	Assumed ratio	BOE	Mcf
Energy	5.6-to-1	1 million	5.6 million
Value	10-to-1	1 million	10 million

Many companies use an energy conversion ratio of six Mcf per barrel, which is the required ratio for certain income tax rules in Internal Revenue Code Section 613A(c)(4).

In countries that use the metric system, crude oil is measured by weight, expressed in metric tons, or by volume, expressed in kiloliters (equivalent to 6.29 barrels). A metric ton of crude oil approximates 7.33 barrels of crude oil, but the ratio varies, since some crude oil mixtures are heavier per barrel than others. Gas volumes are measured in cubic meters and energy is measured in gigajoules. A cubic meter approximates 1.31 cubic yards and 35.3 cubic feet. A gigajoule (or one billion joules) approximates 0.95 MMBtu.

History of the U.S. petroleum industry

To understand the ramifications of financial accounting and reporting in the petroleum industry, it is helpful to understand the basic history of the industry. This text emphasizes U.S. operations and how exploration and production (E&P) companies have adapted to the emerging global marketplace. The U.S. petroleum industry began in the early 1800s, when dwindling supplies of whale oil were supplanted by illuminating oils: kerosene and coal oil. Kerosene was extracted from coal, asphalt and surface crude seepage (known as rock oil). American settlers, drilling for salt brine, occasionally found crude oil mixed in.

In 1856, George Bissell, an investor in the Pennsylvania Rock Oil Co., surmised that a similar type of well could produce crude oil for making kerosene. Although there is mention of an oil discovery in Ontario, Canada, a year earlier, it generally is accepted that Bissell's company was the first commercial oil drilling venture. Drilling began in 1859 near Titusville, Pennsylvania, under the supervision of Colonel Edwin L. Drake, a retired railroad conductor.

A steam-powered, cable-tool rig with a wooden derrick was used to drill a 69 foot well, which produced approximately five barrels per day (BBLD). Additional drilling and production in the Titusville area dramatically increased the supply and reduced the price of crude oil from $10 per barrel in January 1860 to about 10 cents per barrel two years later. Shortly thereafter, refineries began distilling valuable kerosene from crude oil. Nearly four decades later, in 1897, the first offshore well was drilled off the coast of Southern California. H.L. Williams designed a wharf and erected a drilling rig on top of it. At a depth of 300 feet, the well successfully produced oil.

The Industrial Revolution: The growth of 'Big Oil'

At the start of the Civil War, about 200 wells were producing more than 500,000 barrels of crude oil annually. The introduction of petroleum-based lamp fuel was the first of an increasing variety of uses for crude oil and its refined products. The Industrial Revolution and wartime manufacturing created a demand for lubricants to replace turpentine. By 1870, annual production of crude oil exceeded 25 million barrels.

Transportation was a challenge from the earliest days of oil production. Craftsmen called "coopers" constructed wooden barrels with capacities of 42 to 50 gallons. These were filled with oil and hauled by teamsters on horse-drawn wagons to railroad spurs or riverside barge docks. The oil was emptied into large wooden tanks placed on flatbed railroad cars or barges. Only a limited quantity of oil could be moved by these methods. However, the industry's attempts to construct pipelines were thwarted by railroad companies and unions that stood to lose this lucrative business. The first pipeline, built in the 1860s, was constructed of wood and measured less than 1,000 feet long.

In 1870, John D. Rockefeller moved to the forefront of the burgeoning petroleum industry when his firm merged with four other companies to form Standard Oil Co. Their goal was to lead the industry in petroleum refining, transportation and marketing. Shortly after the merger, the company also moved into oil production.[1]

During the 1880s, Standard Oil Co. controlled approximately 90 percent of the U.S. refining industry and dominated the global petroleum industry. Its control of refineries, as well as its ownership of railroads, pipelines and marketing outlets, forced most U.S. petroleum customers to purchase products from the company.[2]

Its dominance drew the attention of federal and state regulators. After discovery of the Spindletop field near Beaumont, Texas, in 1901, the Texas Legislature passed laws barring Standard Oil Co. from the field. This opening of the market encouraged the organization of new companies. Some evolved into vertically integrated companies, such as Texaco founded in 1901. Between 1911 and 1915, federal antitrust laws forced the breakup of Standard Oil Co. into several different companies.

The 1920s and 1930s: Demand, supply and regulation

The 1920s witnessed increased oil industry competition, as more companies formed and demand was spurred by economic growth and the proliferation of automobiles. Production increased to meet demand, but the industry experienced regular price fluctuations and regulatory changes.

American companies began to search for oil in foreign locations beginning in the early 1920s. U.S. policymakers encouraged this outbound investment, fearing a domestic oil shortage. By the mid-1920s, some 35 companies had invested more than $1 billion exploring for and developing reserves in the Middle East, South America, Africa and the Far East.

The 1930 discovery of the giant East Texas Oil Field created a worldwide oil surplus. Abundant East Texas oil, combined with the prevailing economic depression, temporarily slashed oil prices by 90 percent.

Offshore production added a new dynamic to the oil and gas market. Some shallow offshore drilling took place as early as the late 1800s, but it was not until the late 1930s that wells were drilled from structures resembling today's offshore drilling platforms.

From the earliest years of the industry, states monitored the environmental impact of exploration and production. For example, in 1933 the Texas Legislature recognized the need for conservation measures to prevent waste and rampant overproduction of oil fields. The state assigned enforcement and oversight duties to an existing state agency, the Railroad Commission of Texas. Over time, other oil-producing states created similar agencies or commissions to regulate the development and production of oil reserves.

In 1938, Congress passed the Natural Gas Act, which extended the jurisdiction of the Federal Power Commission to include the wholesaling and transportation of natural gas. Federal regulation of the interstate movement of gas continues today under the Federal Energy Regulatory Commission (FERC).

World War II: Defense and growth

Economic recovery from the Great Depression accelerated in the U.S. with the onset of World War II in 1939. Airplanes, automotive equipment and ships were powered by petroleum. The industry easily met the Allied Forces' early demands for petroleum. However, as the conflict progressed, the U.S. and British governments feared an eventual shortage of crude oil. As a preventive measure, they made huge capital investments to develop the enormous reserves in the Persian Gulf.

At the end of World War II, two events stimulated tremendous growth in the natural gas industry: the advent of longline pipe and the birth of the petrochemical industry.

Large quantities of natural gas had been found in Texas, Louisiana and other Southeastern states. However, without reliable longline pipelines, gas transportation proved challenging. New techniques for welding large pipe joints enabled the delivery of gas supplies to the heavily populated Midwest and East Coast. Wartime emergency pipelines, first constructed to move crude oil from Texas to the East Coast, were sold to private enterprises and converted to transport natural gas.

The World War II demand for synthetic rubber and chemicals for explosives prompted the development of a highly specialized petrochemical industry. With readily available feedstocks, petrochemical plants flourished in tandem with broader industry growth. By the 1960s, this specialized industry segment burgeoned along with the range of petroleum-derived products it offered to consumers.

The 1950s and 1960s: Imported oil and the formation of OPEC

During the 1950s and 1960s, world oil production was ample to meet demand. Prices remained stable, averaging $3 per barrel. However, the U.S. began to rely more heavily on imported crude oil and refined products. In 1950, 10 percent of the oil used in the U.S. was imported; by 1970, imports had grown to 23 percent.

In 1960, a world oil cartel, the Organization of the Petroleum Exporting Countries (OPEC), was formed by Saudi Arabia, Kuwait, Iran, Iraq and Venezuela.

Later, eight more countries joined OPEC: the United Arab Emirates and Qatar from the Middle East; Algeria, Gabon, Libya and Nigeria from Africa; Indonesia; and Ecuador. Ecuador withdrew from the cartel in late 1992, but rejoined in 2007.

The 1970s: Embargo and price controls

Prudhoe Bay, one of the top five largest U.S. oil fields, was discovered in 1968 on the North Slope of Alaska, bordering the Arctic Ocean. A year later, the Kuparuk field, one of the top 10 largest U.S. oil fields, was discovered adjacent to Prudhoe Bay. Prior to the Prudhoe Bay discovery by Atlantic Richfield Co. (ARCO), seven very expensive, but unsuccessful, exploratory wells had been drilled nearby.

By 1973, OPEC members produced 80 percent of the world's oil exports, and member countries began to nationalize oil production within their borders. In October 1973, OPEC members cut off all oil exports to the U.S. in response to a U.S. proposed $2.2 billion military aid package to Israel, which had suffered recent surprise attacks from Egypt and Syria. Saudi Arabian oil prices rose from $1.80 per barrel in 1971 to $11.65 per barrel in December 1973. World crude oil prices rose slowly until Iran's 1979 Islamic Revolution created another escalation, peaking at $42 per barrel for some U.S. crude oil.

Even after discovery, development of the Prudhoe Bay and Kuparuk fields stalled. Additionally, a large portion of U.S. oil imports were cut off for several months during the 1973 OPEC oil embargo. The impact of these combined factors compelled Congress to approve the construction of the Trans-Alaska Pipeline, which began in 1975. Finally, in 1977, Prudhoe Bay and Kuparuk crude oils were produced and marketed.

The OPEC oil embargo also prompted the U.S. government to create the Federal Energy Administration in 1974 (predecessor to the U.S. Department of Energy), endowed with control over crude oil prices.

Price regulations were complex: a two-tier oil pricing structure included a lower price for old or lower-tier oil, and a higher price for new or upper-tier oil. Lower-tier oil generally came from properties that were producing prior to 1973; upper-tier oil came from properties that began producing after 1972. Producers often had ownership in both kinds of properties and therefore sold some oil at less than half the price of other oil that was of the same quality. By 1979, the U.S. allowed free-market prices for U.S. oil from newly drilled properties or properties producing less than 10 barrels per day (Bbld) per well.

The Strategic Petroleum Reserve (SPR) was established in December 1975 by President Gerald Ford. The first crude oil was delivered to the SPR in July 1977 and stored at the West Hackberry site near Lake Charles, Louisiana. Other major storage sites include Bryan Mound and Big Hill in Texas and Bayou Choctaw in Louisiana. Total storage capacity of the SPR is approximately 727 million barrels.

Foreign oil continued to be imported (at prices exceeding domestic prices) to meet growing domestic demand. By 1977, some 47 percent of the country's needs were met by imported oil.

The 1980s: Boom and bust

Global market factors, coupled with U.S. regulatory actions, set the stage for a U.S. petroleum industry boom in the early 1980s, which culminated in a bust by the decade's end.

- World oil price increases in 1973 and 1979 improved exploration economics and created an expectation of substantial future price increases.

- Expropriations of U.S. interests in Libya and elsewhere in the 1970s encouraged U.S. companies to explore within domestic borders.

- The Natural Gas Policy Act of 1978 created incentive pricing mechanisms to stimulate the discovery and development of domestic natural gas reserves.

- U.S. price controls on crude oil were removed in 1981, freeing up additional cash for producers to reinvest.

- In 1981, U.S. tax laws reduced the highest individual income tax rate from 70 percent to 50 percent and reduced windfall profit taxes on new oil fields.

- Consequently, in 1981 and 1982, U.S. individuals invested billions of tax-advantaged dollars in limited partnerships for petroleum exploration and production.

All of these factors created a U.S. drilling boom: in 1984 alone, the industry spent $65 billion for exploration and production. However, when Saudi Arabia refused to reduce its market share in 1986, world oil prices plunged 50 percent. With the price collapse, global and U.S. exploration and development activity plummeted, and oil prices hovered at $15 to $18 per barrel for the remainder of the 1980s.

The 1990s: Advent of the modern market

The 1990s were marked by five trends:

- Growing U.S. natural gas demand, production and value.

- Use of oil and gas futures.

- Continued success with offshore deepwater drilling, aided by impressive technological and operational efficiencies.

- Continued restructuring of the U.S. gas industry.

- Increased focus by U.S. companies on foreign E&P investments.

Fluctuating crude oil market. The early 1990s brought new price volatility. Oil prices spiked briefly after Iraq's invasion of Kuwait, but fell quickly after Kuwait was liberated.

Responding to weakening demand in Asia, combined with other factors, oil prices declined briefly in late 1998 to around $11 per barrel, creating fears of a prolonged price decline. Several major producing countries agreed to cut their production in early 1999, and oil prices more than doubled.

Mergers. Growing prosperity for oil and gas companies was eclipsed in 1997 and 1998 by both the Asian economic crisis and a sharp drop in oil prices. These conditions precipitated a frenzy of cost-cutting and consolidations that led to the formation of a group of global companies known as super majors:

- BP was formed by the merger of British Petroleum and Amoco in 1998, followed by the BP Amoco merger with ARCO in 2000.

- Chevron was the result of the merger of Chevron and Texaco in 2000, which acquired Unocal in 2005.

- ConocoPhillips, though not currently a super major, was formed by the merger of Conoco and Phillips 66 in 2002, which resulted in an entity that historically was included in the super major category. ConocoPhillips subsequently split from Phillips 66 in 2012 to form two separate companies: ConocoPhillips, a pure-play upstream company, and Phillips 66, a pure-play downstream company.

- ExxonMobil resulted from the merger of Exxon and Mobil in 1999.

- Royal Dutch Shell was formed from the merger of Royal Dutch Petroleum and Shell Transport & Trading in 2005.

- TOTAL was the result of the merger of TOTAL with Petrofina in 1999, followed by the merger with Elf Aquitaine in 2000.

Additional mergers involving French, Spanish, Belgian, Argentine, Russian and Ukrainian companies continued in the early 21st century, augmenting the global scale of the industry's consolidated footprint.

Exploration trends. The U.S. was viewed as a poor area for new discoveries. It had been heavily drilled (by global standards), and its most promising regions for new fields were in environmentally protected areas. However, in the 1990s, those dismal prospects were reversed by technological advancements that dramatically reduced both the risks and costs for exploration and development. As a result, expenditures for domestic petroleum exploration more than doubled from 1990 to 1999.

Offshore fields in deeper waters proved to be highly productive. As explained in Chapter 5, onshore and offshore exploration success was improved by 3D seismic used to identify likely reservoirs, therefore requiring fewer exploratory wells. Drilling cost per reserve volume declined with the advent of horizontal drilling, in which the wellbore starts vertically and then bends to become a horizontal shaft through wide reservoirs.

The industry also developed economic techniques to extract large quantities of oil and natural gas from nontraditional sources. These included oil from mined oil sands, such as those found in Alberta, Canada, natural gas from tight-sands formations and methane from underground coalbeds.

With advancements in science and engineering, U.S. natural gas supplies shifted from scarce to self-sufficient. New technologies such as horizontal drilling and hydraulic fracturing (fracking) made it possible to explore unconventional resources and revolutionized the global natural gas market. Shale gas success in North America prompted other countries around the globe to assess their unconventional natural gas resources.

Figure 1-2 lists the top U.S. petroleum companies as of December 31, 2018.

Figure 1-2

Top 15 U.S. oil and gas companies, ranked by total assets

Company	Total assets	Worldwide Liquids reserves	Rank	Worldwide Natural gas reserves	Rank
	(in millions)	(MMBbl)		(Bcf)	
ExxonMobil	$346,196	15,657	1	51,816	1
Chevron	253,863	6,790	2	31,576	2
ConocoPhillips	69,980	3,238	3	12,149	4
Occidental Petroleum	43,854	2,069	5	4,095	8
Anadarko Petroleum	40,376	935	7	3,230	9
EOG Resources	33,935	2,146	4	4,687	7
Concho Resources	26,294	750	13	2,624	10
Diamondback Energy	21,596	817	10	1,049	15
Apache	21,582	815	11	2,514	11
Hess	21,433	889	9	1,815	13
Marathon Oil	21,321	902	8	2,275	12
Noble Energy	21,010	723	14	7,231	5
EQT	20,721	169	15	20,805	3
Devon Energy	19,566	1,133	6	4,761	6
Pioneer Natural Resources	17,903	806	12	1,459	14

Source: S&P Capital IQ Company Screening Report, "Top 100 Oil and Gas Companies by Total Assets," March 14, 2019 and SEC filings.

In addition to domestic investments, U.S. petroleum companies doubled their E&P expenditures outside the U.S. during this same time period. Foreign E&P opportunities emerged due to political restructuring within the former Soviet Union and growing sophistication in, and interest by, other countries in attracting E&P investments from around the world. By 1998, imported crude and refined products supplied more than half of U.S. demand.

The 2000s: Global economic decline

The year 2000 started off with oil prices below $30 per barrel. Prices further declined below $20 per barrel towards the end of 2001 but returned to the $30 range by the end of 2002. After 2003, prices began to increase and reached above $60 per barrel in 2005, peaking higher than $130 by mid-2008. Market analysts attributed these price increases to several factors: extensive growth in the financial sector, soaring demand from China, increasing tension in the Middle East and the weakening of the U.S. dollar.

The autumn of 2008 marked the beginning of the Great Recession. A period of general economic decline worldwide, it is considered the worst global recession since the Great Depression of the 1930s. As a result, by December 2008, the price of oil had dropped again to the $40 range.

As the recession slowly passed, prices crept up as the transportation industry saw exponential growth with new demand for gasoline and jet fuel. From 2010 to 2014, prices ranged broadly from $70 to $110 per barrel, whereas in 2015 and 2016 the price of oil again dropped to the $30 to $40 per barrel range experienced in 2002 and 2008. By 2016, prices gradually recovered, reaching as high as $70 per barrel by mid-2018, although $55 to $60 per barrel became the new normal in late 2019 and early 2020. However, by March 2020, prices again dropped below $30 per barrel.

The new millennium: Unprecedented and unconventional

For the petroleum industry, the past two decades have brought extraordinary change and activity. Socioeconomic factors and world events played key roles in this timeframe, including:

- The September 11, 2001, terrorist attacks.

- Ongoing wars in Iraq and Afghanistan.

- Environmental activism focused on climate change.

- The meltdown of the financial markets in 2007 and 2008.

- China's growing demand for energy.

- The Deepwater Horizon oil spill in 2010.

- Rise of unconventional oil and gas.

- Large fluctuations in commodity prices due to technological advancements in drilling.

Deepwater Horizon oil spill. The most momentous event in the oil and gas industry so far in this millennium was the explosion of the Deepwater Horizon offshore rig on April 20, 2010. Occurring in the Gulf of Mexico's Macondo field, the spill brought consequences on many fronts: legislative, regulatory, operational, environmental and financial.

The leaking well was finally sealed five months after the explosion. According to the National Incident Command's Flow Rate Technical Group, an estimated 206 million gallons (4.9 million barrels) of oil leaked into the Gulf of Mexico, making it the largest oil spill in U.S. history.[3]

Unconventional oil and gas. Exploration for and production of shale oil and gas has increased dramatically in the past decade due to technological advances that provide access to petroleum locked in shale formations. The high price of oil, relative to natural gas, has also spurred large investments in liquid-rich shale plays.

In 2008, chasing high prices for natural gas, independents invested heavily in drilling shale formations for gas. After many years of growth, this production eventually created an abundant gas supply that prompted a sizable price drop. The drop was exacerbated by OPEC actions that increased supply at the same time.

Although the lower gas prices hurt the producers, this new source of crude oil lessened U.S. dependence on foreign oil. Two prominent examples are the Bakken Shale and Eagle Ford Shale formations. By the end of 2017, drilling in the Bakken formation was so frenzied that production reached more than one million barrels per day and outstripped the industry's capacity to ship the oil to market.

Despite the challenging price environment, shale gas is the primary growth engine for North American natural gas production and is becoming a major global energy source as well. U.S. dry natural gas production is forecast to grow from 30 trillion cubic feet in 2018 to 43.4 trillion cubic feet in 2050. By 2050, tight oil plays and shale gas resources will likely comprise nearly 90 percent of all U.S. dry natural gas.[4]

The eight key U.S. shale regions are:

- Anadarko (Texas and Oklahoma).

- Appalachia (Ohio, West Virginia, Pennsylvania and New York).

- Bakken Shale (Montana and North Dakota).

- Barnett Shale (Texas).

- Eagle Ford Shale (Texas).

- Haynesville/Bossier Shale (Louisiana, Texas and Arkansas).

- Niobrara (Colorado, Wyoming, Nebraska and Kansas).

- Permian Basin (Texas and New Mexico).

Natural gas is a low-carbon, clean-burning fuel with relatively few environmental effects. It has gained widespread support as a cheap and widely available alternative to coal and other fossil fuels. However, concerns over the effects of fracking (fracing) on groundwater could lead to increased regulatory oversight, which could jeopardize unconventional natural gas production in the U.S.

Current state of the industry

Applying new techniques has enabled the industry to produce more energy resources from increasingly remote locations with reduced environmental impact. Companies continue to seek access to huge natural gas resources that are locked in gas hydrates and thus unattainable by current E&P methods. The industry is studying other technologies to recover oil and gas deposits from hot, high-pressure environments deep inside the Earth.

Fracking, a process that typically involves injecting water and sand, via the well, into a bedrock formation under high pressure, increases the size and extent of existing bedrock fractures, cleaning them and enabling them to interconnect with nearby water-bearing fractures. Oil, gas and brine can then flow back through these fractures and into the well at a faster rate than before. This technique is used to increase or restore the rate at which oil, gas or water can be produced from a reservoir.

Several environmental and human health concerns are associated with fracking: potential mishandling of toxic waste, potential risks to air quality, potential contamination of groundwater and unintended migration of gases and hydraulic fracturing chemicals. Therefore, environmental regulations affecting fracking have increased more recently.

New drilling and recovery methods have catalyzed industry collaboration. Dozens of organizations have partnered to share best practices and increase productivity. Companies have found competitive advantage in sharing the risks of exploration and spreading the enormous capital outlays. For example, large, integrated oil companies partner with U.S. and foreign independent companies to share expertise, workforces and resources.

Industry leaders are also pushing for rapid development of alternative fuels using existing and emerging technologies. In the automotive industry, electric engines or "dual-powered" (electric and gasoline) hybrid engines are becoming more common replacements for internal-combustion engines. Most metropolitan areas have seen sizable expansion of an accessible distribution network consisting of electric power and charging stations for these new technologies.

Additionally, many companies that focused on fossil fuels in years past have more recently become major investors in renewable energy, including wind, solar, biomass and geothermal initiatives. Although these sources are potentially useful, scientists do not expect them to account for a sizable portion of our nation's energy mix for many years. The energy industry must overcome major technological hurdles to make alternative sources reliable, cost-effective and convenient for consumers.

● ● ●

1 Carr, Albert Z. Rockefeller's *Secret Weapon*. New York, McGraw-Hill Book Co., Inc., 1962.

2 McLean, J.G. and R.W. Haigh. *The Growth of Integrated Oil Companies*. Boston, Harvard University Graduate School of Business Administration, 1954.

3 National Commission on the BP Deepwater Horizon Oil Spill and Offshore Drilling. *Deep Water The Gulf Oil Disaster and the Future of Offshore Drilling*, January 11, 2011.

4 Energy Information Administration. "Annual Energy Outlook 2019." January 24, 2019, www.eia.gov/outlooks/aeo/pdf/aeo2019.pdf.

Petroleum Operations and Economics

- **U.S. oil and gas in the global economy**

- **Oil and gas value chain**

- **E&P organizations**

- **Performance and economics**

This book focuses on accounting for petroleum operations. Therefore, it is important for readers to understand the nature of the industry and the role oil and gas plays in the global economy. This chapter and others address critical elements related to supply and demand; the oil and gas value chain, industry structure and key players; as well as recent industry performance and basic project economics.

It is easy to take for granted the ready supply of gasoline, natural gas and electricity. The petroleum industry is integral to providing the day-to-day conveniences our society has come to expect. Petroleum products keep cars, trains and planes moving, industrial complexes humming, and our homes warm in the winter and cool in the summer. As a result, the petroleum industry has become one of the largest, most complex and important of global industries.

Exploration and production companies have a basic challenge: to stay in business, they must find or add more petroleum resources than they produce, and they must do so in an economical way. In addition to their economic, environmental and social concerns, these companies operate in a risky business environment. In the expanding global marketplace, success requires proper management of the inherent risks and a complete understanding of project economics.

U.S. oil and gas in the global economy

Because the world depends on fossil fuels, the industry's ability to meet demand is crucial to our way of life. Globally, the demand for energy continues to increase due to population growth and the evolution of developing nations.

Global consumption of petroleum and other liquids reached an average of over 100 million barrels per day (MMBbld) in 2018.[1] By 2034, projected net exports from the U.S. are expected to peak at more than 3.7 million barrels per day, before gradually reversing as domestic consumption rises. The U.S. will likely return to being a net importer of petroleum and other liquids on an energy basis as a result of increasing domestic gasoline consumption and falling domestic crude oil production near the end of the projection period in 2050.

Lower 48 onshore tight oil development continues to be the main driver of total U.S. crude oil production, which is expected to account for 68 percent of cumulative domestic production through 2050, although production is expected to level off at about 14 million barrels per day through 2040 as tight oil development moves into less productive areas and well productivity declines.

The percentage of dry natural gas production from oil formations increased from eight percent in 2013 to 17 percent in 2018 and is expected to remain near this percentage through 2050. Growth in drilling in the Southwest region, particularly in the Permian Basin, is the main driver for natural gas production growth from tight oil formations.[2]

Currently, oil and natural gas discoveries in the deep water of the Gulf of Mexico lead the lower 48 states' offshore production, which is projected to reach a record 2.4 million barrels per day in 2022. Many of these discoveries resulted from exploration when oil prices were higher than $100 per barrel before the late-2014 oil price collapse. After peaking in 2022, offshore production is expected to decline through 2035, before flattening through 2050, as new discoveries are anticipated to offset declines in legacy fields.[2]

Supply and demand

Global supplies of petroleum are expected to satisfy demand for the next several decades. The industry's ability to find and produce oil and gas from both new and existing sources continues to expand. Its application of more economical means of extracting oil and gas from various sources could extend the estimated future supply by many years.

This delicate balance of supply and demand affects the commodity price. When supply exceeds demand, prices drop; when demand exceeds supply, prices rise.

The price collapse that began in late-2014 highlights the effects of supply and demand on oil prices. Leading up to the collapse, the price per barrel averaged between $90 and $100, and demand outpaced supply. At the lowest point, barrels were priced below $30, and supply outpaced demand for six straight quarters across 2014 and 2015.

Many factors contribute to the price of oil, but fundamentally, all of them revolve around supply and demand. Understanding how lower prices diminish margins is an important component of project economics and will be explained later in this chapter.

Production evolution

The recent sharp production increase was spurred by growing demand and changing energy needs. Booming populations and fast-growing emerging economies demand more energy than ever. In addition, technological advancements have improved the economics of recovering both new and existing oil and gas reserves. Environmental concerns are also changing consumption habits, as evidenced by the continued shift to renewable energy.

All of this is propelling an evolution in how the world produces and consumes energy. Indicative of a global shift, U.S. natural gas and renewable energy consumption is expected to grow, sometimes dramatically, by 2040, reducing both oil and coal consumption.

The U.S. Energy Information Administration (EIA) reports that non-hydroelectric renewable consumption will grow the most, on a percentage basis, due to state and federal policies that encourage the use of renewables. Natural gas consumption will rise as well, driven by projected low natural gas prices. The industrial sector will become the largest consumer of natural gas, beginning in the early 2020s, and consumption in the power sector will grow in response to low natural gas prices.[2]

The EIA predicts that liquid fuels will be consumed at a rate of nearly 102.4 million barrels per day by 2020. Outside the countries represented by the Organization for Economic Co-operation and Development (OECD), India and China are projected to lead global economic growth through 2040. The center of gravity for energy demand is shifting, with expanding Asian middle classes accounting for much of the growth in global gross domestic product (GDP) and energy consumption over the next 20 years.

Natural gas currently supplies nearly one-third of U.S. energy consumption and is the primary heating fuel for approximately one-half of U.S. households.[3] In the U.S. today, electrical generation dominates the natural gas market. In fact, low natural gas prices and favorable costs for renewables have made them the primary sources of new generation capacity.[2]

Figure 2-1 lists current members of the OECD.

Figure 2-1
OECD member countries

Australia	France	Korea	Portugal
Austria	Germany	Latvia	Slovak Republic
Belgium	Greece	Lithuania	Slovenia
Canada	Hungary	Luxembourg	Spain
Chile	Iceland	Mexico	Sweden
Czech Republic	Ireland	Netherlands	Switzerland
Denmark	Israel	New Zealand	Turkey
Estonia	Italy	Norway	United Kingdom
Finland	Japan	Poland	United States

Source: The Organization for Economic Co-operation and Development.

The EIA estimates that fossil fuels, natural gas and natural gas plant liquids (NGPLs) will top the production growth charts, and NGPLs alone will account for almost one-third of cumulative U.S. liquids production by 2050.[2]

During the past 10 years, the U.S. has become the world's leading producer of oil and natural gas. In 2018, U.S. crude oil and natural gas production grew 16.3 percent and 12 percent, respectively, compared to 2017.[4] Projections show that U.S. crude oil production will continue to set annual records through 2027, exceeding 14 million barrels per day through 2040.

Liquefied natural gas (LNG) also has garnered a critical role in worldwide supply and demand balances. This is especially true as pipeline demand outstrips supply, and demand grows in developing countries.

Shale revolution

The emergence of hydraulic fracturing (fracking) in the U.S. has expanded oil and gas production by more than 57 percent in the past 10 years.[5] Fracking technology has been a game-changer in the U.S., enabling cost-effective oil and gas production from unconventional sources. Currently, two-thirds of the natural gas produced in the U.S. comes from hydraulically fractured wells.

According to the EIA, U.S. natural gas production increased from 29.2 million cubic feet (MMcf) in 2017 to 32.7 million cubic feet in 2018.[6] Annual U.S. crude oil production reached a record level of 11.0 million barrels per day in 2018, surpassing 2017 by 1.6 million barrels per day, a 17 percent increase that topped the previous record in 1970.[7]

Although shale oil and gas have been produced in the U.S. for many decades, they were not significant resources until new technologies, predominantly horizontal drilling and hydraulic fracturing, enabled their economic production. After the "shale revolution," the U.S. became the world's top producer of natural gas beginning in 2009, when its production surpassed Russia's. Beginning in 2013, the U.S. surpassed Saudi Arabia as the world's top producer of petroleum hydrocarbons.

Since 2008, U.S. petroleum and natural gas production has increased by nearly 60 percent.[8] This achievement highlights the significant impact of rapid technological advances in drilling. Fracking unlocks vast sums of trapped oil and natural gas that were previously inaccessible, which has also resulted in dramatic declines in drilling costs. Innovation, and in particular the shale revolution, is imperative to meeting the ever-growing demand for oil and gas.

All of these statistics point to a massive shift in both the production base and consumption habits. By 2040, natural gas will likely supply 26 percent of the world's energy, compared to 22 percent in 2018.[9] The shale revolution and other technology-driven changes are essential to this continued growth.

Increased consumption

In 2018, U.S. petroleum consumption averaged about 20.5 million barrels per day, including about 1.2 million barrels per day of biofuels. The EIA projects that petroleum and other liquids will continue to meet the largest share of total U.S. energy consumption through 2050.[10]

Natural gas volumes are expected to grow faster than any other fossil fuel, and natural gas demand is expected to exceed coal demand by 2030. The International Energy Agency (IEA) reports that this will result from efforts to reduce air pollution, as well as increased use of LNG. Global gas demand, as reported by the IEA, will increase by 1.6 percent each year to 2040, exceeding 2018 demand by 45 percent.[11]

The global population has grown significantly in recent years, and this growth is expected to continue. In 2019, the world population was approximately 7.7 billion, with an annual growth rate of around 1.07 percent (down from 1.14 percent in 2016). Experts project it will grow by another 27 percent, reaching approximately 9.8 billion by 2050.

Most of this growth will occur in developing regions. Currently, Asia accounts for 59.4 percent of the global population, while North America accounts for a meager 4.8 percent. Viewed differently, half of all population growth will occur in nine, mostly developing, countries (listed in order of expected contribution to total growth): India, Nigeria, Democratic Republic of the Congo, Pakistan, Ethiopia, the United Republic of Tanzania, the U.S., Uganda and Indonesia.

The world's 47 least-developed countries are home to around 880 million people, or 12 percent of the global population. However, they face severe structural impediments to growth, as they currently account for less than two percent of world GDP and around one percent of world trade.[12] As these countries develop and their populations grow, their infrastructure will advance and their energy needs will escalate.

Developing countries that previously were not highly energy-dependent will become more so. Excluding the 36 member nations of the OECD, the non-OECD nations are projected to account for approximately 65 percent of global energy consumption by 2050, continuing a trend that began in 2007. Asia is projected to post the largest consumption increase among all non-OECD regions.[13]

Role of OPEC

The petroleum industry is dominated by regulations and government interventions. OPEC was founded in 1960 with five participating countries; today, OPEC represents government intervention on a global scale and plays a crucial role in the industry.

OPEC states that its mission is "to coordinate and unify petroleum policies of its Member Countries and ensure the stabilization of oil markets in order to secure an efficient, economic and regular supply of petroleum to consumers, a steady income to producers and a fair return on capital for those investing in the petroleum industry." OPEC heavily influences oil markets by managing oil production for its 14 member countries, which control approximately 80 percent of the world's proven oil reserves.[14]

OPEC decisions play a major role in the global oil market and international relations. In the 1970s, OPEC's reduced oil production led to increased oil prices and OPEC revenue, with serious negative consequences to the global economy. In the 1980s, a major oil glut forced OPEC to cut its oil production several times and even impose production limits on its members to stabilize prices. During the price collapse that started in late-2014, OPEC was slow to cut production, which drove oil prices lower, resulting in severe negative effects on its member countries.

Global reserves

Based on EIA data, 95 percent of total proved oil and gas reserves are located in 26 countries. Nearly 84 percent of the world's oil and gas reserves, and the majority of global production, occur in the top 10 countries. New estimates of worldwide proved oil reserves total 1.7 trillion barrels, while proved gas reserves total 7.1 quadrillion cubic feet (quads).[15]

The world's top 25 countries with proved oil reserves (including lease condensate) based on EIA data are ranked in Figure 2-2. Data for the U.S. is as of December 31, 2019, while data for other countries is from the Oil & Gas Journal as of January 1, 2020.

Political and regulatory risks

Political and regulatory risks also pose concerns for oil and gas companies, which are subject to numerous regulations dictating where, when and how they can operate. The laws and regulations vary from country to country and state to state; they also change constantly. Companies may make economic decisions based on current rules, regulations and political climate, but they also must concern themselves with what may occur in the future.

In the U.S., changes tend to be more predictable, but international operations often come with increased political risk. Compliance with local regulations is imperative in all cases, as noncompliance often results in major costs or even withdrawal of production rights.

Figure 2-2
Top 25 countries with crude oil reserves

Rank	Country	Reserves (MMBbl)
1	Venezuela	302,809
2	Saudi Arabia	266,260
3	Canada	167,401
4	Iran	155,600
5	Iraq	147,223
6	Kuwait	101,500
7	United Arab Emirates	97,800
8	Russia	80,000
9	Libya	48,363
10	United States	47,053
11	Nigeria	36,182
12	Kazakhstan	30,000
13	China	25,927
14	Qatar	25,244
15	Brazil	12,835
16	Algeria	12,200
17	Angola	8,384
18	Ecuador	8,273
19	Norway	8,047
20	Azerbaijan	7,000
21	Mexico	6,427
22	Oman	5,373
23	Sudan	5,000
24	India	4,423
25	Vietnam	4,400

Nationalization, in varying degrees, has long been a risk for international operators. Some countries have made abrupt policy changes that have created complications for oil and gas companies operating within their borders. Local political turmoil also can disrupt operations and cause serious economic consequences. In addition, the possibility of guerrilla action presents serious challenges in certain countries where offshore platforms and other operations can be disrupted.

Before investing in operations, companies must develop a clear understanding of the current political and regulatory climate, while also weighing the risk of change.

As technological developments and economic growth drive increased production, the oil and gas industry constantly strives to maintain the delicate balance between supply and demand. This balance will always be challenged by various strategic risks, including price volatility and geopolitical change. Mitigating these risks is critical to meeting the growing global demand for petroleum.

Oil and gas value chain

The value chain of oil and gas operations contains three primary segments:

- **Upstream.** Exploration and production.

- **Midstream.** Linking production and refining; includes gathering, transportation, storage and wholesale marketing.

- **Downstream.** Refining, distribution and retail.

Upstream

Exploration uses geologic science, drilling technology and skilled personnel to find subsurface traps that contain hydrocarbons. Production removes the hydrocarbons from underground reservoirs and delivers them to a midstream transportation provider. Because they both explore and produce, upstream companies often are called E&Ps. Service and supply companies provide the specialized equipment and skills needed for exploring, drilling, testing, producing, maintaining and reclaiming oil wells and gas wells.

Exploration and production is a complex and capital-intensive business, which typically involves:

- **Identifying areas to explore.** Using seismic equipment and computer processing to identify areas where oil and gas is likely to be discovered and could be economic to develop (see Chapter 5).

- **Securing rights to drill and produce.** Negotiating for mineral rights and structuring a lease agreement that may include paying the property owner a percentage of future production (see Chapter 7) and possibly identifying joint interest or joint venture partners (see Chapter 10).

- **Drilling on leased property.** Drilling an exploratory well, often using a subcontractor who drills and provides drilling equipment (see Chapter 8).

- **Evaluating and completing wells.** Testing for sufficient reserves of oil and gas and completing any well that appears to be economically productive (see Chapter 8).

- **Developing the productive area.** Drilling additional wells and installing surface equipment to efficiently and economically bring the oil and gas to the surface (see Chapters 8 and 11).

- **Producing the oil and gas.** Producing, separating and selling oil and gas according to an economic timetable dictated by reservoir pressure and equipment efficiency (see Chapters 11 and 12).

- **Plugging wells and abandoning the property.** After each well reaches its economic limit, plugging and sealing the well(s) below the surface and removing surface equipment; such end-of-well life activities are interchangeably referred to as plugging and abandonment (P&A) or dismantlement, restoration and abandonment (DR&A) (see Chapter 19).

Midstream

Midstream is the vital link between petroleum producing regions and the population centers where most end users live and work. In most cases, oil and gas are not found in the same geographic locations as either processing facilities or major consumers. Midstream concerns itself with transporting oil and gas from its extraction point to downstream processing facilities, primarily refineries and petrochemical plants, where it is transformed into a variety of finished products for consumer use.

Figure 2-3 illustrates upstream and midstream activities.

Figure 2-3
Upstream and midstream schematic

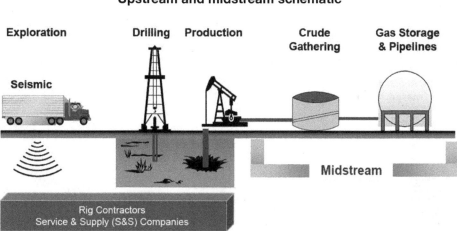

Transportation is a big part of midstream activities, with pipelines, trucks, tanker ships and rail cars used to move oil, gas and other refined products. Pipelines are the most common means of transporting oil and gas. This requires vast pipeline networks, which must be both constructed and maintained. In many ways, pipelines serve as the highways of the industry, linking buyers and sellers.

Storage is another major midstream element. Storage facilities may house oil, gas and other refined products in above-ground facilities, deep caverns, depleted oil and gas reservoirs and depleted aquifers. Storage facilities also manage inventory and supply the natural gas needed to maintain balance in pipelines. They often capitalize on the seasonality of market prices for natural gas, storing their inventory in the summer, when prices generally are lower, and selling it in the winter, when the demand created by colder weather drives prices higher. Success in midstream depends on several external factors, including: growth in the upstream segment and continuous development of reserves, refinery profit margins and a political environment that favors construction of assets such as pipelines.

Downstream

Downstream operations include refineries, petrochemical plants, fuel products distributors and retail outlets, as well as specialty manufacturers and distributors. Companies in the downstream segment refine crude oil and natural gas into products used by consumers. Thousands of products are created downstream, including gasoline, diesel, jet fuel, heating oil, asphalt, lubricants, synthetic rubber, plastics, fertilizers, antifreeze, pesticides, natural gas and propane. Refined products are transported by various means to distribution points for consumption.

Figure 2-4 illustrates various downstream activities.

Figure 2-4

Downstream schematic

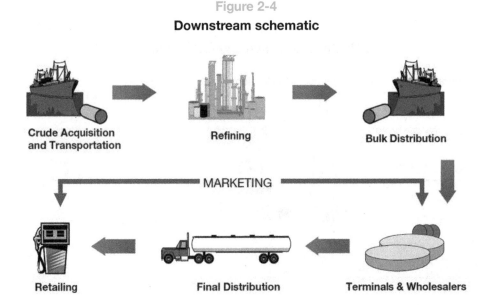

Through marketing outreach, the industry reveals its public face. Advertising, customer management, product mix and wholesale/retail strategies promote sales and brand awareness. Wholesale activities include channel choice, site management and product expansion.

Service companies

Service companies provide labor, equipment and necessary support services to the various industry segments. Major service companies include Baker Hughes, Halliburton and Schlumberger.

Operational risks

Petroleum companies across the value chain face a variety of operational risks that can increase production costs and reduce a project's profitability. Major operational risks include:

- **Geological.** As the world's easy-to-reach reserves decline, exploration must focus on more complex drilling environments (e.g., offshore). The two aspects of geological risk in these environments are: (1) the difficulty of extracting petroleum and (2) the potential that reserves will be smaller than expected. Although new technologies continue to improve the industry's ability to extract reserves, both onshore and offshore, companies try to mitigate the risk through frequent and comprehensive geological testing.

- **Safety.** Given the risky and complex business of exploration, accidents are always possible, and they can produce major consequences. For example, the cost of the 2010 Deepwater Horizon incident alone is estimated as high as $40 billion. To mitigate this risk, the American Petroleum Institute (API) maintains nearly 700 safety standards across all segments of the production process. Maintaining safe working environments is a priority for all companies.

- **Weather.** To meet energy demands, oil and gas producing companies frequently operate in areas that are subject to extreme weather. When making investment decisions, they must consider the potential for hurricanes, tornadoes, earthquakes and arctic conditions. For example, Hurricane Harvey, which hit the Gulf Coast in August 2017, caused reductions to Texas Gulf Coast onshore and offshore production, as onshore production activities were halted, and offshore platforms in the path of the storm were evacuated during the last week of August. However, Hurricane Harvey's impact on overall energy markets was limited, as natural gas production and consumption steadily recovered after the storm passed. The diminished proportion of offshore Gulf of Mexico production, coupled with onshore shale gas production growth, played a role in reducing price impacts compared to previous natural disasters such as Hurricane Katrina in August 2005, when Gulf of Mexico operations supplied 10 percent of the oil and 24 percent of the natural gas consumed in the U.S.

As part of operational decision-making, petroleum companies must weigh their future earnings from production sites against unexpected and unfortunate possibilities related to these sizable risks.

E&P organizations

The E&P industry comprises three basic types of organizations: integrated oil companies, national oil companies and independents. Each type conducts business in some or all of the upstream, midstream and downstream segments.

Companies involved exclusively in upstream typically are referred to as independents, whereas integrated companies operate across the energy value chain. In the petroleum industry, large integrated companies are known as majors, while the largest are known as super majors, as mentioned in Chapter 1.

Integrated oil companies

Companies that are vertically integrated throughout the upstream, midstream and downstream sectors are known as integrated oil companies (IOCs). Their integrated business structure puts them in direct contact with the energy end market, which can offer a competitive advantage. Market knowledge may help a company better manage its production in response to changing market demands. Integration also creates a natural hedge against price drops.

Integrated companies often operate and compete at a global level. Examples of well-known, publicly held, integrated oil companies include BP, Chevron, ExxonMobil, PetroChina, Royal Dutch Shell and Total.

National oil companies

Companies controlled by national governments that manage the country's hydrocarbon resources are referred to as national oil companies (NOCs). Despite this definition, some NOCs operate globally, such as Eni (Italy), Equinor ASA (Norway), PJSC Gazprom (Russia), Petrobras (Brazil) and Saudi Aramco (Saudi Arabia). Others focus solely within their own borders, such as Pemex (Mexico).

Although NOCs vary, they often are part of the government ministry of petroleum or energy. They provide financial support to government energy programs and often subsidize domestic fuel prices. As a result, NOCs are not necessarily profit-driven. Rather, they focus on providing jobs, furthering government policies, paying for government initiatives and supplying inexpensive energy domestically.

NOCs are majority-owned by the state, sometimes with partial ownership by outside investors. Most OPEC countries have at least one NOC, although most also allow investor-owned companies to operate within their borders. Regardless, NOCs often lack the incentives or resources to explore for, produce and market oil and gas to the same degree as other companies. Some NOCs are strategically and operationally autonomous and strive to balance profit and growth, while taking into account national priorities.[16]

When ranked by proved oil and gas reserves, 14 of the top 20 global companies are NOCs. Currently, NOCs also control nearly 80 percent of total oil reserves, whereas IOCs hold only about six percent of the world's oil reserves, a key dynamic in E&P planning.

Independent oil companies

Independent producers are non-integrated, meaning they conduct only upstream activities. They are also typically concentrated in a single country, although they may have limited international operations. The decline of independents, as a result of industry consolidations driven by low oil prices has left a hole in the market. These companies were aggressive explorers, if not always financially successful, and helped access new reservoirs while also fully exploiting mature ones. Some still operate, but at a fraction of the market capitalization as IOCs.[17]

More recently, a new wave of independents has emerged: well-funded groups led by experienced executives, backed by large private equity groups. They are following the trail blazed in the U.S., where investors have poured capital into new companies developing shale formations. But outside North America, these independents are not active in unconventional reservoirs.[16]

In 2019, per the Independent Petroleum Association of America (IPAA), approximately 9,000 E&P independents existed, far more than integrated companies. Although independents lack the diversification that helps IOCs cope with market volatility, they can respond with more agility to ever-changing market conditions.

Performance and economics

Since its inception in the 1850s, the oil and gas industry has experienced many booms and busts. During the last 50 years, several key market adjustments have highlighted the cyclical nature of the industry and emphasized the effect of supply and demand on the industry's financial performance.

Recent industry performance

Oil prices will continue to be under pressure in 2020 as the world's major suppliers consisting of Russia, Saudi Arabia and the U.S. continue to pump more oil into the market. While the oil and gas sector, especially oil, had slowly recovered from the post-2014 downturn, prices collapsed again in March 2020 to similar levels as they did in 2015 and 2016, driven primarily by the same factors as the prior downturn, discussed subsequently herein. As a result, the industry is currently operating in a $30 per barrel price environment, despite oil prices reaching a high above $70 per barrel in the latter half of 2018 and stabilizing around $60 per barrel in late-2019.

The late-2014 price collapse ravaged the industry's financial performance. From the highs of 2008 to the lows of 2015 and 2016, the 50 largest global energy companies saw their market capitalization slashed by 50 percent and their operating profits reduced by approximately 80 percent. Three main factors contributed to this most recent downturn:

- **OPEC.** Watching an imminent price decline due to the supply and demand imbalance, OPEC was slow to cut its production, instead voting in November 2014 to keep its production steady, which significantly caused prices to plummet.

- **Growing supply.** Vast U.S. production from the shale revolution created excess supply while OPEC held its production steady. Today, the U.S. produces nearly double the amount of oil it did in the mid-2000s. Other countries also increased their production, particularly Canada, Libya and Russia.

- **Slowing demand.** Although the U.S. has recovered from the Great Recession, Japan and Europe still face economic difficulties. As a result, their demand for oil has slowed. In addition, as vehicles become more fuel-efficient, gasoline demand is decreasing.

This extreme collapse in oil and gas prices, and its expected long-lasting nature, forced petroleum executives to rethink all aspects of their businesses. Many shifted their strategies to focus on profit per barrel and free cash flow, rather than on producing high volumes and growing reserves at any cost.

Maximizing returns in the oil and gas industry has always required disciplined project evaluation and capital allocation. The most recent price collapse increased the importance of this critical capability.

Project economics and evaluation

In the oil and gas business, each project has a break-even point, when it begins to yield more cash than was spent to develop it. When the price of oil drops drastically, companies must respond by cutting costs on existing projects and developing only those in which anticipated revenues exceed the capital investment and operating costs. After the recent price collapse, E&P companies increasingly allocated capital to projects that produced positive cash flow.

During a long period in the mid-to-late 2000s, the cost to produce was higher than the price received. This trend reversed when companies cut costs in response to the 2014 price collapse and made more economical decisions about capital expenditures.

As emphasized in the energy value chain overview, the decision to explore and produce depends on each well's economics, requiring a detailed evaluation of the relative return on capital investment. Careful evaluation is especially important when prices are low, including analysis of cash-flow sensitivity and comparing various potential investments to identify which ones promise greater profits. Key questions that are often considered include:

- How will the well withstand price volatility?

- What is its break-even point?

- What is the pro forma effect on financial metrics?

With this information, executives can make educated decisions about capital allocation. The cash flow of a well is cyclical. Initially, cash flow will be negative, as the operator invests in exploration and development. As production ramps up, the well begins to show positive cash flow and eventually breaks even, generating a profit in periods after initial production. In later years of the well's life, production slows, cash flow decreases and ultimately the well reaches the end of its productive life.

Figure 2-5 depicts a simple example of how E&P companies analyze the economic practicality of a particular investment.

Figure 2-5

Representative cash flow analysis

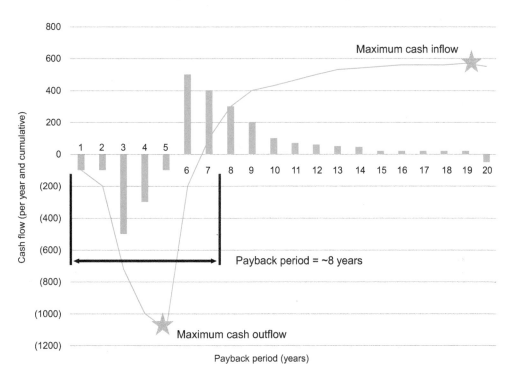

By understanding the long-term cash flow of a well, executives can plan capital expenditures and stagger project development. A well-rounded portfolio contains projects in the early stages of investment, balanced with assets near peak production as well as mature assets nearing the end of their productive lives. The peak-production assets generate high cash flow to support the capital needed for the new and aging assets, and the new assets will generate future cash flow.

● ● ●

1   Energy Information Administration. "Short-Term Energy Outlook." May 2019, www.eia.gov/outlooks/steo/archives/may19.pdf.

2   Energy Information Administration. "Annual Energy Outlook 2019." January 24, 2019, www.eia.gov/outlooks/aeo/pdf/aeo2019.pdf.

3   Office of Fossil Energy. "Liquefied Natural Gas." Energy.gov, www.energy.gov/fe/scienceinnovation/oil-gas/liquefied-natural-gas. Accessed October 2019.

4   "U.S. Oil and Natural Gas Led For New Energy Jobs in 2018," Forbes, March 2019, www.forbes.com/sites/judeclemente/2019/03/08/u-s-oil-and-natural-gas-led-for-newenergy-jobs-in-2018/#5d06eeb56805.

5   Matthews, Christopher M. "The Shale Revolution's Staggering Impact in Just One Word: Plastics," Wall Street Journal, June 25, 2017, www.wsj.com/articles/the-shale-revolutionsstaggering-impact-in-just-one-word-plastics-1498411792.

6   Energy Information Administration. "U.S. Natural Gas Marketed Production." www.eia.gov/dnav/ng/hist/n9050us2a.htm. Accessed April 2019.

7   Energy Information Administration. "Today in Energy." April 9, 2019, www.eia.gov/todayinenergy/detail.php?id=38992.

8   Energy Information Administration. "Today in Energy." May 21, 2018, www.eia.gov/todayinenergy/detail.php?id=36292.

9   Shelor, Jeremiah. "Natural Gas to Lead as Fossil Fuels Dominate Global Energy Mix Through 2040, Say Exporters." Natural Gas Intel, December 11, 2018, www.naturalgasintel.com/articles/116748-natural-gas-to-lead-as-fossil-fuels-dominateglobal-energy-mix-through-2040-say-exporters.

10 Energy Information Administration. "Oil: Crude and Petroleum Products Explained – Use of Oil." www.eia.gov/energyexplained/index.php?page=oil_use. Accessed October 2019.

11 CNBC. "Gas to overtake coal as world's second largest energy source by 2030, says IEA." November 13, 2018, www.cnbc.com/2018/11/13/gas-to-overtake-coal-as-second-largestenergy-source-by-2030-says-iea.html.

12 United Nations Conference on Trade and Development. "Least Developed Countries" unctad.org/en/Pages/ALDC/Least%20Developed%20Countries/LDCs.aspx.

13 Energy Information Administration. "International Energy Outlook 2018." July 2018, www.eia.gov/pressroom/presentations/capuano_07242018.pdf.

14 Amadeo, Kimberly. "OPEC and Its Goals, Members, and History," The Balance, www.thebalance.com/what-is-opec-its-members-and-history-3305872. Accessed November 2019.

15 Oil & Gas Journal. "Worldwide oil, natural gas reserves exhibit marginal increases." December 4, 2018, www.ogj.com/articles/print/volume-116/issue-12/special-reportworldwide-report/worldwide-oil-natural-gas-reserves-exhibit-marginal-increases.html.

16 Energy Information Administration. "Oil: Crude and Petroleum Products Explained – Where Our Oil Comes From." www.eia.gov/energyexplained/index.cfm? page=oil_where. Accessed May 2019.

17 Mills, Robin. "New wave of energy independents may change oil landscape." The National, October 28, 2018, www.thenational.ae/business/energy/new-wave-of-energy-independents-may-change-oil-landscape-1.785121.

CHAPTER 3

Organizational Structures of E&P Companies

Key concepts

- Considerations for structural decisions

- Key functions in independent E&P companies

- Organization of the accounting function

- Information systems

- Internal controls

- Considerations for restructuring

- Outside professional organizations

Like all enterprises, E&P companies implement organizational structures to meet their needs. The structures delegate authority and assign accountability in operations. Financial procedures, as well as the flow of paperwork, follow these lines of responsibility. Petroleum accountants should understand the roles and functions of departments within an E&P company. They can obtain this information through experience, inquiry and by reviewing organizational charts and company operating manuals.

One important aspect of an organization's structure is its system of internal controls. This chapter describes the source of internal control standards and suggests ways to assess and quantify risks. Although the organizational structures of companies in the petroleum industry vary widely, an E&P company is structured to perform the primary steps in the E&P life cycle, which is dependent on the company's size and diversity of activities.

Oil and gas producers in the U.S. are classified as either independents or integrated companies. Globally, they may also be classified as NOCs, as discussed in Chapter 2. Independents typically are viewed by the public as smaller companies with few employees, while integrated companies are typically thought of as being much larger entities. In practice, however, several large oil and gas companies do not refine or market and some integrated companies are small by comparison.

A company's size and degree of integration often determine its organizational structure, as does the geographical dispersion of its activities. It makes sense for an E&P company that operates in a single region to expect close managerial control from its top officials. When operations expand geographically, top management can look to regional and district managers to exert local control, while the primary or corporate office manages overall activities. An integrated company requires an even greater degree of delegated authority and responsibility from top management to those directly involved in its diverse operations.

Considerations for structural decisions

Designing an organization is not simply an exercise in drawing boxes and lines to create an organizational chart. It defines how the organization will look in terms of organizational structure, as well as the functional operating model to achieve business objectives.

By taking a methodical approach to answering several key questions, enterprises can ensure that their resources are aligned to their strategic intent, they are organized to make the most of their distinct competitive position and culture, and their capital, operating and administrative costs are optimized for their business. Organizations should consider many factors and assess a number of questions when structuring or restructuring their companies, as discussed herein.

Aligning to strategic intent

Organizations should ensure the function of each organizational component **aligns to the strategy** of the enterprise.

- *Critical work is organized effectively.* Should operational support functions (marketing, drilling, etc.) be centralized or decentralized?

- *There is adequate management coverage.* Do we need executive leaders for both onshore and offshore operations, or does the scale of our business better justify having just one executive leader?

Another factor to consider is whether the structure will achieve the desired level of **accountability**.

- *Roles are defined and decision rights established.* How do we operate the organization and clarify accountabilities?

- *Performance measurement and management criteria are clearly established and communicated.* What changes are needed to the planning and performance management cycle (long-range planning, incentive programs, etc.) to promote the desired behavior and performance outcomes?

Integration of the enterprise's business processes is another key component requiring analysis.

- *Effective links exist between organizational components that prevent siloed behavior.* Do people in the organization work together well or are there missed opportunities and/or friction in handoffs?

- *The organizational structure promotes the development and protection of specialists.* Are we organized around current capabilities or are we strategically building the right capabilities for five, 10 and 15 or more years from now?

Enterprise structures are **optimal** when companies have the right people doing the right tasks at the right time.

- *The organization is flexible and responsive to change.* Is the right work being done, by the right people, at the right cost point?

- *The right people are within the organization and their skill levels match appropriately to the roles they are filling.* Are organizational efficiencies lost due to under-trained or over-qualified employees?

- *The organization is cost-optimized and right-sized.* Does the overall cost structure achieve the targeted results in the long-range plan? Are these costs properly consumed across and within our targeted goals for capital expenditures, operating expenditures and selling, general and administrative expenditures?

Aligning to competitive advantage and culture

E&P companies typically follow three "pure-play" organizational structures; however, many create a hybrid of the three, seeking to maximize their ability to execute strategy among interdependent factors (e.g., strategic differentiators, inherent skills and capabilities, patents and know-how, executive preference, etc.).

The three pure-play organizational structures are:

Functional. Organized around major activities such as exploration, land, drilling, development, production, transportation, accounting, finance, marketing, trading, human resources and environmental, health and safety. Functional structures typically are chosen by organizations that focus on functional excellence. The organization groups itself in specialist-functional teams, bringing together specialist skills and specialist functions to serve multiple customers or constituents. Organizations that align functionally must establish incentives to encourage leaders to work together across functional lines.

Geographical. Organized around regions, producing basins and formations or another basis depending on the company's asset locations. Examples of geographical structures include regions such as North America, Latin America, the Middle East, North Africa and Turkey (MENAT), Asia Pacific (AsiaPac), Europe and Caspian. Companies may also structure on the basis of basins and formations such as the Permian Basin, Eagle Ford Shale, Canadian Tar Sands, North Sea, Gulf of Mexico, etc. Companies that organize geographically seek to quickly deal with and adapt to local and regional requirements and opportunities. Prioritizing regional agility, these organizations typically assign redundant management and back-office functions to support each geography, which can lead to a higher cost structure.

Process. Much more mature than the traditional functional or geographical organizations, process organizations rarely are pure plays, but instead they represent more of a hybrid structure. Resources are allocated to execute a major process such as "explore-to-develop," "quote-to-cash," "hire-to-retire," etc. Because process owners are responsible for optimizing the end-to-end execution of the process, they receive the enterprise resources they need, including cross-functional support. For example, in a quote-to-cash process, the enterprise might require a combination of resources to execute the defined end-to-end process: sales, marketing, production, transportation, accounting, finance, treasury, human resources and supply chain. To optimize execution, all of these resources should work together and report to the enterprise process owner.

Optimizing the organizational structure

With the organizational rationale established, and the broad, preferred structure selected, the enterprise assembles its field and functional assets to achieve its desired outcomes. At this stage, it is important for leaders to understand the functions they already have (versus what they may need), the maturity of the organization's skills and capabilities, their preferences concerning centralization or decentralization of decisions, and their optimal span of control and management layers, each of which is discussed herein.

Function. What does the organization do?

- Are processes well-defined for the work performed?

- Is the work to achieve all processes performed by someone who knows that he or she is responsible?

- What work is being done today and by whom?

- How does the organization group, by function, the work performed?

- Is the work performed internally or externally by a third party?

Organizational skills and capabilities. How well does the organization execute its functions?

- What is the degree of current organizational skill?

- How long has the organization performed the functions?

- How mature is the organization?

- How well-trained are employees in their jobs?

- Are employees currently performing the functional activities or are they managing and coordinating a third party who is performing the activities on their behalf?

Centralization versus decentralization. Who makes what decisions and controls what resources? Centralization decisions form an iron triangle of cost, risk and value. Ultimately, they must be assessed against the ability of the enterprise to sustain them over the long-term.

Centralization is the degree to which coordination and control are managed by a core person or organizational level, usually corporate headquarters. Reasons to centralize include:

- *Regulatory complexity*. Legal or regulatory environments are difficult to interpret.

- *Commonality*. Local decisions affect the entire company (e.g., labor-union negotiations).

- *Cost*. A centralized function can be managed with fewer resources, offering economies of scale.

- *New technology*. Technologies can enable decentralized companies to consolidate their workforce and resources.

Decentralization is the degree to which subunits of the company and individual managers are responsible for coordination and control, rather than corporate headquarters or one specific level of the hierarchy. Reasons to decentralize include:

- *Responsiveness.* When decisions are pushed to the local level, companies can respond faster to opportunities and local conditions.

- *Independence.* Autonomy stimulates creativity and independence in lower-level employees and helps develop them for higher-level roles.

- *New technology.* Technology can help leaders delegate authority to lower levels, while keeping top management informed.

Factors that drive the decision to centralize or decentralize include:

- *Duration.* How far in the future do decisions commit the organization? How quickly can they be reversed? Generally speaking, the more long-term the decisions and the more difficult they are to reverse, the greater the need to involve senior decision-makers in a more centralized structure.

- *Effect.* How does the decision affect other departments, divisions or the organization as a whole? The more decisions affect the entire organization or other parts of the organization, the greater the need for a more centralized structure involving senior decision-makers.

- *Cost.* What is the cost of implementing decisions – not only resources, but also intangibles such as customer confidence, employee morale, brand, etc.? What would it cost to reverse the decision and its consequences? The higher the cost, the greater the need to centralize the organizational structure of the company.

Span of control. Who reports to whom in the organizational hierarchy? Span of control decisions are based on multiple factors including:

- *How many direct reports do supervisors oversee and are there opportunities to consolidate?* More managers equals higher organizational costs.

- *How different are the skill sets that supervisors manage?* Employees expect their supervisors to understand their functional skills well enough to lead, coach and develop their teams successfully. As the breadth of skills under one manager expands, his or her direct reports must compensate for the manager's potential skill gaps. This can affect span of control because it relates directly to the breadth of disparate skills under a single manager.

- *What is the degree of strategy or transaction in a given function?* The more strategic the work, the more narrow the span of control. For example, corporate strategy and highly strategic merger and acquisition functions are typically smaller in span with employee-supervisor ratios of 5-to-1 to 7-to-1. The more transactional the function, the higher the span of control can be, such as call centers with ratios of 50-to-1.

Management layers. What is the nature of the organizational hierarchy and culture?

- *Tall organizations.* With a higher command and control culture, communication is slower and likely less accurate as one moves down the organization. Decisions are also typically slower as individuals must run things up the chain of command. The span of control is narrower, and supervision is tighter; however, more opportunities may exist for promotion as there are more steps in the corporate ladder.

- *Flat organizations.* The culture is more agile and entrepreneurial than in tall organizations. Communication is faster and less distorted, and decisions tend to be faster and more responsive. Employees at lower levels feel more in touch with top management; however, they generally must be more self-sufficient, requiring fewer support structures. Additionally, there may be fewer opportunities for promotion within the organization.

Key functions in independent E&P companies

Independent E&P companies have much in common, especially at the executive level. Below is a summary of the four distinct activities conducted by almost all producers. Each activity is discussed in more detail in the subsequent sections herein.

Exploration. The exploration department locates and acquires oil and gas reserves. This includes obtaining mineral properties and conducting geological and geophysical (G&G) studies, either through the use of company-owned equipment and personnel or through contracts with exploration support companies. Many E&P companies, even very small ones, keep one or more geologists on staff, although most companies also hire outside professionals or organizations for G&G services.

Drilling, development and production. The drilling, development and production department is responsible for exploratory drilling, development drilling, enhanced recovery operations and field production. In some companies, this may be the petroleum engineering department.

Marketing. The sale and transport of produced oil and gas is typically arranged by the marketing department. U.S. crude oil is typically sold near the well site and transported by pipeline, truck or rail car. Natural gas, on the other hand, is frequently sold to large gas consumers and utilities situated far from the lease, which requires pipeline infrastructure to transport the product from the well site.

Administrative. With responsibility for handling general office functions and stakeholder relations, the administrative department oversees human resources, accounting, finance, tax compliance, information systems, public relations and legal services. Some companies break these functions into separate departments, depending on their organizational structure.

The organizational chart in Figure 3-1 reflects this basic structure. Note that some companies have modified their approach by creating multidisciplinary teams of geologists, petroleum engineers, accountants and other specialists to manage assigned fields or geographic areas.

Typically, especially in smaller independent E&P companies, the CEO has a technical background (e.g., petroleum or reservoir engineer, geologist, geophysicist) and not only serves as CEO, but also may direct the company's exploration, development or production activities. The CEO of a small company may also negotiate joint venture agreements, major property acquisitions and divestitures and financing arrangements.

Exploration department

The exploration department identifies and acquires properties that may contain oil and gas, conducts G&G studies and, in some cases, supervises the drilling of exploratory wells. The work of the exploration department may be delegated to several different groups, as depicted in Figure 3-1 and described below.

Figure 3-1

Basic structure of an independent petroleum company

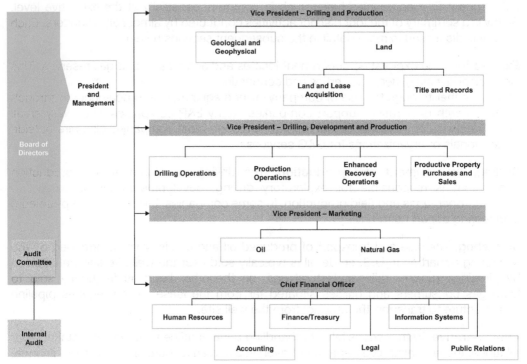

Geological and geophysical. Accumulates and analyzes geological and geophysical (G&G) information to help decide:

- Which leases to obtain in an area of interest.

- Whether exploratory wells should be drilled and in what locations.

Land. Acquires mineral properties and maintains records of properties owned. As shown in Figure 3-1, the work is carried out by two divisions: (1) the land and lease acquisition division and (2) the title and records division.

The manager of the land department is called a landman. He or she identifies and communicates with mineral rights owners to negotiate leases. A landman may also refer to an independent lease broker. Land departments sometimes ask independent lease brokers who are familiar with a particular state, region or basin to represent the company when negotiating with owners of mineral and surface rights and to check local title records.

The land and lease acquisition group advises exploration department managers about leasing activities. It also makes pooling and unitization agreements with lessees of properties that adjoin the company's leases. The title and records division checks new leases for legal propriety, maintains a complete file for all properties and ensures the timely payment of authorized lease rentals.

Drilling, development and production department

The overall objective of the drilling, development and production department is to safely manage the company's wells and production operations. This group seeks to maximize production value while complying with applicable government regulations. It often is called the petroleum engineering department, and its managers and core personnel typically are petroleum engineers.

Larger companies may group petroleum engineers into categories such as exploitation engineers, reservoir engineers and production engineers:

- Exploitation engineers address how best to exploit a field via drilling and enhanced recovery methods. They prepare or review justifications for drilling expenditures and advise about the technical phases of exploitation, drilling, completion, fluid recovery and remedial work.

- Reservoir engineers study oil and gas reservoir performance, calculate recovery and profitability and devise means of increasing ultimate recovery. They prepare internal reports of estimated reserves by well, field, region and company. They also work with independent engineering firms that produce reports of the company's reserves.

- Production engineers manage producing fields, including drilling, well completion, production handling and treatment, and equipment selection and design.

Drilling operations. In most cases, an E&P company outsources drilling operations to contractors rather than maintaining its own equipment. It is not unusual, however, for the owners of an E&P company with producing properties to organize and operate an independent drilling company. In this case, the drilling superintendent oversees all drilling activities, including rigs, tools and equipment. Drilling operations are described at length in Chapter 8.

Production operations. A typical oil and gas producing company hires a production foreman or manager for each field. In addition, pumpers or gaugers measure and control production, as discussed further in Chapter 11. Maintenance, infrequent repairs and mechanical tasks often are carried out by specialist subcontractors.

Enhanced recovery operations. Some companies distinguish between the routine operation of fields where normal reservoir pressure propels oil and gas into the wells and those that supplement reservoir pressure to increase production. Enhanced recovery includes secondary recovery methods, such as waterflooding, and tertiary recovery methods, such as steamflooding. Because of their technical natures and extremely high costs, secondary and tertiary projects require special attention and supervision.

Productive property purchases and sales. A separate department often handles the purchase and sale of property with proved reserves. In some cases, these duties may be assigned to the production department since petroleum engineers evaluate potential acquisitions and sales of proved property.

Other departmental functions. Many support activities are necessary to operate an oil and gas company efficiently. For example, materials needed in the field must be warehoused and trucks or other forms of transportation must be available. Field associates carry out routine functions, such as correspondence and payroll. Although supervised by a production manager, field associates frequently work under the functional supervision of the administrative department.

Marketing department

Depending on its organizational structure and size, a company will sell its oil and gas production through one or more marketing departments or subsidiaries. Close coordination is required among marketing, production and administrative departments.

Oil marketing is in a mature stage, especially when compared with natural gas marketing. Generally, oil is marketed under 30-day contracts and sold at the lease site at wellhead prices that are posted (published) by the oil purchaser or a major oil company. While the contract term is typically 30 days, most contracts are considered evergreen, whereby they automatically renew each month.

Natural gas sales have undergone many changes in recent years. Historically, natural gas and casinghead gas (wet gas produced along with crude oil) were marketed to pipeline companies which then sold the gas to others. Today, gas is marketed by producers, large and small, to many types of gas customers (except residential).

Chapter 27 describes in more detail how both oil and gas are marketed, while Chapter 28 outlines the accounting treatment of these sales under Accounting Standards Codification (ASC) 606, *Revenue from Contracts with Customers*.

Administrative department

In smaller, independent oil and gas companies, the CFO typically oversees the administrative department. Administration encompasses a variety of activities and may consist of multiple divisions, sections or offices, as shown in Figure 3-1. The administrative structure of an E&P company differs little from that found in other types of businesses. Accounting functions related to oil and gas companies are described briefly in the next section.

Organization of the accounting function

A number of groups comprise the accounting department of an E&P company, although the organizational structure for integrated companies is typically more complex than that of independents.

Integrated E&P companies

The organizational structure for an integrated E&P company's accounting department typically includes additional levels of corporate and functional oversight roles common in larger companies, particularly those with international operations. Similar to an independent E&P company in Figure 3-3, Figure 3-2 identifies the corporate controller as having direct oversight of the accounting department.

Figure 3-2

Integrated E&P – Organization of the accounting function

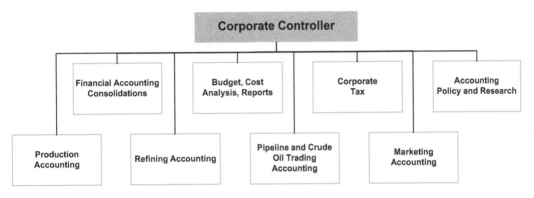

Independent E&P companies

As depicted in Figure 3-1, the organizational structure for an independent E&P company's accounting department is typically within the realm of responsibility of the CFO, although it may also reside with the CAO depending on company-specific roles. Within the accounting department, the controller or assistant controller reports to the CFO or CAO and is responsible for the various groups within the department as depicted below.

Figure 3-3

Independent E&P – Organization of the accounting function

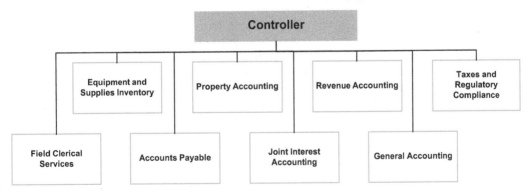

Common tasks within each group are discussed in further detail below.

Equipment and supplies inventory. Responsible for equipment and supplies inventory records, inventory pricing, warehouse tracking and field transfers.

Property accounting. Maintains subsidiary records for proved and unproved properties, work-in-progress, lease and well equipment and field service units; accounts for property and equipment acquisitions, reclassifications, amortization, impairment, retirements and sales; calculates capital expenditure accruals and performs analysis of accrual amounts to budgeted amounts and actual costs incurred.

Revenue accounting. Maintains oil and gas revenue records for each property; accounts for volumes sold and verifies prices reflected in revenues received; computes and validates production taxes; maintains property records for regulatory compliance and production taxation; invoices purchasers for sales of natural gas and calculates revenue accruals.

The group also typically validates amounts due to royalty owners and joint interest owners based on division of interest (DOI) information provided by the land department and maintains ledgers of undistributed revenue payments for:

- Owners with unsigned division orders.

- Owners whose interests are suspended because of estate issues.

- Other undistributed production payments.

Taxes and regulatory compliance. Prepares required federal, state, county and local tax returns for income, production, property and employment taxes; prepares other regulatory reports as required; addresses allowable options for minimizing taxes.

Field clerical services. Trains and supervises clerical personnel assigned to field operations; develops systems, forms, processes and procedures for field accounting and reporting.

Accounts payable. Maintains records of accounts payable; prepares vouchers for disbursements; distributes royalty payments; maintains corporate delegated limits of authority and verifies that disbursements take place within those limits.

Joint interest accounting. Maintains files related to all joint operations in which the company has a working interest; prepares billings to joint owners; reviews billings from joint owners; prepares statements for jointly operated properties; prepares payout status reports; tracks capital and operating expenditures according to farmin and farmout agreements; arranges or conducts joint interest audits of billings and revenue distributions from joint venture operations; responds to joint interest audits by other joint interest owners.

General accounting. Maintains the voucher register, cash receipts, disbursement records and general ledger; prepares financial statements and other special reports; prepares budgets and associated reports. Depending on the size of the company, some of the general accounting functions may be performed by treasury, finance, or other groups outside of the accounting department.

Information systems

E&P companies vary in their employment of information and accounting systems. System platforms may be mainframe, midsize or desktop computers. Several third-party software packages are available as well. Furthermore, the advent and deployment of cloud technologies is changing the landscape of not only the E&P industry, but also other relevant and related industries.

Ownership complexities

An E&P company's information system typically employs a DOI master file, which reflects how revenues and costs will be shared for each well or other accounting unit for a designated time. The land department typically maintains the accuracy and completeness of the DOI master file. Departments that use the file include property accounting, accounts payable, revenue accounting, joint interest accounting and reservoir engineering.

A revenue information system also allocates incoming sales proceeds to appropriate owners, such as the company, joint venture partners, royalty owners and production taxing authorities. The system's purchasing component includes functions for allocating costs to appropriate parties, such as the company and joint venture partners. Therefore, the revenue system must account for incoming cash as well as outgoing distributions of revenue, and the purchasing system must account for purchases and invoicing of other parties for their contractual shares of those costs.

The information system and its chart of accounts are complicated by the need to account for:

- Revenue and cost DOI at a well level.

- Tax accounting, separate from financial accounting and reporting.

- Each well's and each field's gross revenues and cost activity for management review, as well as the net revenues and costs to the company for external reporting.

Information for agile business decisions

In their daily activities, E&P companies must identify, collect, organize and distribute massive amounts of data. The information systems they employ not only produce accounting records, but also aid in operational decision-making, management of joint interests and risk management. Information system technologies continuously evolve to meet the heavy demands of the oil and gas industry.

Today's information systems track activity, resource allocation, investments and production flow across the life cycle of a well, from initial exploration to decommissioning. These new systems make the most of the "internet of things" (IoT), combining sensors, radio-frequency identification markers and pressure/flow meters to gather data produced in the field. Once aggregated, this data can be manipulated and analyzed using software for advanced data visualization and predictive analytics, supplying business information that was unavailable previously. These new technologies enable management teams, as well as production and reservoir engineers, to make better and faster decisions, improving both return on investment and operating cost metrics.

Technology continues to evolve rapidly, with broad implications for the workforce of an E&P company. The introduction of robotic process automation (RPA) and artificial intelligence (AI) is already affecting areas such as accounts payable, supply chain management and equipment inspections – areas where repeatable tasks can be completed continuously, without error, quickly scaling up or down as business conditions warrant.

As AI evolves, some companies are investigating situations in which technology can perform more value-added functions, such as diagnostic, deterministic, analytic and predictive activities that typically have been the sole responsibility of human employees. This shift will affect traditional organizational structures in myriad ways.

Once AI shifts the workforce composition from entirely humans to include more automations, E&P companies will need to hire more technologists who can program and maintain their RPA co-workers. In addition, internal controls will need to adjust, since automations do not require the same level of anti-fraud protection as their human counterparts. These protections include segregation-of-duty (SOD) and limitation-of-authority (LOA) policies required by regulation, such as Sarbanes-Oxley (SOX) and the Committee of Sponsoring Organizations of the Treadway Commission (COSO), both described in more detail in the next section.

Internal controls

As for any enterprise, internal controls are important for an E&P company. Companies should consider both the 2013 Internal Control – Integrated Framework, commissioned by COSO (the COSO Framework), as well as the requirements of the Public Company Accounting Oversight Board (PCAOB) and the Securities and Exchange Commission (SEC).

COSO Framework

The COSO Framework clarifies that internal control demands more than strict adherence to policies and procedures; it requires the use of judgment exercised at every level of the organization. The COSO Framework defines internal control as:

> "[A] process, effected by an entity's board of directors, management, and other personnel, designed to provide reasonable assurance regarding the achievement of objectives relating to operations, reporting, and compliance... The Framework provides for three categories of objectives, which allow organizations to focus on differing aspects of internal control:
>
> - Operations Objectives – These pertain to effectiveness and efficiency of the entity's operations, including operational and financial performance goals, and safeguarding assets against loss.
>
> - Reporting Objectives – These pertain to internal and external financial and non-financial reporting and may encompass reliability, timeliness, transparency, or other terms as set forth by regulators, recognized standard setters, or the entity's policies.
>
> - Compliance Objectives – These pertain to adherence to laws and regulations to which the entity is subject."

The five integrated components of internal control outlined in the COSO Framework are:

- **Control environment**. This environment sets the tone for an organization and influences the control consciousness of its people. It is the foundation for all other components of internal control, providing discipline and structure. Control environment factors include: the integrity, ethical values and competence of the entity's people, management philosophy and operating style, management's assignment of authority and responsibility, and how it organizes and develops people as well as the attention and direction provided by the board of directors.

- **Risk assessment**. Management identifies and analyzes current and future risks faced by its organization, quantifying them and projecting their likelihood and possible consequences. Management decides how much risk is tolerable and at what cost. Managers of E&P companies should set clear objectives and understand the risks in their areas. In too many cases, risk evaluations are informal and controls are assumed to be adequate. One solution is a tool known as a risk matrix which lists major business components or processes across the top axis and related major risks down the left side. Once the risks are identified within the risk matrix, managers can evaluate the probability of occurrence and the potential effect on the company.

- **Control activities**. To minimize identified risks, managers of E&P organizations must establish and execute control policies and procedures according to company objectives.

- **Information and communication**. E&P companies must implement these systems to support their risk management.

- **Monitoring**. Internal control processes should be monitored and modified as necessary, enabling the company to respond to a changing environment.

Sarbanes-Oxley Act

The Sarbanes-Oxley Act, also known as the Public Company Accounting Reform and Investor Protection Act of 2002 (the Act), was enacted in July 2002, largely in response to major corporate and accounting scandals involving several prominent U.S. companies. These scandals created an unprecedented lack of confidence in the financial markets and a loss of public trust in corporate accounting and reporting. The Act brought about the most extensive reform in U.S. financial markets since the Securities Act of 1933 and the Securities Exchange Act of 1934.

The Act required public companies to develop new practices for corporate governance and financial reporting, seeking to restore public trust in the capital markets. One of the most challenging aspects of the law addressed corporate responsibility for internal controls. Titled *Management's Assessment of Internal Controls*, Section 404 requires most public companies and their auditors to report annually on the effectiveness of the company's internal control over financial reporting.

Section 404 also required the SEC to develop and publish rules for management's assessment of internal control. These rules were completed in 2003 and initially issued in 2004, with subsequent updates as discussed herein. The Act also authorized the PCAOB to establish auditing and related professional practice standards for registered public accounting firms.

The PCAOB issued Auditing Standard No. 5, *An Audit of Internal Control Over Financial Reporting That Is Integrated With An Audit of Financial Statements* (AS 5), in May 2007, which replaced Auditing Standard No. 2 issued in June 2004. On March 31, 2015, the PCAOB adopted amendments that reorganized the auditing standards. Accordingly, AS 2201 became effective as of December 31, 2016.

The SEC rules and the PCAOB standards require: (1) management to formally assess internal controls, including tests to confirm their design and operating effectiveness, (2) management to include in its annual report on Form 10-K an assessment of its internal controls and (3) external auditors to provide two opinions as part of a single, integrated audit – that is, the traditional opinion about the financial statements, plus an independent opinion about the effectiveness of internal controls, although the external auditors may also combine the financial statement opinion and the internal controls opinion.

The SEC requires management to base its evaluation on a suitable, recognized control framework. The majority of public companies required to follow Section 404 use the criteria established in the COSO Framework described herein.

Considerations for restructuring

The global oil commodity market began to experience price declines in late-2014. E&P companies that were structured previously to grow in a price environment of more than $100 per barrel began to downsize when it became apparent that the downturn might be long-term.

The decision to restructure an organization should not be taken lightly. Restructuring can disrupt business performance as employees try to protect their positions while attempting to understand new expectations and how the new business will operate. Removing costs from the business in an effort to survive commodity cycles, as mentioned above, is a normal reason to consider restructuring, but other strategic reasons are equally important.

Prime candidates for restructuring include businesses that face a strategic shift, such as a fundamental change in business strategy, market entries or exits, value proposition or product positioning, as well as those undergoing a merger, acquisition or divestiture. These businesses should typically take a fresh look at their field operations to ensure their resources are properly positioned to execute their new strategy. Markets that were investment targets now may require retrenchment or new partnerships to achieve further growth. Back-office functions such as human resources, finance and supply chain operations may be prime targets for consolidation into a shared services center or outsourcing to lower-cost, third-party providers.

Companies undergoing performance improvement or other enterprise transformations often choose to review how their structures can successfully execute newly designed processes or implement new technology, such as enterprise resource planning (ERP) systems. These companies likely will spend time understanding how their improvement efforts will affect responsibility and decision-governance models, as well as any skill or capability gaps they must close for successful change.

Outside professional organizations

In the course of conducting business, an E&P company interacts with a variety of outside parties. Some provide needed technical services, such as drilling rigs and supplies. Certain governmental entities also regulate the industry. Trade organizations provide membership benefits, such as shared information and training opportunities. The following list, not intended to be comprehensive, identifies several of these organizations.

- **American Association of Professional Landmen.** The American Association of Professional Landmen (AAPL) develops model industry forms, including AAPL Form 610 for operating agreements.

- **American Petroleum Institute.** The American Petroleum Institute (API) fosters cooperation among industry and government agencies. A large and influential organization, it is involved in many research projects for the industry. API also develops and distributes training films and publications.

- **Council of Petroleum Accountants Societies.** The Council of Petroleum Accountants Societies (COPAS) develops educational materials and standardized forms that facilitate the practice of petroleum accounting. Guidelines and forms are issued as COPAS model form accounting procedure exhibits. Virtually every U.S. E&P joint operating agreement includes a completed COPAS exhibit that describes billing, accounting and auditing procedures and rights for joint venture partners. COPAS also issues interpretations of bulletins and publishes the *COPAS Accounts* newsletter. There are 25 regional societies active in major oil and gas producing areas of the U.S. and Canada, with the organization's national office located in Wichita, Kansas.

- **Energy Information Administration.** The Energy Information Administration (EIA) is a division of the U.S. Department of Energy (DOE). The agency monitors the petroleum industry and provides statistical histories, forecasts and analyses of domestic and international petroleum industry activities.

- **Independent Petroleum Association of America.** The Independent Petroleum Association of America (IPAA) is the national trade association for independent producers. On behalf of its members, it lobbies legislative and regulatory bodies. IPAA publishes economic and statistical information about the domestic E&P industry, including historically *The Oil and Gas Producing Industry in Your State*, which provides upstream state-by-state data.

- **National Petroleum Council.** The National Petroleum Council (NPC) is a group of experienced industry executives, many currently employed by petroleum companies. NPC advises on petroleum issues and provides studies for the DOE.

- **Office of Natural Resources Revenue, Bureau of Ocean Energy Management and Bureau of Safety and Environmental Enforcement.** The former U.S. Department of Interior Minerals Management Service was reorganized in 2010 and renamed the Bureau of Ocean Energy Management, Regulation and Enforcement (BOEMRE). Subsequently, to replace BOEMRE, three independent agencies were formed. The Office of Natural Resources Revenue (ONRR) manages the revenue collection function from U.S. offshore resources on the Outer Continental Shelf, as well as onshore federal and Native American lands. The Bureau of Ocean Energy Management (BOEM) manages the development of offshore resources, with a focus on environmental and economic responsibility. The Bureau of Safety and Environmental Enforcement (BSEE) enforces safety and environmental regulations, including permitting, inspections and oil spill responses offshore.

- **Regional trade associations.** Well-known regional associations include:

  - Independent Petroleum Association of Mountain States (IPAMS), based in Colorado.

  - Louisiana Oil & Gas Association (LOGA).

  - Oklahoma Independent Petroleum Association (OIPA).

  - Texas Independent Producers and Royalty Owners Association (TIPRO).

  - U.S. Oil & Gas Association, based in Washington, D.C.

- **Society of Petroleum Engineers.** The Society of Petroleum Engineers (SPE), with headquarters in Richardson, Texas, is an international technical and professional association of more than 150,000 members. It publishes the monthly *Journal of Petroleum Technology* (*JPT*). In June 2018, SPE updated its *Petroleum Resources Management System* (PRMS) framework. Developed in conjunction with the World Petroleum Council, American Association of Petroleum Geologists and Society of Petroleum Evaluation Engineers, the update replaced the joint industry guidelines issued in 1997, 2000 and 2001, as well as the previous PRMS framework from March 2007 (see Chapter 15 for details).

- **Society of Petroleum Evaluation Engineers.** The Society of Petroleum Evaluation Engineers (SPEE), based in Houston, Texas, consists of a few hundred experienced reservoir evaluation petroleum engineers. Each spring, SPEE surveys fair-market-value parameters for oil and gas producing properties. SPEE and SPE jointly developed the 1987 *Definitions for Oil and Gas Reserves* and SPEE developed the 1988 *Guidelines for Application of the Definitions for Oil and Gas Reserves*.

- **State oil and gas conservation commissions.** Each state with petroleum production typically operates an agency that issues permits for proposed oil and gas wells and monitors drilling and production. Well operators may be required to file monthly reports with the state commission regarding each well's production of oil, gas and water. An example of this type of agency is the Railroad Commission of Texas.

• • •

CHAPTER

4

Accounting Principles for Oil and Gas Production

U.S. E&P companies follow one of two methods of financial accounting and reporting for oil and gas properties: successful efforts or full cost. Both methods are specified in the Financial Accounting Standards Board (FASB) ASC as accounting principles generally accepted in the U.S. (GAAP). The comprehensive standard for full cost accounting is Regulation S-X Rule 4-10,[1] which is included in ASC 932-10-S99.

History of accounting methods

Of the 20 largest publicly traded U.S. petroleum companies, 18 currently use successful efforts. Of the next 80 largest oil and gas companies, 49 of them use successful efforts and the remainder use full cost.[2] The full cost concept is especially popular with small and medium-sized oil and gas companies given it is generally less complex than successful efforts. Major provisions of the successful efforts and full cost methods are summarized in the pages that follow.

Evolution of regulation

Successful efforts accounting in various forms has been used for more than 80 years. The application of full cost accounting began in the 1950s. By the mid–1960s, accountants and analysts became concerned about the diversity of accounting methods used by oil and gas companies, not only successful efforts and full cost but also many variations in applying them. Because of these inconsistencies, it became difficult to compare financial statements of oil and gas companies. The American Institute of Certified Public Accountants' (AICPA) 1969 Accounting Research Study No. 11 (ARS 11) suggested the elimination of the full cost method, recommending the successful efforts method as the sole standard for oil and gas accounting.

The next major event was the OPEC oil embargo of 1973. It generated intense public and Congressional interest, culminating in the Energy Policy and Conservation Act of 1975 (EPCA). The EPCA called for establishing a national energy database, complete with financial information. Consistent accounting practices were to be developed for use by all oil and gas producers in their reports to the DOE and all producers would be required to adopt the same accounting method. The SEC assumed responsibility for compiling the practices; however, it was permitted to delegate the task to the FASB as long as the final work product was acceptable to the SEC.

In December 1977, the FASB issued its Statement of Financial Accounting Standards No. 19 (FAS 19), *Financial Accounting and Reporting for Oil and Gas Producing Companies*. FAS 19 prescribed a version of the successful efforts method of accounting for determining capitalized costs, conveyances of mineral interests, comprehensive deferred income tax allocations and specific audited disclosures of proved oil and gas reserves and certain costs related to mineral activities. FAS 19 was to take effect for fiscal years beginning after December 15, 1978.

FAS 19 was harshly criticized at SEC hearings in March and April 1978, primarily by independent oil and gas producers. By August 1978, the SEC issued its Accounting Series Release (ASR) No. 253. It concluded that successful efforts and full cost accounting did not provide meaningful financial statements because neither method: (1) recognized the value of the oil and gas reserves discovered or (2) reflected the discovery activities' true income (i.e., reserves value added, less related discovery costs).

Within ASR No. 253, the SEC proposed a new, revolutionary method known as "reserve recognition accounting" (RRA). Under RRA, a value was to be assigned to proved oil and gas reserves, computed under rather arbitrary rules, with changes in the reserves' value reflected in earnings as the changes occurred. Until the RRA method and standards for valuing new reserves could be developed, the SEC allowed registrants to use either the FAS 19 successful efforts method or an SEC-prescribed full cost method for audited financial statements. The SEC required, however, the inclusion of supplemental information based on the RRA method.

In December 1978, the SEC issued ASR No. 257 and ASR No. 258, addressing rules for successful efforts and full cost accounting, respectively. Successful efforts rules were essentially the same as those found in FAS 19.

After the SEC's action allowing registrants to use either the successful efforts or full cost method, the FASB issued FAS 25 in February 1979 for public and private companies. It suspended most of the accounting provisions of FAS 19 for an indefinite period. FAS 25 preferred the successful efforts method, as prescribed by FAS 19, but it was not mandatory. Certain provisions of FAS 19 relating to deferred income taxes, mineral property conveyances, unproved property impairment and disclosure requirements were substantially retained and made effective.

In 1979 and again in 1980, the SEC postponed its requirement for audited reserve information. Finally, in 1981, the SEC dropped the audit requirement, allowing the disclosure of proved reserves to be outside the financial statements.

In February 1981, the SEC announced that RRA had shortcomings that made it inappropriate for adoption as the primary basis of accounting. At the same time, the SEC announced that the FASB would develop supplemental disclosure requirements for oil and gas companies. FAS 69, *Disclosures about Oil and Gas Producing Activities,* was issued in November 1982, and its disclosure rules were adopted the next month, with only minor revisions by the SEC. The rules did not require an earnings summary, as previously required under RRA, but did call for unaudited disclosures of the present value of the future cash flows from production of proved reserves based on specified assumptions.

FASB codification

Controversy over the two accounting methods flared up again briefly in 1986 when the staff of the Chief Accountant's Office of the SEC recommended the elimination of the full cost method for public companies. Commission members rejected the proposal and both methods continue to be accepted for financial accounting and reporting purposes under GAAP.

Accounting for impairment. In March 1995, the FASB issued FAS 121 regarding accounting for the impairment of long-lived assets. These rules were superseded by the October 2001 publication of FAS 144, *Accounting for the Impairment of Long-Lived Assets* (see Chapter 17). A long-lived asset is deemed impaired if the associated expected future cash flows (undiscounted and without interest or income taxes) are less than the asset's net book value. A loss on impairment is recognized by reducing the impaired asset's net book value to fair value.

Effective July 1, 2009, the FASB released the ASC. Its objective was to simplify user access to authoritative literature and include all authoritative GAAP in a topic-based codification. The guidance for successful efforts and full cost accounting, FAS 19 and Reg. S-X Rule 4-10, respectively, was codified as ASC 932, while FAS 144 was codified as ASC 360.

Appendix 1 in this book contains the SEC rules referred to as Reg. S-X Rule 4-10. The SEC amended Reg. S-X Rule 4-10 in May 1996 to delete specific successful efforts rules. It eliminated Rule 4-10(b) through (h) because the rule was considered redundant to guidance in FAS 19; it also added a revised Rule 4-10(b), which required the reporting entities that used the successful efforts method to comply with FAS 19, as amended (now ASC 932).

ASC 360 addresses impairment of proved properties under successful efforts accounting but not under full cost. Reg. S-X Rule 4-10 is unchanged in its mandate that full cost companies meet a specific, and generally more conservative, impairment test. ASC 360 does not change ASC 932 impairment rules for unproved properties.

Prior to ASC 360 and its predecessors FAS 121 and FAS 144, informal SEC staff interpretations of GAAP held that successful efforts companies should have an impairment accounting policy that is no more liberal than limiting the oil and gas properties' aggregate net book value (less related deferred income taxes) to projected, related, undiscounted future cash flows after income taxes.

Reserve disclosure requirements. In December 2008, the SEC issued its final rule on the *Modernization of Oil and Gas Reporting* (the Final Rule), which significantly changed the disclosure requirements for SEC registrants. The Final Rule was, "... intended to provide investors with a more meaningful and comprehensive understanding of oil and gas reserves, which should help investors evaluate the relative value of oil and gas companies."

Furthermore, it states that, "In the three decades that have passed since adoption of these disclosure items, there have been significant changes in the oil and gas industry," adding that, "The amendments are designed to modernize and update the oil and gas disclosure requirements [and related definitions] to align them with current practices and changes in technology." In January 2010, the FASB issued Accounting Standards Update (ASU) 2010-03 to align the oil and gas reserve estimation and disclosure requirements of ASC 932 with the requirements in the Final Rule.

All of the disclosure requirements of ASC 932 apply to public companies and certain disclosure requirements of ASC 932 apply to private companies as well. Other sections of the ASC also require disclosures that are relevant to oil and gas companies. In addition, SEC regulations require certain other disclosures either in the audited financial statements, as supplemental unaudited information, or elsewhere in an SEC filing (see Chapter 30).

Overview of accounting methods

The successful efforts and full cost accounting methods for each major oil and gas activity are summarized in Figure 4-1 and Figure 4-2, respectively.

To illustrate the different financial outcomes of the two methods (ignoring the differences in impairment rules described herein), assume that a company drills five exploratory wells for $1 million each, one of which results in proved reserves.

The successful efforts method would recognize a $1 million asset; the full cost method would recognize a $5 million asset; however, the proved reserves recognized under both methods would generally be the same.

Capitalized costs under successful efforts

The successful efforts method capitalizes only the costs directly related to specific oil and gas reserves when results are positive (i.e., minerals are found). Costs eligible for capitalization include those for drilling and equipping successful exploratory wells, as well as development well costs. Costs that cannot be linked directly to specific reserves, along with all unsuccessful exploratory drilling costs, are expensed. The costs of exploratory dry holes, most geological and geophysical (G&G) costs, delay rentals and other property carrying costs are charged to expense in the period incurred.[3]

Net unamortized capitalized costs under the successful efforts method are amortized using unit-of-production (UOP) amortization calculations as follows:

- Acquisition costs are amortized over total remaining proved reserves.

- Development costs are amortized over remaining proved developed reserves.

Amortization is computed by lease, property or in aggregate, which typically occurs at a field or reservoir level. For successful efforts companies, ASC 360-10-35 and ASC 932-360-35 address the accounting treatment and related impairment assessment for long-lived assets. ASC 360-10-35 prescribes a two-tier approach (see Chapter 17) for proved properties and related equipment and facilities. Unproved properties are subject to the impairment provisions of ASC 932-360-35 (see Chapter 7).

Capitalized costs under full cost

Under the full cost method, all property acquisition, exploration and development costs, including dry hole costs, are capitalized as oil and gas properties. These costs are aggregated, typically at the country level, and amortized using a unit-of-production method based on volumes produced and total remaining proved reserves. The net unamortized capitalized costs of oil and gas properties, less related deferred income taxes, may not exceed an amount referred to as the cost center ceiling, computed in accordance with Reg. S-X Rule 4-10(c)(4)(i). Full cost companies apply the ceiling test on a quarterly basis, which is based on discounted future cash flows, whereas the ASC 360 impairment assessment for successful efforts companies considers undiscounted future cash flows.

Figure 4-1

Classification of costs – Successful efforts

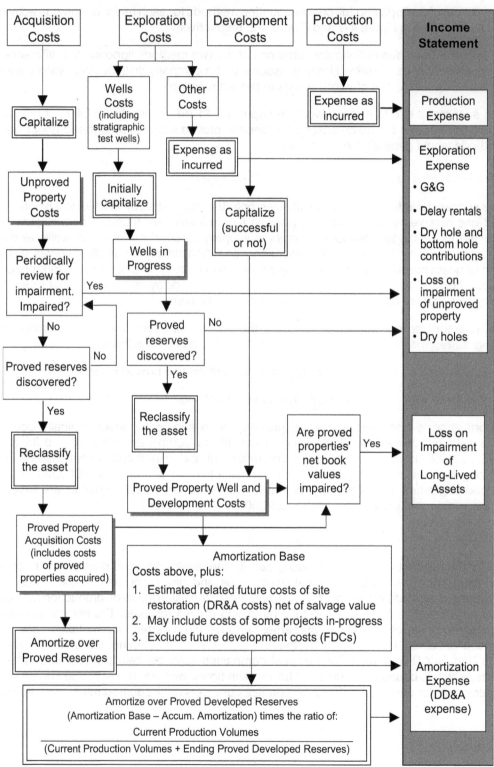

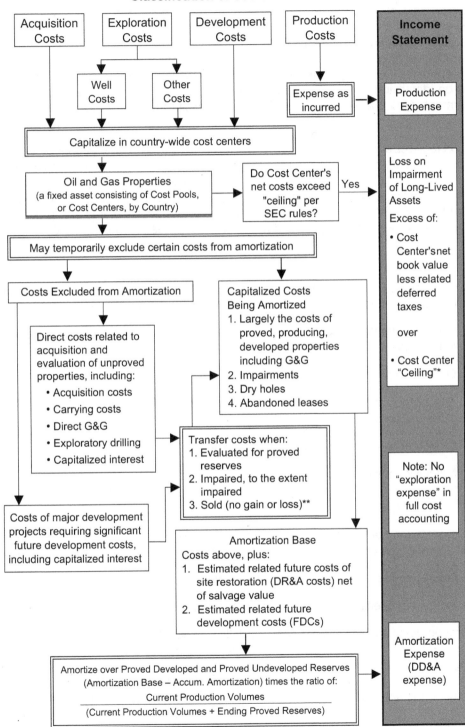

Figure 4-2

Classification of costs – Full cost

* Prescribed in Reg. S-X Rule 4-10 (see Appendix 1).
** See Chapter 18 for related considerations.

Classification of costs

Investors, analysts and other interested parties need to know the true value of proved reserves, which can differ significantly from capitalized historical costs. Although both successful efforts and full cost are historical cost methods, they differ significantly in their accounting for acquisition costs, exploration costs and development costs of oil and gas properties. The distinguishing features of the successful efforts and full cost methods focus on identifying capitalized costs, amortizing them properly and assessing them for impairment. ASC 932 and Reg. S-X Rule 4-10 classify these costs into four categories, described in more detail herein: acquisition, exploration, development and production.

Support facilities and equipment, such as trucks, field service units, warehouses, camp and other facilities, are capitalized and may serve more than one of the four activities. Related depreciation of the capitalized facilities and equipment costs (as well as related operating expenses) is allocated as a cost of acquisition, exploration, development or production. Accounting for all other corporate and overhead costs and acquired equipment is not unique to the oil and gas industry and, therefore, is not described in this text.

Acquisition costs

Acquisition costs include the costs incurred to purchase, lease or otherwise acquire a property or mineral rights. For U.S. operations, these costs generally include:

- The consideration paid by a lessee to a landowner for the execution of a mineral lease, known as a lease bonus.

- Options to purchase or lease properties.

- The portion of costs applicable to mineral rights when land is included in the purchase price.

- Broker fees, recording costs and legal expenses.

- Miscellaneous costs incurred in obtaining mineral rights.

Exploration costs

Certain costs may be incurred both before the related property is acquired (prospecting costs) and after the property is acquired. Accordingly, exploration costs are incurred in:

- Identifying areas that may warrant examination.

- Examining specific areas that might contain oil and gas reserves.

Exploration costs can include the costs of drilling exploratory wells and exploratory-type stratigraphic test wells. Exploration costs can also include the costs of topographical, geological or geophysical studies; rights of access to properties to conduct those studies (shooting rights); and salaries and expenses of geologists, geophysical crews and others conducting the studies. Costs of carrying and retaining undeveloped properties, such as delay rentals and ad valorem taxes on properties, are also included in exploration costs, as are dry hole and bottom hole contributions.

Development costs

Development costs are incurred to obtain access to proved reserves and to provide facilities for extracting, treating, gathering and storing oil and gas. They include the costs of development wells to produce proved reserves, as well as the cost of production facilities, such as lease flow lines, separators, treaters, heaters, storage tanks, improved recovery systems and nearby gas processing facilities. Considering the above, all costs related to drilling and equipping development wells, development-type stratigraphic wells and service wells are considered development costs.

Production costs

Production costs (lifting costs) are the costs of activities that involve lifting oil and gas to the surface and gathering, treating, processing and storing it in the field. In a broad sense, production costs include all costs of acquisition, exploration, development and production. However, for successful efforts and full cost accounting, production costs refer only to those costs to operate and maintain wells, related equipment and facilities, all of which are expensed as incurred as part of the cost of oil and gas produced. Production costs also include the labor to operate the wells and facilities, repair and maintenance expenses, materials and supplies consumed, severance or production taxes, ad valorem taxes and property insurance.

Successful efforts method

According to SEC filings, all of the major U.S. integrated oil and gas companies use the successful efforts method, while just 33 percent of the top 100 U.S. oil and gas companies use the full cost method of accounting.

Figure 4-1 illustrates that the costs of acquiring unproved properties are initially capitalized to an unproved property acquisition costs account. Periodically (typically at least annually, unless circumstances warrant greater frequency), unproved properties are examined to determine whether or not their costs have been impaired. Impairment is recorded as an expense and credited to the allowance for impairment account, a contra account to unproved property acquisition costs.

The capitalized property acquisition costs related to properties where proved reserves have been discovered are amortized as the reserves are produced. Figure 4-1 illustrates that, under ASC 932 rules, all exploration costs, except the costs of drilling and equipping exploratory wells, are charged to expense as incurred. The costs of drilling and equipping exploratory wells (including stratigraphic test wells) are initially capitalized (deferred), pending the outcome of drilling. If the well finds proved reserves, its costs are reclassified to a proved property well and development costs account to be amortized as the related reserves are produced. If the well is dry, accumulated drilling costs are charged to an exploration expense account.

Figure 4-1 also illustrates that all development costs, including the costs of developmental dry holes, should be capitalized to the proved property well and development costs account. These costs are amortized as the related reserves are produced.

Production costs are expensed as incurred, with a few exceptions:

- Enhanced recovery injectant costs are deferred for fields in the development stage, as explained further in Chapter 12.

- A portion of production costs also may be capitalized as the cost of oil and gas inventory, as discussed further in Chapter 14.

Successful efforts amortization

Figure 4-1 summarizes the successful efforts rules for computing amortization of acquisition costs and the costs of wells, related equipment and facilities. Acquisition costs are amortized as the total proved reserves are produced from the property, while well and development costs must be amortized as the proved developed reserves are produced.

This amortization is equivalent to depreciation and is characterized as cost depletion for income tax reporting. Therefore, the amortization of acquisition costs and well and development costs often is referred to as depreciation, depletion and amortization (DD&A). In computing amortization, properties in a common geological structure such as a reservoir or field may be combined into a single amortization center.

If both oil and gas are produced from the same property, the capitalized costs should be amortized on the basis of total production of both minerals. This requires equating the two minerals to an equivalent barrel or equivalent Mcf (explained in Chapter 1).

If only one mineral is produced in sufficient quantities, the other mineral may be considered de minimis. Since minerals produced are assumed to be in proportion to reserves in the ground, the single producing mineral may be used for the computation. A single producing mineral also may be used for the computation if the relative proportion in which the minerals are extracted from reserves is expected to remain consistent over the productive life of the property (see an example and further explanation in Chapter 16).

Successful efforts accounts

While companies today use computerized systems, the discussion that follows demonstrates accounting principles in a manual accounting records environment. In practice, oil and gas companies tailor their procedures, accounts and subsidiary records to meet their operational and organizational needs.

The analysis that follows is presented first for the successful efforts method, followed by the full cost method.

Assets. Many of the accounts named in this section are not unique to the petroleum industry. However, accounts used to record transactions related to exploration, acquisition, development and production costs differ significantly from those of other industries.

- **Inventories.** Often, the amount of oil or gas in storage at a particular time is not significant. Therefore, it typically is not recorded as an inventory item in company accounts. However, if inventories are significant, typically when a company operates storage or pipeline infrastructure, an inventory amount that reflects the cost of production is recorded.

Natural gas inventory recognition is also uncommon, since gas is not stored. However, gas sometimes is injected into underground storage fields in amounts that could be significant; these should be assessed for materiality and potentially recorded in an inventory account.

- **Prepaid expenses.** Prepaid insurance, prepaid rent and similar costs recognized by businesses comprise the prepaid expenses account. Although delay rentals typically are prepaid expenses (in economic substance), industry practice is to expense them (under successful efforts) and capitalize them to oil and gas properties (under full cost) when paid.

- **Unproved property acquisition costs.** This account accumulates the costs of a company's mineral rights in unproved properties, which are properties without sufficient oil or gas reserves to be classified as proved.

  Every major type of unproved mineral interest may have its own general ledger account, where detailed cost data is recorded for each separate property interest. These accounts are charged with applicable costs of unproved properties acquired: purchase price or leasehold bonus, option costs and incidental acquisition costs. Similarly, when proved reserves are found, the accounts are credited with the cost of unproved properties that are transferred to proved. If a portion of an unproved property is sold for less than the total original purchase price of the entire property, the appropriate account is credited for the proceeds up to the property's cost. An unproved property purchase suspense account accumulates costs for acquiring mineral interests of properties to which title has not yet been acquired. The account is credited either when the interest is acquired or when it is ascertained that it will not be acquired.

  For example, ABC Oil Co. (ABC) is a medium-sized independent. If ABC pays a landowner $10,000 for the option to lease a mineral property within six months, the unproved property purchase suspense account is charged. Later, if the acreage is leased, the $10,000 option cost is credited to the unproved property purchase suspense account and charged to an unproved property acquisition costs account. If the acreage under option is abandoned, the $10,000 held in suspense is credited to the unproved property purchase suspense account and charged to exploration expense.

  The allowance for impairment and amortization of unproved properties is more complex. As described earlier in this chapter, the rules for successful efforts require an impairment test for unproved properties. An impairment allowance may be needed for drilling activity that results in a dry hole, for example, or when a lease term expires or management plans to discontinue exploration for reserves on a property, field or other significant area. Chapter 7 provides additional guidance for impairment and abandonment of unproved properties.

- **Proved property acquisition costs.** These accounts reflect the costs and accumulated amortization of costs for proved mineral interests which consist of properties that are producing oil or gas, or where oil and gas reserves are reasonably certain to exist, based on known geological and engineering data.

When a property is found to have proved reserves, its costs are reclassified from the unproved property acquisition costs account to the proved property acquisition costs account. For a property on which impairment has been recorded individually, the net book value (i.e., cost less the impairment allowance) is transferred to the proved property acquisition costs account.

When amortization is recorded, it is charged to a depreciation, depletion and amortization (DD&A) expense account and credited to an accumulated amortization account. See Chapter 16 for additional discussion of DD&A under successful efforts.

- **Proved property well and development costs.** These accounts reflect the costs and accumulated amortization of costs for wells, production equipment and facilities on proved properties. Costs for exploratory wells that do not find proved reserves are not capitalized; instead they are charged to expense in accordance with ASC 932-360-35-13. As discussed further in Chapter 26, primarily for federal income tax determination, well and development costs are divided into two accounts: intangible costs and tangible (equipment) costs.

  Intangible costs are those incurred in drilling the well, such as rig rental and fuel, that have no physical existence and limited salvage value. Labor costs to install casing or other equipment in the well (to the point that valves are installed to control production) are also generally considered intangibles for income tax purposes that are charged to the intangible costs account. Costs to install flow lines, separators, tanks and other lease equipment are classified as equipment for income tax purposes, and thus charged to tangible (equipment) costs.

  Additionally, amortization of well and development costs may be based on individual properties (leases) or groups of properties, if the grouping is related to geological conditions such as a reservoir or field (see Chapter 16).

- **Work-in-progress.** An important part of accounting in an oil and gas company is work-in-progress accounts. Some companies call these accounts incomplete construction. Work-in-progress accounts are closely related to the authorization for expenditures system. Every major construction project or asset acquisition should be controlled by a properly approved authorization for expenditure (AFE). Subsidiary accounts may also be kept for each project and for major cost classifications within each project.

  Work-in-progress accounts may also be used to accumulate the costs of major geological and geophysical exploration projects. The costs related to each major project should be properly analyzed and classified as part of the AFE review and approval process. Accumulated costs are closed to expense at the end of the period. Some companies do not use an AFE system for exploration projects but may establish work-in-progress accounts for these activities (see Chapter 6).

Work-in-progress accounts also are used to reflect all intangible costs of drilling. Each drilling project is properly authorized and costs are accumulated for each AFE. The detailed classification of expenditures is identical to that used in the proved properties account. If an exploratory well finds proved reserves, the accumulated costs in the work-in-progress accounts are charged to a proved properties account. If, on the other hand, the exploratory well is unsuccessful, accumulated costs are charged to an exploration expense account.

The costs of well workovers controlled by AFEs may also be accumulated in work-in-progress accounts. Most companies establish some maximum amount for workovers that can be expensed without an AFE. If the total cost of the workover is estimated at no more than the amount specified, the costs are charged directly to production expense. If an AFE is required, the costs are accumulated for the AFE in a work-in-progress account.

Upon completion of the workover, the accumulated costs are removed from this account and charged to either a production expense account or an asset account. Generally, if the workover does not increase the total proved reserves of the well, the costs are charged to expense. If the workover job increases total proved reserves from the well, the costs are capitalized. Usually, the costs involved are intangible but may include well equipment.

- **Support equipment and facilities.** This account is charged with the capitalized costs of equipment and facilities used in oil and gas operations that serve more than one property or field or more than one function (acquisition, exploration, development or production).

To the extent that support equipment is used in the production process, the related depreciation is charged to expense as required by ASC 932-360-25-16. Staffing camps, regional shops, trucks, barges, warehouses and electric power systems are examples of field service equipment and facilities. As a best practice, companies should be sure to keep appropriate detailed records for individual units and groups of assets.

- **Deferred charges.** These costs are recorded as an asset on the balance sheet until used. Deferred charges typically arise when a company pays for goods or services that have yet to be received or performed. These charges are similar to prepaid expenses, described earlier in the chapter, but fall within the long-term asset category, as they are not expected to be used within the next 12 months.

Liabilities. There are also a number of nuances encountered by E&P companies when recording liabilities, given complex ownership structures in oil and gas properties, among other factors.

- **Revenue distributions payable and revenues held in suspense.** These accounts recognize liabilities due to other joint interest owners or royalty owners for their respective portions of revenues received by the company on their behalf. Suspended revenues may relate to disputed or unknown ownerships or to nominal payables that are paid out quarterly or annually.

- **Production payments and prepaids.** Companies may agree to make future production payments in return for receiving assets (such as cash or an interest in producing properties) upfront. As production occurs, companies are obligated to deliver specified production volumes or pay specified cash amounts.

  Cash received in exchange for future production payments payable in specified cash amounts is considered a borrowing recorded as a debit to cash and a credit to a production payments payable account.

  A company may also record a prepaid asset to reflect cash received for a future obligation to deliver oil or gas, regardless of production. As explained in Chapter 21, the prepaid transaction is not the sale of a mineral interest from the perspective of the company receiving the cash, since it may have to purchase oil or gas in the future in order to satisfy the minimum volumes required for delivery.

  Cash received in exchange for a production payment payable in oil or gas volumes is called a volumetric production payment (VPP). It is regarded as the sale of a mineral interest, and sales proceeds should be credited to a deferred revenue account. See further discussion in Chapter 21.

- **Clearing and apportionment accounts.** Many expenses cannot be charged readily to a single drilling operation, lease or other individual operating function. Instead, they must be accumulated and subsequently allocated to other asset or expense accounts through clearing accounts and apportionment accounts.

  Clearing accounts accumulate expenses during a given period. At the end of the period, the balance of the account is allocated to other accounts, as appropriate, based on the nature of the cost. An apportionment account also may be used to accumulate costs, but in this case account credits are based on fixed rates for services rendered. The balance of an apportionment account, which should be small if rates have been properly established, normally is carried forward from month to month. The account is typically closed to both miscellaneous income and miscellaneous expense at year-end.

  Clearing accounts enhance accounting controls over the receipt and processing of joint venture revenues and billings. E&P companies typically accrue estimated receivables. When they receive net sales proceeds, they use internal information to check the accuracy of the purchaser's calculations. Remittances can be reviewed for accuracy by entering the well's identity, sales month, gross production volumes and cash received from the payer's remittance advice. Accordingly, some companies classify revenue clearing accounts in the accounts receivable section of the chart of accounts.

Revenues. The revenue accounts that are unique to oil and gas production show the company's share of revenues from each major type of mineral interest it owns. Under the proportionate consolidation model (ASC 932-810), revenues that apply to mineral interests owned by other parties are not included in the company's revenues (e.g., revenues that apply to a royalty interest owned by the lessor in a lease operated by the company).

Also applicable to oil and gas companies are forward sales arrangements. Forward sales are agreements in which a producer sells a specific quantity of oil or gas produced, at market prices stipulated on the date of delivery, at a specified point, with a related payment to occur at a future date (similar to fixed price contracts). Revenue recognized under these agreements should be assessed according to ASC 606 (see Chapter 12).

Expenses. Expense accounts unique to exploration and production typically involve the direct expenses required to operate producing properties, such as lease operating expense (LOE). The classification of lease operating expenses varies by company but, in each case, is designed to help control expenses. Items charged to these accounts generally are called lifting costs. Costs are accumulated for each mineral property, permitting the computation of net income for management oversight and income tax accounting. Depreciation, depletion and amortization are not included in this account, rather they are reflected in separate accounts.

Full cost method

Under the full cost method, all acquisition, exploration and development costs are considered necessary for the ultimate production of reserves. Many of these costs are tied to activities not directly related to finding and developing reserves; however, the company expects that the benefits obtained from these activities will be adequate to recover all costs and yield a profit. Establishing a direct cause-and-effect relationship between costs incurred and specific reserves discovered is not relevant to the full cost concept.

Cost centers

Capitalized costs are aggregated and amortized by cost center. Under the SEC's full cost rules, cost centers typically are established at a country level. A rigid interpretation of this rule prohibits grouping countries in a geographical area, except that reasonable groupings may be made of country-wide cost centers that are not significant in the aggregate.

For example, it would be improper to combine activities in the Norwegian, U.K., Dutch and Danish territorial areas under the heading of North Sea operations, unless they are not significant in the aggregate. The rules also would prohibit designating more than one cost center in any individual country.

Costs to be capitalized

The SEC rules for full cost accounting in Reg. S-X Rule 4-10(c)(2) define the costs to be capitalized as follows:

> **Costs to be capitalized.** All costs associated with property acquisition, exploration, and development activities (as defined in paragraph (a) of this section) shall be capitalized within the appropriate cost center. Any internal costs that are capitalized shall be limited to those costs that can be directly identified with acquisition, exploration, and development activities undertaken by the reporting entity for its own account, and shall not include any costs related to production, general corporate overhead, or similar activities.

Under the full cost rules, the following costs are capitalized:

- All G&G costs related to properties in which an ownership interest is held.

- Carrying costs (such as delay rentals and maintenance of land and lease records).

- Dry hole and bottom-hole contributions.

- Costs of exploratory wells (both successful and dry).

- Costs of stratigraphic test wells.

- Costs of acquiring properties.

- All development costs.

When leases are surrendered or abandoned, their costs remain a part of the net capitalized costs of the cost center.

Full cost accounts

Few accounts are unique to full cost accounting, such that those described previously for companies using the successful efforts method are also generally used by those following the full cost method.

Since all costs incurred in each country are capitalized and treated as applicable to all minerals within that country, individual properties and assets conceptually lose their identities. A single oil and gas asset account may accumulate the costs for each country. For example, a company with operations in four countries (U.S., Canada, Norway and Trinidad) might maintain oil and gas property accounts for each country, although the number of accounts needed, or the use of subledger accounts to track costs for each country at a more disaggregated level, may vary depending on the size of the company.

However, even if all oil and gas assets in a country are lumped into a single account, detailed cost records (acquisition, drilling, development and other related costs) should be maintained for federal income tax purposes. Therefore, companies using the full cost method effectively maintain subsidiary records of individual proved and unproved properties, much in the same way as described for successful efforts. Chapter 18 more completely addresses the application of the full cost method by an E&P company.

• • •

---

1   SEC rules for financial accounting and reporting for oil and gas producing companies are found in Rule 4-10 of Regulation S-X (alias S-X·Rule 4-10 or S-X Article 4, Section 10). Regulation App 1 is Part 210 of Title 17 of the Code of Federal Regulations. For the sake of brevity, in this book the applicable regulations are referred to simply as Reg. S-X Rule 4-10.

2   Based on SEC filings as of March 14, 2019, and S&P Capital IQ Company Screening Report as of March 14, 2019.

3   Successful efforts accounting rules do not define the term "incurred." However, FASB Concepts Statement No. 5, *Recognition and Measurement in Financial Statements of Business Enterprises,* clarifies that costs should be recognized when an item meets the four fundamental criteria of, "Definition, Measurability, Relevance and Reliability."

CHAPTER

5

Geological and Geophysical Exploration

- **Nature of exploration costs**

- **Geology and geophysics**

- **Hydrocarbon traps**

- **Exploration methods**

Photograph by istock.com/vvvita

For most companies engaged in oil and gas activities, exploration costs represent an important portion of their annual expenditures. This chapter describes the scope and nature of geological and geophysical exploration costs. Chapter 6 examines the accounting principles and procedures to be used in connection with such costs.

Nature of exploration costs

ASC 932-10-S99-1 incorporates the SEC definition of exploration costs, which Reg. S-X Rule 4-10(a)(12) defines as follows:

> Costs incurred in identifying areas that may warrant examination and in examining specific areas that are considered to have prospects of containing oil and gas reserves, including costs of drilling exploratory wells and exploratory–type stratigraphic test wells. Exploration costs may be incurred both before acquiring the related property (sometimes referred to in part as prospecting costs) and after acquiring the property. Principal types of exploration costs, which include depreciation and applicable operating costs of support equipment and facilities and other costs of exploration activities, are:
>
> (i)   Costs of topographical, geographical, geophysical studies, rights of access to properties to conduct those studies, and salaries and other expenses of geologists, geophysical crews and others conducting those studies. Collectively, these are often referred to as geological and geophysical or "G&G" costs.
>
> (ii) Costs of carrying and retaining undeveloped properties, such as delay rentals, ad valorem taxes on properties, legal costs for title defense, and the maintenance of land and lease records.
>
> (iii) Dry hole contributions and bottom hole contributions.
>
> (iv) Costs of drilling and completing exploratory wells.
>
> (v) Costs of drilling exploratory–type stratigraphic test wells.

Of the five types of exploration costs defined by the SEC, G&G costs are described in this chapter; the other types of exploration costs are described in Chapters 6 and 7.

Geology and geophysics

Geology is the science that studies the planet Earth. It addresses the materials of which the Earth is made, processes that act on those materials, products formed and the history of the planet and its life forms since its origin. Most geological studies are focused on aspects of the Earth's crust because it is: (1) directly observable or indirectly observable through methods such as seismic exploration and (2) the source of energy and minerals for modern industrial societies. The Earth's long geologic history, estimated to be approximately 4.6 billion years, is shown in Figure 5-1.

Geologic setting for oil and gas accumulations

The outer layer of the Earth, known as the lithosphere, contains the Earth's crust and overlays the upper mantle. The crust is composed of three types of rock:

Igneous rocks. Molten rock crystallizes and cools to form igneous rocks at either the surface (e.g., lava) or below the surface (e.g., granite).

Sedimentary rocks. Formed when older rocks eroded, and the eroded materials were transported and deposited as sediments. Through burial and compaction, these sediments transformed into sedimentary rocks, most commonly found as shales and sandstones. Other sedimentary rocks include carbonates, such as limestone, which resulted from the precipitation of water-based organisms (e.g., coral) or changes in the chemistry of the water. Evaporites, primarily halite or common salt, also were precipitated from water under the right conditions of evaporation. Most oil and gas accumulations occur in sedimentary rocks.

Metamorphic rocks. Formed when pressure and heat transformed other rocks. Examples include marble, slate and quartzite. Because organic material is destroyed in this process, metamorphic rocks tend to be poor reservoirs for hydrocarbons, unless they are highly fractured. Geologists in the oil and gas industry are typically only concerned with the ~550 million years following the Precambrian Era, as the evolution of new life forms beginning in the Cambrian period provided an abundance of organic material. This factor, combined with more sedimentary rocks that had not yet metamorphosed, resulted in improved conditions for the accumulation of oil and gas in these younger rocks.

Figure 5-1

Geologic time scale

Era	Period	Millions of years ago (approx.)	Indicative new life forms
Precambrian or Cryptozoic		4,000	Bacteria, algae and jellyfish
Paleozoic *Ancient Life*	Cambrian	550	Plant life, early reptiles, amphibians and fish
	Ordovician	500	
	Silurian	445	
	Devonian	415	
	Carboniferous	360	
	Permian	300	
Mesozoic *Middle Life*	Triassic	250	Large dinosaurs
	Jurassic	100	
	Cretaceous	145	
Cenozoic *Modern Life*	Tertiary	65	Large mammals
	Quaternary	1.6	

The surface of the Earth consists of several lithospheric plates which drift slowly across the underlying asthenosphere, the portion of the upper mantle just below the lithosphere that is involved in plate tectonic movements and isostatic adjustments, in response to heat. The motion of these plates gives rise to the morphology of the Earth's crust.

At divergent boundaries such as the Mid-Atlantic Ridge, new crust is being formed as the African plate and American plate move away from each other. At convergent boundaries, the plates collide. An example of this is the subduction of the oceanic Nazca Plate under the overriding South American Plate, which produced the Andes Mountains. At transform boundaries, the plates grind past each other, such as the San Andreas Fault, which runs more than 800 miles through the state of California.

Earthquakes and volcanic activity are most common along plate boundaries, such as in the Ring of Fire encircling the Pacific Ocean. Over eons, the interactions of plates produced mountain ranges and sedimentary basins. Oil and gas reserves typically are found in these sedimentary basins.

Geologic conditions for oil and gas accumulations

Several conditions existed historically resulting in the creation and accumulation of oil and gas:

- Preservation of source material.

- Maintenance of critical temperatures and pressures.

- Migration of the oil and gas into suitable reservoir formations for production.

- Entrapment of the oil and gas by a barrier, where it accumulated in volume and survived subsequent geologic history.

Source material. Source rocks were abundant organic materials such as the remains of algae and plankton. Most organic materials were of marine origin from the ocean, although lakes and swamps also may have contained sufficient organic remains to generate hydrocarbons. Over time, the organic matter was deposited, along with sediment, and was protected from oxidation, which would have destroyed it. Source rocks tend to be fine-grained rocks, such as shales. With burial and increasing temperature, the organic materials generated hydrocarbons. Accumulations of hydrocarbons often can be traced to their source rocks through chemical analysis.

Reservoir rocks are those possessing sufficient porosity and permeability to produce hydrocarbons. Porosity refers to the pore space, or voids, between the grains of the rock, as illustrated in Figure 5-2. It is measured as a percentage of the total rock volume. Permeability refers to the ability of a rock to transmit fluids, which depends on interconnections between pore spaces.

Figure 5-2
Reservoir rock porosity

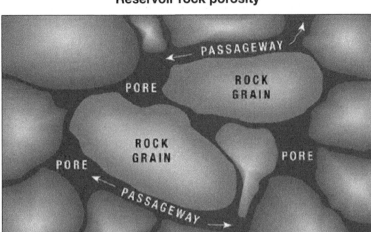

Courtesy of Petroleum Extension (PETEX®)

Almost all reservoir rock grains are coated with residual water and the oil or gas occupies space within this water. Over time, as sediments became buried deeper, the weight of the overburden (layers of rock and soil above) compacted the rocks and expelled the contained fluids, reducing both porosity and permeability. Natural fracturing can greatly enhance the permeability of rocks by connecting pore spaces that were not otherwise connected.

Conventional reservoirs are found in sandstones and various carbonates. However, oil and gas production can occur within many rock types. With improved technology, such as horizontal drilling and fracture stimulation, lower-permeability rocks or other natural materials (shales, carbonates and coals) can serve as unconventional yet successful reservoirs.

These unconventional reservoirs, which include heavy oil and tar sands, tight-gas sands, oil and gas shales and coalbed methane, require different recovery solutions, such as stimulation treatments or steam injection. Typically, these solutions must overcome economic constraints.

In some cases, circulating fluids used during exploration or explicit well-treatment techniques such as acidizing can dissolve certain minerals, thereby enhancing porosity and permeability.

Temperature and pressure. With respect to maintaining critical temperatures, geologists often refer to the desired temperature range in which oil forms as an oil window. Below the minimum temperature, oil remains trapped in the form of kerogen; above the maximum temperature, oil converts to natural gas through the process of thermal cracking. Sometimes oil that is formed at extreme depths may migrate and become trapped at much shallower depths than where it formed, such as in the Canadian Athabasca oil sands.

Overpressured conditions occur when the fluids cannot escape; in this case, they support some of the weight of the overburden. The recovery of natural gas is greatly increased in an overpressured environment because of the compressibility of gas. However, drilling and completion costs increase significantly in overpressured sediments due to safety concerns.

Migration of oil and gas into reservoirs. During the oil and gas formation period, as source rocks were buried and subjected to compaction, most of the original fluids, including saltwater for the dominant marine sediments, were expelled. These fluids carried with them much of the oil or gas that had been generated. Seeking lower pressure, the fluids moved to more permeable, reservoir-quality rocks. Because oil and gas are more buoyant than the dense formation fluids like saltwater, they rise to the top of any permeable layer they encounter. In many low-permeability reservoirs, the source rock and the reservoir are the same, such as coalbed methane and unconventional shales, and no migration occurs.

Trapping of oil and gas. Once the oil or gas encounters a barrier to its migration, it is trapped and can no longer migrate. The overlying impermeable layer, the cap rock, prevents upward migration from the reservoir. Within the reservoir, migration is prevented by either structural configuration or lost permeability, which creates a barrier.

Many trapped accumulations have been lost over time. Subsequent erosion or structural activity may compromise existing traps. For example, large tar-sands accumulations have been breached and degraded, leaving only the residual heavy ends. Much exploration work focuses on the identification of oil and gas traps, as described below.

Hydrocarbon traps

Oil and gas traps can be classified in numerous ways and a detailed explanation is beyond the scope of this book. Petroleum accountants should be aware that traps differ in size, shape and type due to the manner in which they were formed. A simple classification for conventional oil and gas traps includes: (1) structural traps, (2) stratigraphic traps and (3) combination traps.

Structural traps

Structural traps are formed by geological structures that result from horizontal and vertical movements in the Earth's crust related to plate motions and intrusions of minerals like salt from lower strata. The most common types of structural traps are anticlines, faults and domes.

Anticlines. Formed by the upfolding of strata into a dome or arch as the result of either upthrusts from below or lateral compressive forces. Anticlines, which retain hydrocarbons, are covered with a cap rock or other impervious layer. The anticline is filled by the movement of water, oil, gas or some combination of these through porous strata until halted by the seal or cap rock. Figure 5-3 is a simplified illustration of an anticline.

Historically, anticlines have been the most effective traps for oil and gas reserves. An example of an anticlinal reservoir is the giant Sadlerochit reservoir in the Prudhoe Bay field on the North Slope of Alaska.[1]

Figure 5-3
Anticline

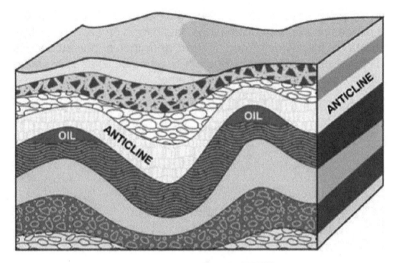

Courtesy of Petroleum Extension (PETEX®)

Faults. Formed by the breaking or shearing of strata due to significant shifting or movement within the Earth's crust. When faulting occurs, the relative placement of the strata is changed to the extent that a porous bed holding hydrocarbons can be sealed off by an impermeable formation, thus establishing a seal or trap. Most individuals think of faults in connection with earthquakes; few realize that these shifts have resulted in accumulated oil and gas deposits. A simple fault is illustrated below.

Figure 5-4
Simple fault

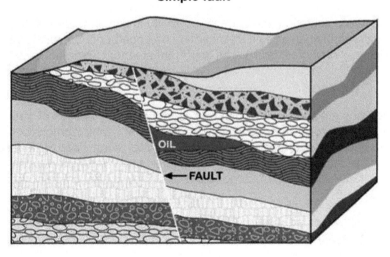

Courtesy of Petroleum Extension (PETEX®)

Domes. Among the first formations to be associated with the accumulation of oil, salt domes, which typify this type of formation, consist of salt that has intruded upward into overlying sediment. A nonporous bed of salt, which is less dense than overlying rocks, is pushed upward, piercing or otherwise deforming weak points in the overlying formations. When the salt pierces one or more formations, faults form on each side of the salt dome. When upper strata are merely deformed or lifted, anticlines or domes become part of the formation. This process is illustrated in Figure 5-5. Some of Texas' most famous oil fields, such as Spindletop, were formed around salt domes.

Figure 5-5

Piercement salt dome

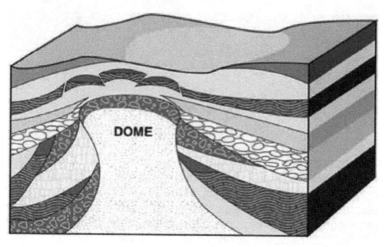

Courtesy of Petroleum Extension (PETEX®)

Oil can be trapped above salt domes (when an anticline is formed), alongside salt domes, or, in some cases, beneath salt pillows or salt sills. The presence of salt is considered very favorable for oil accumulation. Its inherent instability is known to cause the formation of domes or anticlines. Salt also seals off migrating hydrocarbons. Subsalt formations in the Gulf of Mexico and offshore Brazil are an important area for exploration today.

Stratigraphic traps

Stratigraphic traps are the result of differences in the characteristics of strata at various points. Oil and gas become trapped in the porous and permeable portions of the formation and are surrounded by impermeable sections. Stratigraphic traps can be caused by abrupt changes in the porosity and permeability of the formation, irregular depositions of sand and shale or changes in types of carbonate rocks. Typical stratigraphic traps are shown in Figures 5-6 and 5-7.

Some stratigraphic traps are called unconformities or truncation traps because they are associated with erosional unconformities in the strata. A classic example of a truncation trap is the East Texas oil field. Others include the West Edmond field in Oklahoma and part of the Central Kansas uplift.

Figure 5-6
Stratigraphic trap – Example 1

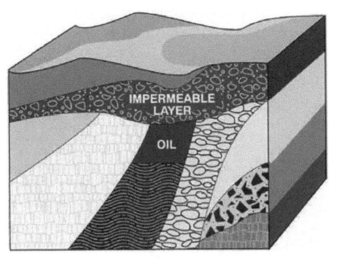

Courtesy of Petroleum Extension (PETEX®)

Figure 5-7
Stratigraphic trap – Example 2

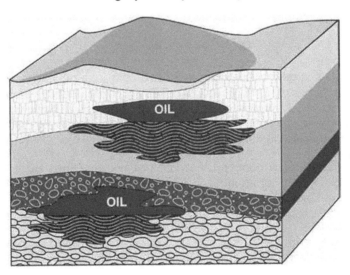

Courtesy of Petroleum Extension (PETEX®)

Commonly, three types of unconformities are distinguished by geologists: angular unconformities, nonconformities and disconformities. An angular unconformity is one in which older sediment was tilted, truncated by erosion and new sediment deposition occurred on top of the previous surface (see Figure 5-8). A nonconformity separates igneous or metamorphic rocks from overlying sedimentary rocks. A disconformity is similar to an angular unconformity, but the older sediment was not tilted prior to deposition of the new sediment.[2]

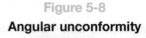

Angular unconformity

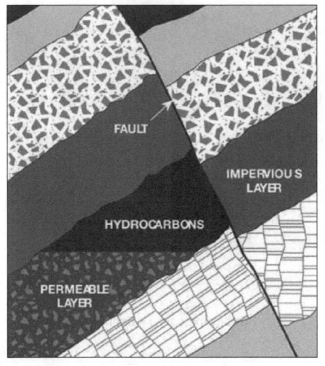

Courtesy of Petroleum Extension (PETEX®)

Many of the world's largest accumulations of hydrocarbons occurred due to enhanced porosity development along unconformities or sealing of the underlying porous reservoirs by impermeable rocks. Examples include the major oil fields of Saudi Arabia, including Ghawar, the world's largest conventional oil field (enhanced porosity), and the largest oil field in the U.S., Eagleville, in the Eagle Ford Shale gas formation.

Stratigraphic traps are also common in carbonate rocks. The original deposition can be variable, producing abrupt changes in porosity and permeability. Reefs are the most dramatic examples. Carbonate rocks are also often subjected to post-depositional changes caused by circulating fluids, which can alter porosity and permeability by dissolving some of the rock matrix.

Combination traps

When two or more types of formations combine due to folding, faulting and other conditions in the subsurface, they can create combination traps. These often involve a stratigraphic or truncation trap combined with a structural trap. The Oklahoma City oil field is an example of this type of reservoir, as is the Rangely oil field in Colorado.

Unconventional reservoirs

Chapter 1 introduced the 1990s development of gas production from tight oil plays or shale reservoirs and coalbeds – continuous formations that historically have been uneconomical to develop. New technology has led to significant new exploration in areas previously considered unlikely to contain recoverable hydrocarbons, especially deeper centers of petroleum basins. As conventional traps become more difficult to find, development of these new reservoirs has become increasingly important.

These unconventional formations typically are referred to as "resource plays" as opposed to "exploration plays," since there is little risk of failing to find hydrocarbons. However, production and profit per well generally are lower in resource plays than in traditional gas plays. They differ from conventional reservoirs in the sense that the hydrocarbons do not flow freely from the reservoir, due to either low porosity or low permeability of the rock formations or high viscosity of the liquid hydrocarbons.

Unconventional reservoirs primarily consist of the following:

Oil sands. Oil sands only recently have been considered part of the world's oil reserves. New technologies, such as steam-assisted gravity drainage and vapor extraction, enable profitable extraction and upgrading to usable petroleum products. However, oil sand production generally has a greater environmental impact than traditional forms of oil and gas extraction. Substantial quantities of oil and gas are contained in tight formations with typically poor permeability. The formations may be vast and continuous; however, because of the low permeability, production rates are low and usually require enhancement.

Tar sands. These high-viscosity bitumen sands contain naturally occurring mixtures of sand, clay, water and bitumen, an extremely viscous (thick) and dense form of hydrocarbons. Significant tar sands deposits have been found in the Athabasca oil sands in Canada and in the Orinoco belt of Venezuela. The Athabasca oil sands are extracted through large-scale surface mining using some of the largest shovels and trucks in the world. Mined bitumen is separated from the sand and clay before being upgraded into synthetic crude oil. Because it is so viscous, bitumen requires dilution with lighter hydrocarbons to make it transportable through pipelines. Approximately two tons of mined oil sands are required to produce one barrel of synthetic crude oil.

Tight sands. These sandstone reservoirs cannot be produced via conventional means such as natural flow or artificial lift due to their very low permeability. In many cases, these reservoirs can be developed more easily than shale reservoirs because their quartz-based rock tends to be more brittle and fractured. Examples such as the Codell and Niobrara formations in Northeastern Colorado have produced large amounts of natural gas and some condensate from thousands of wells. The Cotton Valley sandstone formation in Texas and Louisiana, although primarily a tight gas play with approximately 140 trillion cubic feet of technically recoverable resources in place, also has some tight oil production from the same formation.

Shale gas. This natural gas is trapped within shale formations composed of fine-grained sedimentary rocks. From the late-1990s to the present, a combination of horizontal drilling and hydraulic fracturing has accessed large volumes of shale gas that previously were uneconomic. The Barnett Shale is the prototype of a low-permeability or tight reservoir that has been economically exploited using this technology. After more than two decades of production, it is a hub of technology, experience and information that has improved the efficiency of shale gas development across the country, especially in the Marcellus Shale. The Marcellus play extends across 100,000 square miles in the Northeastern United States, from central-upstate New York, across Western Pennsylvania and into parts of Ohio and West Virginia.

Shale oil. The shale oil revolution trailed the shale gas success by about a decade and owes much of its success to techniques pioneered in the Barnett Shale boom. The first major success was the commercial exploitation of the Bakken play in the Williston basin of North Dakota, Eastern Montana and parts of Southern Manitoba and Saskatchewan. Since then, major activity has occurred in the Eagle Ford formation in south-central Texas and shale formations in the Permian Basin of West Texas and Southeastern New Mexico. However, unlike conventional oil wells, which can produce for decades, shale oil wells tend to decline rapidly. Maintaining production levels from a given field requires the continuous drilling of many additional wells.

During the past 10 years, as the price of oil plummeted from more than $120 a barrel to below $30 per barrel, before partially recovering to current levels, operators in these areas remained profitable by reducing costs through innovation and technological advancements. Standard well designs, multi-well drilling pads and even walking rigs, which can move themselves to new drilling locations without disassembly and reassembly, have been used to drill wells faster, at lower cost and with greater safety than previously possible.

Coalbed methane. Coalbed gas, or methane gas, refers to gas that is stored in naturally occurring coal deposits by a process called adsorption. Unlike conventional natural gas, coalbed methane contains very few other hydrocarbons, such as propane or butane, and no natural gas condensate. To economically recover coalbed methane, wells are drilled into the coal seam, where a decrease in pressure as a result of pumping water from the wells desorbs the methane from the coal. It flows as a gas up the wellbore to the surface for further processing. The most important U.S. coalbed methane basins include the Piceance in Colorado, the San Juan in Southern Colorado and Northern New Mexico, the Black Warrior in Alabama and Mississippi and the Powder River in Wyoming and Montana.

Exploration methods

The goal of oil and gas exploration is to identify new hydrocarbon reserves that can be produced at a profit. While geologists, geophysicists and reservoir engineers cannot search directly for oil and gas, there are a number of methods whereby they can perform exploration activities. G&G exploration identifies areas where conditions are favorable for the accumulation of oil and gas. Varied techniques explore both the surface and subsurface for this purpose. These techniques can employ geology, geophysics, geochemistry and even satellite imagery. The dominant form of exploration, however, is typically an integrated geologic-seismic approach.

The exploration method chosen depends on the level of previous exploration in a basin. If the basin has not been drilled, a basic regional study will determine the geologic setting and favorable factors for the accumulation of oil or gas. At the other extreme is an intensely drilled basin, where the primary concern is to identify any remaining traps missed by previous explorers. Improved technologies have given current explorers exceptional advantages over their predecessors. This is especially true for unconventional reservoirs, where hydrocarbons trapped in the source rocks now can be produced economically.

Technology has also transformed exploration by providing tools for combining many sources of data, especially seismic data, and allowing explorers to manipulate and analyze the data in a variety of ways.

Surface mapping

Surface mapping is commonly used in unexplored, undrilled areas where direct subsurface information is unavailable. Aerial photography, satellite imaging and geochemical surveys assist geologists in interpreting the surface geology. The geologist's goal is to better understand the geological setting, structural style, source rocks and reservoir rocks. However, the extrapolation of surface data alone to predict subsurface conditions can be risky.

Surveying

Gravity and magnetic surveys measure small deviations in the gravitational attraction and magnetic fields caused by variations in the density and magnetic properties of underlying rocks. They generally are used as low-cost tools to assist in the structural reconstruction of a basin.

Existing well data

The primary source of information about subsurface conditions is the data available from previously drilled wells. Downhole logging surveys, conducted during drilling of a well, provide a wealth of information about formation characteristics and fluid content. Tests at the drill site and core samples add to the data set. With this information, explorers can extrapolate data into undrilled areas, particularly when incorporated with seismic data. They use several types of maps, including those that illustrate particular aspects of the geological formation, such as porosity and sand shale ratios, and structure maps, which illustrate the elevation of a particular geologic formation. Depending on governmental rules, explorers generally release their well data after a prescribed period, providing low-cost information to the entire industry.

Seismic shooting

The word seismic means "of, or having to do with, an earthquake or Earth vibration." In the petroleum industry, the term relates specifically to oil and gas exploration conducted by measuring man-made sound waves as they are reflected from subsurface formations. Several methods generate the energy source for seismic activities, including dynamite, Vibroseis™ (vibration) and air guns. No matter the source of energy, seismic sound waves travel downward through the Earth's crust. Upon striking a layer with different acoustic properties, caused by differences in rock density or velocity, a portion of the sound wave reflects back to the surface.

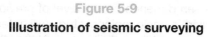

Illustration of seismic surveying

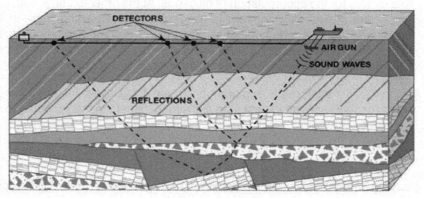

Courtesy of Petroleum Extension (PETEX®)

Figure 5-9 provides an illustrative seismic survey in which the reflected seismic waves are detected at the surface by geophones and recorded digitally for later computer processing. Many geophones are placed around each shot point, the location where energy is transmitted to the subsurface. This array permits subsurface coverage across a large area. Through built-in redundancy, with multiple shot points and arrays of geophones, the same subsurface point is recorded multiple times from different surface positions, thereby increasing the signal-to-noise ratio and clarity of the recording.

For many years, seismic recording was limited to two-dimensional (2D) profiles through the Earth, with time noted on the vertical axis and distance on the horizontal axis. However, improved computer and recording technology now addresses large areas, presenting a three-dimensional (3D) look at the recorded data.

3D seismic. In offshore exploration, 3D seismic processes use several lines of hydrophones in a grid to record the signals. Subsequently, using sophisticated computer software, the signals are translated into "virtual reality," revealing the thicknesses and densities of the subsurface rocks, including those that have been stressed into the types of folds or faults that might trap petroleum as illustrated in Figure 5-10. It is possible to slice the resulting data set in multiple ways, from horizontal to vertical profiles in any direction. The resolution of the subsurface data is greatly enhanced by today's 3D processes, which produce the best data available about petroleum potential, short of actually drilling an exploratory well.

Converting the time scale to depth requires information about the velocity of the rocks through which the sound waves pass. This information is available from well data and by computer analysis of the recorded seismic data itself. In addition to their traditional use of seismic data to define the structural configuration of subsurface layers or formations, geologists can use the data to learn about rock properties and fluid content, particularly when they can integrate well data with seismic data. By calibrating the acoustic properties of the rocks in a well to the seismic data, an interpreter can develop models that make reliable extrapolations of aspects such as porosity or lithology.

In good data areas, such as the offshore U.S. Gulf Coast, hydrocarbon accumulations can be mapped with great accuracy using seismic data. With larger surveys of high quality data, geologists can view sedimentary sequences and relate them to seismic sequence stratigraphic models that predict the likely rock types.

Figure 5-10

3D seismic survey

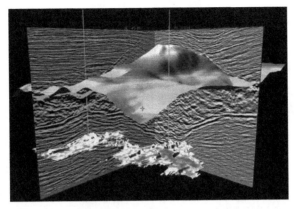

Courtesy of the American Association of Petroleum Geologists EXPLORER publication

4D seismic. Four-dimensional (4D) seismic (also called time-lapse seismic) refers to comparing 3D seismic surveys from the same area but over different points in time. This enables engineers and geologists to track and simulate the behavior of hydrocarbons in a reservoir. The technology is important for deepwater or complex onshore fields, helping to reduce the time and cost of drilling programs. 4D technologies function as: (1) an exploration tool, to identify previously unknown hydrocarbon deposits and (2) a reservoir management tool, to reduce uncertainty in development and production decisions, including improved well placement and infill drilling to tap bypassed reserves. Monitoring the behavior of hydrocarbon reserves can greatly extend the productive life of a field, allowing for positive revisions to drilling and production plans.

Offshore seismic surveys are less expensive than onshore surveys, partly because they can cover larger areas in the same amount of time. Permitting can be problematic for onshore surveys, as can the potential for surface damage. In general, though, seismic surveys can reduce the risk of dry holes by allowing for better well placement. Seismic surveys can be conducted on a proprietary basis, with the recorded data available only to the sponsor. Group shoots can reduce costs because several companies sponsor and share the data, which is quite common for offshore prospects. Costs can be lowered still further if, after a period of exclusivity, the data can be purchased by anyone. Some seismic companies also conduct speculative (spec) shoots, anticipating purchase of the data by interested companies.

Evaluating well logs

A seismic survey often is followed by well logging, illustrated in Figure 5-11, which is one of the most fundamental methods for reservoir characterization. It is an essential method for acquiring more knowledge about subsurface conditions by identifying the physical properties of reservoir formations. This method is very useful to detect a hydrocarbon-bearing zone, to calculate the hydrocarbon volume and to evaluate many other factors. As the search continues for more hydrocarbons, the tools available to explore for oil and gas are becoming much more precise and versatile. With improved computing power and sophisticated programs to analyze and integrate the data, geologists can lower the risks of exploration, while improved production techniques make it possible to access smaller, lower-quality reservoirs economically.

Figure 5-11

Representative well log

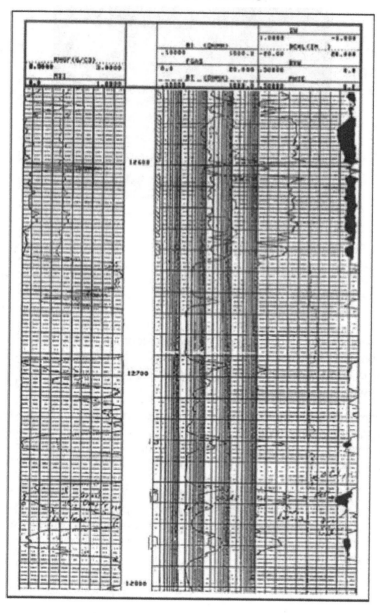

Courtesy of Petroleum Extension (PETEX®)

• • •

1 Harun, Nina. "Eighteen Measured Sections of the Lower Triassic Ivishak Formation in the Sadlerochit Mountains, Northeastern Alaska." Alaska Division of Mining and Geological and Geophysical Surveys, 1986.

2 Indiana University Bloomington. "Unconformities." November 2019, https://geol105b.sitehost.iu.edu/images/gaia_chapter_6/unconformities.htm.

Accounting for Exploration Costs

Key concepts

- Accounting treatment

- Accounting procedures

- Authorization for expenditure

- Accounting challenges

- Subsequent events

- Additional considerations

This chapter examines accounting for exploration costs. It also addresses general financial accounting principles, control systems, recording procedures and accounting challenges. The examples in this chapter focus on the accounting entries for a successful efforts company. The full cost method of accounting is discussed in Chapter 18.

Accounting treatment

Companies employing the successful efforts method expense exploration costs when incurred. The only exception is costs for exploratory wells, including exploratory-type stratigraphic test wells. Until the outcome of exploration is known, exploratory well costs are capitalized as work-in-progress. Exploratory wells that ultimately do not find proved reserves are charged to expense, while successful exploratory wells remain capitalized.

Exploration costs incurred in geological and geophysical (G&G) activities include:

- Topographical, geological and geophysical studies.

- Rights of access to properties to conduct those studies ("shooting rights").

- Salaries and expenses of geologists, geophysical crews and others conducting the studies.

Exploration costs also include costs incurred for the following activities:

- Carrying and retaining undeveloped properties.

- Drilling and equipping exploratory wells.

- Making dry hole and bottom hole contributions.

- Drilling exploratory-type stratigraphic test wells.

To illustrate the accounting treatment for exploration costs, assume that Stoll Oil Co. (Stoll) undertakes an exploratory study at a cost of $165,000. The study identifies two areas of interest: Area A and Area B. Before attempting to acquire the acreage, the company surveys both areas. Survey costs are $20,000 for Area A and $15,000 for Area B. The results for Area A are positive and the company subsequently acquires two leases.

Using successful efforts accounting, Stoll charges these costs to current expense:

Exploration expense	200,000	
Accounts payable		200,000

To record exploration costs associated with exploratory studies and surveys of Areas A and B.

Accounting procedures

The accounting system typically is designed to capture exploration costs for an oil and gas company's financial statements. However, it also supplies data for other business needs in order to:

- Determine a project's ultimate profitability, which may require tracking costs at a more granular level.

- Develop an exploration budget.

- Control costs.

- Report to regulatory agencies, such as the U.S. Department of Energy, which may impose specific requirements for classifying and accumulating data.

- Support federal income tax reporting, which often differs from financial reporting and requires additional, more detailed records.

- Supply the detailed historical cost records required for legal and contractual purposes, including supporting amounts invoiced to other working interest owners.

No single system serves the needs of all oil and gas companies. However, the procedures described in this chapter are common in the industry.

General ledger accounts

According to ASC 932, a company using the successful efforts method must charge all exploration costs to expense as incurred, except for costs of successful exploratory wells, wells in progress and certain circumstances specifically addressed in ASC 932-360-25-11.

Record-keeping depends on a number of variables, including management's needs, organizational structure, and legal, regulatory, compliance or operational requirements. Accordingly, a company's accounting system must do more than just properly record transactions. It also must have the functionality to accumulate information to enhance internal control, provide accurate and timely information to management, support joint interest billings, and collect data for filing federal, state and local tax returns and regulatory reports. Therefore, the elements of each financial transaction must be classified not only by the general ledger accounts involved, but also by other subaccounts, which can make for a complex structure depending on the size of the organization and the activities in which it engages.

The general ledger accounts listed herein are commonly used to record exploration expense and are comparable to the categories found in ASC 932-360-25-9. As mentioned, various subaccounts may be established to further disaggregate costs for record-keeping purposes: (1) geological and geophysical costs, (2) carrying and retaining undeveloped properties, (3) test well contributions, (4) exploratory wells and (5) exploratory-type stratigraphic test wells.

Work-in-progress

Some companies prefer to charge the costs incurred under an AFE to a deferred charge asset account, such as work-in-progress or exploration-in-progress. They accumulate costs pertaining to each AFE in a single account. When work is complete, they charge the costs to exploration expense and credit the deferred charge asset account. This procedure offers additional internal control because all costs pertaining to an AFE are collected initially in one general ledger account, rather than among multiple accounts. Furthermore, as long as the amounts are included in work-in-progress, it is evident that the project is not yet finished.

Successful efforts companies using this method make adjustments when they prepare financial statements at the end of a period to close work-in-progress or exploration in progress accounts into exploration expense. To illustrate, assume from the earlier example that Stoll records the following invoice:

Work-in-progress – G&G exploration	46,000	
Accounts payable		46,000
To record voucher payable for seismic work.		

Note that the only difference in recording this charge is that it is initially debited to a work-in-progress account rather than an exploration expense account.

If the project is not complete at the end of the accounting period, an adjustment closes the accumulated costs into exploration expense for financial statement presentation. For example, if at the end of the accounting period, total exploration costs of $48,300 have been incurred and accumulated in the work-in-progress account for a project that is not complete, the journal entry would be as follows:

Exploration expense	48,300	
Work-in-progress – G&G exploration		48,300
To reclassify exploration costs from work-in-progress to expense.		

Since the project is not complete, a successful efforts company must reverse the above entry at the beginning of the next accounting period to continue the project in progress. After the reversal, additional costs under the AFE are accumulated in the work-in-progress account in the usual manner until the project is complete, at which point an analysis of estimated to actual costs can be prepared, as discussed herein.

Authorization for expenditure

Oil and gas exploration is conducted by project and may extend over a long period, often over several years. Management approvals are required due to the large expenditures, the length of time required and the need to control costs. Company policies dictate the dollar thresholds for expenditure approvals, which in most cases are required from one or more people with functional responsibilities for exploration and, in the case of a joint venture, are required by all working interest owners. Larger expenditures may require a formal AFE, which contains a project description, a list of proposed expenditures and appropriate approvals.

This book uses the term AFE for any planned expenditures that require approval. The definition and requirement for an AFE as used by those in the industry may differ to some degree, as it is most commonly associated with drilling exploratory or development wells.

Figure 6-1

Illustrative completed AFE form

Authorization for Expenditure – Exploration			
Request for authority:		**AFE #:** 01008	
M. Wheeler, Exploration Dept.		**Date:** 8/13/2019	
Location: FN, 2187, Jakku County, Oklahoma			
Purpose: To conduct exploration activities for possible leasing and subsequent drilling and development.			
Item (subaccount)	**Estimated cost**	**Actual cost**	**Variance**
01. G&G contract	$60,000	$58,000	$2,000
02. G&G services – other	0	0	0
03. Field – salaries	7,000	7,800	(800)
04. Field – supplies	0	0	0
05. Field – other	1,000	1,200	(200)
06. Support facilities	0	0	0
07. Shooting rights and damages	2,000	2,300	(300)
08. Mapping expense	0	0	0
09. Equipment rental	0	0	0
10. Other G&G costs	0	0	0
11. Purchased G&G data	0	0	0
Total direct costs	**$70,000**	**$69,300**	**$ 700**
12. Overhead	10,500	9,780	720
Total	**$80,500**	**$79,080**	**$1,420**
Approval: J. Terry 8/20/2019			

For example, assume that Stoll contemplates exploring a certain area. It estimates direct expenditures of $70,000 and requires an approved AFE for work to commence. A district geologist initiates the form depicted in Figure 6-1. Items specified on the exploration AFE correspond to subsidiary accounts for exploration expense. Overhead is an estimate, in this case 15 percent of direct costs, and does not equal expected cash expenditures.

Approval of the AFE does not require an entry in the formal accounting records; instead, it is a form of internal control, ensuring appropriate approval prior to requisition. As costs accumulate for each project, they are compared with the amounts authorized. Columns titled "Actual cost" and "Variance" provide the means to compare these costs when the project is complete.

Accounting challenges

Although ASC 932 clearly defines exploration costs and explains how they are to be accounted for, challenges may arise in the interpretation and application of the guidance as discussed herein.

Determining sufficient progress

ASC 932-360-35-18 through 20 offers guidance in accounting for exploratory wells:

35-18 An exploratory well or an exploratory-type stratigraphic well may be determined to have found oil and gas reserves, but those reserves cannot be classified as proved when drilling is completed. In those cases, the capitalized drilling costs shall continue to be capitalized if the well has found a sufficient quantity of reserves to justify its completion as a producing well and the entity is making sufficient progress assessing the reserves and the economic and operating viability of the project. Note that an entity is not required to complete the exploratory or exploratory-type stratigraphic well as a producing well. For purposes of determining whether capitalized drilling costs shall continue to be capitalized pending the determination of proved reserves, a project may include more than one exploratory well or exploratory-type stratigraphic well if the reserves are intended to be extracted in a single, integrated producing operation (for example, the producing wells will operate with shared infrastructure).

35-19 All relevant facts and circumstances shall be evaluated when determining whether an entity is making sufficient progress on assessing the reserves and the economic and operating viability of the project. The following are some indicators, among others, that an entity is making sufficient progress (see the following paragraph). No single indicator is determinative. An entity shall evaluate indicators in conjunction with all other relevant facts and circumstances. These indicators include:

a. Commitment of project personnel who are at the appropriate levels and who have the appropriate skills

b. Costs that are being incurred to assess the reserves and their potential development

c. An assessment process covering the economic, legal, political, and environmental aspects of the potential development is in progress

d. Existence (or active negotiations) of sales contracts with customers for the oil and gas

e. Existence (or active negotiations) of agreements with governments, lenders, and venture partners

f. Outstanding requests for proposals for development of any required facilities

g. Existence of firm plans, established timetables, or contractual commitments, which may include seismic testing and drilling of additional exploratory wells

h. Progress that is being made on contractual arrangements that will permit future development

i. Identification of existing transportation and other infrastructure that is or will be available for the project (subject to negotiations for use).

Long delays in the assessment or development plan (whether anticipated or unexpected) may raise doubts about whether the entity is making sufficient progress to continue the capitalization of exploratory well or exploratory-type stratigraphic well costs after the completion of drilling. The longer the assessment process for the reserves and the project, the more difficult it is to conclude that the entity is making sufficient progress to continue the capitalization of those exploratory well or exploratory-type stratigraphic well costs.

35-20 If an entity has not engaged in substantial activities to assess the reserves or the development of the project in a reasonable period of time after the drilling of the well is completed or activities have been suspended, any capitalized costs associated with that well shall be expensed net of any salvage value. After a reasonable period of time, the planning of future activities without engaging in substantial activities shall not be sufficient to continue the capitalization of exploratory well or exploratory-type stratigraphic well costs. However, brief interruptions in activities required to assess the reserves or the project, or other delays resulting from governmental or other third-party evaluation of a proposed project, do not require capitalized exploratory well or exploratory-type stratigraphic well costs to be expensed.

Exploration permits

In foreign areas, it is common for petroleum resources to be owned by the government of the host country. U.S. onshore properties, and their underlying mineral rights, may be owned by corporations, private individuals, Native American tribes, or local, state or federal governments. Both onshore and offshore, permission is required to explore for oil and gas. Exploration licenses or permits are issued, many of which require specific activities over their duration, such as drilling a fixed number of exploratory wells or performing agreed-upon seismic studies.

Before a U.S. onshore mineral lease is signed, an exploration permit (shooting rights) may be obtained from property owners. For U.S. offshore exploration, a permit typically is sought from the BSEE. In this specific case, payment of a fee to the U.S. government usually is not required. However, payments for exploration rights to governments or others generally are required and may be awarded through an auction process. See Chapter 7 for a description of the acquisition of unproved properties.

Onshore exploration rights may take one of two forms. Under a shooting rights only contract, the rights holder is allowed to access the property and conduct exploratory activities up to, but not including, drilling an exploratory well. Under successful efforts, the costs involved are classified as exploration expense, as illustrated in the journal entry below:

Exploration expense	2,300	
Accounts payable		2,300
To record exploration permits.		

In other cases, the contract may grant not only shooting rights, but also an option for the grantee to lease all or part of the acreage for a specified sum, usually expressed in dollars per acre.

Acreage selection options

An option agreement typically will specify the amount applicable to shooting rights and separately state the cost of the option. The cost of these exploration rights is treated as any other exploration cost described in this chapter. Accounting for option payments is described in Chapter 7. If none of the acreage in the option is leased, the entire option cost is charged to expense. If the entire acreage is leased, the entire option cost is capitalized as the cost of acquiring mineral rights. Under successful efforts, if only part of the acreage is leased, an allocated portion of the cost is capitalized. A full cost company capitalizes all option costs in every case.

Test well contributions

Frequently, the owner or lessee of a property will contribute cash to the operator of a nearby lease to cover a portion of the drilling costs of a test well. In return, the owner or lessee receives certain information, such as cuttings, core samples and reports obtained during drilling.

In the case of a dry hole contribution, funds are paid to the drilling party only if the well is dry or does not result in a producing well. Bottom hole contributions are paid when the drilling party reaches the proposed depth or a specific geological formation, regardless of the outcome.

For accounting purposes, the recipient of test well contributions treats the payment as a reduction in well costs. The payer of either type of test well contribution treats the payment as an exploration cost.

For example, under successful efforts accounting, the payment of a $12,000 dry hole contribution by Stoll to the operator of a nearby lease is recorded as follows:

Exploration expense	12,000	
Accounts payable		12,000
To record dry hole contribution to operator.		

Exploration performed in return for acreage

In return for an agreement to perform specified exploration work, an operator who owns lease rights in unproved acreage may agree to contribute to another company a portion of interest in that acreage (either an undivided interest in the entire acreage or a divided interest in a fractional share). Accounting for this pooling of assets is addressed in ASC 932-360-55-4. A successful efforts company conducting the exploration charges the costs to exploration expense. The company assigning the acreage records its total acreage cost as the cost of its retained interest. Proper notation for the ownership reduction in the unproved acreage should be made by the land department in the lease records, as the operator is the assignor of the interest.

Assume that Stoll holds leases on 6,000 acres in Coleman County, Texas, that were acquired for $800,000. A contract is executed with XYZ Oil Co. (XYZ), a successful efforts company, in which it agrees to conduct specified exploration. After completion of the work, and regardless of outcome, XYZ receives a one-fourth interest in the property. It spends $350,000 for exploration. XYZ records exploration costs as follows:

Exploration expense	350,000	
Accounts payable		350,000

To record the cost of work performed for an interest in Stoll Oil Co.'s leases in Coleman County, Texas.

XYZ assigns no cost to the leasehold interest acquired. Most companies would assign some nominal amount, such as $1, enabling them to track the interest for future accounting and operational purposes. If this were done in the example, $1 would be charged to an unproved properties acquisition costs account and $349,999 would be charged to an exploration expense account. Stoll makes no entries in its accounting records. It does, however, record the new, reduced property interest in its detailed lease records.

Under a different arrangement, the contract may specify that the party performing the work will acquire an interest in the property only if exploration identifies reserves. This is known as conditional pooling of assets. However, the accounting treatment is the same: a successful efforts company performing the work charges all costs to exploration expense and the party owning the property makes no entry.

A third type of exploration arrangement is outlined in ASC 932-360-25-11 whereby G&G studies may be conducted on a property owned by another party in exchange for an interest in the property if the studies find proved reserves, or for reimbursement of the costs if they do not. G&G costs are accounted for as a receivable when incurred by the party performing the studies. If G&G studies find proved reserves, the costs become the cost of the proved property acquired.

A literal interpretation of this treatment is shown herein. Stoll owns a lease covering 10,000 acres. Under contract, XYZ agrees to explore the property. If it finds proved reserves, XYZ will be assigned a one-fourth working interest in the property. If it finds no proved reserves, Stoll must reimburse XYZ for incurred costs of $90,000. Charges for XYZ's services are posted to a receivable account on its books as follows:

Accounts receivable – other receivables	90,000	
Accounts payable		90,000
To record exploration costs incurred on Stoll lease.		

If XYZ finds no proved reserves, Stoll reimburses XYZ for the $90,000. XYZ records receipt of the payment as follows:

Cash	90,000	
Accounts receivable – other receivables		90,000
To record reimbursement from Stoll for exploration.		

Cost reimbursements to XYZ are recorded as exploration expense on Stoll's books:

Exploration expense	90,000	
Accounts payable		90,000
To record reimbursement to XYZ for exploration.		

Alternatively, if proved reserves are found, XYZ records the acquisition of the mineral interest as follows:

Proved properties acquisition costs	90,000	
Accounts receivable – other receivables		90,000
To record one-fourth mineral interest in Stoll lease.		

Stoll makes no accounting entry if XYZ finds proved reserves; instead, it merely reduces its share of ownership in its detailed lease records.

If drilling is undertaken in return for an interest in a mineral property, the entire drilling cost is included as part of the property acquired within the proved properties acquisition costs account.

Subsequent events

ASC 932-360-35-21 states that subsequent events should be considered when determining the proper disposition of costs for exploratory wells in progress at the balance sheet date:

> Information that becomes available after the end of the period covered by the financial statements but before those financial statements are issued or are available to be issued (as discussed in Section 855-10-25) shall be taken into account in evaluating conditions that existed at the balance sheet date, for example, in assessing unproved properties (see paragraph 932-360-35-11) and in determining whether an exploratory well or exploratory-type stratigraphic test well had found proved reserves (see paragraphs 932-360-35-18 through 35-20).

For example, assume that costs of $230,000 are accumulated for an exploratory well where drilling is completed prior to the balance sheet date of December 31, 2019. At year-end, the well's results are uncertain. However, on February 14, 2020, before the 2019 financial statements are issued, the operator decides that the well does not have proved reserves. With these facts, the costs of $230,000 accumulated at December 31, 2019, are charged to expense in the 2019 financial statements.

A different situation occurs when exploratory drilling continues at year-end. If the well is found to be a dry hole prior to issuing the financial statements, a question arises not only about the proper treatment of costs during the period, but also the treatment of costs incurred after the balance sheet date.

ASC 932-360-35-17 requires that costs incurred after the balance sheet date be charged to expense in the period after the balance sheet date. However, 932-360-40-10 requires that costs accumulated through the balance sheet date must be charged to expense in the period ending with the balance sheet date. Equipment salvage value is considered in the calculations.

For example, suppose XYZ began drilling an exploratory well in November 2019. During November and December, XYZ incurred drilling costs of $265,000. During January and early February 2020, XYZ incurred additional drilling costs of $105,000. On February 8, 2020, XYZ declared the well dry. XYZ issued financial statements for 2019 on March 10, 2020. ASC 932-360-35-17 and 40-10 require XYZ to charge $255,000 to expense in 2019 (costs incurred and accumulated through December 31, 2019, less expected salvage value of $10,000) and $95,000 to expense in 2020 (costs incurred in January and February 2020, net of expected salvage value of $10,000).

Additional considerations

Sometimes oil and gas operators purchase a library of G&G data. The information may relate to a specific area of interest, basin or trend, or it may encompass many areas. As with any type of cost, including those for seismic and support facilities, careful consideration should be given to the proper accounting treatment, as discussed below.

Purchased G&G library

ASC 932 appears to require charging the costs of all purchased exploration data to expense when the costs are incurred. Nevertheless, some successful efforts companies have proposed to treat these costs as deferred charges if they expect to use the information over a period of years and to the extent that the library itself can be resold and its capitalized costs readily recovered in cash. This treatment is analogous to the exception provided in ASC 932-360-25-11.

Companies with this view argue that if the costs can be allocated to specific areas, then they may charge related costs to expense when they use the information. If they cannot identify the costs with specific areas, they may amortize the deferred costs over their estimated useful life, typically two or three years, using straight-line amortization. However, this treatment rarely would be appropriate. Companies using this method should ensure that any deferred costs are truly for a saleable library and recoverable by selling the data. If not, these costs should be expensed at the time they are incurred.

Full cost companies should capitalize a purchased library of G&G data to the appropriate cost center. If the acquired data is for an area that is not covered by existing lease or exploration rights, its cost immediately forms part of the depreciable pool. If the data is for an area covered by an existing lease or permit, the cost is capitalized as part of the costs of unevaluated properties and subsequently accounted for as illustrated in Chapter 18.

Seismic surveys

3D or 4D seismic surveys are widely used for subsurface G&G analysis of both proved and unproved acreage. Successful efforts companies capitalize the costs of these seismic surveys, which assist with production, increase total recoverability and determine the desirability of drilling additional development wells within a proved area. To be eligible for capitalization, these costs must meet the definition of development activities. If they do not, they should be expensed as incurred. Any seismic expenses that relate to both proved and unproved acreage should be allocated between exploration and development costs.

Support facilities and overhead costs

Expenses related to support facilities and overhead costs should be allocated to the particular activities receiving the benefits. Therefore, costs of depreciation, taxes, repairs and equipment operation (such as seismic, construction, grading and drilling equipment, vehicles, repair shops, warehouses, supply points, camps and division, district or field offices) may relate in whole or in part to exploration. The identifiable portion of such costs should be treated as an exploration cost. In successful efforts accounting, only the costs directly related to activities whose direct costs are capitalized should themselves be capitalized.

• • •

Unproved Property Acquisition, Retention and Surrender

To perform any subsurface activities such as drilling exploratory or development wells, petroleum companies first must secure the rights to do so. The question of whether or not minerals actually exist in an area is uncertain until a drilling rig probes to depths where deposits may be found. Despite the risks, a company must negotiate in advance with the owners of mineral rights for permission to drill wells and produce any minerals discovered.

Overview of mineral rights

Occasionally, the rights can be secured simply by purchasing the fee interest in a property for outright ownership of both surface and mineral rights. In nearly every case, though, the right to explore and produce minerals is obtained through an oil and gas lease. This chapter focuses on U.S. leasing practices. Chapter 24 addresses property rights outside of the U.S.

Mineral rights can be severed from surface rights and often are divided among, and owned by, several people. For example, one person or group of people may own the minerals to a depth of 2,000 feet; another person or group may own the minerals from 2,000 feet to 10,000 feet. In this situation, a potential lessee must negotiate with the owners of all the depths through which the drilling will occur. Even more common are situations in which many people (frequently heirs of a decedent) own undivided interests (e.g., 20 percent shares) in a property's mineral rights.

Leasing mineral rights, rather than merely the right to drill and produce, typically allows the oil and gas company to explore, drill, survey, lay pipelines, build facilities, dispose of saltwater and own the minerals during the term of the lease.

When different parties own the surface and mineral rights, the oil and gas company first secures rights from the mineral rights owner(s) and then forges a separate agreement with the surface owner(s). Surface owners cannot legally deny the lessee access to land on which the minerals are leased. Thus, the mineral estate takes precedence over the surface estate.

Surface owners must be paid "adequate compensation" for the damages that occur to surface areas during petroleum operations, such as road construction and brush clearing. If the parties cannot agree on compensation, they may take the matter to court, where the judge typically will apply a rule of reasonable accommodation between mineral and surface owners.

Acquiring mineral rights is a crucial activity for a petroleum company. It typically is handled by personnel in the land department who are responsible for:

- Contacting other oil and gas operators, lease brokers, and land and mineral owners to obtain leases for the desired minerals.

- Advising the exploration department about leasing activities.

- Negotiating joint operating agreements with other operators.

- Securing pooling or unitization agreements.

- Negotiating the drilling of promotional test wells, farmouts and royalty overrides.

- Checking contracts of all newly purchased leases for proper signatures, notarization, dates and other key information.

- Filing the lease contract in the county clerk's office where the leased land is located, which also typically includes filing a memorandum to protect the confidentiality of lease terms.

- Maintaining a complete record about all properties including leases, joint operating agreements, royalty agreements, fee lands and any other rights.

- Verifying that the lease title is clear before drilling commences (by obtaining a title opinion from an attorney who is qualified to examine titles based on abstracts).

- Preparing division orders for proper allocation of revenues and costs.

- Making timely payment for all lease rentals, as authorized.

Lease contracts

In the U.S., oil and gas operators normally acquire rights to mineral properties through leases, which are important for petroleum accountants to understand.

The lease may address oil, gas, related hydrocarbons and other minerals or a combination thereof. In the petroleum industry, a mineral is considered to be a subsurface substance with economic value. Mineral owners who grant rights to others through a lease contract are called lessors, and the entities that acquire the leasehold rights are called lessees.

Lease forms vary widely. Figure 7-1 illustrates a typical lease agreement. Regardless of the language in the printed lease form, the lessor and lessee may strike out certain provisions and add to the document until they reach a final agreement.

Lease bonus

Figure 7-1, Article 1. A lease bonus is cash or other consideration paid to a lessor by the lessee in return for the right to explore for minerals, drill wells and produce any minerals found. The actual amount of the bonus normally is not recorded on the lease form; instead, the document uses wording such as "$10 and other valuable consideration."

The amount paid for the lease bonus is the result of bargaining between the parties and is affected by factors such as the proximity of the property to producing wells, the length of the primary lease term, the competition among potential lessees and the amount of royalty retained by the lessor.

Bonuses usually are computed on a per acre basis and range from a few hundred dollars per acre, in wildcat locations, to tens of thousands of dollars per acre near producing properties. Leases on federal and state owned properties normally are awarded after a bidding process, with each lease granted to the highest bidder. Offshore tracts often encompass 5,000 acres or more; for a single block, a lease bonus of millions of dollars is not uncommon. Some offshore bidding requirements include royalty or net profit bids in addition to (or instead of) bonus bids.

Primary term

Figure 7-1, Article 2. The maximum time allowed for a lessee to commence drilling a well is the primary term. Lessors are eager for an operator to drill as quickly as possible and generally prefer a short primary term. Conversely, the company acquiring the rights prefers more time to evaluate the property, review the drilling budget and obtain nearby parcels. On federal lands or in a wildcat area, five to 10 year terms are common. A three year primary term is common in most other areas, though any number of factors can result in a shorter primary term negotiated by the parties.

Royalty provisions

Figure 7-1, Article 3. Lessors retain a royalty interest in the minerals, which entitles them to receive either a specific portion of the oil and gas produced or a specific portion of the production value, free of development and operating costs. Royalty payments to mineral owners may be reduced only by applicable state severance taxes, production taxes or other costs necessary to make the product saleable. Historically, royalties for oil and gas properties have consisted of a one-eighth share, although they are negotiable and may be larger, as much as one-fifth or potentially more, if the property is near producing oil and gas properties.

To illustrate how royalty interests work, suppose that Indy Oil Co. (Indy), a successful efforts company, acquires a mineral lease on a property in which lessor Jones retains a one-fifth royalty interest. During the current year, 5,000 barrels of oil are produced and sold for $50 per barrel. The state severance tax is eight percent of the value of the oil. Indy, the lessee, must pay all lifting costs and other production costs on the lease. As the lessor, Jones receives payment of $46,000 (1/5 of $250,000 x 92%), which represents the net value of Jones' one-fifth royalty share after withholding severance taxes. In some instances, the lessor may be required to bear a proportionate share of costs to make the product salable.

Shut-in royalties

Figure 7-1, Article 3. Many lease contracts include shut-in royalty provisions, which the operator pays to the royalty owner if a successful well is drilled, completed and capable of producing in commercial quantities, yet has not begun producing within a specified period. Due to the absence of a market, a lack of transportation or the need for permission from a governmental authority, shut-in royalties may be more common on properties that contain gas. Typically, the operator cannot recover shut-in payments from future amounts owed to the royalty owner. Frequently, lease contracts specify that shut-in royalties will be equal in amount to the delay rentals. In many instances, the lessor restricts the shut-in provisions to a limited number of years.

Rights to free use of resources

Figure 7-1, Article 3. Operators customarily receive the right to use, without cost or royalty payment, the amount of oil and gas from the leased property's production that is necessary to carry out all operations covered by the lease contract. However, the royalty owner is entitled to a royalty on any oil or gas from the leased property's production that is used on properties in which the royalty owner has an interest.

Pooling provisions

Figure 7-1, Article 4. While some leases allow the operator to combine (pool or unitize) the leased property with properties leased or owned by others, others may require the lessee to obtain approval from the lessor. Regardless of necessary approvals, once properties are combined, each former owner of an interest in an individual property owns an interest in the total pooled minerals. The ownership interests are normally in proportion to the acreage contributed by each owner.

It may be advantageous to unitize the operation for secondary and tertiary development. Royalties are then divided according to the production capabilities of each producing well, rather than on a contributed acreage basis, with the best wells receiving enhanced portions of the total royalty.

Pooling, or unitization as it is more commonly referred to contractually, may also increase production and make it more efficient. Pooling is especially advantageous to lessees because it typically reduces costs.

Delay rentals

Figure 7-1, Article 5. The payment for deferring the commencement of drilling activities is called a delay rental, which is typically required to be paid to the lessee at the end of each lease year during the primary term in order to keep the lease in effect if no production has been established. Delay rentals are stated on a per acre basis and normally are much smaller than the lease bonus. For example, if a lease contract calls for a lease bonus of $1,000 per acre, the delay rental might be as little as $5 per acre, depending on conditions in the area and the negotiating ability of the parties.

Many short-term leases are paid-up leases, meaning the lease will remain in effect for the entire primary term with no other payments due to the lessor, except the initial lease bonus, unless and until production is established.

Drilling obligation

Figure 7-1, Article 5. The payment of a bonus and signing of a lease ordinarily is enough to keep the contract in force for a specified time. If drilling does not begin within that time, the lease terminates, regardless of the primary term, unless the lessee pays the lessor a delay rental or the lease is paid-up. However, no contract provisions extend the lease beyond the stated primary term. A lease is extended only by production.

Held by production

Figure 7-1, Article 5. Once a successful well is drilled, and commercial production begins, the lease remains in effect for as long as production continues without extended and indefinite interruption. If production ceases, the operator must act in good faith to resume the extraction of oil or gas within a reasonable time, as specified in the lease contract. Prolonged inactivity will terminate the lease, with all mineral rights reverting to the mineral owner, and the lessee required to restore the land's surface to its prior, or otherwise agreed-upon, condition.

Offset clause

Figure 7-1, Article 6. A common provision is an offset clause, which requires operators to drill offset wells on the property, as a prudent operator would drill under similar circumstances. The offset clause comes into play when a successful well is drilled on adjacent land within a specified distance of the property covered by the lease contract.

Right to assign interest

Figure 7-1, Article 9. Lease contracts grant each party the right to assign any part or all of its rights and obligations – which may or may not require approval of the other party. The right to assign interest is extremely important to an oil and gas company.

Lack of standard form

There is no such thing as a standard or statutory oil and gas lease, except those used by governmental authorities. Most oil and gas laws are based on court interpretations and become part of the common law.

Although the actual format of a lease agreement may vary for the numerous reasons outlined herein, the provisions of lease contracts are fairly consistent, such as those included in the illustrative lease agreement provided in Figure 7-1.

Figure 7-1
Illustrative lease agreement

OIL AND GAS LEASE

This agreement made and entered into this _____ day of _____ 20__, by and between _____ (Lessor) and _____ (Lessee).

Witnesseth:

1. Lessor, in consideration of the sum of _____ Dollars ($____), in hand paid, of the royalties herein provided for and of the agreement of Lessee herein contained, hereby grants, leases and lets exclusively unto Lessee for the purpose of investigating, exploring, prospecting, drilling and mining for and producing oil, gas and all other minerals, conducting exploration, geological and geophysical surveys, core tests, gravity and magnetic surveys, injecting gas, water and other fluids and air into subsurface strata, laying pipelines, building roads, tanks, power stations, telephone lines and other structures thereon and over and across the lands owned or claimed by Lessor adjacent and contiguous thereto, to produce, save, take care of, treat, transport and own said products and for the housing of its employees, the following described land in _____ County, State of _____ to wit: This lease also covers and includes all land owned or claimed by Lessor adjacent or contiguous to the lands particularly described above, whether the same be in said survey or surveys or in adjacent surveys, although not included within the boundaries of the land particularly described above. For the purpose of calculating the rental payments only as hereinafter provided for said land is estimated to comprise _____ acres, whether it actually comprises more or less.

2. Subject to the other provisions herein contained this Lease shall be for a term of _____ years from this date (called "primary term") and as long thereafter as oil, gas, or other minerals are produced in paying quantities from said land or lands with which the above described land is pooled hereunder.

3. The royalties to be paid to the Lessor are: (1) On oil, 1/5th of that produced and saved from said land, the same to be delivered at the wells or to the Lessor into the pipelines to which the wells may be connected. Lessee may from time to time purchase any royalty oil in its possession by paying the market price therefore prevailing for the field where produced on the date of purchase. (2) On gas, including casinghead gas or other gaseous substances, produced from said land and sold or used off the premises or for the extraction of gasoline or other products therefrom, 1/5th of the amount realized from said sale at the well, or which would be realized from such sale by the Lessee when computed at the well provided that on gas sold at the well the royalty shall be 1/5th of the amount realized from said sale. Where there is a gas well, or wells, capable of production on this Lease or acreage pooled therewith, whether it be before or after the primary term hereof and such well or wells are shut-in and there is no other production, drilling operations, or other operations being conducted capable of keeping this Lease in force under any of its provisions, Lessee shall pay as royalty to Lessor (and if it be within the primary term hereof such payment shall be in lieu of delay rentals) the sum of $1.00 per year per net royalty acre, such payment to be made to the depository bank hereinafter named or to the Lessor, on or before the anniversary date of this Lease next ensuing after the expiration of 90 days from the date such well or wells are shut-in and thereafter on the anniversary date of this Lease during the period such wells are shut-in and upon such payment, it shall be considered that this Lease is maintained in full force and effect. A "gas well" as used in this paragraph shall be construed as a well capable of producing gas and condensate, gas and distillate, or any other gaseous substances in commercial quantities. (3) On all other minerals mined and marketed, 1/10th either in kind or value at the well or mine at Lessee's election, except that on sulphur mined and marketed the royalty shall be fifty cents ($.50) per long ton. Lessee shall have free use of oil, gas, coal and water from lands, except water from Lessor's wells, for all operations hereunder and the royalty on oil, gas and coal shall be computed after deducting any so used.

4. Lessee, at its option, is hereby given the right and power to pool or combine the acreage covered by this Lease or any portion thereof as to oil and gas or either of them with other lands covered by this Lease and/or with any other land, lease, or leases in the immediate vicinity thereof to the extent hereinafter stipulated, when in Lessee's judgment it is necessary or advisable to do so in order to properly explore or to develop and operate said leased premises in compliance with the spacing rules of (listed authorized authority), or when to do so would in the judgment of Lessee promote the conservation of oil and gas in and under and that may be produced from said premises. Units pooled for oil hereunder shall not substantially exceed 40 acres each in area and units pooled for gas hereinunder shall not substantially exceed 640 acres in area plus a tolerance of 10% each for such units, provided that should governmental authority having jurisdiction, prescribe or permit the creation of larger units than those specified for the drilling or operation of a well at a regular location, or for obtaining maximum allowable from any well to be drilled, drilling or already drilled, units created may conform substantially in size with those prescribed or permitted by governmental regulations. Lessee under the provisions, hereof may pool or combine

acreage covered by this Lease or any portion thereof as above provided for as to oil in any one or more strata and as to gas in any one or more strata. The units formed by pooling as to any strata need not conform in size or area with the unit or units into which the Lease is pooled or combined as to any other strata and oil units need not conform as to area with gas units. The pooling in one or more instances shall not exhaust the rights of the Lessee hereunder to pool this Lease or portions thereof into other units. Lessee shall file for record in the County in which the Lease premises are situated an instrument identifying and describing the pooled acreage and upon such instrument being recorded the unit shall be effective as to all parties hereto, their heirs, successors or assigns, irrespective of whether or not the unit is likewise effective as to all other owners of surface, mineral, royalty or other rights in the lands included in such unit. Lessee may at its election exercise its pooling option before or after commencing operations for or completing an oil or gas well on the leased premises and the pooled unit may include, but is not required to include, land or leases upon which a well capable of producing oil or gas in paying quantities has been completed, or upon which operations for the drilling of a well for oil or gas has therefore been commenced. In the event of operations for drilling on or production of oil and gas from any part of a pooled unit which includes all or a portion of the lands covered by this Lease, regardless of whether such operations for drilling were commenced on, or such production was secured, before or after execution of this instrument, or of the instrument designating the pooled unit, such operations shall be considered as operations for, drilling on, or production of, oil and gas from the lands covered by this Lease whether or not the well or wells be located on the premises covered by this Lease and in such event operations for drilling shall be deemed to have been commenced on said lands covered by this Lease; and the entire acreage constituting such unit or units as to oil and gas, or either of them, as herein provided shall be treated for all purposes except the payment of royalties on production from the pooled unit as if the same were included in this Lease. For the purpose of computing the royalties to which owners of royalties and payments out of production and each of them shall be entitled to on production of oil or gas, or either of them from the pooled unit, there shall be allocated to the lands covered by this Lease and included in such unit (or to each separate tract within the unit if this Lease covers separate tracts within the unit) a pro rata portion of the oil and gas, or either of them, produced from the pooled unit after deducting that used for operations on the pooled unit. Such allocation shall be on an acreage basis and there shall be allocated to the acreage covered by this Lease and included in the pooled unit (or to each separate tract within the unit if this Lease covers separate tracts within the unit) that pro rata portion of the oil and gas or either of them produced from the pooled unit which the number of surface acres covered by this Lease (or in each separate tract) and included in the pooled unit bears to the total number of surface acres included in the pooled unit. Royalties hereunder shall be computed on the portion of such production, whether it be oil or gas or either of them, so allocated to the lands covered by this Lease and included in the unit the same as if such production were from such land. The production from an oil well will be considered as production from the Lease or the oil unit from which it is producing and not as production from a gas unit and production from a gas well will be considered as production from the Lease or gas unit from which it is producing and not from an oil unit. The formation of any unit hereunder shall not have the effect of changing the ownership of any delay rental or shut-in royalty which may become payable under this Lease. If this Lease now or hereafter covers separate tracts, no pooling or unitization of royalty interest as between any such separate tracts is intended or shall be implied or result merely from the inclusion of such separate tracts within this Lease, but Lessee shall nevertheless have the right to pool as provided above with consequent allocation of production as above provided for. As used herein, the words "separate tracts" shall mean any tract with royalty ownership differing, now or hereafter, either as to parties or amounts, from that of any other part of the leased premises.

5. If operations for drilling are not commenced on said land or on acreage pooled therewith as above provided for, on or before one year from the anniversary date of this Lease, the Lease shall terminate as to both parties, unless on or before such anniversary date Lessee shall pay or tender to Lessor or to the credit of the Lessor in the _____ Bank at _____, (which bank and its successors shall be Lessor's agents and shall continue as the depository for all rentals payable hereunder regardless of changes in ownership of said land or rentals) the sum of _____ Dollars ($_____), hereinafter called rentals, which shall cover the privilege of deferring commencement of drilling operations for a period of twelve (12) months. In like manner and upon like payment or tenders annually, the commencement of drilling operations may be further deferred for successive periods of twelve (12) months each during the primary term hereof. The payment or tender of rental under this paragraph and of shut-in royalty on gas wells as above provided for shall be by check or draft of Lessee mailed or delivered to Lessor, or to said bank on or before the date of the payment. If such bank or any successor bank shall fail, liquidate or be succeeded by another bank or for any other reason fail or refuse to accept rental, Lessee shall not be held in default for failure to make such payment or tender until 30 days after Lessor shall deliver to Lessee a proper recordable instrument naming another bank as agent to receive such payments or tenders. The cash payment for this Lease is consideration for this Lease according to its terms and shall not be allocated as mere rental for a period. Lessee may at any time or times execute and deliver to Lessor, or to the depository above named or place of record a release or releases of this Lease as to all or any part of the above described premises, or as to any mineral or horizon under all or any part thereof and thereby be relieved of all obligations as to the land or interest released. If this Lease is released as to all minerals and horizons under a portion of the land covered by this Lease, the rentals and other payments computed in accordance therewith shall thereupon be reduced in the proportion that the number of surface acres within such released portion bears to the total number of surface acres which was covered by this Lease immediately prior to such release.

6. If prior to the discovery of oil, gas or other minerals on said land, or on acreage pooled therewith, Lessee should drill a dry hole or holes thereon, or if after the discovery and production of oil, gas or other minerals, the production therefrom should cease from any cause, this Lease shall not terminate if Lessee commences operations for drilling or reworking within 60 days thereafter, or if it be within the primary term, commences or resumes the payment or tender of rentals, or commences operations for drilling or reworking on or before the rental paying date next ensuing after the expiration of 60 days from the date of completion of dry holes, or cessation of production. If at any time subsequent to 60 days prior to the beginning of the last year of the primary term and prior to the discovery of oil, gas or other minerals on said land, or on acreage pooled therewith, Lessee should drill a dry hole thereon, no rental payments or operations are necessary in order to keep the Lease in force during the remainder of the primary term. If at the expiration date of the primary term, oil, gas, or other minerals are not being produced on said land, or on acreage pooled therewith, but Lessee is then engaged

in drilling or reworking operations thereon, or shall have completed a dry hole thereon within 60 days prior to the end of the primary terms, the Lease shall continue in force so long as such operations on said wells or the drilling or reworking of any additional well are prosecuted with no cessation of more than 60 consecutive days and if they result in production of oil, gas or other minerals, so long thereafter as oil, gas or other minerals are produced from said lands or acreage pooled therewith. Any pooled unit designated by Lessee in accordance with the terms hereof may be dissolved by Lessee by an instrument filed for record in the County in which the leased premises are situated at any time after the completion of a dry hole or cessation of production on said unit. In the event a well or wells producing oil or gas in paying quantities should be brought in on adjacent lands, Lessee agrees to drill such offset wells as a reasonably prudent operator would drill under the same or similar circumstances.

7. Notwithstanding anything in this lease contained to the contrary, it is expressly agreed that if Lessee shall commence operations for drilling at any time while this Lease is in force, this Lease shall remain in force and its terms shall continue so long as such operations are prosecuted; and, if production results therefrom, then so long as production continues under the terms of this Lease.

8. Lessee shall have the right at any time during or after the expiration of this Lease to remove all property and fixtures placed by Lessee on said lands, including the right to draw and remove all casing. When required by Lessor, Lessee will bury all pipelines below ordinary plow depth and no well shall be drilled within 200 feet of any residence or barn now on said land without Lessor's consent.

9. The rights of either party hereunder may be assigned in whole or in part and the provisions hereof shall extend to their heirs, successors and assigns: but no change or division in ownership of the lands, rentals or royalties, however accomplished, shall operate to enlarge the obligations or diminish the rights of the Lessee; and no change or division in, such ownership shall be binding on Lessee until 30 days after Lessee shall have been furnished by registered U.S. Mail at Lessee's principal place of business with a certified copy of recorded instrument or instruments evidencing same. In the event of an Assignment hereof in whole or in part, liability for breach of any obligation hereunder shall rest exclusively upon the owner of this Lease, or of a portion thereof, who commits such breach. In the event of the death of any person entitled to rentals hereunder, Lessee may pay or tender such rentals to the credit of the deceased, or the estate of the deceased, until such time as Lessee is furnished with proper evidence as to the heirs or devisees of the deceased and that all debts of the estate have been paid. If at any time two or more persons be entitled to participate in the rental payable hereunder, Lessee may pay or tender said rental jointly to such persons or to their joint credit in the depository named herein; or, at Lessee's election, the proportionate part of said rentals to which each participant is entitled may be paid or tendered to him separately, or to his separate credit in said depository; and payment or tender to any participant of his portion of the rentals payable hereunder shall maintain this Lease as to such participant. In the event of assignment of this Lease as to a segregated portion of said land, the rental payable hereunder shall be apportionable as between the several leasehold owners ratably according to the surface acreage of each and default in rental payment by one shall not affect the rights of the other leasehold owners hereunder. If six or more parties become entitled to royalty hereunder, Lessee may withhold payment thereof unless and until furnished with a recordable instrument,

executed by all such parties designating an agent to receive payment for all.

10. The breach by Lessee of any obligation arising hereunder shall not cause a forfeiture or termination of this Lease nor cause a termination or reversion of the estate created hereby, nor the grounds for cancellation hereof in whole or in part. In the event Lessor considers that operations are not at any time being conducted in compliance with this Lease, Lessor shall notify Lessee in writing of the facts relied upon and constituting a breach hereof and Lessee, if in default, shall have 60 days after receiving such notice in which to commence compliance with the obligations imposed by virtue of this instrument. After the discovery of oil, gas or other minerals in paying quantities on said premises, Lessee shall develop the acreage retained hereunder as a reasonably prudent operator, but in discharging this obligation shall in no event be required to drill more than one well per 40 acres of the area retained hereunder and capable of producing oil in paying quantities and one well per 640 acres plus an acreage tolerance of 10% of 640 acres of the area retained hereunder capable of producing gas or other minerals in paying quantities.

11. Lessor hereby warrants and agrees to defend the title to said land and agrees that Lessee at its option may discharge any tax, mortgage or other lien upon said land, either in whole or in part, and in the event Lessee does so, it shall be subrogated to such lien with right to enforce same and apply rentals and royalties accruing hereunder towards satisfying same. Without impairment of Lessee's rights under the warranty in event of failure of title, it is agreed that if this Lease covers a lesser interest in the oil, gas, or other minerals in all or any part of said land than the entire and undivided fee simple estate therein, or no interest therein, then the royalties, delay rentals and other monies accruing from any part as to which this Lease covers less than such full interest shall be paid only in the proportion which the interest herein, if any, covered by this Lease, bears to the whole and undivided fee simple estate therein. All royalty interest covered by this Lease, whether or not owned by Lessor, shall be paid out of the royalty herein provided. Should any one or more of the parties named above as Lessors fail to execute this Lease, it shall nevertheless be binding upon the party or parties executing same. Failure of Lessee to reduce rental paid hereunder shall not impair the right of the Lessee to reduce royalty.

12. Should Lessee be prevented from complying with any express or implied covenant of this Lease, from conducting drilling or reworking operations thereon, or from producing oil, gas or other minerals therefrom by reason of scarcity of, or inability to obtain, or to use equipment or material, or by operation of force majeure, or because of any federal or state law or any order, rule or regulation of governmental authority, then while so prevented, Lessee's obligation to comply with such covenant shall be suspended and Lessee shall not be liable in damages for failure to comply therewith; and this Lease shall be extended while and so long as Lessee is prevented by any such cause from conducting drilling or reworking operations on or from producing oil, gas or other minerals from the leased premises; and the time while Lessee is so prevented shall not be counted against Lessee, anything in this Lease to the contrary notwithstanding.

[Signatures of Parties]

[Notary Public]

The interest conveyed or transferred under an oil and gas lease varies dramatically from state to state. In many states, the interest conveyed is a determinable fee interest in the minerals. It terminates when the primary term expires or at the cessation of production. In other locales, an oil and gas lease creates only a license to explore and search, much like a hunting lease for game animals.

Miscellaneous provisions of leases

The foregoing are potential provisions in an oil and gas lease agreement. However, many other provisions may be inserted into leases that give one party special rights or impose selected obligations on the other party to the lease. For example:

Option payment. Frequently, an operator will initiate a pre-leasing agreement with a mineral owner requesting a stated period within which to lease the property. An option payment made by the operator may include the cost of rights to explore, or a separate payment may be required for those rights. The option typically specifies the amount of the bonus per acre, if and when the lease is executed.

Fixed or mandatory rentals. The lease contract may require rental payments that cannot be avoided, even if the property is abandoned or drilling begins. In effect, these payments are a deferred bonus, typically paid in installments.

Compensatory royalties. Petroleum companies pay compensatory royalties to offset royalty owners' loss of income during periods when the company has not fulfilled its obligation to drill. This situation includes failure to drill an offset well or failure to follow an agreed-upon plan to develop the property.

Guaranteed or minimum royalties. For properties with a high probability of production, mineral owners may require lessees to guarantee a specified minimum royalty payment monthly or annually. If a royalty owner's share of net proceeds from production is less than the specified amount, the lessee must pay the difference. Guaranteed payments may be nonrecoverable or recoverable out of future royalties due to the royalty owner. This provision typically is found in federal leases, but it may be negotiated in fee leases (i.e., leases of private lands).

Right to take in-kind. When a lessor owns a significant amount of minerals or requires quantities of oil or gas for business purposes (such as manufacturing or farming), the lessor may wish to take its royalty share in-kind. The lessor takes its royalty share of actual production and then secures the transportation and marketing for its own account. This provision requires additional metering or volume monitoring by the lease operator.

Call on production. Lessors who are in the business of refining, purchasing oil or marketing gas may negotiate an option to purchase, or a call on production, in their lease contracts. This provision gives them the first opportunity to purchase production at terms equivalent to market rates. It often is used by lessors that are vertically integrated oil and gas companies.

Executive rights. Of increasing importance in oil, gas and mineral transactions, executive rights give a person or entity exclusive rights to lease and manage the minerals belonging to another. Executive rights can be useful when several parties own undivided interests in minerals or for the convenience of an oil and gas company. Executive rights resemble a power of attorney in that the holder does not necessarily own minerals in the tract.

Types of mineral interests

The lessee in a mineral lease has rights and obligations associated with drilling and equipping wells and producing the oil and gas. Lessees possess an operating interest or working interest in the property (sometimes also used interchangeably with a leasehold interest). Lessors receive a specified fractional share of the minerals produced or the value thereof in the form of a royalty. The lessor has no right or obligation to carry out exploration, drilling or production. Lessors also bear no part of the costs incurred, except for their proportionate share of production taxes and, if applicable, a share of costs necessary to make the oil or gas salable. Thus, the lessor possesses a nonoperating interest.

Three other types of nonoperating interests may be created out of the working interest: (1) overriding royalty interests, (2) production payments (oil or gas payments) and (3) net profits interests. All are discussed in detail in subsequent chapters of this textbook. Petroleum accountants must distinguish between the terms mineral rights and mineral interests. Mineral rights usually refer to fee ownership rights that are not created by a lease. However, for applying ASC 932, the term mineral interests means more than fee ownership. As defined in ASC 932-360-20, they also include any concession or "other interest representing the legal right to produce or a revenue interest in the production of oil or gas subject to such terms as may be imposed by the conveyance of that interest."

Unproved leasehold acquisitions

All capitalized costs related to unproved mineral properties are charged to the appropriate unproved mineral properties accounts.

Bonus payments

A lease bonus, ordinarily the initial investment in an unproved lease, is capitalized by the lessee as part of unproved properties acquisition costs. Assume that Indy acquires a lease on 800 acres from landowner Johnson, paying a lease bonus of $125 per acre. The $100,000 lease bonus is the initial capitalized cost of the lease and is recorded by Indy as follows:

Unproved properties acquisition costs	100,000	
Accounts payable		100,000
To record lease bonus for acquisition of Johnson lease.		

Incidental lease acquisition costs

Reg. S-X Rule 4-10(a)(1) and ASC 932-360-25-7 state that the cost of a mineral property includes incidental costs, such as broker's fees, recording fees, legal costs and other acquisition costs. A broker fee of $6,500 is paid to acquire the Johnson lease, recorded by Indy as follows:

Unproved properties acquisition costs	6,500	
Accounts payable		6,500
To record broker fee paid to acquire Johnson lease.		

Similar entries are made for recording fees and other acquisition costs. Most companies require a minimum amount before capitalizing costs, although the threshold varies by company. If acquisition costs are insignificant, they may be charged to expense when incurred.

ASC 932 is silent on the proper treatment of overhead costs related to acquiring mineral properties. In identifying and acquiring leases, an E&P company may incur internal costs for scouting, civil engineering, surveying and mapping, usually called leasing costs. One problem faced in properly accounting for leasing costs is that personnel often do more than lease properties: they may service leases already acquired, assist with drilling, work in exploration and even work on producing leases.

Overhead costs incurred by a company's own leasing staff generally are accounted for in one of three ways:

1. Expensed at the time incurred.

2. Capitalized by allocating them using a reasonable allocation methodology (e.g., by acreage, equally to all leases acquired during the period, etc.).

3. Capitalized to the extent associated with specific lease acquisitions, with the balance recorded to operating expense.

From the viewpoint of accounting theory, the third method is perhaps the most desirable; however, practical difficulties often prohibit it. Detailed time sheets can help determine the labor costs that apply directly to specific properties. With adequate record-keeping, operating costs of equipment also may be charged to individual properties. In reality, the bulk of leasing costs cannot be traced to specific leases. To be capitalized, they must be allocated on a predetermined basis.

Because of the practical difficulty involved, Indy Oil Co. treats all leasing overhead costs as operating expenses. The *2019 PricewaterhouseCoopers Survey of U.S. Petroleum Accounting Practices* (Question B1) reports that 20 of 24 responding companies using the successful efforts method charge to expense a portion of internal land department costs associated with acquiring unproved leases. According to Reg. S-X Rule 4-10(c)(2):

> Any internal costs that are capitalized shall be limited to those costs that can be directly identified with acquisition, exploration and development activities undertaken by the reporting entity for its own account and shall not include any costs related to production, general corporate overhead, or similar activities.

Option to acquire leasehold

An operator may not be sufficiently interested in an area to pay the bonuses necessary to acquire leases. Instead, it may wish to acquire the rights for shooting seismic, with an option to lease any part or all of the acreage covered by the option. In these cases, the company must obtain an exploration permit, or shooting rights, from the property owner.

Any costs for these rights typically are considered geological and geophysical (G&G) costs recorded as exploration expense under successful efforts. If the shooting rights include an option to lease the mineral interest, the portion that applies to the shooting rights is expensed and the portion that applies to the lease option is capitalized under the successful efforts method. If the costs cannot be separated, the entire amount is capitalized. If none of the acreage is leased, the costs are expensed.

For example, on March 17, 2019, Indy pays landowner Carson $2 an acre for the right to explore a 2,000-acre tract. It also pays $3 per acre for the right to take three-year leases within the next six months on any part of the acreage by paying a lease bonus of $400 per acre when exercising the option. The journal entry recorded by Indy on March 17, 2019 would be as follows:

Unproved properties purchase suspense ($3 x 2,000 acres)	6,000	
Exploration expense ($2 x 2,000 acres)	4,000	
Accounts payable		10,000
To record lease option and G&G rights on Carson tract.		

On September 3, 2019, Indy exercises the option on 900 acres, acquiring Lease No. 10019 and allowing the option to lapse on the remaining 1,100 acres. The journal entry recorded by Indy when it exercises the option would be:

Unproved properties acquisition costs	362,700	
Impairment expense – unproved properties ($3 x 1,100 acres)	3,300	
Accounts payable ($400 x 900 acres)		360,000
Unproved properties purchase suspense		6,000
To record Lease No. 10019 and lapse of option on remaining 1,100 acres of Carson tract.		

Alternatively, if after six months Indy did not lease any acreage, the amount held in suspense would be expensed as follows:

Impairment expense – unproved properties	6,000	
Unproved properties purchase suspense		6,000
To record lapse of options on Carson tract.		

Acquisition of fee interests

An E&P company typically obtains mineral rights through an oil and gas lease. However, sometimes it obtains a fee interest in a property (i.e., outright ownership of both minerals and the surface rights). In this case, the purchase price, including incidental acquisition costs, should be allocated proportionately between the minerals and surface rights based on the relative fair market values of the two interests.

For example, assume that Indy pays $1,500 per acre for the fee interest in 300 acres, with the surface to be held for investment purposes. In recent transactions near the property, surface rights for similar land without any minerals attached sold for $1,400 per acre. The journal entry recorded by Indy would be as follows:

Land ($1,400 x 300 acres)	420,000	
Unproved properties – fee interests ($100 x 300 acres)	30,000	
Accounts payable		450,000
To record purchase of the fee interest in surface and mineral rights.		

Maintenance and carrying costs

In addition to acquiring leases, the land department should maintain accurate property records. They must keep leases in force, with good title, until either the property becomes productive or the company decides to surrender or abandon it. Delay rentals, legal fees for title defense and clerical costs are considered maintenance or carrying costs, which must be expensed as incurred under the successful efforts method of accounting.

Delay rentals

Assuming that the lease is not paid-up, a delay rental is due to the lessor to defer commencement of drilling operations for an additional year within the primary term. If operations have not commenced, or if the delay rental is not paid by the anniversary date, the lease automatically terminates. For a successful efforts company, ASC 932-360-25-9 stipulates that delay rentals must be charged to expense as incurred.

For example, the 450 acre Flanders Lease calls for an annual delay rental of $980. Operations have not commenced by the first anniversary of the lease but the company wishes to keep the lease in force. It pays the delay rental and records the journal entry as follows:

Delay rental expense	980	
Accounts payable		980
To record annual delay rental expense on the Flanders Lease.		

Property taxes

Many state and local governments levy property taxes on both mineral rights and surface rights. These taxes on mineral rights owned by a lessee are considered another carrying cost of the property and charged to expense. These taxes are incurred after the lessee acquires the mineral rights and should not be confused with any delinquent taxes assumed by the lessee when it acquires the lease. If property taxes assessed on the Flanders Lease are $200, the expenses are recorded as follows:

Ad valorem tax expense	200	
Accounts payable		200
To record property taxes on the Flanders Lease.		

Other carrying costs

Under the successful efforts method, other types of lease maintenance and carrying costs, such as clerical and record-keeping costs and legal fees for title defense, are charged to expense in the same manner as delay rentals and property taxes.

Unproved impairment and abandonment

Generally, a substantial portion of the unproved acreage acquired by an operator is later surrendered or abandoned without production having commenced. Various methods have traditionally been used to account for these known or reasonably anticipated losses. ASC 932 and Reg. S-X Rule 4-10 provide guidance for companies in accounting for the decreased value of unproved properties. ASC 360's guidance for impairment does not address unproved properties.

Under ASC 932-360-35-11, unproved properties must be assessed periodically to determine whether or not their book values have been impaired. If so, a valuation allowance is established to reflect the reduced value. Although it does not define impairment, ASC 932-360-35-11 provides several example indicators for when a property is impaired:

> ... A property would likely be impaired, for example, if a dry hole has been drilled on it and the entity has no firm plans to continue drilling. Also, the likelihood of partial or total impairment of a property increases as the expiration of the lease term approaches if drilling activity has not commenced on the property or on nearby properties...

Impairment of value can be recognized in two ways: (1) individually for unproved properties with relatively significant acquisition costs or (2) by group for a relatively large number of unproved properties whose acquisition costs are not individually significant. The method chosen also determines how to handle costs of abandoned leases and leases transferred to proved properties.

When recording impairment of individually significant properties, a company should maintain detailed individual property records. This will facilitate the need to charge an impairment allowance account with the accumulated impairment on a property when it is sold, surrendered, assigned or becomes proved. If amortizing on a group basis, keeping a single impairment allowance for the entire group (or for each group if there is more than one) may be sufficient.

Individually significant properties

If the costs associated with an individual property are significant, impairment is assessed on a property-by-property basis. Individual impairment also may be recorded on leases that are not individually significant, although there is no requirement to do so.

Responses to the *2019 PricewaterhouseCoopers Survey of U.S. Petroleum Accounting Practices* (Question C1) indicate that 13 of 33 responding companies have unproved leases which are considered individually significant for impairment purposes. Companies typically use various criteria for determining significance. Some companies specify dollar amount as a minimum cost for a significant property. To arrive at a floor price, companies should typically consider such factors as the size of the enterprise, total assets, total investments in oil and gas properties, net income and similar factors. Acquired leases should be evaluated for potential impairment on an annual basis in light of these factors.

The concept of impaired unproved property noted in ASC 932-360-35 is somewhat unusual in authoritative accounting literature. Neither the FASB nor the SEC has defined the term, nor has either clearly indicated exactly how to measure the impairment of an individual unproved property. The aforementioned survey (Question C2) found that companies consider various factors in assessing impairment. All survey respondents with individually significant unproved properties consider whether or not the company still intends to drill on the lease. The majority of respondents also consider: (1) results from exploratory drilling related to the same property, (2) time to surrender as specified in the lease, (3) market value of similar acreage in the area, (4) industry activity in the same area and (5) geologists' evaluation of the lease.

Additional considerations may include:

- If the company has definite plans to drill on a lease, its assessed value might be equal to net book value, with no impairment recognized.

- If drilling plans are uncertain, the company's assessed value of the lease may be significantly less than its original cost.

- If the company does not plan to drill on a lease due to recent dry holes on or adjacent to the company lease or a change in drilling plan, the lease may have little or no assessed value and may be substantially impaired.

- A company's impairment policy might recognize partial impairment as time elapses on the primary term of each lease.

To illustrate impairment of individually significant leases, assume that a company has five individually significant leases for which no impairment has been recorded previously. Costs and value assessed by considering impairment indicators at December 31, 2018, are as follows:

Figure 7-2

Impairment of individually significant leases

Property	Cost	Assessed value	Impairment
Lease A	$ 95,000	$ 85,000	$ 10,000
Lease B	325,000	100,000	225,000
Lease C	100,000	120,000	–
Lease D	225,000	350,000	–
Lease E	40,000	200,000	–
Total	**$785,000**	**$855,000**	**$235,000**

Since each lease is deemed to be individually significant, impairment assessments must be made on a lease-by-lease basis. Even though total assessed value exceeds the total cost of all leases in aggregate, an entry is required to recognize impairment of the two individual leases identified in Figure 7-2:

Impairment expense – unproved properties	235,000	
Allowance for impairment – unproved properties		235,000
To record loss on impairment of Lease A and Lease B.		

After impairment is recorded, the net book value of unproved properties is $550,000, calculated as the cost of unproved properties of $785,000, less the allowance for impairment of $235,000.

Surrender of impaired individually significant unproved property. When surrendering an impaired individually significant unproved property, successful efforts companies charge the net carrying value of the lease (capitalized cost minus valuation allowance) to expense.

Subsequent evaluation. After recording impairment, a company cannot record any recovery in value. For example, assume that on December 31, 2019, the company in the preceding illustration prepares a schedule of unproved properties:

Figure 7-3

Subsequent evaluation of previous impairment

Property	Net cost	Assessed value	Impairment
Lease B	$100,000	$575,000	$ –
Lease E	40,000	41,000	–
Lease F (new)	900,000	880,000	20,000

Based on the assessed value compared to the net cost, an impairment of $20,000 would be recorded on Lease F acquired in early 2019 as of December 31, 2019. Even though the assessed value of Lease B now exceeds its net cost, the impairment allowance of $225,000 for Lease B established at December 31, 2018, does not change. No gains are recorded for previously impaired properties, even if the value has subsequently increased.

Individually insignificant properties

For companies using the successful efforts method, ASC 932-360-35-11 states, in part:

> When an entity has a relatively large number of unproved properties whose acquisition costs are not individually significant, it may not be practical to assess impairment on a property-by-property basis, in which case the amount of loss to be recognized and the amount of the valuation allowance needed to provide for impairment of those properties shall be determined by amortizing those properties, either in the aggregate or by groups, on the basis of experience of the entity in similar situations and other information about such factors as the primary lease terms of those properties, the average holding period of unproved properties and the relative proportion of such properties on which proved reserves have been found in the past.

To compute amortization, a single group or multiple groups of unproved properties may be used. If using multiple groups, the aggregation may be based on a number of logical characteristics, for example, by geographic location (onshore or offshore); cost ($500,000 or less, $500,000 to $1 million, $1 million to $10 million, etc.); geological area (Permian Basin, Bakken or Eagle Ford); or year of acquisition. The purpose of this aggregation analysis is to derive an overall estimate of impairment similar to that assessed on individually significant properties.

When recording impairment of unproved properties on a group basis, a company should develop an amortization methodology that considers factors such as the following:

- Time to surrender, based on lease terms.

- Time to surrender, based on historical experience.

- Experience percentage of successful versus unsuccessful leases.

The basic premise behind the group amortization approach is that certain unproved properties will become nonproductive over time and, therefore, they should be impaired. Others ultimately will become producing properties. Using this methodology, a company should estimate, based on past experience, the portion of its unproved properties that will be nonproductive. If a company has limited history or its exploration strategy and activities have changed, it may be more appropriate to consider industry-wide experience with respect to the factors listed above.

The two most common amortization methods for recording impairment of unproved properties on a group basis are:

- Straight-line amortization.

- Amortization based on analysis of annual surrenders.

Straight-line amortization. To illustrate a basic application of the group method of recording impairment using a straight-line basis, assume that a company includes all of its unproved properties in a single group and records amortization on that basis.

The company records leases acquired each year and separately computes amortization for each acquisition. An analysis of leases acquired in 2019 shows that acquisition costs of $1.5 million were charged to the unproved properties acquisition costs account. As of December 31, 2019, there was a $3.6 million balance in the unproved properties acquisition costs account, including leases acquired in previous years, and a $950,000 credit balance in the allowance for impairment of unproved properties account.

The company's experience indicates that ultimately 25 percent of its leases will become productive and the average holding period for the remaining leases will be five years. As a result, $1,125,000 ($1.5 million x 75%) of the leases acquired in 2019 ultimately will be abandoned over a five-year period (beginning in 2020). Amortization of $225,000 ($1,125,000 ÷ five years) will be recorded in 2020 as follows:

Impairment expense – unproved properties	225,000	
Allowance for impairment – unproved properties		225,000
To record amortization of unproved properties acquired in 2019.		

Similar calculations would be required for leases acquired each year, with amortization expense recorded in the same fashion. Assume that amortization on other leases totaled $490,000 for 2020, resulting in total amortization for 2020 of $715,000 ($225,000 + $490,000). When the impairment of individually insignificant properties is measured and recorded as a group, it simplifies the accounting for both surrender of unproved properties and transfers to proved properties. The original capitalized cost of a surrendered lease is charged to an allowance for impairment of unproved properties account and removed at the time of surrender from the unproved properties acquisition costs account. If a property is transferred to proved properties during the period, the proved leasehold costs account is charged and the unproved properties acquisition costs account is credited for its cost.

For example, continuing the previous illustration, assume that in 2020:

- Additional unproved properties are leased for $1.2 million.

- Leases that cost $500,000 are surrendered.

- Leases that cost $350,000 are proved.

The following journal entries would be recorded:

Unproved properties acquisition costs	1,200,000	
Accounts payable		1,200,000
To record cost of additional leases acquired in 2020.		

Allowance for impairment – unproved properties	500,000	
Unproved properties acquisition costs		500,000
To record cost of surrendered leases.		

Proved leasehold costs	350,000	
Unproved properties acquisition costs		350,000
To record cost of properties transferred to proved during the year.		

Subsequent to recording these journal entries, the accounts would appear as follows:

Unproved properties acquisition costs			
Balance – 12/31/2019	$3,600,000		
Additions	1,200,000		
		Surrenders	$ (500,000)
		Transfers to proved	(350,000)
Balance – 12/31/2020	$3,950,000		

Allowance for impairment – unproved properties			
		Balance – 12/31/2019	$ (950,000)
		Amortization	(715,000)
Surrenders	$ 500,000		
		Balance – 12/31/2020	$(1,165,000)

Amortization expense for 2021 on leases acquired in 2019 is again $225,000 and assuming no change to the company's estimate of surrenders, amortization on leases acquired in 2020 is $180,000 (1/5 x 75% x $1.2 million). Those amounts, along with amortization on acquisitions from previous years, would be charged to an impairments and abandonments of unproved properties account and credited to an allowance for impairment of unproved properties account. If the allowance previously provided is inadequate to absorb the cost of a surrendered lease, a loss should be recognized upon the surrender of the property. The loss should equal the difference between the cost of the property surrendered and the balance in the allowance for impairment of unproved properties account.

Amortization based on analysis of annual surrenders. Another approach for computing amortization is to use annual rates based on experience. In considering its experience, a company should use at least one complete cycle of lease acquisition and exploration and all leases acquired during the base period. If that is not feasible, a representative sample of leases is permissible. Calculations can be based on monetary amounts or acreage when leasehold costs per acre fluctuate widely.

Assume that a company has analyzed its cycle for leases with primary terms of three years. Figure 7-4 is a three-year recurring analysis performed in early 2019.

In this example, the company's history suggests that 60 percent of its unproved properties costs relate to leases that are ultimately nonproductive and become partially impaired, until they are deemed to be worthless. Three different methods can calculate annual amortization rates for the 60 percent of worthless costs.

Method 1 in Figure 7-5 uses a straight-line calculation over the three-year primary term. Annual amortization is one-third of 60 percent, or 20 percent.

Method 2 in Figure 7-6 calculates annual amortization rates by allocating costs over the properties' expected lives. For example, for the 18 percent of costs related to properties expected to be found worthless and abandoned in Year 2, assume that one-half is impaired and expensed in Year 1 and one-half in Year 2.

Figure 7-4
Ultimate cost allocation

Year acquired	Total Cost	Property found to be nonproductive in year:			Ultimately productive property
		1	2	3	
2014	60,000	*	*	$21,000	$26,000
2015	50,000	*	$ 8,500	17,000	16,000
2016	100,000	$12,500	14,500	31,000	42,000
2017	70,000	6,000	15,500	**	**
2018	80,000	5,000	**	**	**
Total		$23,500	$38,500	$69,000	$84,000
3 year avg %***		9%	18%	33%	40%

* Known, but not part of the latest three-year average.
** Unknown at the time of analysis performed in early 2019.
*** For example: 23,500 ÷ (100,000 + 70,000 + 80,000) = 9%.

Figure 7-5
Amortization on a straight-line basis

Abandonment %	Year 1	Year 2	Year 3
60%	20%	20%	20%

Figure 7-6
Amortization based on allocation over properties' expected lives

Year after acquisition	Abandonment %	Allocated straight-line over 3 years		
		1	2	3
1	9%	9%		
2	18	9	9%	
3	33	11	11	11%
	60%	29%	20%	11%

Method 3 in Figure 7-7 calculates amortization by allocating a specific portion (e.g., 20 percent) in each year prior to the expected year of abandonment. For example, for the 18 percent of costs related to properties expected to be abandoned in Year 2, assume 20 percent of 18 percent, or 3.6 percent, is impaired and expensed in Year 1 and 14.4 percent in Year 2, as shown in below.

The third approach should reflect management's judgment and experience in determining that leases retain much of their value until the year in which they are found to be nonproductive.

Figure 7-7
Amortization based on specific portion of abandonment per year

Year after acquisition	Abandonment %	Allocated at 20% per year until deemed worthless		
		1	2	3
1	9.0%	9.0%		
2	18.0	3.6	14.4%	
3	33.0	6.6	6.6	19.8%
	60.0%	19.2%	21.0%	19.8%

It should be noted that in the previous tables, first-year amortization varies from 19.2 percent to 29 percent, but it always exceeds the nine percent of costs attributed to leases expected to be found worthless in Year 1. For this example, one should not calculate first-year amortization as simply nine percent of costs; otherwise, the accounting merely expenses the estimated costs of worthless property in the year it is found worthless.

Amortization is intended to reflect lease impairment, including partial impairment after one year for leases expected to be found worthless in Years 2 and 3. Accordingly, first year amortization should reflect both: (1) the nine percent of costs attributed to leases expected to be found worthless in Year 1 and (2) a portion of the remaining 51 percent of total lease acquisition costs that will be found worthless during the primary term.

Full cost accounting considerations

Refer to Chapter 18 for additional information about measuring impairment of unproved properties under the full cost accounting method.

Evaluating subsequent events

ASC 932-360-35-21 states that information that becomes available after the end of the period covered by the financial statements, but before those financial statements are issued or are available to be issued, should be considered in evaluating conditions that existed at the balance sheet date. This guidance should be considered in assessing unproved properties for potential impairment.

Top leases and lease renewals

In some cases, the operator may be unable, or unwilling, to drill on an unproved property before its primary term expires; however, it may wish to retain the property for possible future drilling. The operator may negotiate with the mineral owner to either extend the primary term of the original lease or sign a new lease contract. Under successful efforts accounting, the bonus for signing a new lease should be capitalized.

A new lease signed before the original lease expires is called a top lease. Under the successful efforts method, the book value of the original lease may be treated as a part of the capitalized cost of the top lease. However, if the original lease expires, and the lessee gives up all rights before obtaining a new lease, the expiration of the old lease should be treated as an abandonment.

• • •

Drilling and Development

When subsurface formations point to the presence of hydrocarbons and related leases are executed, the operator still faces significant hurdles of navigating complex regulatory issues with various agencies and planning the well, including choosing a contractor and drilling method. Once the contractor drills the well, the operator must decide to complete the well and begin production or abandon the site.

Regulatory requirements

Drilling and development activities are subject to various regulations depending on location. Environmental and safety requirements are also important considerations for operators to consider.

Onshore regulatory requirements

The operator must secure a drilling permit from the appropriate state or federal regulatory agency. Many states require permits and specific minimum spacing for wells. Greater spacing is required for gas wells because gas moves through a formation more easily than oil and fewer wells are needed to physically deplete it economically. Offshore well spacing normally is driven by either the constraints of the installation or the seabed infrastructure.

Operators must supply certain information to government agencies up front, including:

- Proof of financial assurance, supported by either a bond from an insurance company or a letter of credit from a bank.

- An application to drill, which requires the exact legal location (staked location) of the well, its planned total depth (TD), spacing, targeted geological formation (reservoir), well type (oil or gas), distance to nearest completed well in the reservoir and lease name.

- A plat, which is a scaled diagram of the lease showing the proposed drilling location, spacing unit boundaries, distance to nearest well in the same reservoir, northerly direction and legal name of surveyed acreage.

- Payment of the applicable regulatory drilling fee, which is typically assessed according to well depth.

The total amount of oil and gas recovered from a reservoir, known as the ultimate recovery, may be only moderately affected by the number of wells drilled into the reservoir. However, the speed at which the reservoir is physically depleted can be very important.

If production accelerates beyond certain technical limits, it will reduce ultimate recovery. Uneven flow from different portions of the reservoir can isolate pockets of hydrocarbons, with possible early water breakthrough or loss of reservoir drive mechanism. Secondary recovery methods can help, but the potential ultimate recovery seldom can be achieved after poor initial reservoir management. More wells may be drilled to evenly deplete the reservoir, maximizing recovery and accelerating cash flow from production. The high cost of drilling, however, impedes overdevelopment unless it is critical to optimize the reservoir development plan.

Drilling on federal lands

In the U.S., drilling activities on federally owned lands are governed by the Bureau of Land Management (BLM). BLM is responsible for oil and gas leasing on about 700 million acres of subsurface mineral estate.

BLM issues two types of leases for oil and gas exploration and development: competitive and non-competitive. In 1987, Congress passed the Federal Onshore Oil and Gas Leasing Reform Act, which requires all public lands available for oil and gas leasing to be offered first through competitive leasing. A non-competitive lease can be offered only after the land has been offered competitively at an auction with no bid received.

The maximum competitive lease of federal property is 2,560 acres in the lower 48 and 5,760 acres in Alaska outside of the National Petroleum Reserve-Alaska. The maximum non-competitive lease in all states is 10,240 acres. Both competitive and non-competitive leases are issued for 10 years and may continue as long as oil or gas is produced in paying quantities.

Offshore regulatory requirements

The Outer Continental Shelf (OCS) comprises federal lands submerged off U.S. coasts. The Bureau of Ocean Energy Management (BOEM) leases and manages the development of U.S. OCS energy and mineral resources, while the Bureau of Safety and Environmental Enforcement (BSEE) is responsible for permitting and offshore regulatory programs. Extensive information is required before a permit to drill is granted, including a description of the drilling vessels, platforms or other structures; details about equipment; pollution control and prevention; location of each well; targeted locations for directionally drilled wells; and structural interpretations of exploration data.

Few events have impacted the offshore regulatory environment like the Deepwater Horizon drilling rig explosion in April 2010, which killed 11 platform workers and injured many others. Former President Barack Obama's administration issued a moratorium on new deepwater drilling permits for the U.S. portion of the Gulf of Mexico so that lawmakers could review existing safety regulations. In addition, the oil and gas industry formed four task forces to identify improvements needed in prevention, intervention and oil spill response.

The Offshore Operating Procedures Task Force was charged with reviewing critical processes associated with drilling and completing deepwater wells to identify gaps between existing practices and industry best practices. The Offshore Equipment Task Force was created to review current blowout preventer (BOP) equipment designs, testing protocols and regulations. The moratorium was subsequently lifted in October 2010.

In April 2016, BSEE issued the *Oil and Gas and Sulfur Operations in the OCS — Blowout Preventer Systems and Well Control final rule (WCR)*. The rule's primary goal was to reduce operational risk and prevent future well control incidents. The rule also updated the equipment and operational requirements for well control activities associated with drilling, completion, workover and decommissioning. The final regulation, which addressed various issues and errors that BSEE identified during implementation of the WCR, became effective on July 15, 2019.

Environmental and safety requirements

Good business principles dictate that drilling companies operate prudently and protect both their workers and the environment. These practices are part of a company's overall risk management.

The U.S. Environmental Protection Agency (EPA), Occupational Safety and Health Administration (OSHA) and various state agencies regulate the energy industry. Their rules promote safety and environmental protection during drilling; some even prohibit drilling in certain areas, such as off the Florida coast. Organizations such as the American Petroleum Institute (API) guide and update energy companies about industry-specific regulations.

The industry has made great strides to improve its safety performance over the past decade. For example, injuries during OCS operations decreased from 738 incidents in 2007 to 429 incidents in 2017, with injuries decreasing more than 50 percent.[1]

The federal government plays a key role in regulating safety and environmental issues. Among the most significant federal regulations and oversight agencies are:

- The EPA oversees protection of the environment and enforces related laws.

- The Comprehensive Environmental Response, Compensation and Liability Act of 1980 (CERCLA), commonly known as Superfund, addresses liability, compensation, cleanup and emergency response for hazardous substances released into the environment, as well as the cleanup of inactive hazardous waste disposal sites.

- The Superfund Amendments Reauthorization Act (SARA Title III), including a free-standing law, the Emergency Planning and Community Right-to-Know Act of 1986 (EPCRA), encourages and supports emergency planning efforts at state and local levels. It informs government officials about potential chemical hazards in their communities.

- The Resource Conservation and Recovery Act (RCRA) is the primary federal law governing municipal and industrial waste. Waste recycling and reduction are its two main objectives.

- The Clean Water Act (CWA), adopted in 1972, protects the quality of surface water. Amendments have changed its focus from municipal grants to partnerships with states to address water quality. The most recent amendment was the Great Lakes Legacy Act of 2002. It authorized $270 million to clean up contaminated sediments in the Great Lakes.

- The Safe Drinking Water Act (SDWA), passed in 1974 and amended in 1986 and 1996, protects drinking water and its sources in rivers, lakes, reservoirs, springs and groundwater wells.

- The Oil Pollution Act of 1990 (OPA 90) amended the CWA and established a trust fund to help clean up oil spills and offer resources for prevention and response.

- The Clean Air Act of 1990, a federal law that also is enforced by the states, limits air pollutants.

- OSHA, organized under the U.S. Department of Labor, protects the safety and health of U.S. workers through the inspection of workplaces.

- A division of the Department of the Interior, the U.S. Fish and Wildlife Service (FWS), conserves fish, wildlife and plants. The Migratory Bird Treaty Act of 1918 gave the FWS authority to establish reservations for migratory birds and protect them from contamination or injury.

Individual states oversee both their radiation regulations and their licensing and disposal of naturally occurring radioactive material (NORM). Certain subsurface formations contain radioactive materials, such as uranium.

Complying with numerous regulations is complicated for E&P companies because the rules continuously evolve. To comply, companies typically track environmental and safety matters at all of their properties. Larger companies dedicate employees solely to environmental and safety concerns, whereas smaller ones may hire consultants for the same purpose.

Noncompliance with environmental regulations can be very costly. For instance, RCRA penalties can reach $50,000 and up to five years in prison for most violations. If a RCRA violation places a person in danger of death or serious bodily injury, penalties can reach $250,000 ($1 million for companies) and up to 15 years in prison. The Clean Air and Clean Water Acts each impose fines for each day of violation, up to $25,000, one year in prison or both. SDWA fines range from $5,000 to $10,000 a day, with no imprisonment.

Energy Policy Act of 2005

The Energy Policy Act of 2005 is a comprehensive legislative package that addresses oil and gas, ethanol, hydrogen, nuclear, coal, conservation, efficiency, and research and development, as well as taxes and incentives. Selected provisions relate to oil and gas companies as follows:

- Permanently authorizes the SPR and can fill the reserve to one billion barrels.

- Establishes an inventory of OCS oil and gas resources enabling the federal government to assess the extent of offshore resources.

- Streamlines the permitting and siting processes for pipelines, with the Federal Energy Regulatory Commission (FERC) named as the lead agency for consolidating records.

- Clarifies FERC's exclusive authority to approve new sites for LNG facilities.

- Establishes a task force addressing the leasing of U.S. oil shale and tar sands.

- Conducts a research and development program for oil shale.

The Energy Policy Act of 2005 was amended by the American Recovery and Reinvestment Act of 2009, Section 406, authorizing loan guarantees for innovative technologies that reduce greenhouse gases. Advanced designs for nuclear reactor, as well as clean coal and renewable energy, may also be included in this program.

Drilling contracts

The drilling of oil and gas wells normally is carried out by independent contractors. Their specialized skills enable them to drill more economically and efficiently than most oil and gas operators. Three types of contracts are available: footage rate, day rate and turnkey. The option chosen depends on the category of drilling, the location of the well and environmental factors. In the early 1980s, the demand for rigs exceeded supply and almost all contracts were day rate arrangements. Although these remain the most common contracts offshore, footage rate contracts dominate the onshore arena.

Footage rate contracts

In a typical footage rate contract, the drilling contractor receives a specified amount per foot of drilling. Costs increase significantly with well depth and drilling is more expensive offshore than onshore.

A footage rate contract usually specifies drilling to a certain depth or to a defined number of feet below a specific geological horizon, whichever comes first. The footage rate is set by adding a risk factor and profit to the estimated costs required to drill to that depth (including bit and rig costs), dividing the total by the targeted depth. The contractor furnishes the rig, crew, services and certain materials and supplies. The operator normally furnishes the well equipment and may provide drilling mud. Several activities are not included in a footage rate arrangement, such as taking a core sample, running certain tests and logging. These activities usually are considered extraneous to drilling and are charged to the operator separately at a day rate.

Each drilling contract includes payment terms, which may specify time or depth intervals. A drilling contractor may require prepayment of a portion of estimated costs. Except for factors outside the contractor's control, payment usually is contingent upon reaching the contract depth.

Day rate contracts

Day rate, or day work, contracts are conceptually simple. The drilling contractor provides drilling rigs and crews, receiving a fixed amount per day to drill the wells, regardless of the number of feet drilled. The operator bears most of the ancillary costs for well construction and the supporting operations, as well as the economic risks. Usually, the contract specifies two different day rates: one for when the contractor is actually drilling, and a lesser figure for standby time while the operator is running tests or overseeing other services.

Virtually all offshore work uses a day rate contract. Like footage rates, onshore day rates vary depending on the location, environmental issues and local demand for rigs. Offshore day rates depend on the type of equipment (e.g., submersible, jackup rig, semi-submersible platform or drillship), drilling conditions and drilling depth.

Turnkey contracts

Used for many years, turnkey contracts originate from U.K. real property law. In a turnkey contract, the drilling contractor performs specified services for a set price. The operator merely has to "turn the key" when the project is complete, assuming no liability until the contract requirements are met. The partners of an operator may require a turnkey contract as a means to increase their confidence in the project.

A turnkey well offers advantages and disadvantages for both contractors and operators. Contractors often have greater latitude in their drilling program and selection of drilling mud and drill bits. Operators benefit because, no matter what problems occur, the cost of the well is fixed. In addition, the operator is assured that appropriately skilled employees will be available to handle peak workloads.

A disadvantage for drilling contractors is that they must complete the well within the fixed cost, regardless of the potential for unpredictable and costly events. However, these uncertainties can be addressed through contractual-loss caps and walk-away rights.

Other arrangements

Alternative approaches usually involve modifications to, or combinations of, the three basic contracts. Alternative compensation can include transferring to the drilling contractor an operating or nonoperating interest in a lease. The contractor also may be given an overriding royalty interest (ORRI) in return for services and supplies.

Drilling preparations

Before drilling can commence, operators take appropriate measures and precautions to gain access to the intended drilling site, ensuring that the well will be drilled in the best location possible.

Staking the well

Although exploration in a new production area may point to a certain property, additional geological work is needed to identify the best well site and to survey and stake the well. Staking is the analysis of scientific data by geologists and geophysicists (including seismic, magnetic or gravity surveys) to determine the best drilling target in the structure. Although subsurface structure is the most important factor, surface conditions are important when they constrain drilling. Constraining conditions include natural phenomena, such as bodies of water, marshes, hostile terrain or other obstructions.

Drilling constraints also may derive from the written lease: for example, clauses that preclude drilling within a specified distance of existing structures or within a municipality. In each of these cases, the well site should be staked in a satisfactory area; a directional well may also be drilled to reach the target formation. Operators must pay particular attention to lease and property boundaries to ensure that the well is drilled on property for which the operator holds a working interest.

Preparing the location

At this stage in a project, the well has been surveyed and staked, or at least the location has been pinpointed. After obtaining the permits to drill, the driller prepares the well site, often developing a well proposal that outlines the objectives and type of well to be drilled. Studies are performed of the surface location, downhole targets and descriptions of varying depths and strata, identifying the information that must be gathered from the well, as well as anticipated post-completion concerns.

The driller must take several additional steps before drilling an onshore property. Access to the location may be a simple matter of grading an access road. However, transportation can present a major problem in some areas. It may be necessary to build roads and bridges that are rated for extreme loads. In swampy areas, such as portions of southern Louisiana, temporary roads may be built using heavy timbers. Uneven terrain may require the use of bulldozers or roads may need to be blasted through the sides of mountains. Occasionally, a drilling structure is so complex that it is equivalent to offshore construction. Platforms also are required in marshy areas and regions in Alaska and the Arctic where permafrost must be protected from the heat generated by the drilling rig. Once access is secured, and the site is level, the delivery of drilling equipment can begin.

Offshore locations present their own challenges. Navigational warnings must be installed and environmental requirements must be addressed. Most of the problems relate to transportation, installation and positioning of the drilling rig rather than well site preparations. Once the rig is on location, however, the most daunting set of challenges concerns the continuous supply of drilling materials and consumables to the site.

Oil and gas leases give operators the right to explore for and produce oil and gas and include the right of ingress and egress. However, operators may have to pay for use of the surface and almost certainly will pay for any damages to the site. Most leases now include requirements for the operator to restore the surface to its original condition, including making damage payments to the surface owner, which represent an additional cost of locating and preparing the well site prior to drilling.

Drilling rig components

Components of a typical drilling rig (see Figure 8-1) include: the derrick (or mast), hoisting system, power system, rotary system, mud system and blowout preventer.

Derrick

The derrick (mast) is the structure placed over an intended drilling location. Although the terms are used interchangeably, a derrick is a structure assembled piece by piece, whereas a mast is a single, portable structure. The rig floor, at the base of the derrick, houses much of the equipment needed for drilling and serves as a base for the derrick itself. Loads from the derrick are transmitted through the rig floor to the substructure of the rig. For shallow-well drilling and some workover operations, drillers may use a self-contained rig mounted on a large truck. For most onshore work, however, drillers use a jackknife mast, consisting of a series of modules that can be erected at the well site.

Figure 8-1
Onshore rig

Courtesy of Petroleum Extension (PETEX®)

Derrick and mast structures range in height from 65 feet to more than 200 feet. By design, they must be capable of withstanding extremely heavy loads up to 1.5 million pounds or more in vertical capacity. Due to their size and varied operating locations, the structures must also be designed to withstand high winds.

Hoisting system

Hoisting equipment must bear heavy loads to support the drill string and its movements in and out of the hole. The hoisting system consists of the hoist (drawworks), mast, crown block, traveling block and wire-rope drilling line. Drilling line is essentially steel rope that can be as large as two inches in diameter. Depending on the loads anticipated, the line can be strung multiple times (as many as 16 lines). Figure 8-2 illustrates a hoisting system.

Figure 8-2
Hoisting system

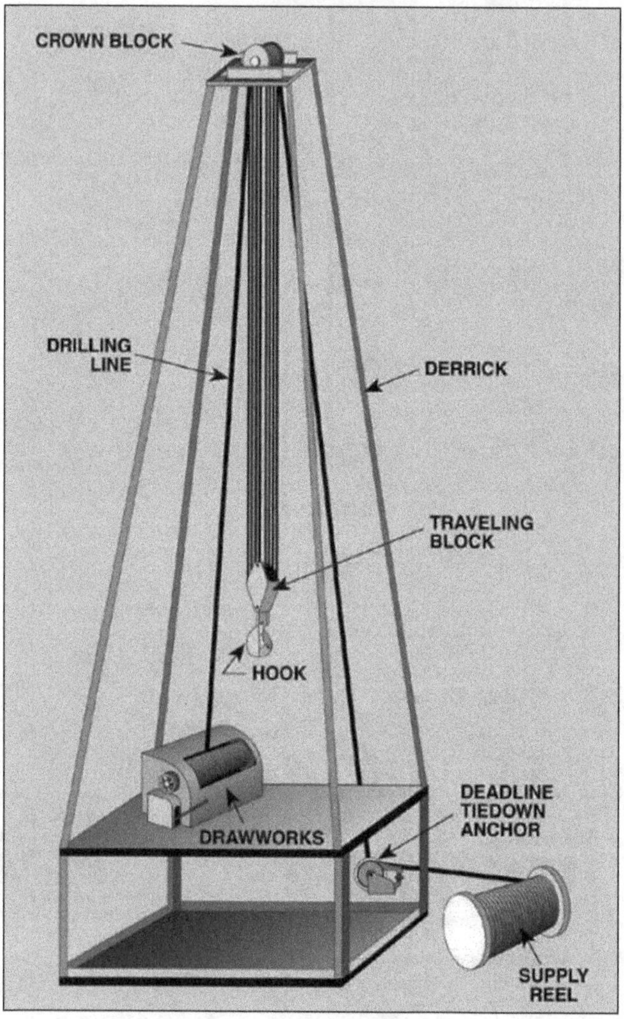

CROWN BLOCK

DRILLING LINE

DERRICK

TRAVELING BLOCK

HOOK

DEADLINE TIEDOWN ANCHOR

DRAWWORKS

SUPPLY REEL

Courtesy of Petroleum Extension (PETEX®)

Power system

The power system furnishes power for rotating the drillstring and bit, hoisting, circulating fluids, compressing air, providing lights and other functions. Land rigs capable of drilling to shallow or moderate depths may require only 1,000 horsepower, whereas those capable of drilling beyond 20,000 feet may require more than 3,500 horsepower. These systems use diesel, diesel-electric, gasoline and other power sources.

Rotary system

A simple rotary system begins with the rotating swivel at the top of the kelly and ends with the drill bit at the bottom of the hole. The swivel enables the entire system to rotate while being held by the hoisting system. Power is applied to the rotary table and, when the kelly bushing is engaged, the drillstring, collars and bit rotate so that the bit cuts into the formation. Advances in technology, including topdrives and downhole motors, have been developed to meet the increasing demands placed on the modern drilling rig. These demands include the need to drill much deeper and more efficiently.

Mud system

In rotary drilling, the drilling mud plays several important roles. Circulating through the drillpipe from the surface to the bottom of the hole and back up through the annular space (annulus), drilling mud carries the cuttings, in suspension, from the formation to the surface. The driller analyzes these cuttings to identify the drilled formation and detect hydrocarbons. Drilling mud also lubricates and cools the drill bitand coats the wellbore. This seals off the formations and stabilizes the wellbore walls. In addition, the weight of the drilling mud offsets the underground (reservoir) pressure, which helps prevent a blowout. Drillers constantly monitor fluid mixtures and specific gravity to optimize both drilling and well control.

Figure 8-3 shows the path taken by the drilling mud as it circulates through the well. From the mud pumps, mud travels through the discharge line to a standpipe, then into a rotary hose connected to the swivel (on the rotary table) or the topdrive. Mud travels down through the kelly, or through a passage inside the topdrive, and then through the drillpipe to the drill bit. At the bit, the drilling mud washes cuttings from the bit and the bottom of the hole and moves upward, carrying them back to the surface. At the surface, a pipe carries the cuttings in suspension to a shale shaker, which removes cuttings from the mud. From the shaker, the cleaned mud flows to a holding tank (shaker tank), then to the active tank, and the whole cycle begins again.

The mixture of materials that comprise the mud determines the weight of the fluid column. To achieve specific objectives, drillers use different weights of drilling mud. A common mixture is a special clay, water-weighting material and chemicals. The mineral barite adds weight to the drilling fluid; barite is about 4.2 times heavier than water. Because certain types of formations can be damaged by water, drillers sometimes use oil-based drilling muds. Even during the drilling of a single well, the driller may make several changes to the mixture of drilling mud.

To remove finer particles and contaminants, mud can be sent through additional cleaning systems, including desanders, desilters, mud cleaners and mud centrifuges. Another piece of equipment, a degasser, removes any gas that might invade the drilling mud as it circulates.

Figure 8-3

Rotary rig mud system

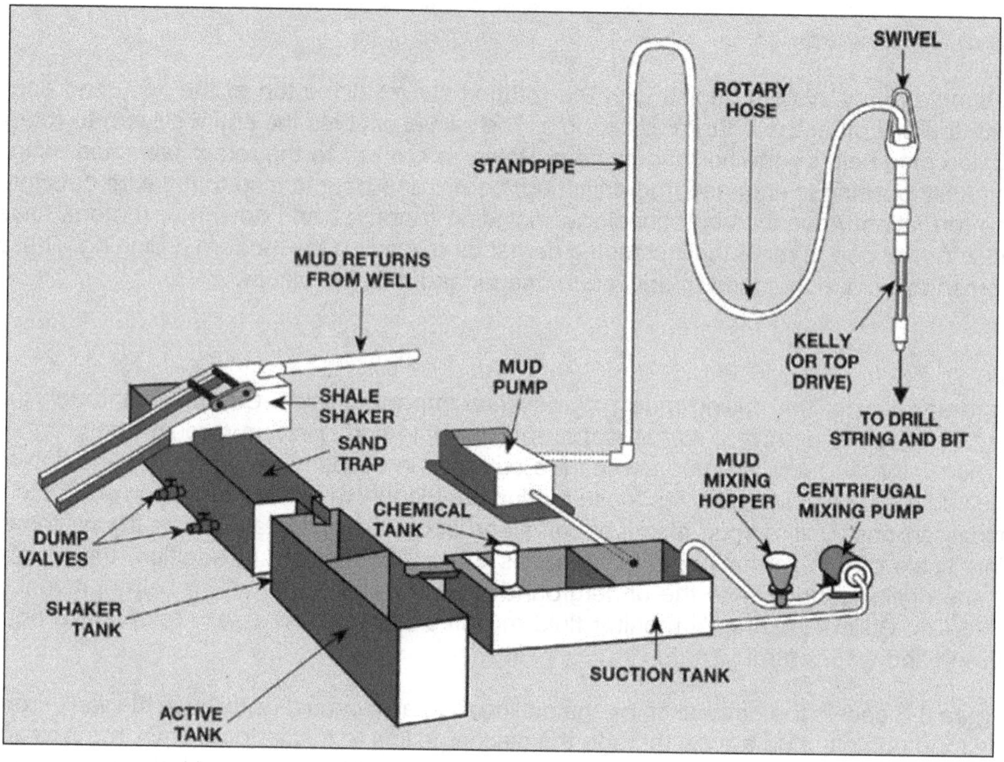

Courtesy of Petroleum Extension (PETEX®)

Blowout preventer

A blowout can occur when formation pressure exceeds the pressure maintained by pumping drilling mud into the wellbore. To protect the well site from this danger, BOPs are installed on the wellhead to provide essential secondary well control protection. They usually comprise two or more stacks, or large valve packages, capable of withstanding high pressures. One set of valves allows the well to be shut-in while the drillstring remains in the hole. The other closes when the drillstring is removed from the hole. BOPs usually include two sets of controls: one on the rig floor and the other at a remote location for safe operation in emergencies. The placement of the blowout preventer stack on a surface wellhead system is shown in Figure 8-4.

BOPs vary in size, according to the wellhead bore, and typically are rated to contain pressures as high as 15,000 psi. In some extreme cases, specialized equipment has been used to withstand wellbore pressures of 20,000 psi.

Figure 8-4
Installed blowout preventer stack

Courtesy of Petroleum Extension (PETEX®)

In addition to setting requirements for blowout preventers, the Blowout Prevention Act of 2010, enacted after the Deepwater Horizon explosion, increased accountability: it requires safety certifications of BOPs, well designs and cementing procedures by third-party inspectors selected by the federal regulator.

Rotary drilling

For many years, the cable-tool method was used to drill into the Earth's surface. A cable-tool rig drilled the Drake well in Titusville, Pennsylvania, in 1859 and marked the beginning of today's oil industry. It used a walking beam mounted to a derrick to raise and lower a cable with a heavy bit attached. Each time the bit was lowered, its blunt, chisel end cracked, chipped and smashed the subsurface formation, slowly drilling a hole.

Although cable-tool drilling was suitable for shallow wells in hard rock formations, softer formations required different technology. The rotary method came into major use just prior to 1900 and is used extensively today to drill oil and gas wells, both onshore and offshore.

Rotary drilling uses a sharp, rotating bit to drill through the Earth's crust. Operating like a common hand-held drill, the bit spins and penetrates with pressure even the hardest formations. Part of the art of rotary drilling is matching the bit type and the downward pressure to the formation's characteristics, using drilling fluid (drilling mud) to wash the hole clear of the chipped-away formation cuttings and to keep the bit lubricated so it does not overheat due to excessive friction.

A rotary table at the drill floor turns the drillstring via a kelly, a hollow bar attached at one end to the top of the drillstring and at the other to the top joint of the drillstring. The kelly enables the lowering and raising of the drillstring during rotation. Power turns the rotary table, which in turn rotates the kelly, drillpipe, drill collar(s) and drill bit. As the drill bit rotates, it chips away formation cuttings.

As drilling proceeds downward, drillers connect new sections of drillpipe at the surface, lengthening the drillstring as it descends. To keep cuttings cleaned out of the hole, the drilling fluid circulates under pressure through the descending drillpipe and is pushed out through small holes in the drill bit at the bottom of the hole into the wellbore. The fluid then pushes upward outside the pipe through the annulus, returning to the surface, carrying the formation cuttings with it.

The need to drill deeper and directionally has prompted many design improvements for rotary drilling. For example, topdrives (overhead rotary drilling systems) have generated improvements versus the kelly system. A kelly can be as tall as 54 feet but a topdrive stands 90 feet or taller. Added height reduces the need for pipe connections, which improves both efficiency and safety.

Downhole motors also have improved drillers' capabilities. A downhole motor looks like a piece of pipe. For directional work, it usually is attached to a bent sub, which is a connector between the pipe and drill collar that allows for one to three degrees of angle. Using drilling fluid to power the motor, these units do not turn the entire drillstring. Instead, mud pumped down the drillstring powers the motor, which then turns the drill bit.

The advantages of using downhole motors include less wear on equipment, such as the casing and drillstring, and improved control of drilling direction. Using measurements while drilling (MWD) techniques, the crew can monitor drilling progress and determine the direction of the wellbore via computer.

Offshore drilling

The first offshore platform was erected in the Santa Barbara channel in California around 1897. Offshore drilling has grown steadily since then. The most dramatic advances have enabled drillers to reach extraordinary depths, with some wells today surpassing a total depth of more than 35,000 feet.

Offshore rig types

- **Submersibles.** Drilling structures that are floated into shallow locations, usually 80 feet or less, and then ballasted down to rest on the seabed.

- **Jackup rigs.** Used in waters as deep as 600 feet, depending on the length of their legs and environmental conditions, jackup rigs are towed or otherwise transported to the drilling location. While they float over the well location, they usually have three legs that are lowered ("jacked down"). As the legs touch the seabed and continue to be jacked down, the hull of the floating rig rises above the water by about 50 feet.

- **Semi-submersibles.** Mobile structures that are towed or propel themselves to the well site. The rig structure is steadied on hulls or pontoons, which often are ballasted below the waterline. A semi-submersible rig is frequently used in deepwater or at locations where severe weather threatens. The stability of these rigs maximizes drilling uptime during unfavorable conditions.

- **Drillships.** Most often used in deepwater, drillships are positioned dynamically over the well location, using satellites or acoustic beacons. Their large capacities, for both people and equipment, suit them for remote locations that are common in exploratory offshore drilling.

Once exploratory wells have been drilled and field development commences, operators erect a production platform as a more permanent structure at the well site. This mode of development depends on the water depth, number of wells and type of reservoir. Many subsea developments, that is, clusters of subsea wells, do not have a dedicated platform but are instead connected to nearby production facilities.

Offshore considerations

Mobile offshore rigs are preferred by drillers because they can be moved from one drill site to the next. Whether bottom-supported (such as submersibles and jackups) or floating units (semi-submersibles and drillships), offshore rigs consist of a platform that is towed or propels itself to the drilling site. The platform is the base for the derrick and drilling equipment. A derrick either sits on the platform deck or is cantilevered on steel arms connected to the platform. Figure 8-5 illustrates an offshore rig.

Offshore rigs contain most of the same functioning parts as onshore rigs but with modifications to suit an ocean environment. The legs of bottom-supported rigs, such as jackups, support the drilling platform and rest on the ocean floor or a special mat. Floating units, anchored to the seafloor, can be raised or lowered by using air or water to fill the hull or legs.

A distinct difference between onshore and offshore operations is the transportation and housing of workers. Personnel must be carried by boat or helicopter to offshore locations. For that reason, a helipad often is a component of offshore rig platforms, which also include accommodations for workers to sleep, eat and live. Electrical, water and waste systems also are maintained on the units.

Figure 8-5

Offshore rig

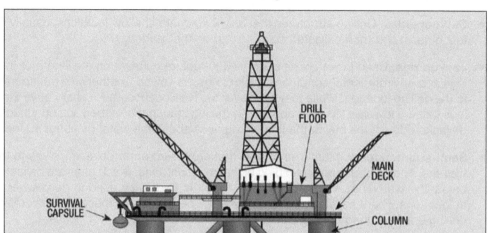

Courtesy of Petroleum Extension (PETEX®)

Derrick. Derricks on offshore drilling units are almost identical to those of onshore rigs, except that they are on floating vessels. In the case of offshore, vessel motion adds dynamic loading to the structure. Some ultra-deepwater drilling vessels have derricks that may stand 200 feet or taller and are rated to sustain dynamic loads of as much as three million pounds.

Hoisting equipment. Hoisting equipment on offshore rigs is also very similar to that of onshore rigs, with two differences: (1) deepwater floating units are much larger and (2) the hoisting system must accommodate vessel motion, which can be addressed by passive or active motion compensators.

Power system. In addition to supplying power to the drilling equipment, the power system on an offshore rig also may be used for the vessel's main propulsion. On ultra-deepwater and harsh-environment units, the main engines can deliver more than 60,000 horsepower.

Rotary system. Most offshore rigs are fitted with topdrives to improve drilling performance; they also may use downhole motors to improve directional drilling into the reservoir.

Mud system. Depending on the mud used, drill cuttings may be dumped overboard after they have passed over the shakers to recycle returned mud. Increased shaker retention time increases the volume of drilling mud recovered from the cuttings and can eliminate the need to dry the cuttings before dumping. In some cases, the cuttings cannot be discharged overboard; they must be transferred, as slurry, onto barges and transported for appropriate disposal.

Larger deepwater drilling units may operate as many as four mud pumps and more than eight shakers. Active and reserve drilling mud volumes can be sizable for deepwater wells; some capacities exceed 20,000 barrels.

BOP. Offshore rigs use BOP stacks, which are BOPs placed on top of each other. Floating units (semi-submersibles and drillships) normally attach their subsea BOP stack to the wellhead, which is cemented into the seafloor.

In deepwater operations, these 15,000 psi-rated BOP stacks can contain as many as six rams and two annular preventers, reaching as high as 60 feet and weighing around 350 tons. Multiplexed systems control these BOP stacks, enabling rapid shut-in of the well in an emergency – before quickly moving off location.

Drilling activities

Onshore drilling crews remove up to 35 feet of dirt to create a cellar, a rectangular pit where they install the base of the rig. Rigs that use a kelly require a rathole, meaning a shallow hole drilled to the side of the main wellbore, also called a borehole.

Spudding is the industry term for beginning to drill. A special bit is used for initial drilling of the main hole. This section is relatively large to permit installation of any casing required by the drilling plan. Large conductor casing may be installed at the surface to prevent cave-ins and form a foundation for subsequent casing strings. Surface casing is installed and cemented to a point safely below all freshwater formations to prevent contamination, although the driller may install additional casing strings as needed. The types of casing and pipe typically used on an onshore well are shown in Figure 8-6.

Depending on the rig and well type, offshore conductor casing ranges from a standard 48 feet to more than 80 feet long. This casing is designed to withstand high wellhead bending loads. A joint can range in diameter from 20 inches to 48 inches. Using high-pressure streams of water, the rig crew creates a hole for the conductor casing.

Although drilling progresses rapidly near the surface, the drillers continuously watch the drilling mud indicators, including cuttings from the bottom of the hole. These indicators provide crucial information about the drill bit's condition. More importantly, they reveal the type of formations downhole. When formation material changes significantly, or the drill bit begins to wear, the bit must be changed. Depending on formation hardness, the same bit may be used for only a few hundred feet or up to several thousand feet. Bits are available in a variety of sizes and materials to drill in formations that range from soft to very hard and abrasive. Bits are commonly manufactured from tungsten carbide and synthetic or natural diamonds.

Figure 8-6
Casing and pipe — Onshore well

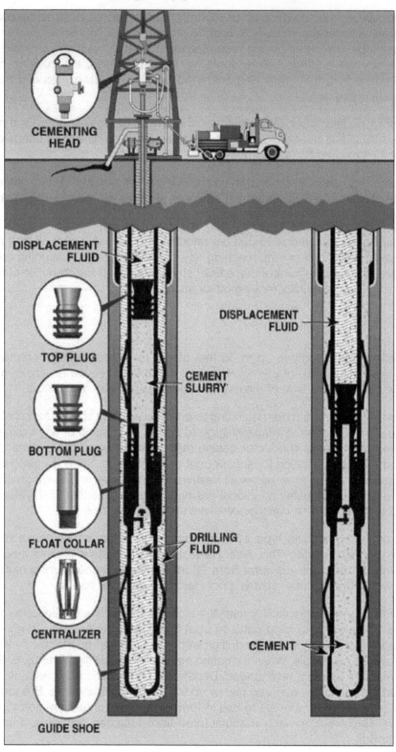

CEMENTING HEAD

DISPLACEMENT FLUID

TOP PLUG

BOTTOM PLUG

FLOAT COLLAR

CENTRALIZER

GUIDE SHOE

DISPLACEMENT FLUID

CEMENT SLURRY

DRILLING FLUID

CEMENT

Courtesy of Petroleum Extension (PETEX®)

Bits come in two main categories: roller cone and fixed head. The steel teeth of roller cone bits roll over the bottom of the hole, crushing the formation as they turn. Fixed head bits use jets of drilling mud to move cuttings out of the way as the fixed head rotates. Normally, additional weight is needed to help the bit work more effectively: drill collars, placed on the bottom section of the drillstring, add weight to the bit. These drill collars usually are 31 feet long and can weigh over 9,000 pounds. Multiple drill collars support the thousands of pounds of weight on the bit.

As the hole is drilled, additional pieces of drillpipe, ranging in length from 18 to 45 feet, are added to the drillstring. When the drill bit must be changed, all drillpipe must be pulled from the hole. The old bit is removed, a new bit is attached and all the lengths of drillpipe are re-inserted in the hole. This process is called making a trip (tripping out and tripping in) and the entire process is called "making a round trip."

In making a round trip, the drillstring is disconnected and reconnected in stands consisting of one, two, three or even four sections of drillpipe, depending on the size and type of rig. Making a round trip at a depth of 14,000 feet can take anywhere from five hours to half a day. Therefore, good planning and careful selection of drill bits is essential to ensure drilling efficiency. Throughout the drilling process, the crew tests the drilling fluids, pressures and cuttings. Once they reach the target depth, they evaluate the formations to determine if they hold sufficient hydrocarbons to justify completing the well.

Even when cuttings indicate the presence of hydrocarbons, the operator needs more information: specifically, a core sample from the formation. To retrieve it, the drillstring is removed from the hole, a core barrel is attached in place of the drill bit and the drillstring is lowered back into the hole. The core barrel is a long bit with a hollow center, designed to capture a formation core. The size of the core varies; it may be one inch to slightly more than four inches in diameter and can be longer than 100 feet. The core is brought to the surface for evaluation (core analysis). A "sidewall sampler" also can be lowered into the wellbore to penetrate the formation and cut a small core. Geologists evaluate these cores for reservoir characteristics such as porosity, permeability, saturation and fluid content.

A drill stem test provides additional information. This test is essentially a temporary completion of the well. The crew inserts a "packer" into the hole and expands it to seal off drilling mud from the tested formation. The packer allows formation fluids to flow upward through the drillstring, where the operator can collect data about the fluid content, formation pressure and other factors. During drill stem tests on offshore wells, oil and gas may come to the surface. In these instances, the crew employs special burners to flare these substances safely into the atmosphere, or the liquids can be captured and stored in tanks, while any gas is flared.

Certain tests, referred to as well logs, can be performed at virtually any point during drilling, but they usually take place when drilling reaches its approximate target. Using a sonde (a tool that measures electrical, radioactive and acoustic formation properties), experts can evaluate the transmitted logs to determine if hydrocarbons are present. Each formation and each fluid responds differently to logging tests. Proper interpretation of these well logs indicates the type of formation and fluids present at various depths.

Newer technologies, such as MWD and logging while drilling (LWD), provide real-time information about the well, even from a remote location. The need to provide more accurate and faster information about the well while it is being drilled will continue to drive technological advancements.

Tests performed during drilling determine whether or not the well has commercial potential. At all depths, tests help geologists and petroleum engineers make better decisions about the future of a well.

Drilling crews

Drilling operations normally continue around the clock, using two or three crews. The person in charge of rig equipment is called the "toolpusher" or "rig manager" and is responsible for overall operations. Normally, the toolpusher is on call 24 hours a day. A driller leads each crew and operates the drilling controls. Crew members include: (1) a derrickman (in the absence of automated pipe-handling equipment) who works in the derrick when pipe is lowered into or raised from the hole and (2) two or more rotary helpers, or roughnecks, who work on the rig floor. A motorman also may be included in the crew to take care of engines and power equipment, although this additional responsibility is sometimes given to the derrickman.

Onshore, it is normal for each of three crews to work an eight-hour shift (or tour, pronounced tower). For logistical reasons, offshore crews typically work 12 hours and are off-duty for the next 12 hours. Even when not on duty, offshore crews remain on the drilling platform for at least seven days and then return to shore for the same number of days. Since most drilling today is performed by independent drilling contractors, an engineer or geologist employed by the operator may also remain on location at all necessary times.

Offshore crews usually are larger than land crews because of their remoteness. The offshore installation manager is responsible for overall rig operations. Crane operators load and unload supplies using the rig's deck cranes. Additional workers (roustabouts) comprise the general labor force and perform various daily tasks to keep the main deck operating efficiently. Engineers, marine crew, maintenance technicians, caterers, radio operators and emergency medical staff are among other personnel who work offshore.

Directional and horizontal drilling

In the early days of the industry, wells drilled with cable-tool equipment were assumed to be vertical. But the advent of rotary drilling revealed that it is nearly impossible to drill a truly vertical well. Changes in the angles of layered formations ("dip angles"), differing formation strength and drilling practices cause the drill bit to drift away from true vertical. Drillers learned how to purposely drill in a certain direction; this allowed them to reach oil and gas in areas where drilling directly down from the surface was not possible, such as offshore near Huntington Beach, California and under the Oklahoma State Capitol building in Oklahoma City, Oklahoma.

When offshore platforms began to be installed in the Gulf of Mexico, directional drilling become even more important. The wells on a typical offshore platform branch out in multiple directions, enabling each platform to drain a much greater area than would be possible with just one well. Drilling a directional well requires vertical drilling, then deflection in a particular direction, as illustrated in Figure 8-7.

Figure 8-7

Illustrative directional well

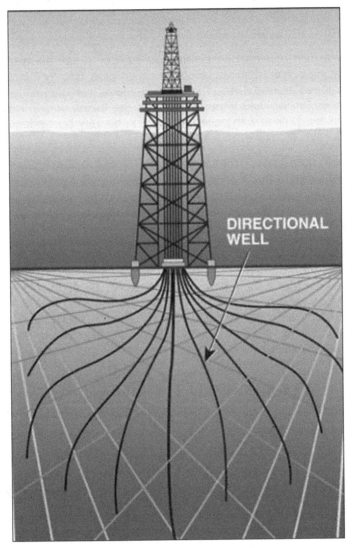

Courtesy of Petroleum Extension (PETEX®)

Subsequent holes (called side tracks) can be drilled from the same original vertical hole. The distance reached from the platform of a directional well depends on many factors, particularly the depth of the target formation; a reach of one mile or more is not uncommon.

One of the main factors governing the rate of oil or gas flow into the wellbore is the length of reservoir formation exposed to the wellbore. The industry has long recognized that, if drillers could lengthen this exposure by drilling horizontally instead of vertically along the productive strata in the formation, they could increase both production rates and recoverable reserves. With technological advances, such as downhole motors and bits, new metallurgy, downhole gyroscopic steering tools, mud systems and logging tools, horizontal drilling has become a reality.

Directional and horizontal drilling employ flexible drillpipe that allows the drillstring to bend. Other specialized equipment often is used, such as downhole motors. The motor is paired with the MWD technique. A MWD tool attached to the drillstring sends information to a computer at the surface. A directional operator monitors the information and steers the drilling.

On a smaller scale than conventional drilling, coiled tubing can be used for directional drilling. Coiled tubing is a continuous length of coiled pipe, usually 2 inches in diameter or less, that is wrapped around a reel. The tubing is reeled into the well with a mud motor attached to its end. Drilling fluid is pumped down the tubing, which rotates the motor and spins the drill bit. Drilling with coiled tubing can be very cost-effective for the right application, particularly small wellbore sidetracks.

A typical horizontal well begins much the same as a vertical one. At a predetermined point above the target formation (the kickoff point), a special directional drillstring is lowered to begin the turn from vertical to horizontal. The radius of curvature depends on the tool design and other factors; it can vary from a few feet to several hundred feet. In a typical well design, the wellbore path will be horizontal by the time it reaches the target formation, where it remains horizontal.

To further increase the flow from a reservoir, multiple wellbores (branches) are drilled from a single wellbore through the producing formation. These multilaterals range from a single well with one branch to three or four branches radiating from the main wellbore. Multilaterals can reach different depths and help to drain fragmented reservoirs more evenly. These wells can be more cost-effective than those drilled traditionally, although they add further complexity to the drilling process.

Improved horizontal drilling techniques have aided in unlocking hydrocarbons that previously were bound up in tight formations, such as shale. These methods allow for greater contact with the reservoir and enhanced fracture stimulation (described later in this chapter).

Drilling challenges

Problems often occur during drilling, inevitably increasing the cost of a project. One potential problem is the risk of a high-pressure blowout. If one occurs, workers' lives are endangered, economic and environmental losses can be high and the well must be brought under control.

Losing equipment in the hole is another common hazard. Part of the drillstring may twist off and it normally must be retrieved before drilling can continue. This may require fishing for the pipe or other equipment stuck in the hole. If the material cannot be retrieved, the hole can be sidetracked around the lost pipe. In some cases, the only solution is to move the rig and start a new hole called a twin well.

When a hole partially collapses or sharp bends occur, the pipe can become stuck. If the drillstring cannot be removed, the only alternative is to cut off the string at the stuck point and proceed in the same fashion as when a pipe is lost in the hole.

Although drillpipe appears to be rigid, it becomes flexible when several joints of pipe are connected in a string. Deviations from a true vertical axis are normal but the deviations must be controlled so that the hole is not drilled in an unacceptable direction.

Another problem can be lost mud circulation. This occurs when a drill bit breaks into caverns or other formations with large openings and mud escapes into the formation. In this event, the formation must be plugged before drilling can continue.

Completing the well

After drilling a well to final depth and evaluating tests from each stage, the operator must decide whether to attempt completion or abandon the well. The right answer is often complex: it depends on if the operator believes there are enough hydrocarbons in the reservoir to justify the additional expenditures for completing, equipping and producing the well.

Onshore completion

An operator may find enough evidence to justify the additional costs of completion. A well is typically completed if the anticipated revenues from production will exceed anticipated completion and production costs. To complete a well, the operator must close off the identified formation. Often, the operator will set and cement production casing in the hole, perhaps cementing it only at the bottom of the well and at the surface.

The next step is to perforate the casing to allow reservoir fluids to flow into the wellbore. A perforating gun lowered into the hole via wireline or drillpipe is fired, perforating the casing and the productive formation. Typically, these perforations are made using high-energy shaped charge explosives, creating holes that allow hydrocarbons to flow through the cement and casing, then into the wellbore before flowing to the surface.

Acidizing and hydraulic fracturing. In some cases, the formation's permeability is low, and oil or gas cannot readily flow into the wellbore. Acidizing and hydraulic fracturing can increase permeability. If the formation is composed of calcium carbonate, acid pumped through the perforations will dissolve portions of the formation, creating channels for the oil or gas to flow.

However, the usual process in sandstone formations is hydraulic fracturing (fracking). Coarse sands or synthetic beads (proppants) are mixed in a fluid and pumped at very high pressure down the wellbore, through the perforations and into the formation, causing it to split or fracture. When the pressure is released, the fluid flows back up the wellbore, leaving behind the coarse sand grains or beads, which prop open the fractures and allow hydrocarbons to flow into the wellbore with greater ease.

Hydraulic fracturing permits the production of oil and natural gas from formations deep below the surface of the Earth (e.g., 5,000 to 20,000 feet). At such depths, the formation may not exhibit sufficient porosity and permeability to allow oil and natural gas to flow at economical rates from the formation into the wellbore. Shale reservoirs in particular have very low permeability, such that creating fractures in the formation is essential for producing gas from a shale reservoir.

Fracturing has been used successfully in an area near Fort Worth, Texas, known as the Barnett Shale. After many years of modest production, new technologies have changed outcomes dramatically: with advanced water-fracturing techniques, operators have unlocked the vast reservoir of gas contained in the tight formations. The area is still a blockbuster field, currently producing about 2.93 billion cubic feet of gas per day (Bcfd), although production has declined from its historical peak of more than 5.7 Bcfd in 2012.[2]

Environmental concerns about fracking. The recent increased use of hydraulic fracturing has prompted more speculation about its environmental dangers, with certain states implementing drilling moratoriums, while several have banned fracking entirely, including Maryland, which directly impacts the development of the Marcellus shale in the western portion of the state.

Some of the concerns associated with hydraulic fracturing include the potential for mishandling of solid toxic waste, risks to air quality, contamination of groundwater and unintended migration of gases and hydraulic fracturing chemicals to the surface. The long-term costs associated with possible environmental cleanup and health concerns are undetermined. Regulators are studying the issues and emerging technologies may help drilling companies use the procedure more safely in the future.

Industry groups dispute whether or not hydraulic fracturing has a major environmental impact. Arguments focus on the extent to which fracturing fluid, used well below the Earth's surface, could contaminate surface or near-surface water reservoirs or cause seismic events due to the impact on formations.

Swabbing. When fluid or drilling mud remains in a well, and reservoir pressure is low, it may be necessary to swab the well to remove the fluid. Swabbing is a relatively simple process: a small, expandable packer is lowered into the well, and when it is pulled swiftly out of the hole, the fluid comes with it. Alternatively, a lighter fluid, or even gas, can be circulated into the wellbore to "underbalance" the well and promote flow. Many other methods exist for completing wells, tailored to meet the needs of each specific reservoir.

Completion equipment

The equipment used to complete a well depends, in part, on whether the well produces oil, gas or both. It also depends on whether the well is flowing or being produced by a form of artificial lift. In either scenario, casing is run into the well and wellhead connections are attached in order to control production.

As shown in Figure 8-8, a simple Christmas tree (an arrangement of gauges and meters) measures pressure and liquids, both when a well is flowing from its own reservoir pressure and when the well is produced by means of a pump. Offshore, Christmas trees can be wet or dry. Wet trees are those installed in water on the seabed and electro-hydraulic controls operate their valves remotely. Dry Christmas trees are those installed on a floating vessel or platform.

Onshore, if a well is not capable of flowing from reservoir pressure alone, the operator uses a form of artificial lift or a pumping unit. The most common lift for onshore wells is a walking beam unit, depicted in Figure 8-9. Sucker rods are attached to the beam unit at the surface. The up-and-down movement of the beam unit activates a simple lift pump installed in the formation.

Lifting hydrocarbons to the surface is only one of the operations necessary for producing oil and gas. The other types of equipment required depend on whether the well produces oil or gas and the amount of treatment needed to process the hydrocarbons for sale or use. Treatment of the oil or gas involves the removal of impurities.

Figure 8-8
Christmas tree valve

Courtesy of Petroleum Extension (PETEX®)

Offshore, the drilling platform often becomes the production platform. The derrick lifts and lowers tools into the wells. The most common forms of artificial lift on offshore wells are gas lift and electric submersible pumps (ESPs). If a well is subsea, oil and gas flows either through a pipeline to a nearby platform or to a "production riser" into a buoy that connects to a tanker. At this point, the liquids are separated, treated and either pumped through the pipeline to shore or stored in the ship's tanks until they can be moved to an onshore terminal.

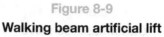

Walking beam artificial lift

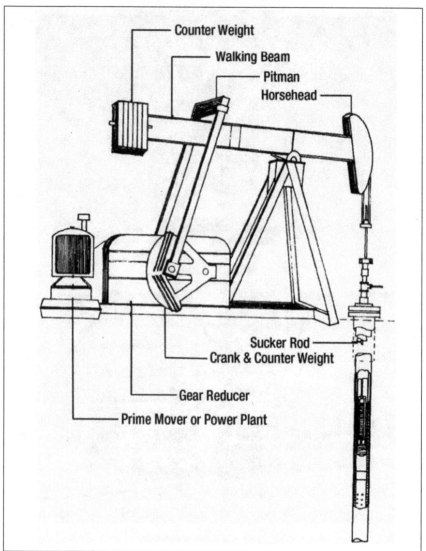

Courtesy of Petroleum Extension (PETEX®)

Wells classified as "oil only" produce no gas or only insignificant quantities. When oil is predominant, but production includes a significant quantity of gas, it is classified as an "oil/casinghead gas" well.

Casinghead gas (also called dissolved gas or solution gas) is dissolved in the reservoir's crude oil, but bubbles out when it comes to the surface and reaches normal atmospheric pressure. Gas in the gas cap overlying the oil is called associated gas. A gas reservoir that contains little or no oil is said to produce nonassociated gas.

To be classified as gas only, production must contain only insignificant amounts of liquid. A gas/condensate well produces both natural gas and condensate. In the reservoir, gas and liquids are part of homogeneous hydrocarbons. When gas is withdrawn from the reservoir, and pressure drops sufficiently, lighter fluid fractions condense, as described in Chapter 1.

Surface casing is cemented through all fresh water formations to prevent contamination and cave-ins. Casing is not usually suitable for producing the well. Small diameter pipe known as tubing is run into the cased well using a packer. Coiled tubing can also be used for production. Oil and gas could be produced through casing, but a string (or strings) of production tubing is normally run into the well. If repairs are later required, it is easier to remove the production tubing than a cemented casing. In addition, the tubing to casing annulus can be monitored for pressure to determine whether tubing integrity has been lost.

Multiple completions, including dual completion, are required when two or more formations will be produced through the same wellbore. The procedures for preparing each formation are identical to those used in single completions. Cement placed above and below each of the producing formations seal the formations so that the oil and gas can flow into the production string.

Placing wells on production

Various surface equipment is required to place wells on production in order to: collect and gather the oil and gas, treat each product for market, briefly store produced oil, measure volumes produced and sold and remove oil and gas from the lease. This process and its associated equipment are described in Chapter 11.

Dry holes

If there are no reserves, or an insufficient quantity to justify completion, the operator may plug and abandon the well. Cement plugs normally are used to seal the well. Equipment in the hole is salvaged and either sold or returned to a warehouse if it is suitable for future use. However, very little of the equipment installed in the hole, such as casing, can be salvaged, due to physical constraints or regulatory requirements. Potentially high formation pressures and other factors can require the entire casing string to be encased in cement.

In any event, surface casing usually cannot be removed because almost all governmental regulatory bodies require it to be cemented in the hole, along with a cement plug at the surface. If the well is never to be re-entered, the protruding section of the wellhead normally is severed to complete the abandonment process.

Reservoir development

Normally, a single well does not constitute complete development of a reservoir. Even though additional wells may not dramatically affect the quantity of hydrocarbons ultimately recovered, the number of wells affects the extraction rate and, thus, the present value of the income stream. Figure 8-10 illustrates the development process for a simple anticline structure.

Figure 8-10

Reservoir development for simple anticline structure

Well	Site	Description
1	D	Discovery field exploratory well is assumed to establish offset sites C and E as proved.
2	E	Offset-development producing well. Well 2 proves Site F.
3	F	Offset-development producing well. Assume data does not prove Site G.
4	B	Step-out exploratory producing well on an unproved drill site. Assume data proves Site A.
5	C	Offset-development producing well.
6	A	Offset-development dry hole. Costs remain capitalized as development costs. Well is plugged.
7	G	Offset exploratory dry hole. Costs are expensed. Well is plugged.

Proving a site means that geological and engineering data indicate, with reasonable certainty, that the site has sufficient reserves, at current prices, to justify drilling the site. Usually, a successful well and G&G data prove only sites that offset the successful well's site. However, as further described in Chapter 15, reasonable certainty also may be established through other means (e.g., reliable technology). The data may or may not prove all offset locations.

Ultimate development of a reservoir depends on several factors. Even though production has been established by drilling a discovery well, the property may not have sufficient potential reserves to warrant further expenditures for complete development.

Volumetric estimates of hydrocarbons can be prepared, initially, when the first well is tested. However, the samples are often quite small. If a 4-½ inch core (a rather large core) is taken in a 40-acre spacing tract, the sample size is only one in more than 13 million. Yet this small sample, along with pressure tests, flow tests and rates, fluid analyses and geological data, is used to decide whether or not the reservoir should be developed.

Depicted another way, Figure 8-11 reflects the field exploratory well as the focal point from which all other subsequent wells are drilled and reserves are established.

Figure 8-11

Reservoir development — Field exploratory well

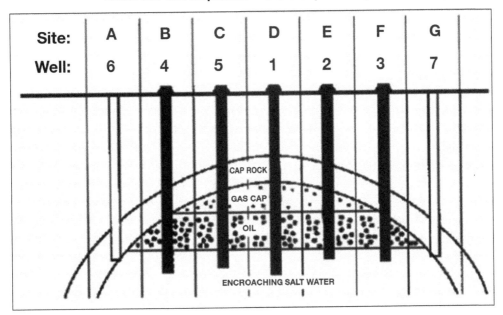

Site:	A	B	C	D	E	F	G
Well:	6	4	5	1	2	3	7

CAP ROCK

GAS CAP

OIL

ENCROACHING SALT WATER

Despite advanced technology, drilling is the only way to identify hydrocarbons. Once a successful well is drilled, the operator continues drilling and development until the boundaries of the reservoir are delineated with marginally economic wells or dry holes.

● ● ●

1   Bureau of Ocean Energy Management, Offshore Stats & Facts. "Stats & Facts / Offshore Incident Statistics." 2017, www.bsee.gov/stats-facts/offshore-incident-statistics.

2   Texas Railroad Commission. "Total Natural Gas Production 2000 through August 2019." November 27, 2019 https://www.rrc.state.tx.us/media/55020/barnett-gas.pdf.

Accounting for Drilling Costs

- **Development costs**

- **AFEs for drilling and development**

- **Interest capitalization**

- **Accounting challenges**

- **Adoption of ASC 842**

This chapter focuses on accounting for the costs of drilling and equipping development wells under the successful efforts accounting method in accordance with GAAP. The accounting for exploratory well costs is addressed in Chapter 6.

Development costs

ASC 932-360-25-14 requires successful efforts companies to capitalize all development costs. Development costs are defined in ASC 932-360-25-12 and 25-13. Reg. S-X Rule 4-10(a)(7) similarly defines development costs.

25-12 Development costs are incurred to obtain access to proved reserves and to provide facilities for extracting, treating, gathering, and storing the oil and gas.

25-13 More specifically, development costs, including depreciation and applicable operating costs of support equipment and facilities (see paragraph 932-360-25-16) and other costs of development activities, are costs incurred to:

a. Gain access to and prepare well locations for drilling, including all of the following:

   1. Surveying well locations for the purpose of determining specific development drilling sites

   2. Clearing ground

   3. Draining

   4. Road building

   5. Relocating public roads, gas lines, and power lines, to the extent necessary in developing the proved reserves.

b. Drill and equip development wells, development-type stratigraphic test wells, and service wells, including the costs of platforms and of well equipment such as:

   1. The wellhead assembly

   2. Pumping equipment

   3. Tubing

   4. Casing.

c. Acquire, construct, and install production facilities such as:

   1. Lease flow lines

   2. Separators

   3. Treaters

   4. Heaters

   5. Manifolds

   6. Measuring devices

   7. Production storage tanks

   8. Natural gas cycling and processing plants

   9. Utility and waste disposal systems.

d. Provide improved recovery systems.

As outlined in Chapter 6, costs are expensed for exploratory dry holes and stratigraphic test wells that do not find proved reserves. Conversely, costs are capitalized for development dry holes and all costs of development-type stratigraphic test wells not completed, as discussed herein. Accordingly, it is important to distinguish between development wells (including development-type stratigraphic test wells) and exploratory wells (including exploratory-type stratigraphic test wells).

The glossary in ASC 932-360-20 makes this distinction by defining the terms development well, exploratory well, service well and stratigraphic test well.

A **development well** is a well drilled within the proved area of an oil or gas reservoir to the depth of a stratigraphic horizon known to be productive.

An **exploratory well** is a well drilled to find a new field or to find a new reservoir in a field previously found to be productive of oil or gas in another reservoir. Generally, an exploratory well is any well that is not a development well, a service well, or a stratigraphic test well.

A **service well** is a well drilled or completed for the purpose of supporting production in an existing field. Wells in this class are drilled for the following specific purposes: gas injection (natural gas, propane, butane, or flue gas), water injection, steam injection, air injection, salt-water disposal, water supply for injection, observation, or injection for in-situ combustion.

A **stratigraphic test** is a drilling effort, geologically directed, to obtain information pertaining to a specific geologic condition. Such wells customarily are drilled without the intention of being completed for hydrocarbon production. This classification also includes tests identified as core tests and all types of expendable holes related to hydrocarbon exploration. Stratigraphic tests are classified as *exploratory-type* if not drilled in a proved area or *development-type* if drilled in a proved area.

The definitions above are similar to those in Reg. S-X Rule 4-10, which also provides a definition of an extension well as "a well drilled to extend the limits of a known reservoir."

These definitions severely limit what can be considered a development well. For example, a well drilled to define a reservoir's perimeters is labeled exploratory, not development. A well drilled to a formation (horizon) with no proved reserves is also exploratory, even if production is occurring from another horizon on the same lease. A well is labeled development only if it is drilled within a proved area and to a stratigraphic horizon known to be productive; thus, an outpost well (step-out well) is also exploratory. Under these definitions, there are very few development dry holes – typically only those that result from faults in the strata or mechanical problems while drilling.

Assume that the DiTirro #1 well is drilled in the proved area of the DiTirro lease with the intent of extracting minerals from a currently producing formation. Drilling costs of $95,000 and casing costs of $5,000 are recorded as incurred, as shown below.

Work-in-progress – intangible costs of wells	95,000	
Work-in-progress – tangible costs of wells	5,000	
Accounts payable		100,000
To record costs incurred for drilling and casing the DiTirro #1 development well.		

Before the well reaches completion, drilling is interrupted by a structure that makes it impossible to continue. The well is abandoned, with none of the casing salvageable. Abandonment is recorded as:

Intangible costs of wells	95,000	
Tangible costs of wells	5,000	
Work-in-progress – intangible costs of wells		95,000
Work-in-progress – tangible costs of wells		5,000

To record abandonment of the DiTirro #1 development well and transfer costs to proved property well costs.

The seemingly inconsistent treatment of costs of unsuccessful exploratory wells and those of unsuccessful development wells is supported by ASC 932-360-25-14. It holds that once proved reserves have been found, development costs result in the creation of a producing system of wells and related facilities much like the production system of a manufacturing company. ASC 932-360-25-14 states:

> Development costs shall be capitalized as part of the cost of an entity's wells and related equipment and facilities. Thus, all costs incurred to drill and equip development wells, development-type stratigraphic test wells, and service wells are development costs and shall be capitalized, whether the well is successful or unsuccessful. Costs of drilling those wells and costs of constructing equipment and facilities shall be included in the entity's uncompleted wells, equipment, and facilities until drilling or construction is completed.

AFEs for drilling and development

Management should closely control expenditures to realize maximum profit, especially when large sums are involved. The tool commonly used for controlling drilling and development costs is the authorization (or authority) for expenditure (AFE) system, as described in Chapter 6.

AFEs are part of capital budgeting. An oil and gas company budgets for capital projects by assessing its major needs and available financing for the coming year. It ranks capital projects according to their expected internal rate of return, overall expected profitability and other factors. Projects with the highest rankings are financed first, although funds typically are allocated to several projects, thereby spreading the risks of exploratory drilling. Some discretion is required because project profitability can change during the year. Also, unexpected projects may arise that require funding, such as major well repairs or the development of a significant new discovery. To finance unplanned capital needs, an oil and gas company may maintain lines of credit and also borrow funds.

The AFE system uses a form to document: (1) expected costs of a project, for review by management and joint venture partners and (2) approvals to proceed. AFEs control the expenditures for all major projects to drill and equip oil and gas properties, purchase drilling equipment and service units and construct field facilities and buildings.

It is typically not practical to obtain specific approval for lesser capital items, such as replacing minor equipment or purchasing supplies for routine operations. Standing authorizations for small purchases may be granted to the responsible department head. In many companies, AFEs are not required for operating expenses other than for costs of significant well workover projects. Even for these projects, an AFE may only be necessary if the estimated cost is greater than a specified amount as determined by the company.

AFE procedures

Summarized below are AFE procedures, suggested forms and records:

- Asset acquisition and construction costs are budgeted at least one year in advance (when possible).

- Even if an oil and gas company has only a small working interest in a well or project, the AFE system tracks and compares budgeted and actual costs for the full 8/8ths or 100 percent working interest. Full project costs are easier for a petroleum engineer to review, compare and evaluate than the company's net costs. However, accounting ledgers and subledgers reflect only the company's net costs for its share of a working interest.

- Authority for carrying out a specific project is assigned to operating personnel, such as the district or division operations manager.

- Selected managers approve each stage of the project. AFE budgets are prepared by project and by subaccount, and AFEs are assigned unique numbers that correlate with the projects.

- Work-in-progress accounts accumulate the project's costs.

- For each project, the actual costs are compared periodically by subaccount to budgeted costs. Differences are assessed and, depending on acceptable limits of cost overruns, may require a supplemental AFE.

As an example, ABC Oil Co. (ABC) budgets for drilling operations a year in advance when possible. ABC plans to drill an exploratory well during the current year on a 200-acre lease obtained from S.W. Perry in Clarke County, Mississippi. The budget calls for drilling one well to 12,000 feet on the property and, if the well is productive, installing necessary lease and well equipment. The projected total cost to drill the well is $616,200 for intangibles and $54,500 for associated well equipment. To complete and equip the well (if it is successful), ABC estimates it will spend $386,600.

AFE forms for drilling are multipurpose. They are used for completing wells, installing production and lease equipment and handling well workovers. Companies typically prepare exploratory well AFEs that show estimated costs to both drill and complete the well. If the exploratory well finds reserves and will be completed, the drilling AFE is used for the completion and equipment. When the well is completed, the revised AFE form contains two totals: (1) the drilling total (all drilling costs to the casing point) and (2) the completion total (all completion costs). The two totals, drilling and completion, are then combined in a third column for total well costs, as shown in Figure 9-1.

Figure 9-1

Illustrative AFE for drilling

Authorization for Expenditure for drilling wells					AFE #	19-017	

Well Description:

Operator:	ABC Oil Company		Well No. 1		Target Depth:	12,000'
State:	Miss.				Target Formation(s):	Smackover
County:	Clarke				Well Type:	Oil
Prospect/Field:	Wildcat					
Well Location	500' FWL & 1250' FNL of Sec. 33-T2n-R17E					

Budgeted Costs:

						Cost to		Total
	INTANGIBLE					Casing Pt.	Complete	Well Costs
001	Footage (or Turnkey)		Ft	@ $	/Ft			
002	Day Rate: 37 and 12 days @ $5,200/day					$192,400	$62,400	$254,800
003	Site Preparation, roads, pits					89,800	3,500	93,300
004	Bits, Reamers, Tools					42,000	2,500	44,500
005	Labor - Company							
006	Labor - Other					1,500	1,500	3,000
007	Fuel, Power, Water					17,000	5,500	22,500
008	Drilling Supplies					1,000		1,000
009	Mud and Chemicals					50,000	5,000	55,000
010	Drill Stem Tests							
011	Coring, Analysis					4,000		4,000
012	Electric Surveys, Logs					40,000		40,000
013	Geological and Engineering					2,000	1,000	3,000
014	Cementing : Surface					21,000		21,000
015	Intermediate							
016	Oil String						20,000	20,000
017	Float Equipment, Centralizers, Etc.					4,000	2,500	6,500
018	Completion, Frac., Acidizing, Perforating						13,500	13,500
019	Rig Transportation, Erection, Removal, Other Transp.					54,500	10,000	64,500
020	Other Services					70,000	15,000	85,000
021	Overhead					2,000	800	2,800
022	Miscellaneous					25,000		25,000
	TOTAL INTANGIBLE COST					616,200	143,200	759,400

	Tangible							
030	Casing							
031	Surface	Ft	16" OD@	$/Ft		3,500		3,500
032	Intermed.	3000 Ft	9 5/8" OD@	16.00 $/Ft		48,000		48,000
033	Production	12550 Ft	5 1/2" OD@	10.75 $/Ft			135,000	135,000
034	Liner	Ft	OD@	10.75 $/Ft				
035	Tubing	12300 Ft	2 3/8" OD@	2.75 $/Ft			33,800	33,800
036	Rods	Ft	OD@	$/Ft				
037	Wellhead and subsurface					3,000	17,000	20,000
038	Pumping Units							
039	Tanks						5,300	5,300
040	Separators						20,000	20,000
041	Heaters - Treaters						30,000	30,000
042	Engines and Motive Power							
043	Flow Lines							
044	Miscellaneous Equipment						2,300	2,300
045	Installation Costs of Surface Equipment							
	TOTAL TANGIBLE COST					54,500	243,400	297,900

Total Well Costs		$670,700	$386,600	$1,057,300

APPROVALS

			Name	Date
		Prepared by	E.N. Gineer	4/10/2019
Operator's internal approvals:		Division	T. Boss	4/10/2019
		Corporate	T. Rex	4/12/2019

Approval of Working Interest Owners:

		Costs to			
Owner	WI%	Casing Pt.	Complete	Approved By	Date
Operator	60%	$402,420	$215,760	See above	See above
ABC Oil Co.	40%	268,280	143,840	A.B. Cloud	4/16/2019
Total	100%	$670,700	$359,600		

ABC's numbering system for AFEs uses five digits: the first two numbers identify the year and the last three numbers are sequential for each AFE created in the year. The illustrative AFE in Figure 9-1 shows the approval of drilling an exploratory well and breaks down expected drilling costs: $616,200 for intangibles and $54,500 for tangibles consisting of casing and other subsurface equipment. Authorization is complete when all signature(s) are obtained. The authorizer typically sets a time limit for project commencement.

If the deadline passes, a revised AFE may be required. This requirement promotes more accurate estimates and control of the project's financial needs. A request for approval of expenditures usually is accompanied by detailed statements showing how the costs were estimated. In many companies, supporting analysis identifies the costs that require cash outlays and those that use items already on hand.

Supplemental AFE

As the project progresses, incurred expenditures are compared periodically with the estimates. It may become evident that the authorized amounts for certain expenses are insufficient. Company policy, the initial AFE or the joint venture operating agreement may require a supplemental AFE for costs that exceed a stated percentage of the original budget.

Operating agreements normally do not require joint venture operators to issue supplemental AFEs to joint venture nonoperators. Therefore, the AFE may be prepared to reflect the operator's preference that no supplemental AFE is required for budget overruns. Conversely, an AFE may contain language requiring a supplemental AFE for expenditures exceeding 10 or 15 percent of the original budget. This language would be considered beneficial to nonoperators.

Rather than simply examining AFE totals, petroleum accountants should analyze overexpenditures, in detail, by category. Comparisons of authorized costs to actual costs help identify errors in accounting, vendor billing and AFE budgeting.

Interest capitalization

ASC 835-20-05-01, *Capitalization of Interest*, requires capitalizing a portion of the interest costs incurred during asset construction:

> This Subtopic establishes standards of financial accounting and reporting for capitalizing interest cost as a part of the historical cost of acquiring certain assets. The historical cost of acquiring an asset includes the costs necessarily incurred to bring it to the condition and location necessary for its intended use. If an asset requires a period of time in which to carry out the activities necessary to bring it to that condition and location, the interest cost incurred during that period as a result of expenditures for the asset is a part of the historical cost of acquiring the asset.

Capitalization period and qualifying costs

Assets that qualify for interest capitalization are those produced for a company's own use, including oil and gas properties and facilities. Conceptually, capitalized interest is a cost that would not have been incurred had the project not been undertaken. The appropriate interest rate (detailed in ASC 835-20-30-3 and 30-4) is applied to the project's average capitalized costs for the year. Total capitalized interest in an accounting period should not exceed the total interest costs incurred by the company during that period.

Interest costs may be capitalized when they meet these three conditions:

1. Capital has been expended.

2. The activities are in progress to ready the asset for its intended use.

3. Interest costs are being incurred.

For successful efforts companies, the major questions regarding interest capitalization focus on the applicable time period. For example, assume that these activities take place on the dates indicated:

Figure 9-2

Successful efforts interest capitalization period

Date	Activity
January 2, 2018	Leases acquired on a prospect
July 1 – August 31, 2018	Seismic and other exploration carried out on leases
June 1, 2019	Exploratory drilling commenced
August 15, 2019	Exploratory well completed as a producer

It might be argued that ASC 835-20-25 permits capitalized interest on the project only during the periods July 1 to August 31, 2018, and June 1 to August 15, 2019, because physical activities occur during these periods. However, ASC 835-20-20 and 20-25-6 state:

> **20** The term activities is to be construed broadly. It encompasses physical construction of the asset. In addition, it includes all the steps required to prepare the asset for its intended use. For example, it includes administrative and technical activities during the preconstruction stage, such as the development of plans or the process of obtaining permits from governmental authorities. It also includes activities undertaken after construction has begun in order to overcome unforeseen obstacles, such as technical problems, labor disputes, or litigation.
>
> **25-6** ... Similarly, interest is not to be capitalized during periods when the entity intentionally defers or suspends activities related to the asset. Interest cost incurred during such periods is a holding cost, not an acquisition cost. However, delays that are inherent in the asset acquisition process and interruptions in activities that are imposed by external forces are unavoidable in acquiring the asset and as such do not call for a cessation of interest capitalization.

Due to the ASC's broad interpretation of "activities," successful efforts companies have developed a variety of practices when choosing starting and ending dates for interest capitalization. Analyzing seismic charts, obtaining financing, arranging for drilling rigs and other nonphysical activities are qualifying activities, according to some companies. These companies capitalize interest on the average balance of unproved properties, as well as on costs for drilling and development in progress.

The *2019 PricewaterhouseCoopers Survey of U.S. Petroleum Accounting Practices* (Question N4) found that nine of 24 successful efforts respondents begin to capitalize interest on unproved leasehold costs when some type of significant construction activity begins. Three of the responding companies begin interest capitalization when the first well is spud, while a handful of companies responded that interest capitalization begins when some type of exploration activity occurs, commitment is made to the development plan or when the lease is acquired.

In light of ASC 835-20-15-5, the following assets qualify for interest capitalization:

- **Undeveloped leases.** These leases qualify for interest capitalization as long as exploration activities necessary to prepare a lease for its intended use are in progress. Interest capitalization begins with the first expenditure to explore the lease and continues (assuming exploration activities are continuous) until the property is ultimately written off or produces oil or gas. Qualifying activities can include pre-field administrative and technical work such as:

  - Work performed by internal or external geologists and engineers to identify areas that may warrant further examination and to examine specific areas that are believed to contain oil and gas.

  - Title opinion curative work.

  - Procurement of work permits from regulatory agencies.

  Payments of delay rentals are inadequate evidence that exploration activities are underway. In the case of an undeveloped lease that covers large acreage, the situation must be reviewed carefully to determine if the work done on a portion of the acreage allows interest capitalization on the entire block of acreage.

- **Shut-in properties.** As suggested by ASC 932-360-35-16 and 35-17, occasionally an exploratory well may find oil and gas reserves, but those reserves cannot be classified as proved until additional testing and evaluation occurs. ASC 932-360-35-13 and 35-19 provide indicators that support continued capitalization of the exploratory well's costs. If continued capitalization is appropriate, interest capitalization can continue as long as exploration is continuous.

  Wells that are capable of production, but are awaiting the construction of additional facilities (e.g., gas wells awaiting construction of a pipeline), are considered to be qualifying assets. Interest capitalization continues as long as development activities on the pipeline are continuous. However, wells that are shut-in due to lack of a market or because of depressed gas prices do not qualify for interest capitalization.

- **Drilling and development costs.** For proved properties, these costs, including costs of unsuccessful development wells, are capitalized as part of the cost of oil and gas properties. Assuming that development activities are continuous, their costs qualify for interest capitalization until the related property is capable of producing and delivering oil or gas.

  Significant development costs (e.g., costs of an offshore production platform) often are incurred in connection with a planned group of development wells before all the planned wells have been drilled. ASC 932-360-35-7 allows exclusion of a portion of those development costs and proved developed reserves in determining the unit-of-production amortization rate until additional development wells are drilled. In these circumstances, interest capitalization continues on the portion of development costs deferred, once again, as long as development activities are continuous.

- **Leases held for resale or contribution to a partnership.** In many cases, these leases do not qualify for interest capitalization because qualifying activities are not occurring on the property. If the company performs activities (e.g., geological and geophysical work) to prepare the lease for resale or contribution, the property should qualify for interest capitalization as long as the activities are continuous.

To qualify for interest capitalization, activities do not have to take place on each asset every day. Brief interruptions in activities, interruptions that are externally imposed, as well as delays inherent in asset acquisition, do not require cessation of interest capitalization. However, if essentially all the activities related to an asset's acquisition are suspended, interest capitalization ceases until activities resume. For example, if a company determines that an exploration project is too expensive or risky to pursue without joint venture partners and it suspends all project activities until it can identify partners, interest capitalization should cease. When activities resume, the project will once again qualify for interest capitalization.

ASC 835-20-25-5 states that interest capitalization must end when an asset is substantially complete and ready for its intended use. Generally, this occurs when a property is ready for production. The lease then becomes part of a producing asset system under successful efforts rules. However, ASC 835-20-25-5(c) identifies an exception to this rule for successful efforts companies:

> Some assets cannot be used effectively until a separate facility has been completed. Examples are the oil wells drilled in Alaska before completion of the pipeline. For such assets, interest capitalization shall continue until the separate facility is substantially complete and ready for use.

Immaterial activity

Most larger companies (and some smaller ones) do not capitalize interest unless the cost of an individual project or program is expected to exceed a specific threshold. ASC 835-20-15-4 acknowledges the common use of minimum thresholds for the capitalization of inventory and property, plant and equipment. It notes that thresholds are justified on the basis that any difference would be immaterial, both individually and in the aggregate.

This subtopic goes on to state that it does not preclude using thresholds established to conform with materiality tests. The *2019 PricewaterhouseCoopers Survey of U.S. Petroleum Accounting Practices* (Question N1) found that 15 of the 33 responding companies (45 percent) establish an expenditure threshold before interest is capitalized on an individual project or program.

Another convention is the minimum time required before capitalizing interest on expenditures. Minimum times should be based on when the interest becomes material. These conventions eliminate the administrative costs of capitalizing insignificant interest costs for numerous small capital-construction projects and short construction periods.

Accounting challenges

Situations frequently occur in drilling and development that create complicated accounting questions. Some lie in distinguishing between exploratory and development wells. Others arise after a halt or delay in drilling. Successful efforts companies may choose alternative procedures to account for the situations described herein; however, these practices are generally accepted within the E&P industry.

Deeper drilling beyond producing horizons

If a well is drilled within the proved area of an oil or gas reservoir to the depth of a stratigraphic horizon known to be productive, and it continues to be drilled deeper into unproven strata, the petroleum accountant must determine if it is a development well or an exploratory well. For accounting purposes, it is reasonable to treat the well (i.e., the single hole) as two wells: (1) calling the costs to drill to the proven horizon development costs and (2) calling the incremental exploration costs to drill to a deeper horizon exploratory costs.

When drilling an exploratory well, an operator frequently discovers oil in commercially productive quantities and completes the well (or plans to complete the well) at that horizon. The operator then drills deeper into the same hole to explore another formation, which may be noncommercial.

The costs of drilling to the producing horizon are capitalized as those of a successful exploratory well but the incremental costs of drilling deeper, without finding proved reserves, are charged to expense as unsuccessful exploratory costs. Similarly, if the operator enters a producing well and drills deeper to an unproved horizon unsuccessfully, the incremental costs should be charged to expense.

Plug back and completion at shallower depths

The inverse of the situation just described also may occur. For example, suppose that the operator drills an exploratory well targeting a formation at 12,000 feet. At 8,000 feet, the drill encounters a hydrocarbon-bearing formation. Drilling continues to the 12,000-foot test depth but finds no hydrocarbons. The operator then plugs back to 8,000 feet and completes a producing well.

The incremental costs for drilling between 8,000 and 12,000 feet are charged to expense as unsuccessful exploratory costs and the costs of drilling to the producing horizon at 8,000 feet, along with completion costs, are capitalized as costs of wells and related facilities.

Some companies also charge to expense a portion of the drilling costs to reach the upper producing horizon, asserting that these costs were necessary to drill the lower portion of the well that has been abandoned. Drilling costs should be allocated between the portion of the well that is abandoned and the portion that produces. The incremental costs of the abandoned portion should be charged to expense.

Costs of abandoned portion of a well

When drilling an exploratory well that targets a specific formation or trap, difficult conditions can force the operator to abandon the hole and start a new well nearby. If the second hole is completed as a producer, the accountant must decide how to treat the costs of the abandoned hole: the costs of the abandoned hole may be charged to expense or capitalized as part of the cost of the completed well with proved reserves.

Typically costs of the abandoned hole are charged to exploratory dry hole expense because the abandoned hole added nothing to the utility or value of the completed well. If the original well is labeled a development well under ASC 932-360-25-13, all costs involved are capitalized. If it is necessary to abandon the lower portion of the well in order to plug back and sidetrack to reach the same objective via directional drilling, the cost of the abandoned portion is likewise charged to exploratory dry hole cost expense.

Some companies capitalize the costs of an abandoned well if the target of the second well (the sidetrack) is the same. The second well (twin well) and the sidetrack are simply unexpected additional costs to reach the target formation.

Adoption of ASC 842

In 2016, the FASB and International Accounting Standards Board (IASB) issued new standards for leases, ASC 842 and IFRS 16, respectively. ASC 842 became effective beginning in 2019 for calendar year-end public business entities (2021 for nonpublic entities), while IFRS 16 became effective for all entities beginning in 2019.

The new guidance requires lessees to bring virtually all leases onto their balance sheets. Balance sheet recognition for lessees, along with more detailed disclosure requirements for both lessees and lessors, introduces change for all those who are party to a lease. The change varies by entity, but it affects accounting, process and controls, financial reporting and perhaps even decisions about whether to lease or buy an asset. This section highlights areas that may be challenging for the energy industry during the transition and afterward.

In a lease, one party obtains the right to use an asset legally owned by another party for a period of time, as defined in ASC 842-10-15-3. It is this right of use that distinguishes a lease from other executory contracts. The rights of a lessee are different from those of an owner of an asset or a party to a service agreement that does not transfer a right of use. Nonetheless, a lessee does have certain rights that receive accounting recognition as an asset (with a corresponding liability for the obligation to make payments for that right of use) because a lessee has control over an economic resource and is benefiting from the use of the asset.

> A contract is or contains a lease if the contract conveys the right to control the use of identified property, plant, or equipment (an identified asset) for a period of time in exchange for consideration. A period of time may be described in terms of the amount of use of an identified asset (for example, the number of production units that an item of equipment will be used to produce).

A reporting entity should consider the application of lease accounting in ASC 842 to all arrangements that meet the definition of a lease per ASC 842-10-15-3, with the exception of the following:

- Leases of intangible assets subject to ASC 350.

- Leases to explore for or use minerals, oil, natural gas and similar nonregenerative resources subject to the guidance contained in ASC 930 and ASC 932.

- Leases of biological assets (such as plants and animals).

- Leases of inventory.

- Leases of assets under construction.

As discussed in ASC 842-20-25-2, a lessee may elect not to apply the recognition requirements of ASC 842 to short-term leases (generally with a lease term less than one year). This election should be made by class of underlying asset. If a lessee chooses to elect this short-term lease measurement and recognition exemption, it should recognize the lease payments in net income on a straight-line basis over the lease term. Variable lease payments should be recorded in the period in which the obligation for the payment is incurred.

ASC 842 requires lessees to capitalize all leases with a term of more than one year. A lessee's income statement recognition of lease-related expense depends on the lease's classification as either an operating or financing lease. Although the pattern of expense recognition may be similar to the previous accounting treatment under ASC 840, the amount of lease expense recorded will likely differ due to changes in how certain elements of rent payments are treated.

The accounting model for lessors under ASC 842 is substantially equivalent to that provided in existing GAAP (i.e., ASC 840), but lessors will also need to consider the implications of ASC 606, Revenue from Contracts with Customers. Lessors will classify leases as operating, direct financing or sales-type based on criteria similar to those used by lessees, plus an additional requirement to assess collectability of lease payments for direct financing lease classification. In addition, when control does not transfer to the lessee (i.e., when the payment indicator is only met as a result of a third-party residual value guarantee), the arrangement will not qualify as a sales-type lease but may qualify as a direct financing lease.

Definition of a lease

Regardless of the arrangement's legal form, lease accounting guidance applies when the arrangement conveys control of an identified asset to another party for a specified period in exchange for consideration.

Use of an identified asset. To meet the definition of a lease, the arrangement must require the use of an explicitly or implicitly identified asset that is physically distinct. A physically distinct asset may be an entire asset or a portion of an asset. For example, a building is generally considered physically distinct. One floor within the building may also be considered physically distinct if it can be used independent of the other floors.

Certain assets may lend themselves to use by more than one party and need to be carefully evaluated to determine if they are physically distinct. For example, a contract providing the use of a portion that is less than substantially all of the capacity in a pipeline to transport natural gas is not physically distinct because it cannot be distinguished from other concurrent users of the pipeline. A portion of an asset that is not physically distinct is not an identified asset unless it represents substantially all of the capacity of the asset and thereby provides the customer with the right to obtain substantially all of the economic benefits from use of the asset.

Conversely, a portion of a pipeline (such as a lateral pipeline) could be physically distinct if an entity can separate (e.g., through use of a valve) and use the portion of the asset independent of the mainline pipeline.

When thinking about whether an asset is physically distinct, entities may need to consider the nature of the asset and evaluate how the asset was designed to be used. This evaluation could include the type of functionality the asset will provide and to what parties it will be provided.

The existence of substitution rights may result in the determination that a specific asset has not been identified. If an asset is implicitly specified because the supplier does not have any alternative assets available to fulfill the contract, substitution rights do not exist. If, however, an asset is explicitly specified in a contract, but the supplier has a contractual right to substitute that asset, the entities would need to evaluate the following ASC 842-10-15-10 criteria to determine if the substitution rights are substantive.

Even if an asset is specified, a customer does not have the right to use an identified asset if the supplier has the substantive right to substitute the asset throughout the period of use. A supplier's right to substitute an asset is substantive only if both of the following conditions exist:

a.   The supplier has the practical ability to substitute alternative assets throughout the period of use (for example, the customer cannot prevent the supplier from substituting an asset, and alternative assets are readily available to the supplier or could be sourced by the supplier within a reasonable period of time).

b.   The supplier would benefit economically from the exercise of its right to substitute the asset (that is, the economic benefits associated with substituting the asset are expected to exceed the costs associated with substituting the asset).

The supplier's right or obligation to substitute an asset for repairs, maintenance, malfunction or technical upgrade is generally not considered substantive and would not preclude the arrangement from being considered a lease.

Right to control the use of an identified asset over the period of use. A customer controls the use of the identified asset by possessing the rights throughout the period of use to: (1) obtain substantially all of the economic benefits from the use of the asset ("economics" criterion) and (2) direct the use of the identified asset ("power" criterion).

- **Economics criterion.** To be a lease, the arrangement must convey the right to obtain substantially all of the potential economic benefits that can be obtained from directing the use of the asset throughout the period of use, which could be consecutive or nonconsecutive periods of time. A customer would not control an asset if another party has the right to more than an insignificant portion of the potential economic benefits, which should be assessed based on the contractual rights of the respective parties, and not as a probability analysis as to who is likely to receive the benefits. More specifically, the rights to the output and other economics derived from use of the asset should be considered.

  If the asset produces more than one type of output or benefit, this assessment should be made based on the fair value of the contractual rights. In other words, the assessment should be performed based on the potential economic returns associated with those contractual rights. The assessment should be based on the asset as it exists at the time of entering into the arrangement by considering the capacity level at which the asset is expected to operate, maintenance schedules and type of physical asset. The standard does not define "economic benefits" but ASC 842-10-15-17 provides examples of ways the benefits can be obtained, including the use of an asset directly or indirectly, such as by using, holding or subleasing the asset.

- **Power criterion.** To meet the power criterion, the customer must hold the right to direct how and for what purpose the asset is used throughout the period of use. If the contract explicitly states how and for what purpose an asset will be used throughout the term of the arrangement and neither party can change the purpose, other factors should be considered to determine which party is directing the use of the asset as discussed in ASC 842-10-15-20(b). If the relevant decisions about how and for what purpose the asset is used are predetermined, the customer has the right to direct the use of an identified asset throughout the period of use if at least one of the following conditions exists:

  - The customer has the right to operate the asset (or direct others to operate the asset in a manner that it determines) throughout the period of use without the supplier having the right to change those operating instructions.

  - The customer designed the asset (or specific aspects of the asset) in a way that predetermines how and for what purpose the asset will be used throughout the period of use.

Embedded leases

Under previous lessee guidance, embedded leases often were off-balance sheet operating leases. Therefore, applying lease accounting to an arrangement may not have been important. Under ASC 842, however, this determination is likely to be more important, since virtually all lessees will recognize a lease's right-of-use asset and lease liability, which must be reflected on the balance sheet. This determination is particularly important during the transition to the new standard.

Drilling contracts. To assess whether or not an arrangement is a lease (or contains a lease), reporting entities should start by determining if it contains an identified asset. In most cases, drilling contracts specify the drilling equipment and the supplier (drilling company) does not have a substantive substitution right (i.e., the costs to substitute would outweigh the benefits). When an asset is distinct and identified in the contract, and when the supplier lacks substantive substitution rights, the supplier and customer (typically the operator) must determine who holds the decision-making rights that most affect the economic benefits derived from using the asset.

The new standard describes decision-making rights that could potentially affect the economic benefits derived from use of an asset. These include the right to change: (1) the type of the asset's output, (2) the timing of the output, (3) the place of the output, (4) whether the output is produced and (5) the output quantity.

The economic benefits of drilling equipment derive from a customer's ability to use the equipment throughout the contract period, and to decide where, when and how to use it. A supplier's right to constrain the customer's decision-making to protect the safety of the rig or its personnel or to comply with legal or other requirements is considered a protective right and does not rebut the customer's exclusive use of the equipment.

In this situation, even when the customer might not be able to operate the drilling equipment, the customer's power to decide when or where to drill, how to alter the drilling plans to address conditions, and other relevant decisions suggest that the customer controls the asset. A similar assessment is likely to be needed for other types of oil field equipment, including rentals.

Although drilling rigs represent a potential embedded lease under ASC 842, they may not have been similarly assessed as such under ASC 840.

Transportation and storage contracts. Under the new guidance, arrangements involving pipelines, gathering systems and storage tanks may contain leases. The assessment requires identifying the instances in which there is a physically distinct asset.

For example, a customer may use the entire capacity of a distinct storage tank, even though that particular tank may not be specified in the contract. Assume that the customer is storing a hazardous chemical and the supplier has only one tank suited to the purpose (due to safety or other considerations). Also, assume that the customer will use the entire tank. In this case, it may be difficult to assert that the arrangement does not rely on an identified asset. If the customer controls when and how much of the storage capacity it uses at any given time, the arrangement is considered a lease.

In contrast, a supplier who owns a tank farm and agrees to store a commodity that can be held in more than one tank, or that can be commingled with inventory owned by others, is unlikely to rely on an identified asset (this assumes that the customer does not use essentially the entire capacity of the tank farm).

The accountant must determine when the asset is physically distinct. In some instances, a customer uses the entire capacity of a distinct pipeline segment. When a customer has sole access to a pipeline's capacity for the "first mile" or "last mile," the accountant must ascertain whether or not that sole access represents a physically distinct asset, as discussed in the following example.

Facts. Shipper, Inc. ("customer") agrees with Midstream, LP ("supplier") to use 100 percent of a specific natural gas pipeline's capacity. The supplier operates and maintains the pipeline. The customer pays the supplier a fixed capacity charge each month and, when the customer chooses to use that capacity, a variable amount for each unit of natural gas transported. The supplier cannot use the customer's portion of the capacity to transport natural gas for any other customer.

Analysis. The arrangement contains a lease of the pipeline.

The pipeline is physically distinct and the customer uses 100 percent of its capacity. Therefore, the arrangement relies on an identified asset.

The customer has the right to control the identified pipeline's use during the specified period because:

- The customer makes the relevant decisions about how and for what purpose to use the pipeline by deciding when and how much natural gas to transport during the period of use.

- The customer has the right to obtain substantially all of the economic benefits from transporting natural gas through the pipeline because no one else can use the pipeline during the period of use.

Joint operating agreements

Most oil and gas producing activities are conducted through a joint operating agreement (JOA), in which the mineral interest is owned by two or more parties through a legal, undivided interest held by each party. Although some joint operations are organized as legal entities, most are not.

The parties to a JOA typically designate one mineral interest owner to be the operator (typically the one with the largest undivided interest). The other parties to the JOA are designated as nonoperators. The operator manages the day-to-day operations during drilling and also during the production phase if the drilling phase is successful. Therefore, the operator usually is the named customer in a drilling contract with a supplier of drilling equipment. However, all owners of mineral interests vote on major decisions affecting the joint operation. The decision-making rights of the nonoperators are substantive and are a key reason (along with the legally undivided nature of mineral interests) that the operator does not consolidate the joint operation.

Although arrangements vary, the most common transaction structure is one in which a supplier executes a multiyear arrangement with the operator to provide drilling equipment and related goods and services. The drilling equipment cannot be replaced by the supplier except if it malfunctions. The parties to the JOA (both the operator and nonoperators) collectively make decisions under the JOA and the nonoperators reimburse the operator for their portion of costs incurred in connection with the use of drilling equipment for activities specified in the JOA. In case of a default under the contract between the supplier and operator, the supplier has recourse only to the operator and not to the joint operation or its nonoperator members.

Analysis by the supplier. The supplier is party to a lease. From the supplier's perspective, it has surrendered control of its asset since decision-making resides with the operator during the period of use. Classification must be considered, but applying lease accounting to a typical drilling contract is unlikely to result in a sales-type or direct-financing lease.

Analysis by the customer. Determining whether or not the drilling contract contains a lease requires considering: (1) the legal rights conveyed by the contract with the supplier and (2) the intended use of the equipment.

The operator is the named party in the drilling contract and is legally responsible for fulfilling all obligations, including incurring the costs of the drilling equipment. In case of a default, the supplier has recourse only to the operator, not to the joint operation or its nonoperator members. Therefore, the contract between the operator and the supplier is a lease because: (1) the asset (drilling equipment) is explicitly identified, and the supplier cannot substitute it for other drilling equipment unless it malfunctions (which is not a substantive substitution right of the supplier) and (2) the operator directs the use of the asset and obtains substantially all of the benefits derived from it.

The supplier has ceded control of the drilling equipment to the operator alone. The fact that the operator has a JOA with nonoperators does not alter the arrangement between the supplier and the operator. The accounting effect with respect to the JOA requires evaluation of its terms and conditions. For example, the JOA will need to be evaluated to determine if it creates a sublease between the operator and nonoperators (i.e., is there a physically distinct asset under the arrangement with respect to each nonoperator).

The operator records a right-of-use asset and liability associated with the lease in its financial statements. Under ASC 932, the operator capitalizes (if appropriate) all of the costs incurred in connection with the contract and shows nonoperator reimbursements as a reduction of capitalized costs. This example assumes there is no sublease between the operator and the nonoperators.

Lease and nonlease components

A contract may contain one or more leased items, as well as nonlease goods and services. The lease accounting model need not apply to nonlease contract components (items or activities that transfer a good or service to the lessee). Land is a separate lease component unless the accounting effect of treating it as such would be insignificant (e.g., the new amount recognized for the land lease component would be insignificant, or separating the land lease component would not affect the lease classification of any individual lease component).

Previous leasing guidance allocated property taxes and insurance separately from minimum lease payments. Under ASC 842, however, reimbursements to the owner for property taxes and insurance are not separate goods or services. Therefore, they are not considered components and any associated lessee fixed or variable payments should be treated as part of overall contract consideration, allocated between the lease and nonlease components. In contrast, maintenance services involve delivery of a separate service and are therefore considered a nonlease component if provided by the lessor to the lessee.

Determining lease and nonlease components may be challenging. For instance, in a typical drilling rig contract, a large portion of the fee typically relates to: (1) the supplier's employees who operate the rig and (2) goods and services used for drilling, such as concrete and piping.

After identifying the lease and nonlease components, the contract consideration should be allocated to each component. A lessee should allocate the contract consideration to the separate lease and nonlease components based on their relative standalone prices. As a practical expedient, a lessee may, as an accounting policy election by class of underlying asset, choose not to separate nonlease components from the associated lease component and instead account for them as a single lease component. A lessor should allocate contract consideration to the separate lease and nonlease components according to the transaction price allocation guidance provided in ASC 606.

The practical expedient now available to lessees for lease and nonlease components was not available to lessors when the standard was issued. However, in July 2018, the FASB approved an additional practical expedient that allows lessors to make an accounting policy election, by class of underlying asset, to choose not to separate lease and nonlease components.

Said differently, lessors, like lessees, may now account for lease and nonlease components as a single, combined component. However, the lessor's practical expedient is limited to circumstances in which the nonlease component otherwise would be accounted for under ASC 606. It must also meet two additional criteria: (1) the timing and pattern of transfer for the nonlease component and the associated lease component must be the same and (2) the stand-alone lease component, if accounted for separately, must be classified as an operating lease.

Once lease and nonlease components are combined under this practical expedient, the lessor must determine how to account for the combined component considering whether it is predominantly a lease or nonlease. If the nonlease component predominates, the lessor should account for the combined component according to ASC 606. If the lease component predominates, the lessor should account for the combined component according to ASC 842.

Evaluating predominance requires judgment. However, a lessor generally should be able to determine if the combined component is predominantly a lease or a revenue arrangement, without any detailed quantitative or theoretical analysis required.

Rights of way and easements

Rights of way and easements take different forms, ranging from a perpetual easement to a finite-lived easement (right of way). In some cases, full payment for the easement is made upfront. In others, payments are required at periodic intervals throughout the period of use. Under previous leasing guidance, certain easements and rights of way were accounted for as intangible assets.

Applying ASC 842 requires petroleum accountants to evaluate carefully whether or not these easements and rights of way lie within the scope of the new standard, since rights of use and consideration may vary from one arrangement to another.

To assist with the transition to the new standard, the FASB issued ASU 2018-01, Land Easement Practical Expedient for Transition to Topic 842, which is codified in ASC 842-10-65-1(gg) as follows:

> An entity also may elect a practical expedient to not assess whether existing or expired land easements that were not previously accounted for as leases under Topic 840 are or contain a lease under this Topic.... A land easement (also commonly referred to as a right of way) refers to a right to use, access, or cross another entity's land for a specified purpose. This practical expedient shall be applied consistently by an entity to all its existing and expired land easements that were not previously accounted for as leases under Topic 840. This practical expedient may be elected separately or in conjunction with either one or both of the practical expedients in [ASC 842-10-65-1 paragraphs] (f) and (g). An entity that elects this practical expedient for existing or expired land easements shall apply the pending content that links to this paragraph to land easements entered into (or modified) on or after the date that the entity first applies the pending content that links to this paragraph as described in [ASC 842-10-65-1 paragraphs] (a) and (b). An entity that previously accounted for existing or expired land easements as leases under Topic 840 shall not be eligible for this practical expedient for those land easements.

• • •

Key concepts

- Legal forms of joint activities

- Joint ventures

- Recording joint interest transactions

- Material transfers

- Joint interest audits

- Electronic data interchange

Previous chapters emphasized the costly and high-risk nature of oil and gas exploration and development. Significant exploration costs are incurred prior to knowing if reserves of oil and gas exist and, if so, in what quantities. Therefore, it is not surprising that otherwise fierce competitors routinely combine their capital and expertise in joint operations.

Cost and risk sharing arrangements allow companies to acquire, explore for, develop and produce oil and gas under costly and hazardous conditions. For example, new drilling technologies have allowed E&P companies to prospect for reserves in the deepwater regions of the Gulf of Mexico and offshore Brazil and Africa. These projects require large upfront investments as leasing an offshore block can cost $25 million or more. Ultra-deepwater drilling has been successful in the Gulf of Mexico to maximum drilling depths of 30,000 to 40,000 feet under maximum water depths of 7,500 to 12,000 feet. With daily rental costs of $500,000 or more, offshore drilling rigs may be booked on a project for several years and incur costs of several hundred million dollars.

In regions that are not especially hazardous or costly, cooperation can make good economic sense or can be dictated by social concerns. If several operators own working interests in small leases in a common area, it is wasteful for every operator to drill wells on every property; it is unnecessary for producing the reservoir and state spacing laws actually might prohibit it. In addition, the administrative and supervisory efforts required by each operator to carry out a drilling project involving only one or two wells, and producing the reserves from those wells, may be greater than any potential benefits.

In recent years, regulators and the general public have renewed their focus on the operations of oil and gas companies. Several contributing factors to this include:

- Volatile commodity prices.

- Hydraulic fracturing.

- Significant global dependence on oil and gas for energy.

- High-profile oil spills in the Gulf of Mexico and Alaska.

- Concerns about security in certain major oil-producing areas in the Middle East and Africa.

Consequently, the industry has seen increased regulation from both the legislative and executive arms of the U.S. government. Because joint interest operations are an important part of the oil and gas industry, they too are affected by these recent changes.

Legal forms of joint activities

In some instances, development and production activities are almost impossible to carry out unless the mineral owners join forces. For example, it is not economical to employ recovery techniques on only part of a reservoir underlying a single lease. Instead, the techniques must be applied to the entire reservoir to maximize operational efficiencies and potential reserve recovery.

Good conservation practices dictate careful planning and control to produce minerals from the reservoir. This requires cooperation among all mineral owners. Therefore, jointly conducted operations are routine throughout the petroleum industry. Parties to the joint operations combine their financial resources and/or personnel and share in the revenues and expenses that result from the arrangement.

In general, while joint interest operations are not always straightforward, they typically take one of three legal forms, as discussed herein. Operations are structured according to operating agreements that address specific facts and circumstances of each joint operation.

Joint ventures of undivided interests

By far, the most important and most common form of industry joint venture is one of undivided interests (unitized interests). Working interest owners jointly drill, develop and operate a jointly owned or unitized property (or properties) according to a written agreement executed by all parties. One of the parties in the joint venture typically is designated as the operator and takes the lead on development projects and operations.

The term "joint venture" usually refers to a project that combines leases; the parties own an undivided interest (joint interest) for the purpose of jointly producing resources. The undivided interests include divided interests that, through unitization, effectively become undivided interests. An undivided interest owner has a share in the entire lease or property. For example, a joint owner might own a 50 percent interest in a tract of 640 acres. Alternatively, an owner might own a divided interest of 100 percent of the interest in 320 acres included in a 640 acre lease.

Legal partnerships

Limited partnerships managed by an E&P company as the general partner and substantially funded by individual investors (limited partners) were popular in the 1970s and early 1980s. Limited partnership (LP) investments in exploration and development were called "drilling funds." Other limited partnerships acquired producing oil and gas properties and were called "income funds."

A master limited partnership (MLP) is publicly traded but retains the legal form of a partnership. The general partner of an MLP manages the partnership's operations, while individual investors are limited partners.

Oil and gas entities may form a partnership, under state law, to jointly explore and develop a project. The partnership is a legal entity: it holds title to assets, incurs debts in its own name and otherwise carries on business activities. Traditionally, joint ventures in the upstream sector of the industry have not been structured as legal partnerships; however, such arrangements are more common in other sectors of the industry, especially midstream.

Accounting for partnership interests is described in Chapter 23 and MLPs are described in greater detail in Chapter 29.

Jointly owned corporations

Certain legal, political or economic reasons may encourage oil and gas companies to undertake cooperative ventures by forming a separate corporation. For example, three domestic oil companies may wish to explore and produce in a foreign country. They may form a new corporation in the foreign country, with each domestic enterprise owning one-third of the stock. Frequently, these enterprises own stock in the foreign corporation, along with either the foreign government or a foreign corporation local to that country. Similarly, corporations may jointly form a new corporation to build a pipeline, explore a new area or construct secondary recovery facilities.

Other considerations

The global demand for energy, driven by both U.S. consumption and increased consumption in emerging economies such as India and China, creates an incentive for producers to explore for replacement reserves. The International Energy Outlook 2019, prepared by the U.S. Energy Information Administration, projects that energy demand in non-OECD Asia is projected to almost double between 2018 and 2050, making it both the largest and fastest-growing region in the world for energy consumption.

To meet the substantial capital outlay required to fund these projects, E&P companies likely will continue to establish unique and innovative forms of joint ventures. This trend already is apparent in the Gulf of Mexico, where independents are exploring and producing in areas once dominated by large, integrated companies. These independents have formed unique partnerships to jointly own the capital-intensive floating production platforms used for deepwater operations.

Joint ventures

This chapter focuses on how joint interest owners account for joint venture activities, particularly the sharing and recording of joint costs. Formation of a joint venture reflects either a pooling of capital or an exchange of like-kind assets. Joint ventures establish definitions and guidelines under which all parties to the joint venture must operate. Fortunately, the U.S. oil and gas industry has a long history of cooperative enterprises from which to draw various model forms for these agreements.

It is common for joint interest owners to use the proportionate consolidation method of accounting. This method enables each owner to record its proportionate share of assets, liabilities, revenues and expenses according to its own account classifications. The joint venture is not regarded as a unique accounting entity; therefore, separate financial statements are not necessary for the venture.

If a joint venture uses a corporate structure, which is rare in the U.S., proportionate consolidation generally is not appropriate. The authoritative guidance in ASC 323 requires the equity method of accounting for corporate joint ventures. However, the industry practice of recording investments in unincorporated joint operations, using a proportional basis, is recognized by the FASB and is allowed by authoritative literature in ASC 932. See Chapter 23 for further discussion of the accounting for joint ventures.

To conduct a joint operation, a mineral interest (or multiple mineral interests) is identified as the subject of the venture. The joint venture may cover a single well, project or lease. Typically, a joint venture covers a group of jointly owned leases of mineral interests and takes one of three forms:

- **Jointly owned leases within an area of mutual interest specified in a joint venture agreement.** Working interests in oil, gas or other mineral leases are acquired and held, as undivided ownership interests, by two or more E&P companies.

- **Pooled drilling and production unit.** Relatively small leases or portions of leases, each separately owned by E&P companies or individuals, are pooled or combined into a single drilling and production unit. Not all of the lease owners in a field may choose to participate in the enterprise.

  A pool or unit may be created under several different scenarios. Working interest owners can invoke the express pooling provisions contained in their separate oil and gas leases, which grant the right to pool their working and royalty interests. Another type of pool can be created by a separate voluntary agreement that joins working interest owners and royalty interests in separate tracts. In other cases, royalty owners may not be involved in the pooling arrangement.

  Drilling and production units frequently do not involve all owners in a field and may be either purely voluntary or forced by government controls. For example, state spacing requirements may decree that a minimum of 40 acres is required for an oil well or a minimum of 640 acres is required for a gas well. The owner of a 20-acre lease must join with other owners to pool their leases in order to establish a drilling block.

- **Fieldwide unitization.** All separately owned tracts in a field are unitized into a single unit or property. All working interest owners and all royalty owners in the field contribute their separate properties to the unit. In return, they receive smaller, fractional interests in the combined properties, and sometimes pay or receive money under equalization settlements.

  Field-wide or reservoir-wide unitization is especially common when performing operations such as secondary or tertiary recovery, pressure maintenance or gas cycling. Field-wide unitization agreements are more complex than those found in simple arrangements for pooling of drilling and production units.

Typically, two types of agreements guide participants in joint operations: (1) the joint venture agreement, which establishes the venture and (2) the joint operating agreement (JOA), which governs the joint operations.

Among oil and gas companies that operate internationally, some joint operations also are governed by production sharing contracts. A production sharing contract (PSC) stipulates the basis of sharing the output of oil and gas operations among the joint parties. Under a PSC, a partner (typically the operator) bears the entire cost and risk of exploring and developing the lease. If the operation achieves commercial success, the operator recovers its costs through its allocation of production, as stipulated by the PSC.

Joint venture agreements

The terms "exploration agreement," "pooling agreement" and "unitization agreement" refer to specific types of pooling arrangements. The more general term "joint venture agreement" applies to oil and gas companies that own undivided interests in specific leases or leases within a specified land area, such as a large portion of a county.

A joint venture agreement identifies the companies, the leases within the venture and the respective working interests in the leases. Normally, these leases include adjoining acreage or acreage within a small area. When property is exchanged for an interest, the agreement includes a clause assigning the interest.

The agreement designates an area surrounding the leases as an area of mutual interest (AMI). Any venture participant that acquires leases in the AMI must do so on behalf of the joint venture. This precludes an owner from unfairly profiting from joint venture information, such as a new discovery on venture leases. Certain joint venture agreements also include drilling and development guidelines.

Regardless of whether they involve a single tract of land, a block of leases jointly owned or a field-wide unitization, formation of a joint interest is negotiated by management representatives. Company specialists in geology, land, engineering, law, tax and accounting may participate. Management may seek outside expertise, depending on the size of the company, its available resources and the project scope. Before execution, the agreement's form and terms should be reviewed carefully by qualified representatives of each party. When executed, the written joint venture agreement becomes effective on the date specified. Joint operation of a single property or block of properties is carried out under a JOA, as described in the next section.

Joint operating agreements

A separate document from the joint venture agreement, the JOA sets out the duties, obligations, rights and responsibilities of the working interest owners to the joint venture operations and specifies how costs and benefits will be shared. The JOA is crucial to accounting procedures and principles for joint operations and is examined in detail herein.

Operating agreements for smaller pooled drilling and production units or single tracts of land are less complex than field-wide unitizations. However, the general principles, purposes and certain provisions of operating agreements are the same in all situations and may address the following:

1. **Definitions.** Defines terms used in the agreement, such as operator and nonoperator. For pooled units and field-wide units, this section also defines unitized substances, unitized formation, working interest owner, royalty interest owner and other terms.

2. **Creation and effect of joint operation or unit.** Describes the oil and gas leases and property involved for a single tract of land and any restrictions regarding depth or formations. For pooled units and field-wide units, it describes the mineral leases, interests, separate properties, mineral or minerals unitized and producing zones that comprise the unitized area.

3. **Interests of parties.** Sets out the participating interest of each working interest owner in the costs and production of the unit. For field-wide units, the agreement may set out participation factors by individual tracts.

4. **Title.** Represents the title examination for the lease of any proposed drilling or production site prior to drilling. The information examined typically includes working interest, minerals royalty, overriding royalty and production payments required under the applicable lease(s).

5. **Plan of operations.** Provides for a drilling or development program, workover operations, abandonment and similar activities. This section may be separated into several articles.

   For a single tract or drilling unit, the drilling of the first well is agreed on expressly and the mechanics are provided to obtain an agreement for drilling additional wells. Also, if not all working interest owners agree to participate in drilling a subsequent well or wells (referred to as nonconsent or going nonconsent), this section includes provisions to permit independent operations. In this case, the party that desires to drill, complete, rework and recomplete can do so without the consent of the other parties.

   The consenting parties absorb all costs of the operation, including those of a dry hole. When such a well produces, the driller is permitted to recoup a specified percentage of the drilling and equipment costs out of production attributable to the nonconsenting parties' interests.

6. **Operator.** Identifies the party with operational control over and supervision of the joint operation. Provides that the operator will conduct its JOA activities reasonably and prudently, in a good and professional manner, with due diligence and dispatch and in accordance with accepted industry practices.

7. **Duties and obligations of operator.** Sets out the powers and duties of the operator to develop and operate efficiently; requires lands and leases in the covered area to be kept free from third-party statutory liens; describes records and reports required by nonoperators and governmental authorities; explains the procedure for resignation or removal of the operator and selection of a successor; and sets out other similar requirements.

8. **Relationship of parties.** Specifies that the duties, obligations and liabilities of the parties are intended to be several, not joint or collective. It also specifies that nothing contained in the JOA creates an association or trust or imposes a partnership duty, obligation or liability with, or to, any of the parties; each party is individually responsible for its obligations.

   Related to this provision is an agreement that the parties do not intend to operate, or to be taxed, as a partnership under federal income tax laws. The operator agrees to file appropriate forms with the Internal Revenue Service (IRS) in order to elect out of Subchapter K partnership provisions.

9. **Effective date and term.** Specifies the effective time frame for the agreement. In field-wide units, this section requires execution of the agreement by a specified percentage of all working interest owners and royalty interest owners. It specifies the term (period of time) that the agreement remains in effect after its effective date (e.g., so long as the leases continue in effect, operations are conducted or production continues).

10. **Allocation of production.** States that each party has the right to take oil or gas in-kind or to dispose of its proportionate share of the oil or gas produced from the joint operation. The right to take oil and gas in-kind is a defense against an IRS assertion that the joint venture is really a taxable corporation.

    This section may state that each party is responsible for royalties on its share of production, holding other parties free from that liability. Alternatively, the duty to keep the records and handle the payment of royalties may be delegated to the operator.

11. **Abandonment and salvage.** Sets out the responsibilities of each party for plugging and abandoning exploratory and producing wells on properties covered by the agreement.

12. **Taxes.** May require the operator to render, for ad valorem tax purposes, all jointly owned property, and to pay property taxes for the benefit of the parties, according to the provisions of the accounting procedure (described in the next section).

    This section may specify that each party pays its proportionate tax obligation separately. Also, it may state that each party is responsible for paying production, severance, excise, gathering and all other taxes on its proportionate share of the oil and gas produced.

13. **Insurance.** Requires the operator to carry specific insurance, such as workers' compensation, employer's liability, comprehensive public liability and comprehensive automotive liability. The limits of coverage also may be prescribed. Wording may state that, if the operator does not comply, it assumes all risks and sole liability. This section establishes that premium payments will be made according to the provisions of the accounting procedure.

14. **Development and operating costs.** Other than for named exceptions, this section requires the operator to promptly pay and discharge all costs and expenses incurred in the development and operation of the joint interest area and to charge all parties with their proportionate shares on the basis set out in the accounting procedure.

    The operator is granted the right to demand and receive payment from other parties for their shares of the estimated costs to be incurred during the next succeeding month ("cash calls"). The operator may be required to avoid any single project that is reasonably estimated to require expenditure beyond a stipulated amount without consent from nonoperators.

15. **Liability, claims and litigation.** States that, if any party to the agreement is sued on an alleged cause of action arising from operations in the joint interest area, involving titles of any single tract subject to the agreement, the party shall give prompt written notice to the operator and all other parties. It further specifies that lawsuits may be settled only with the consent of all parties.

    This section of the JOA states that no charges shall be made for the services of staff attorneys retained by the parties and that outside attorneys may be employed only with the consent of all parties. Legal costs, along with other costs related to the defense of suits, when properly authorized, are considered costs of operation, to be charged to and paid by all parties in proportion to their interests in the joint operation.

16. **Force majeure.** Requires that all obligations of each party, except for payment of money, are suspended if that party is prevented from complying because of strikes, fire, war, civil disturbances, acts of God, laws, regulations, inability to secure material or other causes beyond the reasonable control of the party.

17. **Notices.** States that all notices authorized or required between the parties, and required by any of the provisions of the agreement, must be furnished in writing by mail or other specified means and addressed to the party to whom the notice is given at the address listed in the agreement.

18. **Other provisions.** Adds any other provisions deemed necessary to set out the rights, duties and obligations of the parties to efficiently and economically carry out the operations of the joint venture.

The list provided is only a sampling of terms frequently found in joint operating agreements. Petroleum accountants should be aware that additional provisions may add layers of complexity to the parties' understanding. A commonly used model for JOAs comes from the American Association of Professional Landmen (AAPL) Model Form Operating Agreement. For single-tract units and small pooled units, operating agreements usually are prepared by one of the parties to fit each particular situation.

JOAs typically include an exhibit that addresses joint venture accounting procedures, such as the basis of direct charges and credits to the joint account, overhead charges, equipment disposal, basis of materials transferred on and off the property, inventories, billings, advance payments and audits.

Over the years, COPAS has developed several model Accounting Procedure Joint Operations exhibits. Note that when COPAS issues a new exhibit, it does not impact an accounting procedure previously adopted as part of a JOA. When a joint operation is formed and the JOA is signed, it adopts the applicable COPAS accounting procedure joint operations form, either without modification or with agreed-upon changes, as an exhibit to the JOA.

Although standard forms of operating agreements and accounting procedures are widely available to the industry, they are not used in every case. Contractual rights and obligations vary in every joint operation, which can present a challenge to accountants and tax advisers.

Accounting procedure exhibits

Accounting procedure exhibits for joint operations commonly include two major parts: (1) the exhibit form itself and (2) interpretive guidance on applying its provisions.

The exhibit form consists of five sections:

1. **General provisions.**

   A. **Definitions.** Defines terms used in the contract, including joint property, joint operations, joint account, operator, nonoperators, parties, first-level supervisors, technical employees, personal expenses, materials and controllable materials.

   B. **Statements and billings.** Most agreements require the operator to bill nonoperators monthly for their share of charges. Billing is made on or before the last day of the following month and must contain appropriate detail. The invoice should identify the lease, facility or authorization for expenditure (AFE). It also summarizes charges and credits by appropriate classifications of investment and expense. The invoice provides additional details for controllable materials, unusual charges and credits.

   C. **Advances and payments by nonoperators.** Usually, operators have the right to make cash calls. According to the accounting procedure, each nonoperator must pay its bill within 15 days of receipt. Interest is charged, at a specified rate, on any late payments.

   D. **Adjustments.** To take exception to billings and claim any adjustments, nonoperators are given 24 months after the end of a calendar year in which the billing took place.

   E. **Audits.** Nonoperators generally have the right to audit the operator's records related to the joint account. The right to audit typically extends to 24 months after the fiscal year-end. Joint interest audits are described later in this chapter.

   F. **Approval by parties.** An operator must give proper advance notice of all items requiring approval or agreement to parties or nonoperators. Agreement or approval of a majority (in interest owned) of nonoperators is binding on all nonoperators.

2. **Direct charges.** Certain items are charged directly to the joint operation, including:

   A. Rents and royalties on the properties.

   B. Labor costs directly related to the joint interest operations, including salaries, wages and incentive compensation for the operator's field employees directly employed on the property, first-level field supervisors and technical employees working directly on the property (if technical costs are not already included in overhead rates). Other labor charges include the related costs of holiday, vacation, sickness, disability, relocation, training, award payments and other allowances, as well as expenditures or contributions imposed by governmental authorities.

   Related personnel expenses and employee benefits applicable to direct labor costs also are direct charges. Benefits customarily are limited to a percentage of labor costs; amounts are recommended by COPAS on a periodic basis. Current recommendations are included in COPAS MFI-27, *Employee Benefits and Percentage Limitation.*

C. Materials purchased or furnished by the operator for use on the joint property. Detailed provisions related to materials and equipment are described later in this chapter.

D. Transportation of employees and materials necessary for joint operations and subject to site conditions.

E. Costs of contract services, equipment and utilities, with specified exceptions and limits.

F. An operator has the right to charge the joint account for use of operator-owned equipment and facilities at rates commensurate with the costs of ownership and operation. Detailed suggestions for bases to be used in making charges for these costs are included in Section II-8 of the explanation portion of MFI 17. In lieu of charging for actual costs, an operator may charge an amount for services equal to normal commercial rates in the area, less 20 percent.

G. Goods and services that are provided by affiliates and detailed in an approved AFE do not require approval of the parties unless the amounts exceed specified limits. The costs of an affiliate's goods and services may not exceed average commercial rates in the area of operation unless approved by nonoperators.

H. Damages and losses to joint property, except those resulting from the operator's gross negligence or willful misconduct.

I. Legal expenses related to joint property for services provided by an outside firm. Special provisions may allow for use of the operator's legal staff.

J. Taxes of all kinds on the joint property, its operations and production.

K. Insurance costs for joint interest property, personnel and operations.

L. Communication costs for the joint operations.

M. Ecological, environmental and safety costs.

N. Plugging, abandonment and reclamation costs for joint property.

O. Other necessary direct costs.

3. **Overhead.** Misunderstandings can arise easily among joint interest owners over direct costs, overhead charges and costs that may not rightfully belong to the joint account. Therefore, the agreement usually includes detailed provisions for these items. Salaries, wages and personal expenses of technical employees and contract personnel may be charged directly to the joint account or included in the overhead rate.

As compensation for administration, supervision, office services and warehousing costs (and, if applicable, technical personnel), an operator can charge overhead as either a fixed rate or a percentage of drilling and producing costs. Under fixed rates, the venture sets a rate, per well per month, for the wells being drilled and a lower rate, per well per month, for the wells being produced.

The three major subheadings of the overhead section are:

A. Overhead – drilling and producing operations.

B. Overhead – major construction and catastrophe.

C. Amendment of overhead rates.

4. **Pricing of joint account material purchases, transfers and dispositions.** The operator of a joint interest frequently transfers materials and equipment from its own warehouse or solely owned property to the jointly owned property and vice versa. Also, operators routinely purchase materials and equipment designated for the joint operation. Later, these items are removed and sold.

Since material prices change frequently, it is not feasible for joint owners to negotiate each transaction. Therefore, the industry has developed widely accepted rules that govern the pricing of material and equipment purchases, transfers and dispositions. COPAS has been the guiding force behind these standards. For example, this chapter describes the industry term "condition value" of materials acquired or disposed of, as found in Section IV of COPAS MFI-4.

5. **Inventories.** The accounting procedure requires an operator to maintain detailed records of controllable materials and conduct periodic and special physical inventories.

Recording joint interest transactions

Oil and gas companies may use seemingly conflicting terms to describe aspects of the business. Petroleum accountants should understand these distinctions. For instance, holders of operating interests who are not responsible for operating the property are called nonoperators, even though they hold working interests in a property. Holders of nonoperating interests, such as royalty owners, are not referred to as nonoperators. Likewise, accounting procedure exhibits refer to any owner of an operating interest that is not the operator of the property as a nonoperator.

Records of operators

Most operating agreements require an operator to pay all costs and expenses incurred, charging each nonoperator its proportionate share. The operator's accounting system must properly accumulate and classify expenditures for preparation of monthly billings. Also, the system should support the accounting procedure adopted in the joint operating agreement. Oil and gas companies use software to facilitate these processes. Working interest amounts and other information that is entered into the software system must be consistent with the joint operating agreements.

Operator overhead cost reimbursements. Accounting for operator overhead cost reimbursements has been the subject of scrutiny in recent years. Many operators treat these reimbursements by nonoperators as reductions of expense (i.e., netted with both operator and nonoperator overhead charges), with the initial cost recorded by the operator as a debit to expense. Many believe this approach is consistent with proportional consolidation to reflect the provisions of the joint operating agreement. In this approach, it would not be appropriate to record the overhead cost reimbursement in a separate account from the initial debit.

Charging costs to joint interest accounts. Typically, operators match each charge or credit with the related individual joint operating agreement and record it to the related property at the 100 percent gross (8/8ths) amount of a vendor invoice. They maintain subsidiary records, by account number, for each joint operation. Customarily, these records agree with the operator's work-in-progress, wells and related facilities, revenue and lease operating expense subsidiary ledgers. The property's identifying number contains allocation information for each working interest owner.

For example, if Big Oil USA, operator of the N. Moore 2, receives a statement for $301,903 from the contract driller of N. Moore 2, it would record the following entry:

Work-in-progress – intangible costs of wells	301,903	
Accounts payable		301,903
To record receipt of statement from drilling contractor on N. Moore 2.		

The operator's proportionate share of each cost is netted, in the appropriate account in its financial records, while it records the nonoperator's share of total charges as accounts receivable (or a similarly titled account).

Based on the working interest percentages shown in Figure 10-1, the operator's joint interest billing (JIB) system makes the following entry at the end of April related to the contract drilling costs on N. Moore 2 (see Figure 10-2).

Accounts receivable – joint interest billings	184,243	
Work-in-progress – intangible costs of wells		184,243
To record receivable from nonoperators for shares of N. Moore 2 drilling costs. *[(1.0 - 0.3897298) x $301,903.89].*		

Since the joint interest billing system is processed at the end of each month, only the operator's interest and a receivable from the other working interest owners appear in the monthly financial statements. During the month, when costs are accumulated for each joint activity, the detailed records form a joint interest ledger.

Some companies use a variation of the method noted above, processing joint interest entries daily, using joint venture accounting software; however, JIBs continue to be distributed at the end of the month.

Allocating each transaction to each joint interest owner's account. Another approach to recording joint venture transactions is to analyze each transaction prior to recording it. The portion applicable to nonoperators is recorded immediately as accounts receivable, and the operator's share is recorded in its usual asset and liability accounts.

For example, if this method were used by Big Oil USA on a statement for $301,903 from the drilling contractor on N. Moore 2, the entry would be:

Work-in-progress – intangible costs of wells	117,661	
Accounts receivable – joint interest billings	184,242	
Accounts payable		301,903
To record receipt of statement from drilling contractor on N. Moore 2.		

Records of nonoperators

Joint interest billing procedures. Nonoperators are billed monthly by the operator for their share of charges and credits. Amounts typically include costs and cost adjustments related to the joint operation. The JIB statement is the principal source document delivered to nonoperators each month. Prepared by the operator, the JIB statement contains sufficient detail to enable nonoperators to debit or credit appropriate accounts in their own records.

COPAS MFI-26, *Joint Interest Billing Summary Classifications* (revised October 1994), suggests categories and classifications for use in JIB statements. These lists identify various types of costs but do not necessarily coincide with GAAP or income tax accounting. Therefore, nonoperators must exercise judgment in recording these costs. An operator cannot accommodate every nonoperator's chart of accounts. In practice, however, JIB statements usually meet the broad accounting classifications of successful efforts and full cost companies, as well as their tax reporting requirements.

Monthly billing for a joint account contains: (1) a summary statement and invoice showing total charges and amounts due from every working interest owner, along with an individual invoice to any nonoperator receiving the statement and (2) supporting schedules that help identify the expenditures and properly account for them according to the project's AFE. When a JIB statement is received from the operator, it is routed for approval to the engineer or department responsible for monitoring operations. Approval should entail a review for reasonableness of amounts and cost descriptions of the stated classifications, property, well, AFE and month of occurrence. Next, the billing is routed to the JIB department, where it is checked for evidence of approvals, coded and entered into the accounting system.

From the JIB statement, nonoperators make entries in their detailed subsidiary records. This step may require professional judgment in classifying billed items from the operator using the nonoperator's chart of accounts. Account titles used to record charges from the billing are the same as if the properties involved belonged solely to the nonoperator. Only the subsidiary accounts reflect the fact that the properties are jointly owned and operated. Payments made to the operator are charged to vouchers payable. Advances may be charged to either the payable account or a prepayment account.

Joint interest billing illustration. Country Service Co., a nonoperator, owns a 0.0547563 interest in the N. Moore Lease. Joint venture costs incurred from the prior month include certain costs of a new well known as N. Moore 2 and the prior month's production costs of the N. Moore 1 well. Figures 10-1 through 10-4 illustrate a nonoperator's accounting treatment for the monthly billing from the operator.

The journal entry made by Country Service Co. to record the April 2019 billing is:

Work-in-progress – intangible costs of wells [0.0547563 x (items 133 – 283)]	20,159	
Work-in-progress – tangible costs of wells [0.0547563 x (items 104 – 122)]	8,944	
Lease operating expenses (0.0547563 x $5,085.66)	278	
Accounts payable		29,381
To record receipt of joint interest billing for April for N. Moore wells.		

Figure 10-1

Joint interest billing – Lease summary

Big Oil USA, Inc.
P.O. BOX 12345, Denton, TX 76201

Country Service Co.	Invoice No.: 1023174
15467 East 107TH Avenue	Invoice Date: May 24, 2019
Houston, TX 77046	Term: Net 15 upon receipt
	Month: April 2019
	Property: N. Moore Lease

Summary Statement and Invoice

Owner #	Owner name	Working interest	Amount
1123500	ABC Oil	0.0447897	$ 24,033.14
1118600	Estes Park Partners	0.0635633	34,106.62
5117300	Cougar Petroleum	0.0153747	8,249.72
2954800	Will B. Smith	0.0226632	12,160.55
1431400	Country Service Co.	0.0547563	29,380.99
0488500	J.B. Jones	0.0258106	13,849.38
8224400	EBT Oil & Gas	0.3833124	205,676.74
0000001	Big Oil USA, Inc.	0.3897298	209,120.17
		1.0000000	

Total current-period charges to joint account	$536,577.31

To invoice you for:	
Drilling and development charges	$29,102.52
Lease operating expenses	278.47
Total current-period charges	**$29,380.99**

Previous balance carried forward	–
Total due	**$29,380.99**

Remittance instructions
Please reference the above invoice number and mail payment to:
Big Oil USA, Inc.
P.O. Box 12345
Denton, TX 76201

Figure 10-2

Joint interest billing – Drilling costs

Big Oil USA, Inc.
P.O. Box 12345, Denton, TX 76201

Country Service Co.   Invoice No.: 1023174
15467 East 107th Ave.   Invoice date: May 24, 2019
Houston, TX 77046   Term: Net 15 upon receipt
Property: N. Moore Lease   Month: April 2019
Well: N. Moore 2   AFE No.: 102

Drilling and Development Charges

S/L	Description	Amount	Total
104	Tubing	$147,780.21	
105	Wellhead assembly	764.88	
115	Misc. noncontrollable surface well material	684.79	
122	Production and other lease facilities	14,111.02	
133	Installation cost	4,245.70	
244	Permits, site prep and cleanup	8,638.74	
248	Other contract services	116.25	
249	Contract drilling	301,903.89	
251	Direct supervision	7,870.42	
255	Bits	(1,297.06)	
267	Equipment rentals	3,449.50	
268	Small tools and supplies	206.90	
269	Transportation, land	6,156.29	
273	Communications	177.66	
275	Testing, drafting and inspection	22,083.03	
277	Perforating	8,280.20	
280	Drilling overhead charge	5,000.00	
283	Loss and damage	1,319.23	
Total drilling and development charges			**$531,491.65**

Joint interest billing – Facilities costs

Big Oil USA, Inc.
P.O. Box 12345, Denton, TX 76201

Country Service Co.	Invoice No.: 1023174
15467 East 107th Ave.	Invoice Date: May 24, 2019
Houston, TX 77046	Term: Net 15 upon receipt
Property: N. Moore Lease	Month: April 2019
Well: N. Moore 2	AFE No.: 102

Controllable Material Detail

Accounting code	Description	Amount	Total
27-2631-102-104	MT60549 13,005.8" (411 Jts.) 2 7/8 6.5# L-80 AB Mod R-2 tubing, Condition A		**$147,780.21**
27-2631-102-122	M0208		
	30.0 ea.-2150# WN flange w/std bore	$ 331.68	
	7.0 ea.-21N #143 Rockwell plug valve	419.96	
	20.0 ea.-3150# RF WN flange w/std bore	276.16	
	7.0 ea.-31N #143 Rockwell plug valve	690.23	
	4.0 ea.-41N #143 Rockwell plug valve	536.98	
	332.0 ea.-5/8 x 3 1/2 BO7 ht. alloy std. w/2	367.73	
	270.7 ft. – Ft. 3 in sch-40 A-53-B SMLS pipe PE	1,513.48	
	1.0 ea.-4 std. weld cross	243.28	
	5.0 ea.-3 Fig 100 FE #021027-15-BS-285	1,805.00	
	1.0 ea.-2 Fig 100 FE #031027-F-15-BS	220.00	
	139.0 ft.-2 sch 40 SMLS line pipe	625.29	
	3.0 ea-4 PE BLK Pipe x 21'	415.80	
	17.0 ea-2 PE BLK Pipe x 21'	817.08	
	3.0 ea-4 wafer butterfly valve, Demco	323.97	
	Miscellaneous noncontrollable Items	2,558.34	
		11,144.98	
	M0266 30.0 ea.-2150# WN flange w/std bore	144.66	
	M0310 Miscellaneous noncontrollable items	2,631.00	
	M0443 Miscellaneous noncontrollable items	141.60	
	M0444 Miscellaneous noncontrollable items	48.78	
Total production and other lease facilities			**$14,111.02**

Figure 10-4

Joint interest billing – Production costs

Big Oil USA, Inc.
P.O. Box 12345, Denton, TX 76201

Country Service Co.   Invoice No.: 1023174
15467 East 107th Ave.   Invoice Date: May 24, 2019
Houston, TX 77046   Term: Net 15 upon receipt
Property: N. Moore Lease   Month: April 2019
Well: N. Moore 1   AFE No.: N/A

Lease Operating Expenses

S/L	Description	Amount	Total
120	Contract labor	$2,903.61	
121	Rig services	406.71	
125	Gas handling	6.81	
128	Saltwater disposal	375.75	
140	Chemicals	44.72	
141	Small tools and supplies	55.34	
143	Automotive expense	198.36	
170	Telephone and telegraph	53.50	
180	Employee travel and gen. exp	68.13	
800	General services	112.08	
824	Area expense	510.65	
880	Production overhead	350.00	
	Total lease operating expense		**$5,085.66**

Material transfers

Joint interest operations typically pool assets and financial resources for the purpose of exploring, developing and producing resources. Under the proportionate consolidation method, each owner records its share of equipment in tangible costs of wells and related development. Items moved between the joint venture's well sites and the operator's warehouses and equipment yards must be recorded properly. Freight and installation costs are charged directly to the joint interests and treated by all parties as part of the equipment's cost. While COPAS has developed special rules as it relates to material transfers, these rules should be considered in conjunction with authoritative guidance issued by the FASB and the SEC.

Although differences exist between the accounting for costs under the proportional basis of accounting versus the equity method, accounting for the transfer of assets contributed by parties is similar under both methods. As a general rule, when an operator transfers material or equipment to a joint property at formation, the transfer price is the book value of the transferred materials or equipment. For mineral property conveyances, ASC 932-360-40-7 states that, "In a pooling of assets in a joint undertaking intended to find, develop, or produce oil or gas from a particular property or group of properties, gain or loss shall not be recognized at the time of the conveyance."

Differing views exist about the appropriateness of recognizing a gain when one party contributes noncash assets to form joint operations, while other parties contribute cash, and the noncash contributor has no actual or implied commitment to reinvest that cash or support the joint operations. However, in the oil and gas industry, joint operations typically require shared costs, income and royalty payments to all parties. This inherently represents a continued financial commitment to the operations by all parties, as well as a continuation of the earnings process, which would make the recognition of a gain inappropriate.

The COPAS standards in Model Form Interpretations 38 (MFI-38), *Materials Manual*, provide suggested guidelines in pricing material transfers and dispositions to assist operators in ascertaining generic prices for recording material transfers. A database developed by COPAS, known as the Computerized Equipment Pricing System (CEPS) also assists entities with transfer pricing issues and requirements, including calculations for each piece of material or equipment from a published base-price list.

In addition, COPAS accounting procedures state that the following methods can be used to approximate the current market price of material or equipment:

- Manually applying the HPM to published material and equipment price lists.

- Vendor quotes.

- Historical purchase prices.

- Mutual agreement to the transfer prices by the parties involved.

Transfers from wholly owned warehouse to jointly owned lease

When equipment is transferred from the operator's wholly owned warehouse inventory to a jointly owned property, the accounting procedure in the venture's joint operating agreement will specify the use of condition values.

For example, assume that an item of equipment is carried in the operator's warehouse inventory account at an original cost of $20,000. The current price of a new asset is $36,000. The equipment is considered to be in Condition Value B, which means it will be valued at 75 percent of the current new cost when it is transferred to joint interest Property 12103J. Because the operator owns three-fourths of the working interest, the nonoperator owner is charged $6,750 for its new one-fourth interest in the property transferred.

Since the operator's original cost for the one-fourth interest was $5,000 (1/4 x $20,000), it realizes a gain on the portion of the asset sold. However, no gain is realized on the three-fourths interest belonging to the operator because a sale to an outsider did not take place for that portion of the asset.

Ignoring transportation expenses, the operator records the transfer as follows:

Accounts receivable – joint interest billings (1/4 x 75% x $36,000)	6,750	
Tangible costs of wells (3/4 x $20,000)	15,000	
Inventory – materials, supplies and equipment		20,000
Other income		1,750
To record transfer of equipment to jointly owned property.		

As previously mentioned, other procedures can be used to approximate the current market price of material or equipment transferred and to recognize profit or loss on the share of equipment sold to the nonoperator. However, profit is never recognized on the share retained by the operator.

Transfers from wholly owned lease to jointly owned lease

A second example involves equipment transfers between leases during drilling and production which require a slightly different treatment.

Assume that an item of equipment with an original cost of $20,000 is transferred from wholly owned Lease 18610 to Lease 18205, in which the operator owns a one-fourth working interest. The equipment is categorized as Condition Value B and is charged to the joint lease at $25,000 (calculated as the current price of $33,333 multiplied by 75% given that the equipment was new when initially transferred to Lease 18610). In this transaction, three-fourths of the asset is sold for $18,750.

Under the successful efforts method in accordance with ASC 932-360-40-3, no gain or loss is recognized by the operator on the abandonment or retirement (which encompasses sales) of individual wells or items of equipment from producing properties until the last well is abandoned. Until then, all proceeds are credited to the asset account rather than recorded as a gain or loss on sale. If the asset's original cost is known, it should be removed from the asset cost account and the accumulated amortization account should be adjusted to defer the gain or loss, if needed.

The journal entry recorded by the operator is as follows:

Accounts receivable – joint interest billings (3/4 x $25,000)	18,750	
Tangible costs of wells – Lease 18205 (1/4 x $20,000)*	6,250	
Accumulated DD&A – tangible costs of wells		3,750
Tangible costs of wells – Lease 18610		20,000
To record transfer of equipment from wholly owned lease to jointly owned lease.		

* Note there may be alternative methods to arrive at the cost basis of this entry.

Transfers between jointly owned leases

Equipment also may be transferred by the operator between two jointly owned leases.

Assume that a piece of equipment, originally costing $20,000, is transferred to Lease 10723J, in which the operator and Magnolia Oil Co. each own a 50 percent working interest. The equipment was previously used on Lease 10792J, a producing property that is three-fourths owned by the operator and one-fourth owned by Crescent City Oil Co. The equipment is transferred at Condition Value B for used equipment that applies a factor of 65 percent to the new equipment price of $24,615, resulting in a transaction value of $16,000. This transfer scenario creates a challenging problem, without a fully satisfactory solution. A common approach is to split the transaction into two steps.

First, assume that the equipment is removed from the jointly owned property, as shown in the next example for assets removed from jointly owned properties. In effect, the operator purchased one-fourth of the equipment with a condition value of $16,000 from the joint owners of Lease 10792J, where the asset originally was used, and removed the remaining three-fourths of the equipment at a cost of $15,000, without recognizing a gain or loss.

Second, as shown in the previous example of transfers from a wholly owned lease to a jointly owned lease, to account for the transfer of the equipment to Lease 10723J, assume that the equipment is charged to Lease 10723J at a condition value of $16,000. In effect, one-half of the equipment has been sold to the joint owners of Lease 10723J for $8,000, and one-half has been transferred to the operator's account for $10,000. The accumulated amortization account absorbs the residual $1,000 from the entry, since no gain or loss is recognized, in accordance with ASC 932-360-40-3.

The operator's journal entry to record the material transfer is as follows:

Accounts receivable – joint interest billings (1/2 x $16,000)	8,000	
Tangible costs of wells – Lease 10723J (1/2 x $20,000)	10,000	
Accumulated DD&A – tangible costs of wells [1/4 x ($20,000 - $16,000)]	1,000	
Accounts receivable – joint interest billings (1/4 x $16,000)		4,000
Tangible costs of wells – Lease 10792J (3/4 x $20,000)		15,000
To record transfer of assets between joint interest properties.		

* Note there may be alternative methods to arrive at the cost basis of this entry.

Asset removal

A fourth example illustrates an entry for assets removed from jointly owned producing properties and transferred to the operator's warehouse.

Assume that the operator removes an asset originally installed new at a cost of $20,000 from Lease 06203J. The operator owns one-fourth of the working interest in the lease. The asset is transferred to the operator's warehouse, where it will be reconditioned for use on the operator's wholly owned Lease 17304.

At the time of removal, a new identical asset would cost $32,000. The removed asset is Condition Value C, which establishes a value of 50 percent of the current new cost. In effect, the operator purchased three-fourths of the equipment from the nonoperator for $12,000 and removed one-fourth of the equipment at a cost of $5,000. The transfer is recorded by the operator as follows:

Inventory – materials, supplies and equipment	17,000	
Accounts receivable – joint interest billings (3/4 x $16,000)		12,000
Tangible costs of wells (1/4 x $20,000)		5,000
To record transfer of equipment from jointly owned Lease 06203J to operator's warehouse.		

Joint interest audits

After receiving, approving and processing joint interest billings, nonoperators can gain further assurance about the accuracy of the charges by examining the operator's internal records. Referred to as joint interest audits, these examinations are authorized by the accounting procedure exhibit of the JOA. Most JOAs define the audit period as the current year and prior two years. COPAS Accounting Guideline No. 19 (AG-19) offers additional guidance about joint interest audit protocol and procedures.

Generally, the nonoperator with the largest working interest initiates the audit, contacts the operator, and plans and executes the work. The nonoperator appoints an experienced person, within or outside the company, as the lead auditor. He or she alerts the operator of the desire to audit the records, requests the necessary documents and decides on the timing of the audit.

The lead auditor prepares a confirmation letter to the operator including: (1) names and addresses of all working interest owners, (2) properties to be addressed in the audit, (3) on-site visitation dates and estimated number of participating auditors, (4) time period that will be audited, (5) arrangements to access pertinent original records and (6) a description of records requested in advance.

The operator's original records generally include:

- Chart of accounts and organizational charts.

- Field schematic.

- Drilling contracts and permits.

- Daily drilling, tour, cementing, completion, mud, chemical, bit usage and plugging and abandonment reports.

- Casing specifications.

- Journal vouchers with backup.

- Material transfers.

- All pertinent records from the operations department.

The lead auditor prepares and sends a ballot letter to the nonoperators, informing them of the operator's consent to the audit. The letter includes pertinent information, such as the date of the audit, the properties to be audited, and the estimated cost and completion time. The auditor asks nonoperators to agree to the audit and either share in the costs or send their own auditors. The letter also includes a date on which the nonoperators' agreements should be returned to the lead auditor.

In planning an audit, the lead auditor assesses the risk, asking questions such as:

- Has the nonoperator had previous associations with the operator? If not, what is the reputation of the operator?

- Has a previous audit been completed? If so, what were the results?

- How many properties should be audited?

- What types of expenditures should be examined?

- What amount of billed expenditure is too small to evaluate?

- Has the lead auditor's management requested the audit of specific wells?

The lead auditor prepares the audit program, coordinates the work and supervises the staff. He or she communicates with all parties about audit findings, the operator's response, follow-up, the billing of audit costs and any other issues. The lead auditor should ensure that as much work as possible is completed upfront before reaching the operator's office. These procedures can include: reading the daily drilling reports to get a history of the properties; reviewing the information contained in any previous audit reports and files; and preparing any lead schedules, with information from the operations department or Joint Audit Data Exchange (JADE), an electronic file of the cost-detail transactions related to all the properties being audited.

When the audit is complete, the lead auditor presents the findings to the operator, prepares an audit report, identifies the exceptions (either for or against the operator), distributes the audit report to members of the audit team, nonoperators and the operator, follows up on the resolution of open issues and writes a final closure letter.

The general steps for a joint interest audit are summarized in Figure 10-5. COPAS AG-19 includes example forms of the required letters and reports.

Figure 10-5
General steps for a joint interest audit

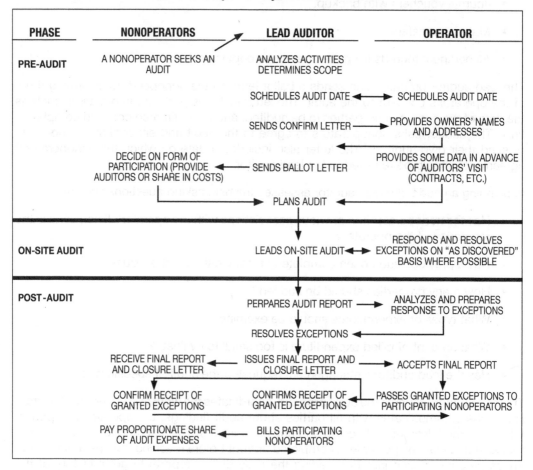

Electronic data interchange

Joint interest operations require oil and gas companies to exchange huge quantities of operating and accounting data. In its early years, the industry compiled, classified and disseminated this information manually. Computer technology later allowed individual companies to develop software programs for accumulating data and preparing reports. However, companies receiving the data would have to enter the information in their own accounting and data systems. Later, some companies adopted the practice of providing computer tapes to interested parties.

Electronic data interchange (EDI) has simplified the problem of information transmittal and receipt in joint operations, and in accounting for other transactions between companies, such as the exchange of petroleum products.

Through the initiative of COPAS members and others, computer programs now facilitate data accumulation, transmittal and receipt. General Electric Information Services' EDI systems may be the best known of these programs. Participating companies retain their in-house coding systems. Before it is transferred to other companies, data is converted to standard codes and formats for transmission. At the receiving end, the data is converted to the company's in-house codes and formats.

Among the most important parts of this exchange are the following:

- **CODE (Crude Oil Data Exchange).** Provides field formats and record layouts to facilitate the transmission of crude oil run tickets, run statements and tank increment records between oil producers and oil transporters.

- **CDEX (Check Stub Data Exchange).** Automates the collection and distribution of check-detail information about jointly owned oil and gas properties.

- **GRADE (Gas Revenue Accounting Data Exchange).** Records information about natural gas and NGL metered volumes, allocated volumes, tests and plant settlement.

- **PETROEX (Petroleum Product Exchange).** Prepares bills of lading and bulk-custody information on product exchange transactions.

- **RECONART (Exchange Reconciliation System).** Produces a record of unmatched exchange transactions on a contract and product basis.

- **TABS (Terminal Administration and Billing System).** Authorizes credit and product at exchange terminals and captures bill of lading information.

- **JADE (Joint Audit Data Exchange).** Compiles information for review and verification of a joint venture operator's source documents. This system helps reduce the audit time required by auditors and the operator's support staff.

- **JIBE (Joint Interest Billing Exchange).** Enables the electronic transmission of monthly joint interest billing statements and invoices to other working interest owners.

● ● ●

Production and Volume Measurement

Key concepts

- Bringing production online

- Gas injection

- Measuring oil volumes

- Measuring gas volumes

- Measuring NGL volumes

- Gas processing

The ultimate objective of oil and gas operations is to produce and sell hydrocarbons for a profit. As such, it is important for petroleum accountants to understand the procedures used to measure, process, market, deliver and ultimately account for these products. Many industry terms related to production and volume measurement appear in this chapter, but keep in mind that the use of terms can vary among petroleum accountants, engineers and other industry participants. Related topics dovetail with this chapter, while Chapter 12 describes the accounting for oil, natural gas and NGL sales.

Bringing production online

After a well is completed, it is placed on production by installing surface equipment. Figure 11-1 illustrates typical surface equipment used in the following processes related to oil and gas production:

- Collecting and gathering the produced emulsion of oil, gas and water from the well.

- Separating the oil, gas and water.

- Treating the oil and gas to minimize any remaining impurities and bringing them to marketable condition.

- Storing the oil briefly prior to sale, which further removes impurities.

- Measuring the volumes produced and sold.

- Facilitating the removal of oil, gas and water.

Several transportation modes are used when a well begins producing. Oil is carried by crude pipelines, barges or trucks; natural gas typically is transported by gas pipelines. Onshore, produced water from the site is treated and injected into underground reservoirs using commercial saltwater disposal wells. Offshore, saltwater is typically released into the ocean.

To collect and gather the oil, gas and water produced from a field, an E&P company connects wellheads to pipes called flow lines which usually are buried beneath the surface. A gathering system refers to any system of pipes installed over a wide area to gather oil and gas from wells and fields for delivery to a major pipeline or processing plant. Accordingly, the collection of flow lines is referred to as a "gathering system" or network which leads to various surface equipment.

Although a well may be classified as an oil well or a gas well, few reservoirs produce only one product. Individual products often must be separated and treated to remove impurities such as sediment, water or water vapor before the product is transferred from the field. Most pipelines and refineries require that: (1) the content of crude oil contains less than one percent basic sediment and water (BS&W) and (2) the content of natural gas contains no more than seven pounds of water vapor per MMcf.

The oil and gas mixture is directed through an enclosed steel cylindrical or spherical piece of equipment called a separator. Gravity, and sometimes centrifugal force, separates the gas from any liquids. Oil and gas flow through the separator in a one to six minute process, depending on the oil density. Gas, which is lighter than liquids, travels through an outlet at the top of the separator and liquids escape through lower outlets.

Figure 11-1

Schematic of lease production facilities

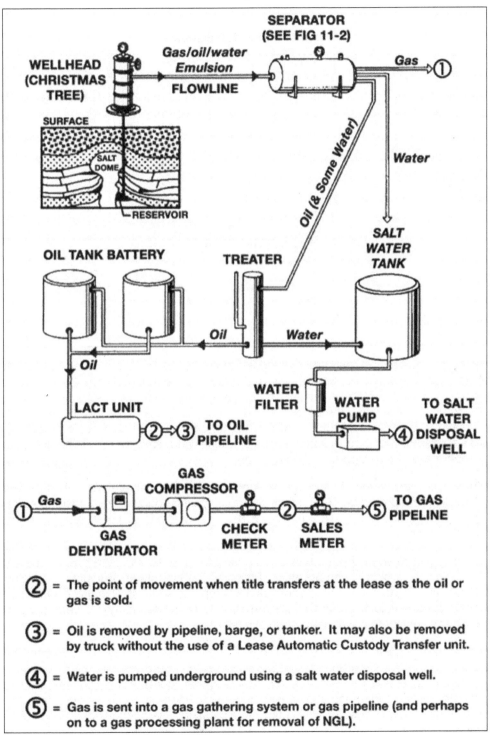

② = The point of movement when title transfers at the lease as the oil or gas is sold.

③ = Oil is removed by pipeline, barge, or tanker. It may also be removed by truck without the use of a Lease Automatic Custody Transfer unit.

④ = Water is pumped underground using a salt water disposal well.

⑤ = Gas is sent into a gas gathering system or gas pipeline (and perhaps on to a gas processing plant for removal of NGL).

Two-phase separators split gas from liquids, while three-phase separators divide oil, gas and water streams. A horizontal three-phase separator is illustrated in Figure 11-2 below.

Figure 11-2

Horizontal three-phase separator

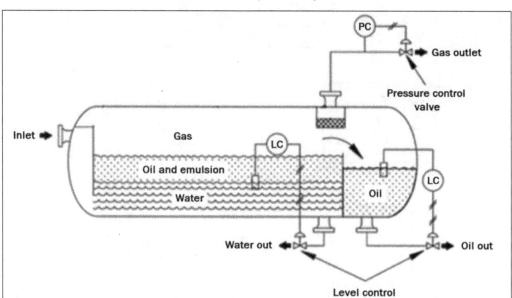

When oil droplets are trapped and suspended in water, the mixture is called "oil-in-water emulsion." When water droplets are trapped and suspended in oil, the mixture is called "reverse emulsion." Both mixtures are treated with demulsifying chemicals and heated to assist gravity in separating the products. A more sophisticated separator (heater treater) can break these emulsions. Another type of treater employs an electrostatic process that applies an electrical charge, instead of heat, to cause water to settle out of the oil. Treaters also separate any gas trapped in the emulsion.

"Stage separation" refers to the process of passing the mixture through separators before selling the products. Three-stage and four-stage separation refers to the number of times the mixture is passed through, at decreasing levels of pressure, to maximize product recovery.

Lease use gas refers to the portion of gas used on a lease as fuel for heater treaters, dehydration units or gas compressors. Typically, the last stage of separation yields a small quantity of gas that is not economical to compress and sell. This gas may be flared if there is enough volume to maintain a constant flame. If not, the gas is vented into the atmosphere, subject to government regulations.

Water and impurities must be removed from natural gas before it will be accepted by a pipeline. Field processing depends on the composition of the gas. Dehydration removes water vapor via several methods: heating, adding drying agents, adding antifreeze agents, expanding the gas and refrigerating it with heat exchangers, or using a glycol dehydrator that works on the principle of absorption and pressure. Gas conditioning (sweetening) removes impurities, such as carbon dioxide (CO_2) and hydrogen sulphide (H_2S), using additives, heat and filters.

Crude oil is transferred from a lease by pipeline, truck, barge or rail tank car to a refinery or an intermediate oil purchaser. For oil delivered into a pipeline, the product may be measured by a lease automatic custody transfer (LACT) unit. This equipment automatically measures, samples and tests the oil, and either returns it for additional treatment or routes it into the pipeline. In place of a LACT unit, some operators may gauge their stock tanks manually, test and measure samples and calculate volumes delivered.

Natural gas is transferred from a lease through a gas meter used for measurement. The product may move to a regional gas-gathering system or directly into an intrastate or interstate gas pipeline.

Gas meters typically are owned by gas purchasers and are referred to as sales meters. Not as accurate or dependable as those used for crude oil, the meters must be recalibrated frequently. Lease operators often install another unit, a check meter, on the pipeline immediately in front of the sales meter, to compare the volumes measured. Contracts usually specify that differences greater than two to five percent are cause for recalibration.

If necessary or economical, gas in the gathering system or pipeline is sent to a gas processing plant for removal of NGLs such as ethane, propane, butane and natural gasolines. Gas processing is described in more detail later in this chapter.

Gas moves through a pipeline because it is under pressure. Gas compressors can be installed to further compress the gas and push it through the pipeline more effectively. Compressors are powered by gas turbines, steam turbines, electric motors or gasoline engines, and compressor stations often are situated every 40 to 50 miles along the pipeline system.

When reservoir pressure is sufficiently high, it pushes produced gas into the gas gathering or pipeline system. In the later stages of a field's productive life, pressure typically will decline and gas compressors may be added at the lease site to enhance delivery of the product.

Gas injection

Gas produced from a reservoir is reinjected into the reservoir when: (1) it will increase the ultimate recovery of oil or condensate or (2) there is no economic market for it. Reinjection typically improves production of the more valuable oil or condensate. Also, the reinjected gas may be produced and sold in the future if economics permit.[1] See Chapter 12 for the accounting related to gas reinjection.

Pressure maintenance in oil reservoirs

In some situations, the ultimate recovery of oil can be increased by maintaining the reservoir pressure above the "bubble point" (the pressure below which gas bubbles out of the liquid). At pressures above the bubble point, all gas molecules stay dissolved and in solution with the crude oil. However, at pressures below the bubble point, gas bubbles begin to break out of the solution and rise to the highest part of the reservoir, forming a secondary gas cap. As the gas escapes, the viscosity of the crude oil increases, which decreases its mobility and ultimate recovery.

Large capital expenditures are required to install the equipment necessary for reinjecting gas. Furthermore, revenues from gas sales are delayed until most of the recoverable oil reserves have been produced. Data from geologists, engineers and financial analysts help determine the merits of a gas injection project to increase ultimate oil recovery.

Artificial gas lift

In an artificial gas lift, gas is injected into an oil well (not the reservoir) between the tubing and casing. Pressure from the injected gas opens a valve in the tubing string, near the bottom of the well, allowing the gas to combine with the crude oil in the tubing. This action lifts oil from the bottom of the well to the surface. Similar pressure-sensitive valves may be installed at selected points along the tubing string to help lift the gas.

Pressure maintenance in gas condensate reservoirs

The ultimate recovery of condensate can also be increased by maintaining reservoir pressure above the dew point. At this pressure, all gas and condensate exist as a single solution. At pressures below the dew point, liquid drops of condensate begin to form and fall out of the solution. Some drops stick to the walls of the subsurface formation, while others fill the pore space around each wellbore. Liquid condensate does not flow through the rock as easily as gas; therefore, a drop in reservoir pressure below the dew point decreases the amount of condensate that can flow to the wellbore and restricts the flow of gas through the reservoir. Reservoirs with these characteristics often are called "retrograde condensate reservoirs."

In a gas cycling operation, lean gas (the resulting gas stream after it has passed through separators and condensate has been removed) is reinjected into the reservoir, where it maintains pressure, absorbs condensate, and ultimately is produced, processed and reinjected. Gas cycling operations are illustrated in Figure 11-3 below.

Figure 11-3
Gas cycling operations

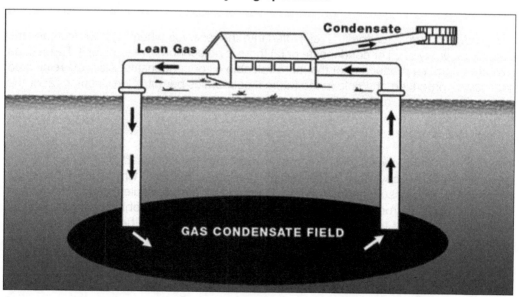

When injection of lean gas no longer contributes to increased liquid recovery from a reservoir, gas injection is discontinued and future produced gas is sold after processing. At that point, the reservoir is said to be in a blowdown phase.

For pressure maintenance of either oil reservoirs or retrograde condensate reservoirs, the injected gas may be part or all of a field's production, or it may be purchased from other sources.

Measuring oil volumes

An important step in revenue accounting is determining the volume and quality of the oil and condensate that are produced and sold. The physical activities of taking readings, testing and measuring are performed by the purchaser and company field personnel. However, revenue accountants must know and understand these procedures to ensure they are applied and accounted for correctly.

Appropriate internal controls are necessary because inaccurate measurements of volume or quality can result in lost revenue. The American Petroleum Institute (API) has issued numerous production and measurement standards; a revenue accountant should apply these procedures and ensure compliance by field personnel and purchaser representatives.

Oil volumes produced and sold

Oil is measured by one of two methods: (1) manually by gauged tank levels when the product is moved by pipeline, truck, barge or rail tank car to a purchaser or refinery or (2) automatically by a LACT unit when the product flows into the purchaser's pipeline.

Manual measurement. Manually measuring the oil volumes sold from a stock tank requires three steps:

- Obtaining volume measurements of an empty stock tank to determine the amount of oil that can be stored at various tank levels.

- Measuring the levels of oil in the tank before and after oil is removed.

- Converting measured oil levels to oil volumes to compute the reduction of oil volume in the tank.

Before a new tank battery is activated, each empty tank is "strapped," that is, the tank dimensions are measured to determine the fluid volume for any given fluid level. The tank normally is measured by an employee of the tank vendor (tank strapper) at four or five key points, according to industry standards. Measurements are witnessed by a representative of the producer and are recorded on a tank strapping report, signed by both the tank company employee and the producer's representative.

The strapping report is sent to an independent tank engineer, who computes the volume of oil contained in each interval of tank height (usually one inch). Although tanks are manufactured to uniform dimensions, they tend to bulge outward in the middle. In a large tank, a slight bulge can account for several barrels of oil.

The standard unit of measurement of crude oil known as a stock tank barrel (STB) is 42 gallons of marketable crude oil held at a temperature of 60 degrees Fahrenheit (°F) and at atmospheric pressure. Tank capacity is recorded on a table, where each one-fourth inch from the bottom to the top is associated with a specific volume of oil.

A portion of an illustrative tank table is shown in Figure 11-4. Volumes for each one-quarter inch from 1 foot to 1 foot 10-¾ inches and from 6 feet to 6 feet 10-¾ inches are illustrated.

The table in Figure 11-4 indicates that if the level of liquid is 1 foot 4 inches, the volume is 86.48 barrels; at 6 feet 10 inches, the liquid volume is 442.92 barrels. If the tank level is 6 feet 10 inches, and liquid is removed, lowering the level to 1 foot 4 inches, the volume of the removed liquid is 442.92 less 86.48, or 356.44 barrels (unadjusted for temperature or gravity).

A tank table (or its equivalent table of tank increment factors) is a basic reference source for calculating the volume of oil produced into or delivered from a lease tank. Tank tables are stored as computer files for fast and accurate conversion of tank levels into volumes produced or sold.

A gauger is a person, usually the oil purchaser's representative, who measures the quantity and quality of products produced from the lease. The term pumper refers to the producing company's employee (or contractor) who operates and maintains equipment on the lease.

The pumper is responsible for an E&P company's testing, gauging and initial recording of volumes produced and sold. Visiting the lease site daily, the pumper gauges the tank and records the results on a pumper's report, sometimes called a gauge sheet. This operational report acts as a check against the purchaser's run ticket, the receipt generated at the point of delivery. The pumper has the right and responsibility to witness the gauger's testing and measurement of the oil. An E&P company does not typically expect the pumper to witness all of the gauger's activity but may require that the pumper reconcile the run ticket data to the crude oil levels noted on the pumper's report.

Immediately before running a tank of oil (i.e., moving the oil) into the pipeline, truck or railcar, the oil purchaser's representative, observed by the oil producer's representative, measures the top level of the oil (opening gauge). This is performed with a steel measuring tape (gauge tape), which is weighted with a brass plumb bob or gauge bob.

A device known as a thief permits the extraction of oil from any desired level in the tank. In a test called a "shakeout," oil samples are taken from several intervals just above and below the pipeline connection. These samples determine if the BS&W content of the oil is low enough, typically less than one percent.

The samples are deposited in glass tubes and spun in a centrifuge, causing BS&W to settle to the bottom of the tube. This allows the representative to determine the BS&W content from marked gradations on the tube. If the tank contains too much BS&W, the measurements will indicate how much of it must be drained from the tank, thereby lowering the oil which can be sold to the level of the pipeline connection.

Figure 11-4

Illustrative tank table*

BARRELS (42 Gallons)										DISTRICT:	COVINGTON
FEET PER ONE-QUARTER INCH										OWNER:	KT OIL
STRAPPED										LEASE:	SANDY
BY: J. SARTWELLE		FOR: KT OIL			P.L.			TANK No.	20-9
BY:		FOR:		OLD No.		CONN.			

1			2		3		4		5		6			7		8	
1	64	86									6	388	95				
¼	66	21									¼	390	30				
½	67	56									½	391	65				
¾	68	91									¾	393	00				
1	70	26									1	394	35				
¼	71	61									¼	395	70				
½	72	97									½	397	05				
¾	74	32									¾	398	40				
2	75	67									2	399	75				
¼	77	02									¼	401	09				
½	78	37									½	402	44				
¾	79	72									¾	403	79				
3	81	07									3	405	14				
¼	82	42									¼	406	49				
½	83	78									½	407	84				
¾	85	13									¾	409	19				
4	86	48									4	410	54				
¼	87	83									¼	411	89				
½	89	18									½	413	24				
¾	90	53									¾	414	59				
5	91	88									5	415	94				
¼	93	23									¼	417	29				
½	94	58									½	418	64				
¾	95	94									¾	419	99				
6	97	29									6	421	33				
¼	98	64									¼	422	68				
½	99	99									½	424	03				
¾	101	34									¾	425	38				
7	102	69									7	426	73				
¼	104	04									¼	428	08				
½	105	39									½	429	43				
¾	106	75									¾	430	78				
8	108	10									8	432	13				
¼	109	45									¼	433	48				
½	110	80									½	434	83				
¾	112	15									¾	436	18				
9	113	50									9	437	53				
¼	114	85									¼	438	88				
½	116	20									½	440	22				
¾	117	56									¾	441	57				
10	118	91									10	442	92				
¼	120	26									¼	444	27				
½	121	61									½	445	62				
¾	122	96									¾	446	97				

* Values for all but two columns have been omitted to simplify the use of this table in the chapter.

Automatic measurement. The LACT unit was an important development in automating oil field functions, as it performs the following critical tasks related to measuring oil volumes:

- Meters oil.

- Records temperatures.

- Takes and stores oil samples at predetermined intervals for later gravity determination.

- Measures BS&W content.

- Diverts the oil back through the treating system if BS&W is too high.

- Directs the oil into the pipeline and shuts off the valves after the oil enters.

If the unit malfunctions, it shuts down, and an alarm sounds in the field office so that personnel can investigate and correct the malfunction.

When a LACT unit records the sale of oil into a pipeline, a meter measures the volume of oil from the unit's dump tank (also called the metering tank or surge tank). The dump tank is not strapped; therefore, there are no tank tables or increment factor sheets. Instead, the LACT meter must be proved regularly to verify its accuracy. The meter proving report supplies an accuracy factor, which is applied to the difference between the opening and closing meter readings to calculate the true gross barrels that entered the pipeline.

All measurements and other data are recorded on a meter ticket for production and accounting records. Depending on the software used, gravity and temperature adjustments may be calculated automatically by the unit, eliminating staff time.

If oil purchasers use computer software to calculate the volume of oil, the tank table is supplemented by a table of tank increment factors. Figure 11-5 lists the barrels of oil per one-quarter inch between each level of the tank.

Run tickets. The run ticket is a legal document on which the gauger, witnessed by the pumper, records the information necessary to establish the correct price and STB volume of the oil removed, including:

- Specific location or tank, which indicates the first two pricing factors: geographic location and type of oil based on sulfur content.

- Date of removal or sale, which is the third pricing factor.

- Observed API gravity and the corresponding observed temperature of the oil sample so it can be corrected to API gravity at 60°F, the fourth pricing factor and a secondary factor in determining STB volume.

- Tank level of oil just prior to oil removal and corresponding crude oil temperature.

- Tank level of oil just after oil removal and corresponding crude oil temperature.

- BS&W content of the oil removed.

Figure 11-5

Figure 11-5

Illustrative table of tank increment factors

13-350-S	**ABC PETROLEUM COMPANY** **INCREMENT FACTOR SHEET**

District ____Newgulf____

Tank Number ____19127____

Date of Table ____December 15, 2019____

Operator Name ____ABC Petroleum Co.____

Pipe Line Company _____

Lease Name _____

Lease No. ____17-583____   Pipe Line Code _____   Gauger District _____

Truck Code _____   State Code _____   Tax Code _____   Price Code _____

Tank Strapped By: _____

No.	INCREMENT		VERTICAL COMPONENTS				Volume in Barrels Per Vertical Component	No. of QTR. INCHES	
	(Use 5 Decimals) Barrels per ¼ Inch		From Feet	To				From	To
	1	.34600	0	0	0	8	43.07200		
	1	.15791	0	8	0	10	9.26328		
	1	.34891	0	10	3	0	140.28664		
	1	.34605	3	0	6	0	193.83120		
	1	.34106	6	0	7	9	112.64904		
				Unadjusted Tank Capacity			499.10216		
				Correction Factor and Cone Capacity			0.00931		
				Total Adjusted Tank Capacity			499.11147		

Tank levels determine gross oil volumes at the corresponding oil temperatures. Gross volumes are corrected to stock tank barrels at 60°F for the calculated API gravity at 60°F. Full correction includes volume reduction to exclude BS&W content. Figure 11-6 illustrates a run ticket that reflects the delivery of oil from the tank previously used to illustrate Figure 11-4.

The gauger measures the oil's API gravity with a hydrometer. Oil temperature is taken by lowering a thermometer into the oil in the tank.

Information recorded on the run ticket also includes the purchaser's name, lease owner's or operator's name, run ticket number, and signatures of the gauger and pumper.

Run tickets also have spaces for recording gravity adjusted to 60°F and the result of volume calculations. These calculations are not completed on the copy of the run ticket supplied to accounting, but instead are made by employees of the production department for their use in the control of operations and compliance. In most large companies, calculations are made with electronic data-processing equipment.

A run ticket generated by a LACT unit, or meter ticket, contains the meter readings for volumes, observed gravity and temperature, average line temperature (if the meter is not temperature compensated) and the BS&W.

API gravity at the observed temperature is corrected to API gravity at 60°F (true gravity or corrected gravity), using a gravity correction table. This table, partially reproduced in Figure 11-7, shows true gravity for each one-tenth degree of observed gravity. For example, if observed gravity is 23.2 degrees API, and observed temperature is 100°F, then the true (corrected) gravity is 20.9 degrees API at 60°F.

Determining the volume correction factor. To calculate volume at 60°F, the amount of observed volume at an observed temperature is multiplied by a volume correction factor. Volume correction is a function of the observed temperature and the oil's API gravity at 60°F. The appropriate factor is selected from a volume correction table, illustrated in Figure 11-8 for various temperatures from 50°F to 104°F and API gravities ranging from 20 to 29 degrees.

Computing the volume run

The steps for computing the standard barrels of oil run from a tank at 60°F are summarized herein and illustrated in Figure 11-9.

Step 1. The observed gravity at the observed temperature is corrected to the true gravity at 60°F. Observed gravity indicated on the run ticket in Figure 11-6 is 23.2 degrees API at 100°F. Referring to the gravity correction table in Figure 11-7, true gravity is determined to be 20.9 degrees API.

Step 2. The gross amount of fluid (oil and BS&W) in the tank before the run is determined by applying the first measurement to the proper tank table (Figure 11-4). The first measurement of oil level indicated on the run ticket is 6 feet, ½ inch, at 102°F. The tank table shows a gross volume of 391.65 barrels.

Step 3. Using the volume correction table in Figure 11-8, the volume obtained in Step 2 is corrected to the volume at 60°F. ABC Petroleum Co. rounds off the true gravity reading of 20.9 degrees API to the nearest whole number to arrive at an adjusted true gravity of 21 degrees API.[2] The volume correction table in Figure 11-8 shows that for gravity of 21 degrees API and an observed temperature of 102°F (the temperature for the first measurement of oil level from the run ticket), the volume correction factor to adjust the volume to 60°F is 0.9835. Multiplying this factor by the volume of 391.65 barrels on the first observed reading yields a corrected volume of 385.19 barrels.

Step 4. The gross amount of fluid remaining in the tank after the run is determined by applying the second measurement to the proper tank table. The second measurement indicated on the specimen run ticket is 1 foot 9-½ inches at a temperature of 86°F. The tank table in Figure 11-4 shows a gross volume of 116.20 barrels.

Step 5. The volume obtained in Step 4 is corrected to the volume at 60°F, as in Step 3. The true gravity is 20.9 degrees API, rounded to 21 degrees. The volume correction table in Figure 11-8 shows that for API gravity of 21 degrees at a temperature of 86°F, the reduction factor is 0.9898. Applying this factor to the volume of 116.20 barrels at the second measurement yields a corrected volume of 115.01 barrels.

Step 6. The net volume of the fluid run (oil and BS&W) is determined by subtracting the result obtained in Step 5 from that obtained in Step 3 (calculated as 385.19 barrels less 115.01 barrels, resulting in 270.18 barrels).

Step 7. The volume of the fluid run is adjusted for the BS&W content. Since the BS&W content indicated on the run ticket is 0.4 percent, the oil content of the volume run is 99.6 percent. Thus, the corrected net volume of oil sold at 20.9 degrees API gravity at 60°F is 269.10 stock tank barrels (calculated as 270.18 barrels x .996). For revenue determination, oil volume is measured to the hundredth barrel. For volume measurement, crude volume at the observed temperature is sometimes called the "gross volume," while the volume of stock tank barrels at the standard temperature is the "net volume." In accounting for an owner's share of 8/8ths production, the terms gross volume and net volume refer to 8/8ths production and an owner's net share of the 8/8ths production, respectively.

When crude oil is used for fuel or other operating or development purposes (either on the lease where produced or on another lease), the amount withdrawn from the tanks is recorded on a standard company run ticket. In this way, a business can properly account for lease revenue, expense and taxes. If the crude oil is subsequently recovered to complete a new well, for example, affidavits to that effect are supplied by production department personnel so that taxes are not paid twice.

Oil storage

Crude oil moves through the flow line and is stored in large steel storage tanks (stock tanks or flow tanks) until sold. The stock tank is counted as one of the stages in three- and four-stage separation because any remaining BS&W will settle to the bottom of the tank.

Depending on the type of crude oil produced, a large amount of natural gas may separate from the oil in the stock tanks, despite several stages of prior separation. Stock tanks may be connected to a vapor recovery system that collects the gas for sale, use on the lease or flaring. If there is enough gas to justify the cost of compressing it for movement to a gas pipeline, the gas may be sold.

Oil is transferred from the stock tanks through an outlet called a sales line, which is approximately one foot from the bottom of the tank. Because sediment and water settle to the bottom of the tank, placing the sales line just above the bottom of the tank ensures that the purchaser or transporter receives only sales-quality oil. Occasionally, residue below the sales line (i.e., tank bottom or bottom oil) is drained and reprocessed through the separators, or it may be sold separately. The lease operator uses metal seals with recorded serial numbers to close the outlet valve on the sales line. These seals are tracked by the lease operator and oil purchaser to safeguard against unauthorized movement of oil from the stock tanks.

Each lease normally maintains two or more stock tanks that can hold several days of oil production. The tanks are connected by flow lines in a tank battery. They are equipped with inlets and valves to control the flow of the oil into and between the tanks. Oil that has been processed through the separators fills one stock tank; a valve is closed to isolate the other tank. This allows the oil to be measured and drained into a pipeline, truck or barge.

Figure 11-6

Pipeline run ticket

OPERATOR (OR FIELD LOCATION)	**ABC Petroleum Co.**			
LEASE OR COMPANY NAME **24001**			Delivery	Receipt **X**
FOR ACCOUNT OF			Crude Grade or Product	
CONSIGNEE (if delivered to connecting carrier)			Reid Vapor Pressure	
CREDIT				

MOVED BY			TO (line or station)	
Pump Gravity	Truck **X**		**XYZ Pipeline Co.**	

TANK SIZE **500**	POWER FURNISHED BY OR TRUCKED BY		

MO. 12	DAY **15**	YR. **2019**	DISTRICT NO.	TICKET NO. **0512**
TANK OR METER NO. **2401**	OFFICE CODES			LEASE NO.

	OIL LEVEL					CALCULATIONS OR REMARKS
GAUGE	FT.	IN.	FRACT	TEMP		
1st	6	0	1/2	102		
2nd	1	9	1/2	86		
OBS. GTY. & TEMP. 23.2 | 100°F		TRUE GRAVITY				
CODES		BS & W				
POWER	TRUCK		0.4%			

METER				
TRANSACTION NO.	PRINTING HEAD NO.	Barrels	Gallons	10ths
OFF				
ON				
AVG. METER PRESS psi	METER FACTOR	METERED BARRELS		
TEMPERATURE COMPENSATED? Yes No		AVG. LINE TEMP °F	COMPRESSIBILITY FACTOR	NET BARRELS

ON	GAUGER **Ernest Hobbs**			TIME **7:00 AM**	
	OPERATOR'S WITNESS OR WAIVER NO. **Terry Roundtree**			SEAL OFF **83661**	
OFF	GAUGER **Ernest Hobbs**			TIME **8:10 AM**	DATE **12/15/2019**
	OPERATOR'S WITNESS OR WAIVER NO. **Terry Roundtree**			SEAL ON **84471**	

Figure 11-7

Gravity correction table

For Observed Temperature of 100 to 114°F	API Gravity at 60°F								
	23.0	23.1	23.2	23.3	23.4	23.5	23.6	23.7	23.8
	Factor for API Observed Gravity of 23.0 – 23.8								
100	20.7	20.8	20.9	21.0	21.1	21.2	21.2	21.3	21.4
101	20.6	20.7	20.8	20.9	21.0	21.1	21.2	21.3	21.4
102	20.5	20.6	20.7	20.8	20.9	21.0	21.1	21.2	21.3
103	20.5	20.6	20.7	20.8	20.9	21.0	21.1	21.2	21.3
104	20.4	20.5	20.6	20.7	20.8	20.9	21.0	21.1	21.2
105	20.4	20.5	20.6	20.7	20.8	20.9	20.9	21.0	21.1
106	20.3	20.4	20.5	20.6	20.7	20.8	20.9	21.0	21.1
107	20.3	20.4	20.5	20.6	20.7	20.8	20.8	20.9	21.0
108	20.2	20.3	20.4	20.5	20.6	20.7	20.8	20.9	21.0
109	20.2	20.3	20.4	20.5	20.6	20.7	20.7	20.8	20.9
110	20.1	20.2	20.3	20.4	20.5	20.6	20.7	20.8	20.9
111	20.0	20.1	20.2	20.3	20.4	20.5	20.6	20.7	20.8
112	20.0	20.1	20.2	20.3	20.4	20.5	20.5	20.6	20.7
113	19.9	20.0	20.1	20.2	20.3	20.4	20.5	20.6	20.7
114	19.9	20.0	20.1	20.2	20.3	20.4	20.4	20.5	20.6

Figure 11-8

Volume correction table

ASTM-IP   20 – 29 degrees API 50 – 104°F

Observed Temperature, °F	API Gravity at 60°F									
	20	21	22	23	24	25	26	27	28	29
	Factor for Correcting Volume at 60°F									
50	1.0039	1.0040	1.0040	1.0040	1.0040	1.0041	1.0041	1.0041	1.0042	1.0042
51	1.0035	1.0036	1.0036	1.0036	1.0036	1.0037	1.0037	1.0037	1.0038	1.0038
52	1.0031	1.0032	1.0032	1.0032	1.0032	1.0033	1.0033	1.0033	1.0033	1.0034
53	1.0028	1.0028	1.0028	1.0028	1.0028	1.0029	1.0029	1.0029	1.0029	1.0029
54	1.0024	1.0024	1.0024	1.0024	1.0024	1.0024	1.0025	1.0025	1.0025	1.0025
85	0.9902	0.9902	0.9901	0.9900	0.9899	0.9899	0.9898	0.9897	0.9896	0.9895
86	0.9898	0.9898	0.9897	0.9896	0.9895	0.9895	0.9894	0.9893	0.9892	0.9891
87	0.9895	0.9894	0.9893	0.9892	0.9891	0.9891	0.9890	0.9889	0.9888	0.9887
88	0.9891	0.9890	0.9889	0.9888	0.9887	0.9887	0.9886	0.9885	0.9884	0.9883
89	0.9887	0.9886	0.9885	0.9884	0.9883	0.9883	0.9882	0.9881	0.9879	0.9878
100	0.9844	0.9843	0.9842	0.9841	0.9839	0.9838	0.9837	0.9835	0.9834	0.9832
101	0.9840	0.9839	0.9838	0.9837	0.9835	0.9834	0.9833	0.9831	0.9830	0.9828
102	0.9836	0.9835	0.9834	0.9833	0.9831	0.9830	0.9829	0.9827	0.9826	0.9824
103	0.9833	0.9831	0.9830	0.9829	0.9827	0.9826	0.9825	0.9823	0.9822	0.9820
104	0.9829	0.9827	0.9826	0.9825	0.9823	0.9822	0.9821	0.9819	0.9817	0.9816

Figure 11-9

Figure 11-9
Computing the volume run

	Example	
	Amount	**Source**
Per run ticket from the field		
Observed gravity of sample	23.2	Figure 11-6, Pipeline run ticket
Observed temperature of sample	100°F	Figure 11-6
1st gauge height	6' ½"	Figure 11-6
1st gauge temperature	102°F	Figure 11-6
2nd gauge height	1' 9-½"	Figure 11-6
2nd gauge temperature	86°F	Figure 11-6
BS&W content	0.4%	Figure 11-6
Production department's calculations		
Step 1. Correct to "true gravity" at 60°F	20.9	Figure 11-7, Gravity correction table
Step 2. Determine "opening" fluid volume	391.65	Figure 11-4, Illustrative tank table
Step 3. Correct to barrels at 60°F	385.19	Figure 11-8, Volume correction table
Step 4. Determine fluid volume left in tank	116.20	Figure 11-4
Step 5. Correct to barrels at 60°F	115.01	Figure 11-8
Step 6. Determine net fluid barrels removed	270.18	= 385.19 − 115.01
Step 7. Adjust barrels to exclude BS&W*	269.10	= 270.18 x 99.6%

*(i.e., 269.10 barrels of 20.9 API gravity crude sold)

Related monthly processes

a. Accumulate adjusted volumes by tank

b. Compare accumulated total to purchaser's run statement

c. Allocate sales volumes to wells

d. Prepare production and sales reports for government agencies and internal controls

U.S. demand for crude oil historically has exceeded U.S. production capacity and minimized the need for field storage. Therefore, crude oil inventories for most companies consist of insignificant amounts of unsold oil in field tank batteries. Tank capacities vary according to a field's early production rates and distance from pipelines. Inventory volume does not vary significantly from quarter to quarter. For this reason, many companies do not record crude oil inventory on their balance sheets.

In the U.S., the only substantial underground crude oil storage is the Strategic Petroleum Reserve (SPR). As mentioned in Chapter 1, in 1977 the U.S. government began storing crude oil in underground leached salt caverns in the Gulf Coast area, Michigan and New York to prevent a major supply disruption such as an abrupt decrease in foreign imports. Approximately 645 million barrels of crude oil were in storage as of October 2019, which is approximately 89 percent of the SPR's current capacity.[3]

Oil prices

In the U.S., crude oil sells at a price per barrel based on a posted price bulletin and tank barrel volume. Prices vary according to:

- Geographic location.

- General degree of sulfur content.

- Date of sale.

- Oil density, measured in degrees of API gravity, at 60°F.[4]

The first two factors, geographic location and sulfur content, are expressed in the price bulletin as a type or name of crude oil, such as West Texas Intermediate or Louisiana Light Sweet and do not change for a given reservoir. Sulfur is a contaminant not typically removed from oil at a lease and it is expensive to remove at a refinery. Thus, crude oil with a higher sulfur content sells for less money. Sulfur content is expressed in three degrees or classes: (1) sweet crude, generally with less than 0.6 percent sulfur by weight, (2) intermediate crude, generally with sulfur content between 0.6 percent and 1.7 percent and (3) sour crude, generally with more than 1.7 percent sulfur.[5]

Posted prices vary by date of sale for several reasons, such as changes in the global and national prices of crude oil and refined products, as well as changes in local supply and demand.

The density of crude oil affects the cost for refining it into valuable products such as gasoline. Heavy crude oil has more mass, but less value per barrel. Light crude oils, with high API gravities, command higher selling prices because they will produce a greater proportion of gasoline without the necessity for expensive refining techniques to break the long, heavy hydrocarbon molecules into the smaller, lighter molecules found in gasoline.[6]

Measuring gas volumes

Natural gas is an important energy resource for the U.S. economy. The U.S. Energy Information Administration forecasts that the U.S. will remain the world's largest natural gas producer throughout the projection period, reaching 43 trillion cubic feet in 2050, with shale resources production continuing to expand in the Appalachian region and in tight oil formations in and around Texas.[6]

To determine the quantity of gas that changes ownership when a sale occurs, the unit of measurement must be specified and the volume calculated according to terms in the gas sales contract.

Gas volumes produced and sold

As mentioned in Chapter 1, natural gas is measured in two ways: by volume and by heat content. The standard volume unit of measure in the U.S. is Mcf, which is the amount of gas expressed in thousand cubic feet at standard atmospheric pressure and temperature.

Residue gas (dry gas) is more than 90 percent methane, with a heat content of about one MMBtu per Mcf at atmospheric pressure. Residue gas volume and heat content are much less than that of corresponding wet gas delivered to the plant. Shrinkage during processing from plant-volume reduction (PVR) and plant-thermal reduction (PTR) results primarily from: (1) using gas as fuel to operate the plant, (2) extracting the NGLs and impurities and (3) plant losses and meter differences due to inaccurate measurements of gas volumes in normal operations. Extraction loss is greater for a gas stream with a high liquid content than for one containing less liquid. This shrinkage factor is considered when determining each lease's share of NGLs and residue gas produced by the plant.

The total volume of residue gas that remains after processing is the sum of residue gas volumes actually delivered from the plant to producers and gas purchasers. This volume, when multiplied by the Btu content of the residue gas, is allocated among the leases or wells according to their respective volumes of theoretical residue gas, using a factor that represents the liquid and extraction loss.

Plant personnel record the products delivered to the plant through inlet meters and the products delivered from the plant through outlet meters. They also report volumes produced and sold. If any inventories of NGLs, or the combined products in the gas stream, remain at the plant, plant personnel maintain inventory records as well. These metering systems and records should be accurate and available for audits by producers and purchasers.

Pressure bases. The standard pressure bases used by the industry for gas volume reporting are approximately sea-level atmospheric pressures of 14.65, 14.73 and 15.025 pounds per square inch absolute (psia). When arriving at contract settlements or filing state and federal production reports, accountants must determine which pressure base is required. Most federal government reports use 14.73 psia. Some state reporting requires 14.65 psia (Texas, Oklahoma) or 15.025 psia (Louisiana). The standard temperature used by all is 60°F.

The heat content measurement, called a British thermal unit or "Btu," is defined as the heat necessary to raise the temperature of one pound of water by one degree Fahrenheit. Historically, many gas sales contracts were priced by Mcf. Most contracts now express prices in terms of one million British thermal units, or MMBtu. Prices are independent of gas temperature or pressure. Some contracts, particularly with utility companies, are expressed in decatherms, which equal one MMBtu.

The Btu content (energy) in a volume of gas does not change with a pressure base change. Therefore, the total Btu determined at one pressure base is equal to the total Btu determined or reported at another pressure base.

Most companies record gas produced in Mcf, which makes it easier to analyze reserves. Most state and federal regulatory agencies require reports in Mcf. The U.S. is the only market that does not use the metric system to measure volumes.

When gas quantities are expressed in volume, but the price initially is expressed in heat content (MMBtu), the price per MMBtu must be converted to the price per Mcf by multiplying the price per MMBtu by the heating value (Btu) of a unit of gas volume (Mcf). For example, if the price is $2 per MMBtu, and the Btu content is 1.1000 MMBtu per one Mcf at 14.73 psia, then the price per Mcf at 14.73 psia is $2.10 ($2 multiplied by 1.1000). For proper comparison, both the Btu content of the gas and the Mcf must be measured using the same pressure base.

To convert gas volumes to MMBtu, the volumes expressed in Mcf are multiplied by the Btu content per Mcf, adjusting for any differences in pressure base. For example, if one Bcf (billion cubic feet) measured at 14.65 psia is sold, then the equivalent volumes sold at the higher pressure of 14.73 psia are smaller (i.e., one Bcf x (14.65 ÷ 14.73) equates to 0.9946 Bcf). If the Btu content per Mcf at 14.73 psia were 1.1000 MMBtu, then the MMBtu sold would be 994,600 Mcf multiplied by 1.1000 MMBtu per Mcf, or 1,094,060 MMBtu.

Volume measurement. Gas volumes are measured when gas flows through a meter that records temperature, pressure or other specific information needed. The oil and gas industry uses three types of meters: (1) turbine, (2) diaphragm positive displacement (the type used to measure most residential use) and (3) rotary gas displacement. However, metering technology is advancing: sophisticated electronic or ultrasonic metering systems are available now, especially for offshore development, where gas quantities are larger and meters are less accessible.

As described earlier, gas flows from wells, through pipelines, to a central facility for separation and processing. Sufficient residues are removed so the gas can continue to the purchaser, transporter or gas processing plant. For proper accounting records, volume readings are taken at both the wellhead and the central delivery facility.

Measurements also are recorded at the points where gas leaves or re-enters the pipeline or gathering system, such as to: (1) run lease equipment, (2) flare into the air, (3) process for NGL removal, (4) return from the processing plant or (5) inject into a reservoir. As with crude oil, a gas producer may install a check meter on the line downstream from the purchaser's or transporter's sales meter to verify and prove the accuracy of the sales meter. Alternatively, E&P company representatives may regularly witness sales-meter calibration by outside specialists.

Because of the complex nature of gas measurements, volume readings rarely agree, such that gas sales contracts typically specify an allowable percentage difference. If an audit of the gas measurement finds a difference larger than allowable, adjustments to recorded volumes may be required.

Gas plant settlement. As previously described, gas processing can be complex. Detailed calculations determine the volumes and proceeds of products sold, as well as products taken in kind. The gas settlement statement is a required schedule prepared by a gas plant accountant. The settlement statement verifies for each lease or well amounts for producers or other buyers, in-kind volumes, and volumes and prices of products sold.

Gas settlement statements provide detail for the gas producers' and buyers' accounting departments to record product sales. Such statements include:

- Property name.

- Actual residue gas and NGLs.

- Theoretical residue gas and NGLs.

- Volume of extraction and processing loss.

- Volumes sold.

- Gallons per thousand cubic feet of each product.

- Btu of the gas.

- Prices paid per product.

- Deductions taken by the plant owner.

- The total settlement amount for the property.

Allocating gas sales

The allocation of sales from multiple leases served by a central delivery facility is a complex procedure requiring several calculations. Used with permission, the following is an allocation example from Section 6 of COPAS Accounting Guideline No. 15.[7] Figure 11-10 is a gas flow schematic (also called a gas flowchart) that illustrates the flow of gas in this example.

In this example, Leases A, B and C contain oil wells that also produce gas. The gas emerges from oil production at separators installed at the lease. During the month, gas production was 11,000 Mcf, 13,000 Mcf and 17,000 Mcf, respectively, from the three oil leases. Leases D, E and F contain gas wells. Production measured at the wellhead was 25,000 Mcf, 22,000 Mcf and 28,000 Mcf, respectively. Based on gas tests from each well, the theoretical dry gas should be 96.0 percent, 93.2 percent and 92.9 percent of the production volume from the three leases, respectively. Thus, the total theoretical volume of dry gas from leases D, E and F is 70,500 Mcf (24,000 Mcf + 20,500 Mcf + 26,000 Mcf).

The gas well gas is passed through a central low temperature extraction (LTX) unit, which removes condensate liquids. The LTX output was 650 barrels of condensate and 70,500 Mcf of lean, high pressure gas. The condensate was piped to storage tanks, where 2,000 Mcf of vapors (flash gas) from the storage tank went to low pressure gathering lines to be commingled with the casinghead gas.

The low pressure casinghead gas (measured at Meter No. 1 to be 40,500 Mcf) and the flash gas (measured at Meter No. 2 to be 2,000 Mcf) pass through a compressor, where they are boosted into the high pressure sales line. A portion of the gas is burned as fuel for the compressor. Total output from the compressor (measured at Meter No. 3 to be 40,800 Mcf) and high pressure gas well gas from the LTX unit (measured at Meter No. 4 to be 70,500 Mcf) were combined and sold. Meter No. 5 on the high pressure gas line indicated that 110,000 Mcf was sold.

Figure 11-10
Gas flow schematic

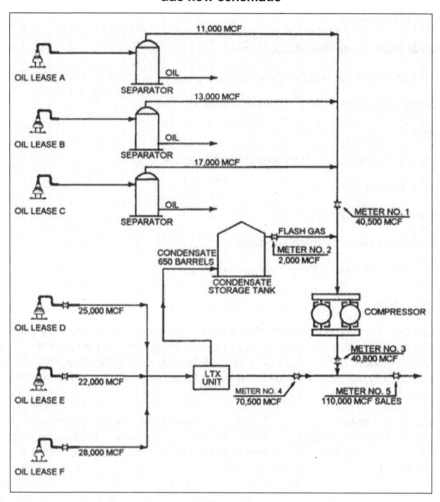

Volumes sold are allocated back to the leases in five steps:

Step 1. Meter No. 5 total sales volume of 110,000 Mcf is allocated to Meters No. 3 and No. 4 in proportion to each meter's throughput into Meter No. 5.

Meter	Metered throughput					Allocated sales
No. 3	40,800 Mcf	x	(110,000 ÷ 111,300)	=		40,323 Mcf
No. 4	70,500 Mcf	x	(110,000 ÷ 111,300)	=		69,677 Mcf
Total	**111,300 Mcf**					**110,000 Mcf**

Step 2. The 69,677 Mcf of sales attributed to Meter No. 4 is allocated to the three gas leases on the basis of theoretical lean gas remaining after extraction of condensate.

Gas lease	Theoretical lean gas				Allocated sales
D	24,000 Mcf	x	(69,677 ÷ 70,500)	=	23,720 Mcf
E	20,500 Mcf	x	(69,677 ÷ 70,500)	=	20,261 Mcf
F	26,000 Mcf	x	(69,677 ÷ 70,500)	=	25,696 Mcf
Total	**70,500 Mcf**				**69,677 Mcf**

Step 3. The 40,323 Mcf of sales attributed to Meter No. 3 is allocated to Meters No. 1 and No. 2 based on metered throughput. This charges the fuel gas used by the compressor to oil well gas and flash gas.

Meter	Metered throughput				Allocated sales
No. 1	40,500 Mcf	x	(40,323 ÷ 42,500)	=	38,425 Mcf
No. 2	2,000 Mcf	x	(40,323 ÷ 42,500)	=	1,898 Mcf
Total	**42,500 Mcf**				**40,323 Mcf**

Step 4. The 38,425 Mcf attributed to Meter No. 1 is allocated to the oil leases based on oil well gas production.

Oil lease	Gas production				Allocated sales
A	11,000 Mcf	x	(38,425 ÷ 41,000)	=	10,309 Mcf
B	13,000 Mcf	x	(38,425 ÷ 41,000)	=	12,184 Mcf
C	17,000 Mcf	x	(38,425 ÷ 41,000)	=	15,932 Mcf
Total	**41,000 Mcf**				**38,425 Mcf**

Step 5. The 1,898 Mcf of flash gas attributed to Meter No. 2 (calculated in Step 3) is allocated to the gas leases based on condensate produced. Condensate produced by well is determined by well tests of condensate-gas ratios. These ratios vary, depending on the density of the sample, so the conversion factor used in the example is only an assumption.

Gas lease	Condensate				Allocated flash gas
D	210 Bbls	x	(1,898 Mcf ÷ 650 Bbls)	=	613 Mcf
E	190 Bbls	x	(1,898 Mcf ÷ 650 Bbls)	=	555 Mcf
F	250 Bbls	x	(1,898 Mcf ÷ 650 Bbls)	=	730 Mcf
Total	**650 Bbls**				**1,898 Mcf**

Based on the allocations in the previous five steps, the summary of the gas sales allocations would be as follows:

Lease	Production	Sales (in Mcf)			
		Oil well gas	Gas well gas	Flash gas	Allocated sales
	(Mcf)				
A	11,000	10,309	–	–	10,309
B	13,000	12,184	–	–	12,184
C	17,000	15,932	–	–	15,932
D	25,000	–	23,720	613	24,333
E	22,000	–	20,261	555	20,816
F	28,000	–	25,696	730	26,426
Total	116,000				110,000

Gas storage

In the U.S., natural gas demand is seasonal, with differing peak and off-peak periods, depending on the region. In northern states, demand is higher in winter (for space heating), while in the south, demand is higher in summer (to generate electricity for air conditioning). Overall, natural gas demand is higher in the winter than in the summer. Gas that is produced during low-demand periods is stored in underground reservoirs for use when demand peaks. Gas storage facilities typically lie downstream of the pipeline system, where they temporarily store gas from numerous fields.

Gas storage traditionally has been defined as a series of operations whereby a quantity of production is injected into an underground depository to meet later demand. Historically, the industry used depleted oil or gas reservoirs for this gas storage. However, in recent years, leached underground salt dome structures, including those holding the Strategic Petroleum Reserve, are used in areas where they occur naturally, such as the Gulf Coast.

This technique for storage is easier and less expensive than using depleted oil or gas reservoirs, which take a long time to fill (sometimes most of a year). Salt dome storage usually can be filled rapidly, commonly with a cycling period (into and out of storage) of just one month or less. Storage capacity in a salt dome is increased by pumping in fresh water that dissolves the salt walls.

Limited pipeline capacity from a producing area to a market can restrict delivery capacity during peak demand. This restricted ability to move gas creates an incentive to produce it at a relatively constant rate throughout the year.

Measuring NGL volumes

As defined in Chapter 1, NGLs are recovered from a wet (rich) natural gas stream. The constituents of the gas stream are determined by analyzing gas delivered from each lease (or combination of leases) serving a gas processing plant, using gas chromatographs and spectrometers.

NGL volumes produced and sold

Dry natural gas is more than 90 percent methane, which is the simplest and smallest hydrocarbon molecule, consisting of one carbon atom bonded with four hydrogen molecules (CH_4). NGLs are the slightly larger natural hydrocarbon molecules of ethane (C_2H_6), propane (C_3H_8), butane (C_4H_{10}) and natural gasolines (five to 10 carbon atoms per molecule, or C_5S to $C_{10}S$). Liquefied natural gas (LNG) is a popular term for methane (CH_4), which is cooled to reduce its volume for transport and used primarily for heating and cooking. LNG production has more than doubled since 2000 as it has become popular as an alternative fuel in trucking, rail, marine and other industries.

Sampling. Like oil and gas from a lease, NGLs produced from a plant must meet minimum quality requirements to be accepted by a carrier or purchaser. The plant operator collects NGL samples to identify gross impurities that might require a shutdown or diversion of plant production until cured. Testing procedures use corrosion-sensitive test strips (commonly made of copper) and color charts (e.g., the Saybolt colorimeter test).

NGLs delivered into a pipeline are spot-sampled by the plant operator or automatically sampled on a continuous basis, depending on contract terms with the purchaser or carrier. During truck or rail deliveries, samples of each load are analyzed using a chromatograph (similar to natural gas measurement). Constituents, including any impurities, are reported on a volume-percent basis.

Chromatograph analyses often report chemically distinct constituents at a far higher level than is recognized in field market arrangements. In such cases, the constituents of the liquids are grouped to their market designation and totalled for settlement purposes. For example, the analysis may report hexanes plus (C_6+), in addition to pentanes (C_5S), when a processing agreement only addresses pentanes plus. The accountant simply adds the two reported percentages attributed to hexanes and pentanes to arrive at the settlement quantity of pentanes plus (C_5+).

Upon carrier acceptance, the liquids are transported to a user or market center. Market centers receive, store and fractionate NGLs and maintain standard exchange and delivery procedures to facilitate the trading of liquids.

Volume measurement. NGL volumes are measured with turbine meters or similar meters. Flowing NGLs spin the turbine in the meter, which records the rotation speed, indicating flow rate for a given type of fluid. Alternatively, a mass measurement meter weighs the gas to indicate the NGL portion of the measured gas.

NGL portions are expressed in gallons per Mcf (GPM). For example, gas with 1.0 GPM contains one gallon of NGLs in each Mcf.

NGL storage

Gas processing plant owners accumulate NGL inventories that must be stored on-site. The most common liquids storage is a one- to three-day supply of NGLs stored in above-ground bullet tanks (an industry term describing the tank shape). Liquids are transported from storage facilities, via connection to an NGL pipeline, or by trucks or rail cars loaded at plant terminals. Underground storage also is used for NGLs, either as a mixture of products or a purity product (referring to the pure product or liquids that meet the purchaser's specifications).

Many underground storage facilities are situated near fractionation plants and wholesale-market delivery or consumption points. At these locations, payment is made in the month the NGLs are produced and stored, with pricing based on actual sales during the current month or the last preceding month of sales. Depending on company policy and contract terms, adjustments may be made, at a later date, for the difference between the settlement price and the price received when the NGLs are withdrawn from storage and sold.

Another pricing method is to defer settlement until the NGLs are withdrawn from storage and sold. These settlements are based on the actual prices received from the sales. Plant owners must maintain monthly records of the stored products to ensure a proper allocation between leases when the products are withdrawn. Sales from storage usually are allocated on a first-in, first-out (FIFO) basis.

Gas processing

Natural gas often contains excessive NGLs and impurities (sulfur, water and carbon dioxide) that must be removed before it can enter downstream pipeline systems. At lease facilities, field equipment frequently is used to remove the heaviest liquids and some impurities.

Gas transported from the lease with significant impurities or NGL content (wet gas) is sent by pipeline to a gas processing plant. Larger, more sophisticated, and far more expensive than field equipment, these plants remove the NGLs and impurities and produce marketable dry gas known as residue gas, which consists mostly of methane and is sold at the tailgates of gas plants. Although gas processing is expensive and reduces the energy content and value of the processed gas, recovered NGLs have many uses in manufacturing and petrochemical industries.

Types of processing

Processing plants combine separation, purification, compression, extraction, and liquids-handling and measurement equipment. Their capacities range from small to more than one Bcf per day. Since the mid-1970s, processing technologies have lent themselves to modular units that fit onto trucks for greater mobility. The opportunity to move readily to new sources of gas extends a processor's lines of business.

Two technologies generally are employed to process natural gas: (1) lean-oil absorption and (2) cryogenics. Both produce liquids and can be applied to most gas streams. However, important differences exist in terms of capital and operating costs.

Lean-oil absorption is an older technology that uses chemical processes to extract NGLs from a gas stream as they pass through a series of special, oil-bearing contactor towers. Lean-oil plants usually are block-mounted; therefore, they cannot be moved easily. These plants are inefficient at extracting the lighter ends of NGL components, such as ethane. The advantages of lean-oil absorption are its minimal use of fuel for compression and a high degree of flexibility in the volume of gas it can process efficiently.

A cryogenic process condenses NGLs from the gas stream by chilling them through one or a combination of two basic methods or cycles: refrigeration and expansion. A refrigeration cycle uses various working fluids to chill the wet-gas stream. Expansion cycles use a large drop in pressure through valves and/or turbines to produce very cold temperatures, sometimes adding a refrigeration cycle to chill the feed gas.

Cryogenic processes require large amounts of gas and refrigerant compression, increasing fuel expenses. However, they are efficient at extracting the available liquids, often achieving extraction of 95 percent of the ethane and close to 100 percent of the heavier components, including butane and natural gasoline.

The efficiency of cryogenic plants falls rapidly at throughput levels below 50 percent of the plant's rated capacity. However, they often can be moved to new locations. In nearly all instances, cryogenic plants are modular, and the primary pieces of equipment fit onto a semi-trailer for ease of transportation.

Types of plants

Gas processing plants are categorized according to the type and extent of processing, use of the residue gas, a plant's location relative to transmission pipelines, and local or company traditions. They are called gas plants or gas-liquids extraction plants.

The names given to these plants, such as lean-oil or cryogenic (or refrigeration), reflect the type of process used to remove the NGLs. For example, a refrigeration plant may refer to a plant that cools the gas to a range of 15°F to (40)°F and, at the lower temperature, recovers about 70 percent of ethane, 90 percent of propane and virtually all of the heavier NGLs. By contrast, a true cryogenic refrigeration plant cools gas to a range of (150)°F to (225)°F, recovering 95 percent of the ethane and close to 100 percent of the heavier components.

Bobtail plant refers to a gas plant that removes the NGLs as a single stream, which is sent to a fractionation plant (described in the next section) to separate the NGLs into their components. A cycling plant handles residue gas that will be reinjected into a reservoir. The term straddle plant generally refers to a plant situated on a transmission pipeline system, as opposed to one that is situated between the field gas-gathering system and the pipeline. Gasoline plant is a confusing, perhaps archaic, term for a gas plant, as it refers to the natural gasolines typically removed from the gas.

Fractionation

A fractionation plant receives an NGL stream from one or more gas processing plants and fractionates the stream into separate products. A single fractionation plant may handle the output of several true gas processing plants, thereby reducing the need for fractionation facilities at each site. This approach also is a more economical means of transporting NGLs from the gas plant to a shipping point because only one pipeline is needed to move the mixed liquids.

Fractionation is accomplished by heating and cooling the NGL mix in tall towers, where components can be drawn off from the height at which they settle. Fractionation facilities operate continuously and have consumers and/or storage for the finished products in close proximity. NGL market prices are established at these sites. Expenses of transportation and fractionation are subtracted to arrive at plant tailgate prices for NGLs.

● ● ●

1   Oil recovery methods fall into two broad classifications: primary recovery and enhanced recovery, as described in Chapter 25.

2   Such rounding has little effect on revenues. Even a full one degree difference in API gravity changes the volume by only 0.01 percent, or about $1.93 for the 385.19 barrels valued at $50 per barrel.

3   Office of Fossil Energy. "SPR Quick Facts and FAQs." Energy.gov, www.energy.gov/fe/services/petroleum-reserves/strategic-petroleum-reserve/spr-quick-facts-and-faqs. Accessed October 2019.

4   The relationship between API gravity and specific gravity is purely mathematical. API gravity varies inversely with specific gravity.

5   The *Dictionary of Petroleum Exploration, Drilling & Production*, PennWell Publishing Co., 1991, added that "sweet crude" may refer to crude with a sulfur content below 1 percent, while "sour" may refer to crude with a sulfur content above 1 percent. *Oil Markets and Prices*, Oxford University Press, 1993, notes that West Texas Intermediate (WTI) actually is a sweet crude with a sulfur content of 0.4 percent and an API gravity of 40 degrees. The NYMEX crude oil futures contract is not strictly for WTI, but for a sweet crude oil with a sulfur content of less than 0.5 percent and an API gravity between 34 degrees and 45 degrees. Several U.S. and foreign sweet crudes meet those specifications.

6   Energy Information Administration. "International Energy Outlook 2019." September 24, 2019, www.eia.gov/outlooks/ieo/pdf/ieo2019.pdf.

7   For the example and Figure 11-10, meter numbers are revised from the presentation in the COPAS Accounting Guideline No. 15 (AG-15), *Gas Accounting Manual* (revised 2010).

Accounting for
Oil, Gas and NGL Sales

Accounting for oil, gas and NGL sales can be a complex matter. Numerous factors can make the proper recording of sales information a challenge, including:

- Multiple owners.

- Changes in ownership interests.

- Royalty rates that vary by property.

- Fluctuating prices.

- Production tax rates that vary by property.

- Gas imbalances.

- Changes in purchasers.

- Purchaser, operator and pipeline accounting errors.

As an example of the effects of multiple owners and multiple forms of distribution, assume AMP Oil Co. (AMP) is the operator of a property in which it has a 40 percent net revenue interest. The property is burdened with a 25 percent royalty and production taxes are 5 percent. During one month, $150,000 of petroleum is sold from the lease.

As further described in the "Adoption of ASC 606" section herein, based on its analysis, AMP has determined it is an agent with respect to the sale of the other interests' production to the ultimate third-party customer. Consequently, assuming that all criteria for revenue recognition have been met, AMP's revenues (net of royalties) are $45,000 ($150,000 x 0.40 x 0.75), and its production tax expenses are $2,250 ($45,000 x 0.05). The purchaser's practice of distributing proceeds could be any one of the following:

- Pay AMP $42,750 for its portion of revenue, net of the royalty burden and production taxes. This method is common for sales of oil production in which the purchaser directly pays the net revenue interest holders, the royalty owner and the local government.

- Pay AMP $150,000, and AMP must distribute the proceeds to the other net revenue interest holders and the royalty owner, as well as pay all production taxes. This method is common for sales of natural gas.

- Pay AMP $142,500, and AMP must distribute the proceeds to the other net revenue interest holders and the royalty owner. The purchaser withholds only production taxes for payment directly to the local government under this method.

Adoption of ASC 606

ASC 606, *Revenue from Contracts with Customers*, was required for adoption by most fiscal year-end public business entities[1] by January 1, 2018 (January 1, 2019, for all other entities and effective in interim periods in 2020), under either a full or modified retrospective approach.

ASC 606 addresses the principles that an entity must apply to report useful information about the amount, timing and uncertainty of revenues and cash flows that arise from its contracts to transfer goods or services to customers.

The core principle requires entities to recognize revenue depicting these transfers in an amount that reflects the consideration they expect to receive in exchange.

Five-step model

ASC 606 outlines a five-step model for recognizing revenue from contracts with customers:

Step 1. Identify the contract.

Step 2. Identify the performance obligation(s).

Step 3. Determine the transaction price.

Step 4. Allocate the transaction price.

Step 5. Recognize the revenue.

For a contract to be accounted for using the five-step model, it must meet certain criteria. Before applying the guidance in the revenue standard, an entity must assess, for example, whether or not it is "probable" that it will collect the revenue. A contract contains a promise (or promises) to transfer goods or services to a customer. A performance obligation is a promise (or a group of promises) that is distinct, as defined in ASC 606. Entities must determine whether to account for performance obligations separately or as a group.

The transaction price is the consideration an entity expects from a customer in exchange for the goods or services it provides. To determine the transaction price, consideration should be given to whether or not there is variable consideration, a significant financing component, noncash consideration or amounts due the customer. The transaction price then must be allocated to the separate contractual performance obligations based on relative, stand-alone selling prices.

ASC 606 sets out several methods for estimating a stand-alone selling price when one is not directly observable. Allocating discounts and variable consideration also must be considered. Revenue should be recognized when (or as) the performance obligations are satisfied. ASC 606 helps determine if a performance obligation is satisfied at a point in time or over time. If a performance obligation is satisfied over time, the related revenue also is recognized over time.

Although revenue recognition for the oil and gas industry may appear simple, complexities can arise for certain types of contracts. The explanation herein focuses on the effect of the new revenue standard on the industry and highlights potential differences from previous practice under GAAP. In the text that follows, the "revenue standard" or the "new revenue standard" refer to ASC 606.

Scope exceptions

The new revenue standard applies to all contracts with customers, except for contracts that are within the scope of other standards, such as leases, financial instruments and certain nonmonetary exchanges. Extractive activities are not specifically excluded from the scope of the revenue guidance. Contracts for the purchase or sale of oil and natural gas often meet the definition of a derivative. However, contracts that are expected to result in physical delivery may be eligible for the normal purchases and normal sales (NPNS) scope exception included in ASC 815, *Derivatives and Hedging*.

Contracts that are accounted for as derivatives are excluded from the scope of the new revenue standard. If a company elects to designate a qualifying commodity sale contract as NPNS, the contract should be accounted for under the new revenue standard. The ultimate settlement of a physically settled derivative accounted for as a derivative is also outside the scope of the new revenue standard. The derivatives guidance does not specify income statement presentation for mark-to-market changes recognized on derivative instruments. Revenue from contracts with customers should be separately disclosed in the footnotes if mark-to-market changes and ultimate settlement of a derivative are presented as revenue on the income statement.

Principal versus agent

Under the new revenue standard, a company is a principal in a transaction if it obtains control of the goods and services of another party before it transfers control of those goods and services to the customer. The revenue standard provides the following indicators to assist in the evaluation of whether a company controls the goods or services:

- Primary responsibility for fulfilling the promise.

- Inventory risk.

- Discretion in establishing price.

The standard provides no relative weighting to the indicators. Instead, oil and gas producers and processors need to understand the relationships and contractual arrangements among the various parties to the sales arrangement (i.e., nonoperating working interests and/or royalty owners) to ascertain if and when control transfers.

If control of another interest holder's production transfers to the producer or processor before it is sold to the third-party customer, the other interest holders have effectively sold their production to the producer or processor. In that case, the producer or processor is the principal and should record revenues on a gross basis.

If, however, control does not transfer to the producer or processor prior to the production being sold to the third-party customer, the producer or processor is an agent and should recognize net revenues based on its proportionate interest.

Various examples are provided herein to illustrate the analysis required. Unless otherwise noted, the examples in this chapter assume that the producer is an agent with respect to the sale of other interest holders' production. Consequently, it will report its revenues net of other working interest owners' interests and royalty owners' interests, as discussed herein.

For example, a midstream company may take control of some or all of the commodities prior to their transfer to the end customer, acting as a principal. Alternatively, a midstream company may provide a service to the producer, selling the commodities on the producer's behalf as an agent. The pricing structure for these contracts (e.g., fee-based, percentage of proceeds, percentage of index, keep-whole, etc.) does not necessarily determine whether or not the midstream company controls the commodities before they are transferred to the end customer. In making this principal versus agent determination, all facts and circumstances of an arrangement must be considered.

Taxes

Entities often collect amounts from customers that must be remitted to a third party (e.g., collecting and remitting taxes to a governmental agency). Taxes collected from customers could include sales, use, value-added and some excise taxes. Amounts collected on behalf of third parties, such as certain sales taxes, are not included in the transaction price as they are collected from the customer on behalf of the government. The entity is the agent for the government in these situations.

Taxes that are based on production, rather than sales, are typically imposed on the seller, not the customer. An entity that is obligated to pay taxes based on its production is the principal for those taxes, and therefore recognizes the tax as an operating expense, with no effect on revenue.

Management should assess each type of tax, on a jurisdiction-by-jurisdiction basis, to conclude whether to net these amounts against revenue or recognize them as an operating expense. The intent of the tax, as written into the tax legislation in the particular jurisdiction, should also be considered.

The name of the tax (e.g., sales tax or excise tax) is not always determinative when assessing whether the entity is the principal or the agent for the tax. Whether or not the customer knows the amount of tax also does not necessarily impact the analysis. Management should look to the underlying characteristics of the tax and the tax laws in the relevant jurisdiction to determine whether the entity is primarily obligated to pay the tax or whether the tax is levied on the customer. This could be a significant undertaking for some entities, particularly those that operate in numerous jurisdictions with different tax regimes.

Arrangements between working interest owners

Because of the economic uncertainties related to exploring for and producing oil and gas, two or more parties often join together to locate and develop prospects. Oil and gas companies will need to apply judgment to evaluate whether or not the parties in transactions between working interest owners have a vendor-customer relationship.

A customer is a party that contracts with a company to obtain goods or services that are the output of that company's ordinary activities in exchange for consideration. Conversely, arrangements where the parties are participating in an activity together and share the risks and benefits of that activity are not considered contracts with customers.

A transaction with another working interest owner will be accounted for under the new revenue standard if the counterparty is considered a customer in the specific transaction. Companies should consider whether other applicable guidance, such as ASC 808, *Collaborative Arrangements*, should be applied when an arrangement is not a contract with a customer.

Example – Working interest owners in a joint operating agreement

Facts. An upstream company is party to a JOA under which each of the parties agrees to participate jointly in exploration and development to extract minerals.

Question. Are the other JOA working interest owners considered customers for the exploration and development activities?

Analysis. No. A JOA is not considered a contract with a customer because the counterparties have contracted to share proportionately in the risks and benefits of the exploration, development and production activities rather than to obtain the output of an entity's ordinary activities. Therefore, these activities would not be performance obligations performed for a customer.

Example – Working interest owner that provides midstream services

Facts. An upstream company is a party to a JOA and also has wholly owned midstream operations (such as gathering, processing, transportation or marketing services). The upstream company performs midstream services for its own production and the production of the other working interest owners that are party to the JOA.

Question. Are the other working interest owners considered customers of the midstream service contracts?

Analysis. Yes. The working interest owners are customers in these arrangements because the upstream company is selling midstream services to the other working interest owners, and the services are an output of the company's ordinary activities. Therefore, the midstream service contracts should be accounted for under the revenue standard.

Commodity sales

Sales of commodities are common in the oil and gas industry. Commodity arrangements that are not accounted for as derivatives are in the scope of the new revenue standard. The table in Figure 12-1 describes the timing of revenue recognition under the new revenue standard as compared to the previous revenue accounting standard.

Allocating the transaction price

The transaction price is allocated to separate performance obligations based on their relative stand-alone selling prices, as determined at contract inception. Although the revenue standard does not require a specific method for determining stand-alone selling prices, it emphasizes the use of observable data. All available information should be considered, such as market factors, company-specific pricing practices, internal costs, classes of customers and availability of observable data, when establishing stand-alone selling prices.

Figure 12-1

Point in time versus over time

New revenue standard	Previous revenue standard
Revenue is recognized upon the satisfaction of performance obligations, which occurs when control of the good or service transfers to the customer. Control can transfer at a point in time or over time. A performance obligation is satisfied over time if it meets one of these criteria:	Revenue is generally recognized when it meets all four of the following criteria:
• The customer simultaneously receives and consumes the benefits of the entity's performance as the entity performs (e.g., certain services).	• Persuasive evidence of an arrangement exists.
• The entity's performance creates or enhances an asset that the customer controls.	• Delivery has occurred, or services have been rendered.
• The entity's performance does not create an asset with alternative use to the entity <u>and</u> the entity has an enforceable right to payment (cost plus a reasonable profit margin) for performance completed to date.	• The seller's price to the buyer is fixed or determinable. • Collectability is reasonably assured.

New revenue standard (continued)	
A performance obligation is satisfied at a point in time if it does not meet one of the above criteria. The new revenue standard provides indicators for the point in time at which control transfers.	Companies typically recognize revenue when the commodity is delivered to the customer (assuming that the other revenue recognition criteria have been satisfied).

	Previous revenue standard (continued)
Many sales of oil and gas commodities likely will be recognized at a point in time under the new revenue standard because the customer does not simultaneously receive and consume the benefits of the commodity. However, some commodity arrangements may meet the "over time" guidance if the customer consumes the commodity immediately. For example, sales of natural gas to a gas-fired power plant with no storage capacity may meet the "over time" criteria. Companies should consider all relevant facts and circumstances when evaluating whether or not a commodity is simultaneously received and consumed by the customer. Considerations include the inherent characteristics of the commodity (e.g., whether or not it can be stored), the contractual terms and information about infrastructure or delivery mechanisms.	**Expected effect** Determining whether control transfers at a point in time or over time can affect other steps in the new revenue model, such as allocating the transaction price for multi-period commodity contracts and applying the "series" guidance, which requires that the commodities meet the criteria to be recognized over time.

Fixed-price contracts. The forward price of a commodity may be a relevant input in determining stand-alone selling price in certain fixed-price contracts. In other cases, the forward index curve may not be a key input used by a company in determining pricing for a commodity sale contract.

For example, a company may price a long-term contract based on internal costs (e.g., depletion, lifting and other operating costs) plus an expected profit margin, and there may not be an observable forward price for the duration of the contract. The forward price may not be a relevant input in determining stand-alone selling price in that situation.

In these instances, a company will need to determine whether the contractually stated prices represent stand-alone selling price of the commodity. This determination may require judgment, particularly if the fixed price per unit is not constant throughout the term of the contract.

Index-based contracts. Certain commodity sale contracts include variable consideration because the consideration is calculated based on an index price at a specified date. Variable consideration is typically allocated to all of the performance obligations in an arrangement based on their relative stand-alone selling prices. However, if certain criteria are met, variable consideration is allocated to only one or more performance obligations in the contract rather than to all performance obligations. Sales of commodities at an index-based price will likely meet the criteria for allocating variable consideration, as illustrated below.

Example – Stand-alone selling price for an index-based commodity sale

Facts. An upstream company enters into a contract to sell 100 barrels of oil each month for the next 12 months (a total of 1,200 barrels) at an index-based price of West Texas Intermediate (WTI) for that day's delivery. The company determines that each barrel of oil constitutes a separate performance obligation and that control transfers at a point in time when the barrel of oil is delivered. Assume that there are no prepayments or payments due after the deliveries.

Question. How should the company recognize revenue under the revenue standard?

Analysis. The transaction price consists entirely of variable consideration. Under ASC 606-10-32-40, the company would allocate variable consideration to each barrel of oil based on the WTI price for that day since the variable consideration relates specifically to the company's efforts to transfer the commodity, and allocating the consideration in this manner is consistent with the allocation objective. Therefore, the amount of revenue recognized each day would be the product of the number of barrels delivered and the WTI price for that day.

Information and accounting systems

Given the complexities described, operators must use an accounting system that accurately and efficiently records oil and gas sales proceeds and properly distributes the proceeds rightfully due to other owners. One key element in the system is the division of interest (DOI) file. This master file contains the revenue sharing percentages for each unique distribution based on the lease identity, month of sale and purchaser.

Companies with sophisticated information systems enter production volumes and related volume measures directly into electronic databases. This role is performed by a production clerk, operations employee, production accountant, gas control clerk or other designee.

In an integrated company, several divisions or subsidiaries may be involved in producing, refining, processing, and marketing oil and natural gas.

The marketing department, responsible for negotiations and sales contracts, enters its agreements into the database on the basis of property or measurement point. DOI owners and their interests are entered into the system using date-sensitive codes. The current revenue deck contains the ownership interest information used to pay these owners.

Revenue accountants verify that settlement statements agree with data collected from other departments. Pipeline information is entered daily or monthly and used for monthly accruals. Production data and other state tax information are entered and verified periodically by tax accountants. When revenue accountants are confident that the correct information resides in the system, they initiate steps for the computer to record entries, make payments and generate reports for monthly closings.

Accounting complexities

As illustrated in the earlier AMP example, a number of industry-specific matters can affect the distribution of proceeds from oil and gas sales, each of which is further described in a subsequent section herein:

- Division orders.

- Distribution accounting.

- Revenues held in suspense.

- Royalty reporting.

- Production taxes.

- Ad valorem taxes.

- Exchanges.

Division orders

As explained in Chapter 7, the contractual agreements between parties determine ownership interests. Usually, no two contracts are exactly the same. These agreements can create many different owners of a single mineral property. Oil and gas sales proceeds from the property must be distributed to each eligible party.

Oil purchasers generally send separate checks to each owner. Conversely, purchasers of natural gas generally pay all net proceeds from the sale to the operator. As a result, the operator becomes responsible for distributing gas proceeds to the various owners of the working interests, royalty interests, overriding royalty interests and net profits interests.

If the working interest owners do not sell their gas collectively, each working interest owner may take its gas in-kind, sell it to the party of its choice and receive a net proceeds check from its gas purchaser. For these reasons, the parties must reach agreement about who distributes the proceeds from gas revenues to whom.

As illustrated in Figure 12-2, a division order is the agreement between the purchaser of production and all the owners of production stating how the production proceeds should be distributed. If the operator or other working interest owners are receiving proceeds on behalf of itself and others, it should create a division order for its distributions to the other parties.

Division orders include the legal description of the property, names of interest owners and the interest owned by each. Sometimes a division order includes the terms of purchase, including provisions that address the passing of title to the products, price, measurement, production taxes and related items.[2]

By signing the division order, each owner represents that its ownership stake is listed correctly, and it agrees to all provisions. In all cases, the operator must carefully consider whether it is the principal or agent based on the terms of agreements entered into with other interest owners as well as purchasers and processors. The operator records revenue from customers on a gross basis if they are a principal or a net basis if they are an agent.

The operator and purchaser retain copies of division orders. These records authorize the accounting department to distribute proceeds from production sales to the various interest owners. New division orders or changes in division orders may be reported on a form titled "Notice of Division Order Changes." It identifies the lease, names and addresses of all interest owners, the fractional interest belonging to each, and any fractional interest or interests held in suspense. For a transfer of interest, fractional interests of the grantor and grantee are recorded before and after the transfer or the change in interests held in suspense.

Division orders may contain special clauses in the body of the order or as attachments which contain the legal language and agreements between the interest owners and the operator or payer. These clauses may define terms, quantity measurement methods, quantity inclusions and exclusions used to calculate payments, circumstances when proceeds may be withheld, dates and methods of payment, valid title and other special arrangements.

Figure 12-2

Figure 12-2

Illustrative division order[3]

NADOA Model Form Division Order (adopted September 1995)			
Division Order			

To: **Date:** February 5, 2019

Property No.:	094-730-8820-1800	**Effective date:**	Commencing at 7 a.m.
Property Name:	Bell Heirs "A"		Date of first purchase
Operator:	Big Oil USA		
County and State:	Montague County, Texas		
Property Description:	[Legal description]		

Production: X **Oil**   X **Gas**   ___ **Other**

Owner Name	Owner Number	Decimal Interest	Type of Interest
Big Oil USA	197954	.50000000	WI
KT Oil	287643	.21375000	WI
Amber Bell	634322	.06250000	RI
Frederick Bell	725873	.03125000	RI
Micah Bell	725874	.03125000	RI
Walter Johnson	697389	.00672550	ORRI
Phyllis Johnson	697390	.00672550	ORRI
Casey Stewart	487653	.00345490	ORRI
Melvin Kirkland	567839	.00962500	ORRI
Lois Kirkland	567895	.00962500	ORRI

The undersigned certifies the ownership of their decimal interest in production or proceeds as described above payable by __Big Oil USA__ (Payer).
                (Company name)

Payer shall be notified, in writing, of any change in ownership, decimal interest or payment address. All such changes shall be effective the first day of the month following receipt of such notice.

Payer is authorized to withhold payment pending resolution of a title dispute or adverse claim asserted regarding the interest in production claimed herein by the undersigned. The undersigned agrees to indemnify and reimburse Payer any amount attributable to an interest to which the undersigned is not entitled.

Payer may accrue proceeds until the total amount equals **$25.00**, or pay on December 31, whichever occurs first, or as required by applicable state statute.

This Division Order does not amend any lease or operating agreement between the undersigned and the lessee or operator or any other contracts for the purchase of oil or gas.

In addition to the terms and conditions of this Division Order, the undersigned and Payer may have certain statutory rights under the laws of the state in which the property is located.

Special clauses:
Owner(s) signature(s):
Owner(s) Tax ID No.(s):
Owner daytime telephone:
Owner fax:

Federal law requires you to furnish your Social Security or Taxpayer Identification Number. Failure to comply will result in 35% tax withholding and will not be refundable by Payer.

Distribution accounting

As discussed previously in the "Adoption of ASC 606" section herein, an E&P company's revenues typically consist of its share of revenues net of the revenue interests owned by others. For example, assume an E&P company is the operator of a producing property in which it owns a 40 percent net revenue interest. The well's gross revenue from gas production for the month is $100,000. The E&P company has determined it is an agent of the other revenue interest owners in the property.

Assuming all other revenue recognition criteria have been met, the operator records a receivable of $100,000, as well as its portion of gas revenues based on its 40 percent net revenue interest. A revenue distribution payable liability is also recorded for the amounts owed by the operator to the other revenue interest owners for their share of the gross revenue. The journal entry recorded by the operator would be as follows:

Accounts receivable – oil and gas sales	100,000	
Revenue distributions payable		60,000
Gas revenues		40,000
To record gas revenue for well [name] for [month, year].		

Exceptions to this rule include: (1) accounting for minimum royalties recorded as a production expense (explained later in this chapter) and (2) recognizing revenues for gas quantities taken and sold that give rise to gas imbalances (explained in Chapter 13).

Revenues held in suspense

Revenues related to interests owned by others may be held in suspense and not distributed for various reasons, including:

- Awaiting an executed division order.

- Awaiting an executed change in ownership interest.

- Awaiting a proof of title or title opinion.

- Awaiting resolution of a dispute regarding ownership interest.

- An interest owner's signature cannot be obtained on the division order or transfer order.

- Minimal size of distribution.

- Uncashed prior distributions to a particular owner, which could mean the owner cannot be found or has abandoned the property.

All revenues may be held in suspense when awaiting an executed division order. If one interest owner's information is in doubt, that portion of revenues alone may be held in suspense exclusive of other interest owners' portions.

The division order typically states that if a particular distribution is minimal (below a stated amount such as the $25 illustrated in Figure 12-2), then it need not be distributed until the cumulative distribution payable exceeds the stated amount. However, it is customary to distribute all amounts owed at the end of each calendar year, even if the total is less than the stated minimum. State or local regulations, or the lease agreement itself, may also set the distribution threshold.

When owners are not known or cannot be located, amounts due must be paid into an escrow account. Whether held in escrow or not, unclaimed distributions fall under state escheat laws that address unclaimed property. Outside companies may be engaged to find the owners; their fees are charged against owner proceeds. After a period of time, as determined by each state, unclaimed revenues held in suspense accounts must be distributed to the appropriate state agency.

Royalty reporting

Depending on contract provisions, either the operator or the purchaser makes periodic payments to royalty owners, which may be monthly or on a less frequent periodic basis. Reporting usually is in the form of a settlement statement or check stub, also called a revenue remittance advice. This document should identify the lease(s) involved, production month(s) included, number of barrels of oil or condensate or Mcf of gas sold, sales price, royalty owner's ownership percentage of production, state production or severance tax withheld and net amount paid to the royalty owner. Contracts or state regulations sometimes call for other data or for the enclosure of copies of supporting documents (e.g., run tickets).

Various regulatory agencies are responsible for collecting and accounting for the royalty interests owned by Native American tribes and state and federal governments, including federal offshore waters. These agencies require the monthly and annual filing of detailed reports on production, sales and other dispositions of products, along with the checks for royalties due. From these reports, the agencies compile information to determine receipt of the correct amounts. Agency regulations change frequently and are beyond the scope of this book. Official manuals used by operators explain how to file required forms. Revenue accountants should remain informed of current regulations, as heavy penalties may be imposed for failure to comply.

Production taxes

Most states levy one or more types of tax on produced oil and gas. Production taxes, or severance taxes, are computed by values or volumes of oil, condensate, gas, NGLs, and sulfur produced and sold or consumed. Taxes usually are levied at the time and place at which minerals are severed from the producing reservoir.

Some states impose a conservation tax to fund energy conservation, oversight and research programs. Many Native American tribes assess a production tax, which usually is credited against amounts otherwise due to the state where the well is located. Each state's and tribe's assessment methods and rates vary. Revenue accountants must be familiar with the current tax laws of the states where producing properties are located. Government regulations mandating different types of taxes and rates are subject to constant change.

The Council of Petroleum Accountants Societies' (COPAS) Oil and Gas Severance Tax Guide, the Commerce Clearing House, Inc.'s *State Tax Reporter*, and other sources periodically update information about taxes on oil, gas and NGL production and sales. The Society of Petroleum Evaluation Engineers' website displays information by state to assist petroleum engineers in economic modeling and reserve estimation.

Calculating production taxes. As stated previously, the basis for determining the amount of tax due is the value or volume of the oil or gas produced and sold during a predetermined period. The accountant should know whether the taxing entity bases tax rates on sales or production from the property. It is also important to know whether the purchaser or the producer is responsible for payment and remittance of the appropriate tax.

State laws specify the tax rate and assessment basis of the particular product. A common tax method applies a fixed percentage to the total gross value of the product sold in a given month. Other states base their tax on the volume of oil and gas sold. A few states combine the two bases of value and volume in assessing taxes due. In these cases, either volume or value is used, whichever generates greater revenue to the state. Several special provisions currently in use by taxing entities are listed below:

- Before applying the tax rate, the gross value of oil may be reduced by a designated per barrel amount to reflect the barge, pipeline and/or trucking charges necessary to transport the oil produced and sold.

- With approval from the state, the value of natural gas may be reduced by documented marketing deductions (e.g., costs incurred beyond the separator, such as dehydration, to make the gas saleable to a purchaser).

- Different rates can be levied based on the producing property's location within counties, school districts or municipalities; in some states, rates vary with the date on which the lease commenced commercial production.

- Other states have different rates for special classifications of wells, such as wells incapable of producing more than a minimum quantity of oil per day based on the well's average daily production during the taxable month.

Paying production taxes. Oil and gas purchasers may deduct taxes from the sales proceeds and pay the producer a net amount. The purchaser remits taxes due, along with tax forms or schedules, to appropriate state collection agencies. Alternatively, a purchaser may pay the producer the gross value for the production and the producer then may remit taxes to the designated state agency.

Some production and certain ownership interests can be exempt from taxation. For example, injection gas, vented or flared gas and gas-lift gas are exempt in some states. Interests owned by the federal government, state government or Native American tribes are exempt from taxes in most states. In certain instances, contractual agreements between the parties result in tax-free interests. In these situations, other owners must bear the non-taxpaying owners' shares. In general, however, production taxes are borne proportionately by all interest owners, including royalty interest owners.

States typically require monthly tax payment and reporting. Usually, both the producer and purchaser file a monthly tax report which is due one to two months after the production month.

To determine that all taxes due were reported and paid correctly, state personnel compare reports submitted by the purchaser and producer. They also may compare the tax reports with production reports generated by the operations department and filed with the state. Many states also require quarterly and annual reports. The level of detail in state tax reports varies. Typically, reports show production volume, production value and tax for each unit or lease with a summary for each county or parish.

Penalties. The tax-assessing agency may impose penalties and interest for any failure to file timely reports or pay taxes, in full, when due. Many states will waive these penalties if the delinquency is not due to taxpayer negligence. Failure to file tax reports can be classified as a misdemeanor with possible fines and/or jail terms. Some penalties for late filing are set at specific dollar amounts; others apply a percentage to production volume or value.

Refunds. Refund procedures for overpaid production and state taxes vary. Some states require the filing of an official claim for a refund, along with supporting evidence; others require the filing of amended tax reports. Certain states allow a reduction for the amount of requested refunds in the amount of taxes due in the current month. The taxpayer is notified if the claim subsequently is disallowed.

Ad valorem taxes

Ad valorem (a Latin term meaning "according to the value") taxes and property taxes generally are levied by counties, school districts and other local taxing entities based on where the production occurs. Ad valorem taxes can be based on either: (1) the amount of production occurring in the previous calendar year or (2) the estimated fair market value of well equipment or economic interest in the property. Tax rates vary widely among local taxing entities, and a county or parish may encompass many different taxing entities.

Although calculated in similar fashion to production taxes (e.g., applying a statutory rate to an assessed value or the gross value of production), ad valorem taxes are noticeably distinct, and they present challenges to revenue and joint interest accountants. For example, certain states impose ad valorem taxes on both the gross value of production and equipment. When paying ad valorem taxes based on gross production value, the distributor of revenues may withhold and escrow estimated taxes from its distributions to all interest owners (except for exempt owners). Working interest owners pay all ad valorem taxes assessed on equipment value.

As a general rule, the operator is responsible for reporting and paying ad valorem taxes. Conversely, the purchaser often withholds and remits production and severance taxes. Another difference between ad valorem taxes and production taxes is the frequency of reporting. Production taxes usually are paid and reported monthly, whereas and ad valorem taxes are paid annually. Many operators withhold estimated ad valorem taxes from monthly revenue distributions. This reduces the risk of uncollectible taxes from the other owners in the event the well unexpectedly ceases production or a joint venture owner becomes insolvent.

Because of the high degree of specialization and varying regulations imposed by state and local taxing jurisdictions, ad valorem taxes may require significant attention. Failure to emphasize their importance can expose a company to sizable losses due to uncollectible taxes from nonoperators or from excessively high property tax appraisals that go unchallenged by the company.

Exchanges

Occasionally an E&P company will exchange its crude oil for another company's crude oil, rather than sell it. These exchanges may be completed to meet location, quality or timing issues (e.g., to reduce transportation costs or to meet an integrated company's need for a different quality of crude for its local refinery).

The exchange may be structured so that one party receives a differential from the other for an agreed-upon difference in value of the exchanged barrels. Alternatively, the exchange may be structured as a sale of the E&P company's crude oil in exchange for its purchase of other crude oil. In such circumstances, each company pays the other the full purchase price of oil received in the exchange. Normally, the acquired oil is sold during the same month the exchange occurs.

Close scrutiny should be given to exchange transactions, as they can give rise to complex accounting issues, such as:

- Does the exchange agreement meet the definition of a derivative as defined by ASC 815, *Derivatives and Hedging*, and related interpretations, and will the contract be settled physically?

- Has consideration been given to gross versus net presentation of resulting revenues and expenses based on guidance in ASC 606?

- Has full consideration been given to the guidance in ASC 845, *Nonmonetary Transactions*?

In evaluating exchange contracts, facts and circumstances in the context of the entity's various activities should be carefully considered, rather than solely the terms of the individual contract.

Revenue accounting department

Because of differences in individual company operations, size and structure, no standard organizational pattern can dictate how to set up the revenue accounting department. Companies with only a few producing properties may employ one accountant to perform all revenue accounting functions or even all accounting functions. As with any position that involves financial transactions, it is important to structure accountability and segregation of duties to achieve effective internal control.

Larger companies may set up numerous specialized positions (such as gas accountant or production tax accountant) or units (production accounting, gas control or royalty owner accounting) to achieve effective revenue accounting. These companies are also more likely to operate sophisticated information and accounting systems, as well as internal controls.

Revenue accountant responsibilities

One of the primary responsibilities of a revenue accountant is to assign and record revenue to the correct property, measurement point, tank or well. Therefore, one of the accountant's first tasks is to identify revenue accounting centers for accumulating and grouping recorded revenue.

Generally, the revenue accounting center is identified by well, but it also may be by field, lease, prospect or other defined aggregation of activity for grouping volume, revenue and cost information. Whichever method is chosen, a distinct accounting center reference is assigned, such as a combined alpha and numeric code. The centers are required in order to properly set up receivables, record production, distribute proceeds to the working interest and royalty interest owners, record accruals and calculate taxes.

In many E&P companies, the revenue accounting center is not determined solely by the accounting department but rather is selected by considering the needs of the entire organization. Revenue centers may define areas of responsibility in production, land and marketing, as well as in accounting. Hence, centers commonly are called accounting cost centers, even within revenue accounting. The amortization cost center for full cost accounting is countrywide; for successful efforts, it generally is the lease or reasonable aggregation of leases. However, the accounting cost center often needs to be configured well-by-well for management oversight, or by lease for income tax reporting.[4]

Revenue accountants are also responsible for the correct recording of revenue entries and accurate distribution of revenue to the other interest owners. They must compare the settlement statement or revenue remittance advice from the purchaser to their internal company records of volumes sold, contract prices, tax rates and net revenue interests. They also must interact with the production, land and marketing departments to access the information required to record proper accounting entries for each property. This verification process varies from company to company and information from other departments also may be needed.

Volume verification

Procedures must be established to compare the volumes measured at the lease or central facility to those noted and paid for by the purchaser. Larger companies, or those with more sophisticated systems, may be capable of allowing the production department to enter sales volumes directly into a system that is accessible by the revenue department.

Methods for volume verification vary by company size, but may include the production clerk or revenue accountant:

- Receiving the pipeline run tickets, internally calculating (or outsourcing) volume calculations, and verifying that the statement of pipeline runs and the volume on the purchaser's check agree with the pipeline run tickets.

- Maintaining the meter tickets and calculating production to report to the revenue department, which must verify that the volumes agree.

- Maintaining the meter tickets and generating a report (such as the lease operating statement described in Chapter 14) of sales volumes received from the purchaser, in which case the production department may verify that the correct volumes were received.

- Maintaining the meter tickets and entering the volumetric amount, gravity and other pertinent data into the company's information system. During the monthly close process, the revenue accounting department accesses this data, verifying that the volumes paid for by the purchaser agree with the volumes entered by the production department.

Companies should also implement a process to verify that the amounts and terms negotiated on sales contracts are considered when revenue is recognized. Sales contracts often are maintained in the marketing department. Procedures must be established to give the revenue accounting department, or other assigned department, a means to verify contract terms and prices. This is more easily implemented with an integrated computer system that allows the direct entry of contract prices by the marketing department and subsequent access by the revenue accounting department as it records monthly closing entries.

Ownership interests

As stated previously, the revenue accountant must ensure that revenues are distributed properly. Division orders and royalty agreements generally reside in the land department, which provides a record (or information to prepare the record) called the revenue deck. The revenue deck contains a list of the interest owners and their respective ownership percentages.[5] This ownership record is assigned a unique code that, when referenced with the property's identifying accounting center number, directs the accountant or the computer system to set up payables to the correct owners according to their current ownership percentages. If an interest owner assigns or sells its interest or part of its interest, a new revenue deck reflecting the new ownership must be set up and assigned a new, unique code.

For example, assume AMP has an 85 percent working interest and a 70 percent net revenue interest in a well that started production on August 11, 2019. AMP's accountant sets up a revenue deck called R1 that contains AMP's 70 percent net revenue interest, with a 30 percent interest to other interest owners. AMP sells half of its net revenue interest to St. Charles Oil Co., effective October 1, 2019. AMP's accountant sets up a second revenue deck called R2 that reflects the new net revenue interests: AMP, 35 percent; St. Charles Oil Co., 35 percent; and other interest owners, which remains unchanged, of 30 percent. The first revenue deck is closed, with any sales occurring after September 30, 2019, to be distributed using revenue deck R2.

To facilitate accounting, agreements that call for ownership changes upon payout should specify an effective date. Payouts are triggered when revenues to a given interest in a well equal all costs allocated to that interest: acquisition, drilling, completion and operations. The governing agreement may make the ownership change effective: (1) the first day immediately after the month when payout actually occurs or (2) the day after payout (APO) is calculated to occur.

If applicable, the second approach requires a special allocation of the joint venture's revenues and costs for the month, as noted in COPAS Accounting Guideline No. 13 (AG-13), *Accounting for Farmouts/Farmins, Net Profits Interests and Carried Interests*.

Oil sales

Revenues are commonly recorded in an operating revenue subledger, with a separate record for each revenue accounting center (generally by well) to facilitate a number of accounting and reporting requirements. A record of the earnings for each lease or well is routinely needed to prepare management reports, complete federal income tax returns and file reports with regulatory agencies.

The information for each oil sales accounting center should typically include the following:

- Property identification.

- Revenue interest owned.

- Oil runs (8/8ths barrels and net barrels based on revenue interest owned).

- Total revenue for the month based on revenue interest owned.

- Cumulative revenue for the year based on revenue interest owned.

Given that revenue checks generally come at least one or two months after the date volumes are produced and sold, E&P companies typically accrue estimated revenue earned, but not yet received, in their monthly financial statements. Accrual estimation varies by company; it may be based on the previous one- or two-month's total revenues or involve a more sophisticated analysis of estimated production and estimated or actual prices. The production department should be able to supply current volume information for company-operated properties. For nonoperated properties, the accountant may need to estimate oil volumes based on the property's production history.

Accrual entries should also include the applicable production taxes and the amount receivable from the purchaser. The accrual entries are typically reversed at the beginning of each month so that the E&P company can record revenue and taxes at the time it receives cash; however, the accrual and reversal process varies by company depending on a number of factors.

Private companies should give careful consideration to accrual and reversal entries that are only performed annually, as a reversal in the new period could cause material distortions across financial statement periods.

Accrual method

As previously mentioned, due to the lag time between the date volumes are produced and sold and the date on which an E&P company receives payment and supporting documentation from the purchaser, an accrual estimate is typically recorded for each cost center's revenue based on internal records of volumes, prices and production tax rates.

Assuming all criteria for revenue recognition have been met, the revenue accountant debits accounts receivable, recording the receivable to an accounts receivable subledger for the particular purchaser, as though the purchaser had been invoiced.

A debit is also recorded for production tax expense, while a credit is recorded to a revenue account. In the event the purchaser does not withhold the production taxes, a credit would also be recorded for the production taxes payable by the E&P company.

When the purchaser's check arrives, an accountant debits cash and credits accounts receivable for the particular purchaser. The statement or voucher receipt attached to the actual check identifies the volumes purchased, related taxes and revenue paid. It is called a remittance advice or settlement statement. An accompanying statement of run tickets also should be provided by the purchaser or transporter.

To illustrate, suppose that AMP receives a statement of oil runs from a lease in which the purchaser withholds taxes and pays each interest owner the net amount due. AMP's share of oil sold is 800 barrels.

Oil revenue at $50 per bbl	$40,000
Less: 5% state severance tax	(2,000)
Net proceeds received	**$38,000**

Further, assume that AMP had previously accrued more volumes at a higher price as compared to the purchaser's remittance advice, as illustrated:

	Per AMP	Per Purchaser
AMP's share of oil sold (in bbls)	805	800
Oil price per barrel	$50.50	$50.00
Oil revenue	$40,653	$40,000
Less: 5% state severance tax	(2,033)	(2,000)
Net receivable	**$38,620**	**$38,000**

In this case, when revenues and production taxes were initially accrued, AMP would have recorded the following journal entry:

Accounts receivable – oil and gas sales	38,620	
Production tax expense	2,033	
Crude oil revenues		40,653
To record sale of oil volumes.		

Subsequently, when the purchaser's check is received, AMP records the following journal entry:

Cash	38,000	
Accounts receivable – oil and gas sales		38,000
To record collection of proceeds from purchaser for oil sales.		

As illustrated, the entries result in a $620 debit in accounts receivable that should be investigated. From AMP's perspective, it should determine whether the purchaser underpaid or whether it previously over-accrued revenues for the period in question. In practice, company-specific controls and processes should dictate review thresholds and procedures for further investigation of discrepancies.

Accrual accounting is also required for gas and NGL revenues, and similar accrual procedures should be followed, although the supporting documentation from the purchaser and the accrual methodology tends to vary and be more complex for gas.

Oil inventory

Virtually all E&P companies have oil in lease tanks, but the volumes and inventory changes typically are immaterial to financial statements. Accordingly, when preparing financial statements, many E&P companies do not recognize the inventory of crude oil in lease tanks.[6]

However, some companies have substantial crude oil inventories, such as those in remote foreign locations or on large ocean tankers. Inventories of these types, measured using any method other than the last-in-first-out (LIFO) method, should be reflected in the financial statements at the lower of cost or net realizable value (NRV). NRV is defined as estimated selling prices in the ordinary course of business, less reasonably predictable costs of completion, disposal and transportation. NRV adjustments should be recorded as an expense and, if material, presented separately on the face of the income statement.

To illustrate, assume that an E&P company's share of crude oil inventory in lease tanks at January 31, 2019, was 100 barrels, carried at an NRV of $50 per barrel. The company's share of February 28, 2019, oil inventory was 60 barrels at an NRV of $45 per barrel. The necessary adjustment would decrease the recorded inventory by $2,300, calculated as:

Beginning inventory (100 bbls @ $50)	$5,000
Less: ending inventory (60 bbls @ $45)	(2,700)
Net decrease in inventory	**$2,300**

The journal entry recorded on February 28, 2019 would be as follows:

LOE – change in inventory	2,300	
Inventory – crude oil		2,300
To record the decrease in oil inventory.		

Natural gas sales

Chapter 11 introduced measurement concepts for various hydrocarbons. As mentioned, the volume of gas produced and recorded in the operating revenue subledger is stated in Mcf. However, most gas sales contracts express price in terms of delivered MMBtu, not delivered Mcf.

Value determination

Revenue is the quantity of Mcf sold times the measured heat content per Mcf (i.e., the MMBtu per Mcf for the gas sold, also called the Btu factor) times the price per MMBtu. An Mcf of gas with a relatively high heat content has more energy, and more value, than an Mcf of gas with low heat content. Generally, dry natural gas that is virtually all methane has a Btu factor of one MMBtu per Mcf.

The heat content can be determined under various conditions, but generally the sales contract will state that the heat content is based on dry Btu (i.e., the heating content in an Mcf of gas, measured and calculated free of moisture). Some contracts may define dry Btu as Mcfs having no more than seven pounds of water. If MMBtu per Mcf is measured as though the Mcf were saturated with water, the MMBtu content would be approximately one percent less than dry MMBtu per Mcf. Note that the terms dry Btu and saturated Btu refer to relative water saturation, whereas the terms dry gas (or residue gas) and wet gas refer to NGL content.

E&P companies typically track revenue in terms of Mcf sold times a price per Mcf. To calculate sales price per Mcf, the revenues received and recorded (and paid on a price per MMBtu) can simply be divided by the recorded corresponding gas sales volume. The price per MMBtu also may be converted to a price per Mcf given the heat content (i.e., MMBtu content of an Mcf of such gas). The basic conversion formula is: (price per MMBtu) x (MMBtu per Mcf) = price per Mcf.

If the measured MMBtu per Mcf reflects an Mcf at a pressure base and water content inconsistent with the measured volume of Mcf, then multiplying measured MMBtu per Mcf by the measured volumes of Mcf will not result in the correct quantity of total MMBtu. In these cases, one or both measurements should be restated for consistent pressure base and water content.

Similarly, in converting a price per MMBtu to a price per Mcf, a consistent pressure base and water content should be used. Typically, the heat content is converted for the pressure base and water content of the volumes recorded in the E&P company's records, generally at 14.73 pounds per square inch absolute (psia) for governmental reporting. For the same mixture of natural gases, one Mcf at 14.73 psia will have less density, fewer molecules and less energy than an Mcf at the greater pressure of 15.025 psia.

Pressure-base and water-content conversion formulas are shown in the tables that follow:

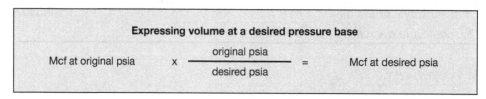

Expressing volume at a desired pressure base

$$\text{Mcf at original psia} \quad \times \quad \frac{\text{original psia}}{\text{desired psia}} \quad = \quad \text{Mcf at desired psia}$$

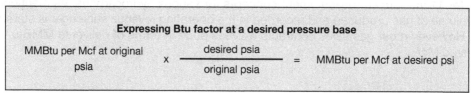

Expressing Btu factor at a desired pressure base

$$\text{MMBtu per Mcf at original psia} \quad \times \quad \frac{\text{desired psia}}{\text{original psia}} \quad = \quad \text{MMBtu per Mcf at desired psi}$$

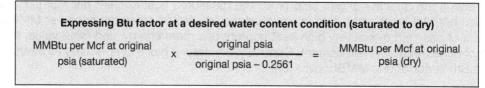

Expressing Btu factor at a desired water content condition (saturated to dry)

$$\text{MMBtu per Mcf at original psia (saturated)} \quad \times \quad \frac{\text{original psia}}{\text{original psia} - 0.2561} \quad = \quad \text{MMBtu per Mcf at original psia (dry)}$$

Expressing volume at a desired water content condition (saturated to dry)

$$\text{MMBtu per Mcf at original psia (saturated)} \times \left[1 - \frac{0.2561}{\text{original psia}} \right] = \text{Mcf at original psia (dry)}$$

Calculating gross value

$$\text{Mcf at desired psia (dry)} \times \text{MMBtu at desired psia (dry)} \times \text{Price per MMBtu} = \text{Gross value}$$

The example that follows uses these formulas. The Btu factor is converted to 14.73 psia.[7] The Btu factor is converted from saturated to dry.[8] The volumes sold in Mcf, measured at 14.73 psia (dry), are multiplied by the MMBtu per Mcf at 14.73 psia (dry) and by the contract price, stated in MMBtu, to arrive at the gross value.

Alternatively, the contract price, stated in MMBtu, can be multiplied by the MMBtu per Mcf at 14.73 psia (dry), calculating the price per Mcf, which is then multiplied by the Mcf at 14.73 psia (dry).

The volumes sold are 20,000 Mcf at 14.73 psia (dry). The Btu factor is 1.079 MMBtu per Mcf at 15.025 psia (saturated, or sat.). The contract price is $2 per MMBtu.[9] The calculations are as follows:

Step 1: $\quad \dfrac{1.079 \text{ MMBtu per Mcf}}{@ \ 15.025 \text{ psia (sat.)}} \times \dfrac{14.73 \text{ psia}}{15.025 \text{ psia}} = \dfrac{1.058 \text{ MMBtu per Mcf}}{@ \ 14.73 \text{ psia (sat.)}}$

Step 2: $\quad \dfrac{1.058 \text{ MMBtu per Mcf}}{@ \ 14.73 \text{ psia (sat.)}} \times \dfrac{14.73 \text{ psia}}{14.73 \text{ psia} - 0.2561} = \dfrac{1.077 \text{ MMBtu per Mcf}}{@ \ 14.73 \text{ psia (dry)}}$

Step 3: $\quad \dfrac{20,000 \text{ Mcf}}{@ \ 14.73 \text{ psia (dry)}} \times \dfrac{1.077 \text{ MMBtu per Mcf}}{@ \ 14.73 \text{ psia (dry)}} \times \dfrac{\$2 \text{ per}}{\text{MMBtu}} = \dfrac{\$43,080}{\text{gross value}}$

As mentioned, Step 3 may alternatively be expressed by first calculating the price per Mcf at 14.73 (dry):

Alternate: $\quad$ (a) $2 per MMBtu $\times \dfrac{1.077 \text{ MMBtu per Mcf}}{@ \ 14.73 \text{ psia (dry)}} = \dfrac{\$2.154 \text{ per Mcf}}{@ \ 14.73 \text{ psia (dry)}}$

Step 3: $\quad$ (b) $\dfrac{\$2.154 \text{ per Mcf}}{@ \ 14.73 \text{ psia (dry)}} \times \dfrac{20,000 \text{ Mcf}}{@ \ 14.73 \text{ psia (dry)}} = \dfrac{\$43,080}{\text{gross value}}$

Recording natural gas sales

Accruing the sales of unprocessed gas works much the same way as accruing the sales of oil, as previously described. For example, suppose that ABC operates the Margaret Theresa Lease 1. The royalty interest is 15 percent. All gas production is sold to RK Gas Resources, Inc. (RKGR) at $2 per Mcf. ABC has determined it is an agent for the other revenue interest owners in the property. Upon meeting the criteria for revenue recognition, the appropriate entry on ABC's books for its share of 20,000 Mcf sold in June 2019 is as follows:

Accounts receivable – oil and gas sales ($2 x 20,000 Mcf)	40,000
Gas revenues ($2 x 20,000 Mcf x 85%)	34,000
Revenue distributions payable ($2 x 20,000 Mcf x 15%)	6,000
To record sale of gas production for June 2019.	

Many automated revenue systems will make a memo entry of the total revenue from the property for internal management and regulatory reporting. The system will allocate the amounts for the working interest and royalty interest owners based on the DOI revenue deck.

When sales are made from a central delivery facility rather than the wellhead, the production department provides to the revenue accounting department the gas sales volumes, allocated by lease. The central delivery facility generally issues a gas allocation statement detailing the sales applicable to each lease. Gas allocation statements also may state the sales price, marketing costs (e.g., gas gathering charges and dehydration charges), production taxes withheld (if any) and net sales proceeds allocated to each lease or well.[10]

Residue gas and NGL sales

Accounting for residue gas and NGLs from a plant can involve complex allocations. In addition, the revenue accountant must clearly understand processing arrangements and contract provisions. Liquids contracts can have innumerable variations such as: the measurement calculation of the products; the location or the point in the process where the control of the gas and/or NGLs transfers; the party(ies) responsible for transportation, processing, fractionation, marketing and other charges; and the method used to charge for processing (e.g., a product retention or fee per Mcf, MMBtu or gallon).

A common question for oil and gas companies when accounting for residue gas and NGL sales is how to present gas processor fees and price deductions in the income statement. As explained earlier in this chapter, oil and gas companies commonly contract with midstream companies to process the natural gas and sell it to the end customer. In other cases, the midstream company might purchase all of the gas from the producer.

The producer's income statement classification of the fees involved depends on whether, for that transaction, the processor is a customer of, or a service provider to, the producer. This assessment determines whether the fees should be presented as a reduction in revenue or as an expense. Determining if the processor is a service provider to, or a customer of, the producer may require judgment in certain circumstances.

Gas purchase arrangements

In some cases, the producer sells "wet" (unprocessed) gas to a processor and the processor obtains control of the commodity when it is received at the processing facilities (i.e., at the wellhead or a central delivery point). As a result, the processor is the principal in the commodity sale arrangement with the third-party customer. There is no service provided to the producer as the processor purchases all wet gas prior to processing the commodities. Gas purchase arrangements may include fees or deductions that reduce the amounts paid by the processor to the producer (e.g., processing fees, low volume fees, dehydration fees, transportation and fractionation (T&F), marketing, etc.). The processor would record these fees/deductions as a reduction of the purchase price for the commodities.

The producer would account for the contract with the processor based on the new revenue guidance, as the processor is its customer. Any fees/deductions should be presented as a reduction of the transaction price for the commodities (rather than as an expense) as the payment does not relate to a distinct service provided by the processor in this type of arrangement.

Example – Product purchase/sale

Facts. Producer sells wet gas at the wellhead to a processor. The processor takes control of the commodity at the wellhead and may process, store or sell the wet gas at its discretion. The processor enters into contracts with third parties for the sale of the processed gas (residue gas) and NGLs, delivers the commodities directly to the third-party customers and negotiates any pricing discounts or premiums relative to the market index.

The price to be paid by the processor to the producer is 80 percent of the index price of the processed commodities at the time the gas is received, less a fixed gathering and processing fee per unit of gas received at the wellhead. These contracts commonly are called "percentage of index" (POI) arrangements.

Question. How should the producer account for this arrangement?

Analysis. The producer recognizes product revenue as the amount to be received from the processor (its customer). The gathering and processing fees should be reflected as a reduction of the transaction price (rather than as an expense) because the processor is not providing distinct services to the producer in exchange for those fees (since the processor purchased the gas at the wellhead).

Gas processing service arrangements

In other situations, a processor may be a service provider of the producer. The processor processes the gas for the producer and provides marketing services on behalf of the producer but it does not take control of the commodities. In these arrangements, the producer would record product revenue for the sale of the processed commodities to the third-party customers. Fees paid to the processor would be classified as expenses. The processor would recognize service revenue for the net fees retained for the processing and marketing services provided to the producer.

Example – Processing services

Facts. Producer enters into a gas processing service contract with Processor. Producer retains title to the wet gas throughout processing. Processor remits the residue gas back to Producer and sells the NGLs to third-party customers.

Processor obtains legal title to the NGLs momentarily before legal title is transferred to a third-party customer as the NGLs are processed and sold on the same day. Processor is contractually required to sell the NGLs upon completion of the processing services at a specified location. Processor cannot store the NGLs or direct them to another location for sale. Processor retains 20% of the actual sales proceeds received for the NGLs as compensation for its services and remits 80% of the sales proceeds to Producer. Processor is also entitled to a fixed gathering fee per unit of gas received from Producer. These contracts are commonly referred to "percentage of proceeds" (POP) arrangements.

Question. How should the parties account for this arrangement?

Analysis. Processor concludes that it does not obtain control of the NGLs before they are transferred to a third-party customer; therefore, Processor is selling the commodities on Producer's behalf (i.e., as an agent). Additionally, Processor is providing the residue gas back to Producer. As such, Processor is providing processing and marketing services to Producer and should recognize service revenue for the net amount retained from the commodity sale (ie., 20% of proceeds) and the fixed gathering fees.

Producer should recognize product revenue for the gross amounts received from the third-party customers for the residue gas and NGL sales. The fees paid to Processor (i.e., 20% of proceeds and fixed gathering fee per unit) should be reflected as expenses.

Embedded derivatives

The sales price of NGLs in contracts often is linked to other commodity prices, such as crude oil, natural gas, or a formula based on a market or index with caps and floors. In contracts where the sales price of NGLs is not clearly and closely related to the market price of NGLs, an embedded derivative may exist. These embedded derivatives may need to be accounted for separately in accordance with ASC 815.

Common royalty provisions

In addition to the basic fractional royalty in all oil and gas leases, two additional royalty provisions are common. The two provisions, first introduced in Chapter 7, are shut-in royalties and guaranteed minimum royalties. These special provisions may apply to oil or gas properties, but more often they apply to gas wells.

Shut-in royalties

Standard lease agreements provide for the payment of shut-in royalties if it is necessary to shut in a well that is capable of production. This situation can occur due to a lack of market or marketing facilities, for example. Shut-in royalty payments (in lieu of production) occur after proved reserves are recognized and must be paid to prevent forfeiture of the lease. The terms of the lease agreement may or may not provide for the recovery of shut-in royalties paid from future royalties on production that would otherwise be due.

Guaranteed minimum royalties

The lease agreement may also stipulate guaranteed minimum royalties, by which the lessor receives a minimum royalty each year, regardless of production volumes. These guaranteed payments sometimes are called fixed cash royalties. Similar to shut-in royalties, fixed cash royalties may or may not be recoverable under the terms of the lease agreement.

Enhanced recovery

Although several types of injection operations exist as discussed in Chapter 25, there are two major accounting questions pervasive to enhanced recovery: (1) accounting for material injected into the reservoir and (2) determining when the related reserves should be included in the reserves disclosures and amortization calculation.

Injection costs

Accounting for materials injected into the reservoir requires management to consider the following significant judgments:

- Are injection costs incurred after a production response to maintain current production and reservoir pressure?

- Alternatively, are injection costs incurred to recover additional hydrocarbons from a reservoir?

- If costs were incurred to recover additional hydrocarbons from a reservoir, were they intended to pressurize reservoirs before incremental production?

Based on management's evaluation, costs of enhanced recovery projects may be classified as either development costs, as defined in ASC 932-360-25-12 and 25-13 and Reg. S-X Rule 4-10(a)(7), or production costs, as defined in ASC 932-360-25-15 and Reg. S-X Rule 4-10(a)(20).

If determined to be development costs, injection costs for these projects should be capitalized, as evidenced by the following example journal entry.

Intangible costs of wells	2,000	
Accounts payable		2,000
To record gas purchased for injection into Lease A.		

Alternatively, if determined to be production costs, injection costs for these projects should be expensed, as demonstrated in the following example journal entry.

LOE – pressure maintenance	2,000	
Accounts payable		2,000
To record gas purchased for injection into Lease A.		

Recognition of reserves

Costs incurred to install enhanced recovery facilities, including the cost to drill injection wells, are properly capitalized as wells and related equipment and facilities. These costs are amortized as the related reserves are produced.

To compute amortization of enhanced recovery facilities, successful efforts companies include these costs in total proved developed costs for the property or field, to be amortized over the related total proved developed reserves, which have been increased for the incremental proved developed reserves from enhanced recovery.

Reg. S-X Rule 4-10(a)(22)(iv) limits the recognition of proved reserves from enhanced recovery:

> Reserves which can be produced economically through application of improved recovery techniques (including, but not limited to, fluid injection) are included in the proved classification when:
>
> (A) Successful testing by a pilot project in an area of the reservoir with properties no more favorable than in the reservoir as a whole, the operation of an installed program in the reservoir or an analogous reservoir, or other evidence using reliable technology establishes the reasonable certainty of the engineering analysis on which the project or program was based; and
>
> (B) The project has been approved for development by all necessary parties and entities, including governmental entities.

As noted in Chapter 15, the SPE industry definition of proved undeveloped reserves requires the successful testing by a pilot project or favorable response of an installed program in the same or an analogous reservoir with similar rock and fluid properties. It must also be reasonably certain that the project will proceed. However, the industry definition of proved undeveloped reserves remains unacceptable to the SEC and for financial reporting under ASC 932, which requires the use of the SEC definition provided in Reg. S-X Rule 4-10.

Full cost companies amortize enhanced recovery facilities as part of the total countrywide full cost pool. They may, however, exclude the capital costs of recovery projects from the amortization calculation until the reserves added by the project have been classified as proved or untill the project is determined to be unsuccessful.

Reinjected gas

In addition to determining whether the project is in the development or production stage, the source of natural gas for injection operations can significantly impact the recording of transactions.

One lease. When gas is produced from, and reinjected into, the same reservoir under a single lease agreement (or unitization agreement, as described in Chapter 22), ownership equity is undisturbed and no royalty payments are necessary. In addition, production taxes generally are not payable for gas injected into the same lease.

Reinjection may be required to extract liquids but it does not enhance the value of the gas or reduce production costs when the gas is ultimately sold. Therefore, economic value should not be assigned to the reinjected gas. All income and lifting costs are assigned to the liquids until the gas is actually sold. Statistical records should be maintained for the gas reinjection. When the gas is produced the second time, sales of the reinjected gas should be recorded as lease revenue.

Multiple leases. A similar situation exists when a single reservoir, into which gas is being reinjected, underlies more than one tract leased by the same group of working interest owners. The treatment of the working interests' shares of gas would be the same as in the single lease scenario. However, a question of royalty payments arises because some of the gas may be produced on one lease and injected on another lease, with different royalty owners. The best solution is to secure the royalty owners' agreement to unitize, which effectively converts several leases into a single property. Injections, using one lease's wells, may increase production from wells on other leases producing from the same reservoir.

Without this agreement, and assuming that a royalty must be paid each time gas is produced and leaves a lease, these royalty payments should be charged to the lease benefiting from the injection operations. All expenses should be considered lifting costs attributable to any oil and NGLs produced from the reservoir, and none of the injected volumes should be included in revenues of the working interest owners.

Gas acquired from other sources. Additional accounting challenges occur if the extraneous gas used for injection (often as part of a secondary or tertiary recovery program) is either purchased from outsiders (including royalty owners) or transferred from other reservoirs owned by the producer that is conducting the injection program. These situations are typical of pressure maintenance operations that inject gas or combined gas and products. Therefore, this section makes frequent references to pressure maintenance operations. Since the accounting problems presented by injected gas are identical to those of injected products, the explanation applies to both.

Royalty owners. If extraneous gas is injected into a reservoir, it is customary for the lease's royalty owners to permit the later recovery of the extraneous gas without receiving associated royalty payments. An important factor in determining appropriate accounting procedure is whether or not all of the injected gas and products will be recoverable. Generally, some injected products and gas will remain in reservoirs because it is not economically feasible to recover all of them.

A cumulative record of gas injected should be maintained and the volume of re-produced gas should be determined at the time of sale. Production taxes and royalty payments may not be due for re-produced gas. Accounting methodologies also vary, which may follow the method prescribed by the tax authority or the lease agreement, although any of the following assumptions may also be reasonable:

- All injected gas is re-produced before any gas reserves.

- All injected gas is produced after estimated reserves.

- Production is proportionate.

Gas purchased from others. The purchase and subsequent re-production of injected commodities acquired from outsiders, including amounts purchased from royalty owners on leases from which gas is transferred, adhere to the principles described above.

Gas transferred from another lease. Gas production and reinjection by the same company generally are not recorded as revenue and expense items. However, they may be recorded as such to better track each field's performance and then eliminated in consolidation.

· · ·

---

1   The SEC would not object to certain public business entities (PBEs) (i.e., entities that are PBEs solely due to the inclusion of their financial statements or financial information in another entity's filing with the SEC) adopting the new revenue standard using the timeline otherwise afforded private companies.

2   Each owner's interest is based on a title opinion, rendered by the legal department after examining title abstracts supplied by the operator of the property.

3   This division order was developed by the National Association of Division Order Analysts (NADOA) and is the primary form used by the industry. The NADOA also publishes the National Association of Division Order Analysts Journal, which contains guidelines for writing division orders.

4   Creating an accounting cost center by well is necessary when joint venture owners elect to "go nonconsent."

5   The revenue deck includes all owners: working interest, royalty, overriding royalty, state, federal and Native American royalty. This deck should sum to 100 percent. Most revenue accounting systems will then establish a payable for each owner in the deck. Payables are aggregated, by owner, for all properties. On a specified date, the system prints and distributes a single revenue check to each owner for the accumulated royalty payable for a given production month.

6   17 of 33 respondents (52 percent) to the *2019 PricewaterhouseCoopers Survey of U.S. Petroleum Accounting Practices* (Question L1) record product stored in lease tanks as inventory in their financial statements, while fewer responding companies record product in pipelines (13 of 33, or 39 percent) and product in gathering systems (nine of 33, or 27 percent) as inventory.

7   To convert to the same pressure base used in the volume measurement recorded in the accounting system.

8   The water content was converted to dry (rather than the volume converted to saturated) because most gas contracts specify Btu measurement in a dry condition, and most accounting systems record the volume and Btu in dry condition.

9   Contract prices stated in MMBtu are independent of gas temperature or pressure. The volume and Btu factor must be stated at the same pressure base to calculate value.

10   An illustration of a gas allocation statement is available in COPAS Accounting Guideline No. 15 (AG-15), *Gas Accounting Manual*, (revised 2010).

Gas Imbalances

- **Producer gas imbalances**

- **Pipeline gas imbalances**

Photograph by istock.com/kodda

Accounting for the sale of unprocessed gas is described and illustrated in Chapter 12, along with accounting for the sale of gas recovered from a gas plant. In those explanations, it was assumed that the operator sold gas to a single purchaser and all working interest owners were allocated revenues in proportion to their contractual ownership interests. However, in many cases, one or more working interest owners may be allocated a volume of gas that is different than their entitled share of production for the period. This producer gas imbalance is sometimes referred to as a "producer imbalance."

Another common imbalance occurs when a working interest owner nominates and sells to a customer (or customers), and the pipeline delivers to that customer a gas volume that differs from the working interest owner's share of gas in the pipeline. This is known as a pipeline gas imbalance, although common industry terms may also refer to it as a transporter imbalance or shipper imbalance.

Pipeline and producer imbalances require coordination among operators, nonoperators, consumers and pipeline companies. COPAS Accounting Guideline No. 8 (AG-8), *Natural Gas Administrative Issues,* and COPAS AG-22, *Producer Gas Imbalances,* provide guidance for accountants regarding these imbalances.

Producer gas imbalances

The rights and responsibilities of the joint venture's working interest owners regarding producer imbalances should be addressed in the gas balancing agreement (GBA) entered into early in the joint venture. The GBA is often attached as an exhibit to the joint operating agreement.

Unfortunately, many operating agreements do not contain GBAs, forcing the parties to work out an acceptable solution for imbalances, which are typically settled by asking those owners who have an under-take in one period to take an extra share of the property's future production. Alternatively, an owner with an over-take may pay cash to the other owners in periods that follow the over-take.

Gas balancing agreements

Typically, a GBA is an integral part of the joint operating agreement executed prior to drilling a well. The GBA reduces operational and settlement conflicts and should be negotiated as soon as possible. Although more fully addressed in COPAS AG-22, major aspects of these agreements include:

- **Balancing unit and geological formation.** Names the geological formation the GBA covers and addresses the computation of balancing (i.e., whether it will be on an Mcf or MMBtu basis).

- **Parties' rights and obligations.** Identifies the rights and obligations of both the operator and nonoperator(s) concerning nominating gas, curtailments, operational questions, limits on over-produced gas and rights of parties in case an over-produced working interest owner declares bankruptcy.

- **Statement of gas balancing.** Specifies the content of the statement, the party responsible for its preparation and the timing of its preparation. Typically, the operator prepares the statement.

- **Ownership interest transfers.** Dictates whether gas imbalances are settled in cash or transferred to the new owner when a working interest is sold.

- **Royalty and production tax payments.** Identifies the responsibility of each producer for paying royalties and taxes.

- **Volumetric balancing methods.** Provides alternatives for settling imbalances volumetrically (e.g., gas make-up, exchange make-up or offsetting of imbalances).

- **Cash settlement methodology.** Describes the frequency of cash settlements and their valuation methodology: actual proceeds; last-in, first-out (LIFO); first-in, first-out (FIFO); or current market value.

Calculating producer gas imbalances

The monthly production volume allocation statement is the primary source for computing producer balancing positions. The statement identifies the quantity of produced gas that was physically transferred to working interest owners. If a well is connected to more than one pipeline, it requires multiple allocation statements. The sum of all allocation statements for the well or property equals its monthly production.

A producer imbalance may be calculated as follows:

Producer imbalance	=	**WI owner's production taken**	–	**WI owner's entitled share of production***

> * Calculated as the volume of produced gas multiplied by the owner's gross WI. If a royalty interest owner takes its royalty in-kind, the WI owner's entitled share of production is based on net revenue interest.

The operator prepares a monthly gas balancing statement assigning each working interest owner a cumulative over- or under-produced position. Nonoperators should verify the accuracy of the statement including their working interest, total production and allocated share. All discrepancies should be communicated to the operator and resolved.

Settling producer gas imbalances

The operator settles producer imbalances according to the terms of the GBA. In the absence of a GBA, working interest owners determine the settlement alternatives prior to fully depleting the reserves.

Gas make-up, cash balancing and offsetting imbalances are the three most common methods of settling producer imbalances. In gas make-up, under-produced owners sell gas volumes larger than their entitled amounts and over-produced owners sell gas volumes smaller than their entitled amounts to eliminate the imbalance. Cash balancing means paying cash to the under-produced party for the imbalance. Working interest owners also may agree to offset imbalances of two or more wells or properties in which they own interests.

Accounting for producer gas imbalances

Historically, gas balancing was accounted for by a policy election: either the sales method or the entitlements method. Both methods met GAAP and SEC requirements under ASC 932-10-S99-5.

However, the ASC guidance was superseded by ASC 606, *Revenue from Contracts with Customers*. Therefore, accounting for production imbalances is no longer a policy election. Entities should evaluate their policies to ensure that they align with the ASC 606 standard, which means accounting for commodity sales contracts by recognizing revenue to depict the transfer of goods or services in an amount that reflects the consideration the entity expects in exchange. Generally, the legacy sales method is viewed as more consistent with the new standard's principles than the legacy entitlements method.

Under the sales method, a working interest owner records revenue only when gas is produced and sold on the owner's behalf. No receivables or payables are recorded for producer imbalances; instead, proved reserves are adjusted.

When a working interest owner over-produces beyond the designated share of remaining estimated reserves, it recognizes the excess gas imbalance as a liability on its balance sheet. An under-produced owner may determine that the over-produced owner's share of remaining reserves is insufficient to settle the imbalance. If so, the under-produced owner recognizes a receivable, to the extent collectible, from the over-produced owner.

Pipeline gas imbalances

The roles and rights of parties involved in a pipeline gas imbalance are established largely by contract and by pipeline rules subject to the approval of the Federal Energy Regulatory Commission (FERC) or other regulatory bodies.

Roles of operators and nonoperators

Field operators monitor and control the flow of gas production from wells. To determine gas availability, operators estimate monthly production to nonoperators, beginning the nomination process. Nonoperators selling their own gas identify a market for their products and submit a nomination to the well operator or pipeline company. During the month after the gas flow, the pipeline company prepares a production volume allocation statement for the nonoperators, allocating actual production to each working interest owner.

Nominations

For a producer to market its own gas, it makes a nomination to the operator or pipeline company. If the pipeline's capacity exceeds the month's total nominated volumes, it confirms the nomination. However, if nominations exceed capacity, the pipeline operator allocates volumes based on service type (firm versus interruptible transportation). After revising the nominations, the producer and pipeline confirm them. The producer's customer also confirms its nominated receipt volume with the pipeline. Differences between confirmed nominations and actual gas flow are minimized to prevent pipeline imbalance penalties.

If actual production varies considerably from the confirmed nomination, the operator may modify the physical gas flow, or the parties may revise the nominations. Nominations are further described in Chapter 27.

Allocations

Despite the parties' best efforts, physical gas flow seldom equals the total of confirmed nominations. When that happens, the parties involved, including the operator, nonoperators, pipeline and shippers, agree to determine an allocation method prior to physical flow. These predetermined allocation agreements address the contractual and regulatory requirements.

Common allocation methods include: (1) pro rata allocation based on confirmed nominations, (2) allocation based on entitlements and (3) allocation based on swing volumes (i.e., the difference between total confirmed nominations and delivered volumes). The producer records over-deliveries or under-deliveries to the pipeline as receivables or payables, respectively.

- Under a pro rata allocation method, every shipper's confirmed nomination volume is divided by the total confirmed nominations to determine the shipper's pro rata share of imbalances.

- The entitlement method involves an allocation of volumes based on a contractually determined proportionate share of gas.

- In agreements containing a swing volume allocation provision, the pipeline company or designated shipper (generally the largest shipper) retains any imbalance while other shippers are allocated their nominated volumes.

Settling pipeline gas imbalances

Since the implementation of FERC Order 636 (issued in 1992), the settlement of imbalances follows one of three common methods: (1) imbalance trading allows two different shippers on the same pipeline to offset imbalances by trading their under- and over-delivered positions; (2) volumetric imbalance make-ups allow the producer to separately identify and nominate additional or lesser volumes; (3) cash in/out settlement enables the producer to pay or receive cash for the imbalance.

Imbalances typically are valued according to contractual requirements. These may require valuing the imbalances at:

- Current mainline index prices.

- The pipeline's weighted average cost of goods sold.

- A weighted average sales price.

- Another accepted method.

In addition, the pipeline may impose penalties for imbalances that exceed specific tolerances in the tariff. Producers should assess the carrying value of unsettled pipeline imbalances to ensure the amounts agree with the pipeline tariff and they have properly accrued any penalties.

Accounting for pipeline gas imbalances

Pipeline imbalances generally are recorded as accounts receivable or payable at values that reflect the contractual arrangements with the pipeline company. The terms of a GBA may also meet the definition of a derivative or contain an embedded option feature requiring recognition under the provisions of ASC 815, *Derivatives and Hedging*.

● ● ●

Production Costs

Reg. S-X Rule 4-10(a)(20) defines production costs as:

> (i) Costs incurred to operate and maintain wells and related equipment and facilities, including depreciation and applicable operating costs of support equipment and facilities and other costs of operating and maintaining those wells and related equipment and facilities. They become part of the cost of oil and gas produced. Examples of production costs (sometimes called lifting costs) are:
>
>   (A) Costs of labor to operate the wells and related equipment and facilities.
>
>   (B) Repairs and maintenance.
>
>   (C) Materials, supplies, and fuel consumed and supplies utilized in operating the wells and related equipment and facilities.
>
>   (D) Property taxes and insurance applicable to proved properties and wells and related equipment and facilities.
>
>   (E) Severance taxes.
>
> (ii) Some support equipment or facilities may serve two or more oil and gas producing activities and may also serve transportation, refining, and marketing activities. To the extent that the support equipment and facilities are used in oil and gas producing activities, their depreciation and applicable operating costs become exploration, development or production costs, as appropriate. Depreciation, depletion, and amortization of capitalized acquisition, exploration, and development costs are not production costs but also become part of the cost of oil and gas produced along with production (lifting) costs identified above.

Accounting for production costs

Production costs (i.e., lease operating expenses or lifting costs) generally are expensed as incurred. However, two exceptions exist:

- The recording of oil and gas inventory at cost.

- The accrual or deferral of production costs, if material, associated with gas imbalances.

The first exception recognizes that production costs otherwise might be allocated to inventory and cost of goods sold. However, because oil and gas inventories often are insignificant, E&P company balance sheets do not always report them. The *2019 PricewaterhouseCoopers Survey of U.S. Petroleum Accounting Practices* (Question L1) found that 17 of 33 (52 percent) responding companies record product stored in tanks as inventory in their financial statements, while fewer responding companies record product in pipelines (13 of 33, or 39 percent) and product in gathering systems (nine of 33, or 27 percent) as inventory.

Applying the second exception requires accruing or deferring production costs to more closely match expenses with related revenues. Chapter 13 further describes accounting for gas imbalances.

Use of subaccounts

Petroleum accountants should be familiar with the functional accounts that E&P companies commonly use to capture production costs. The accounting system must contain sufficient information to satisfy GAAP requirements as well as meet the needs of company management when they evaluate operations. Accounting records also should furnish the necessary data for calculating income taxes.

Records kept at the well and lease levels are most important for management control, joint interest billings, reserve determination and income tax accounting. For financial reporting, lease operating expenses can be aggregated either by country or by large geographical area. Although some costs can be identified readily with a well or lease, other costs must be allocated using a reasonable basis.

Figure 14-1 provides examples of subaccounts for lease operating expenses:

Figure 14-1
Illustrative lease operating expenses subaccounts

Subaccount name	Classification
Salaries and wages	Direct
Employee benefits	Direct
Contract pumping services	Direct
Repairs and maintenance of surface equipment	Direct
Ad valorem, production and severance taxes	Direct
Other taxes	Direct
Fuel, water and lubrication	Direct
Supplies	Direct
Environment and safety	Direct
Shut-in and minimum royalties	Direct
Other royalties	Direct
Pressure maintenance	Direct
Compressor rentals	Direct
Supervision	Indirect
Overhead	Indirect
Well services and workovers	Direct or indirect
Saltwater disposal	Direct or indirect
Auto and truck expenses	Direct or indirect
Insurance	Direct or indirect
Treating expenses	Direct or indirect
Other	Direct or indirect

Assume that E-Lease Oil Co. (E-Lease) charges any lease operating expenses closely related to individual leases directly to the lease operating expenses account. E-Lease accumulates indirect costs in the company's clearing and apportionment accounts and then allocates such costs to the lease operating expenses of individual leases.

Classifications of specific costs will vary by company. Some are considered indirect due to their nature (e.g., depreciation of support facilities and saltwater disposal costs). Others are categorized as indirect due to the practical aspects of cost accumulation.

It may not be immediately clear how to classify a particular cost because subaccounts tend to mix classifications by nature (salaries, supplies, insurance) and by function (well service, repairs, auto and truck). Each E&P company should establish its own practice.

For example, if E-Lease uses field labor in well services activities, it may charge the labor costs to the salaries and wages subaccount, rather than the well services and workovers subaccount. The chosen classification system should be understood clearly and followed consistently throughout the company.

Other apportionment accounts

It can be difficult to choose a reasonable basis for measuring and allocating the activity related to each lease. Accordingly, E&P companies may use other apportionment accounts to accumulate charges that are ultimately allocated to individual lease operating expense accounts or asset accounts.

The typical methods for apportioning various costs incurred depending on the related activity are as follows:

- **District expenses.** Allocated among acquisition, exploration, development and production activities; the portion allocated to production activity is further allocated to individual properties based on the number of producing wells.

- **Regional expenses.** Related to regional activities and the operation of regional offices, these costs may be initially allocated to districts based on their individual expenditures, and subsequently treated like other district expenses by allocating the costs to acquisition, exploration, development and production activities.

- **Drilling equipment.** Apportioned to exploratory and development wells according to a footage or day rate.

- **Air compressor plant and systems.** Apportioned based on volumes.

- **Dwelling.** Allocated like district expenses.

- **Electric power system.** Apportioned based on power used.

- **Fire protection system.** Allocated based on the number of wells or facilities served.

- **Gas compressor plant.** Apportioned based on volumes.

- **Gas gathering system.** Apportioned based on volume and/or wells served.

- **Oil gathering system.** Apportioned based on volumes and/or wells served.

- **Waterflooding system.** Allocated based on volumes of water used.

- **Other service facilities.** Allocated based on hours or days used.

- **Transportation equipment.** Allocated based on miles driven or hours used.

- **Warehouse and shop.** Allocated based on items issued, cost of items issued or direct labor hours, as determined for each lease.

Choosing a reasonable and consistent basis for charging costs to the activities that use the services is essential to using apportionment accounts.

Direct production costs

As previously mentioned, direct costs are closely related to the production of oil or gas from specific mineral properties and are controlled largely at the lease level. Several direct production costs from Figure 14-1 are described in this section.

Salaries and wages

Field employees consist of pumpers, gaugers, roustabouts and other employees ranked below first-level supervisors. Stationed directly on producing properties, these employees are concerned with the basic lease, facility operations and routine maintenance. They customarily use time sheets to record the hours spent on each job, well or lease. These time sheets are the basis for normal charges to individual properties or wells during the monthly joint interest billing cycle.

Employee benefits

Employee benefits are an element of the total cost of labor that may also be allocated to individual leases. Many companies estimate these costs using a ratio of employee benefits to direct labor costs.

For example, E-Lease estimates that its employee benefits represent 20 percent of direct labor costs. The company records actual charges for health care premiums and other benefits in an employee benefits account. At each pay period (or monthly), E-Lease debits lease operating expenses and credits the employee benefits account for 20 percent of its actual labor costs.

Contract pumping services

Pumping and routine maintenance services are typically performed by an individual on a contract basis. The individual contracts with the company to render certain services on selected properties for a defined fee. Compensation depends on the number of wells, locations, type of services, time schedules and other factors.

The individual is an independent contractor, not an employee. Invoices include all contract expenses, including time, vehicle use and travel. Unusual items are billed separately. Monthly invoices from contractors should contain the details necessary for accounting entries.

Repairs and maintenance of surface equipment

This account is typically charged for costs of repairing surface equipment at the lease, such as tank batteries, separators, flow lines, lease buildings, engines, motors, other above-ground production equipment and lease roads.

When company employees make these repairs, the labor costs may be charged to the salaries and wages subaccount rather than to the repairs and maintenance of surface equipment subaccount. However, in general, costs to repair the well or subsurface well equipment should be charged to the well services and workovers subaccount (see discussion in following section).

Ad valorem, production and severance taxes

Ad valorem taxes are accrued as lease operating expenses based on a reasonable estimate of the assessment for the period. Production and severance taxes are accrued when the related production occurs or when recording the revenue upon which the taxes are based. These taxes are based on either the value or volume of product sold (or a combination of value and volume) depending on the tax jurisdiction where the individual property is located.

As an example, assume that in June 2019, E-Lease's share of production from the Eagle Coast lease was 10,000 barrels of oil that sold for $50 per barrel. State production taxes imposed were 6 percent of the revenue value, and the oil purchaser is responsible for making all necessary disbursements to other owners in the lease.

Assuming all revenue recognition criteria have been met, E-lease records revenues and related production taxes, as illustrated in the journal entry below:

Accounts receivable – oil and gas sales	500,000	
Production tax expense	30,000	
Crude oil revenues		500,000
Accounts payable		30,000
To record production and sale of crude oil and related taxes from the Eagle Coast lease for June 2019.		

Indirect production costs

Indirect production costs are:

- Not closely related to oil and gas production on specific leases.

- Not controllable at the lease level.

These costs are accounted for in much the same way as overhead in that costs of a function or activity are accumulated, then allocated to individual properties according to direct labor hours, direct labor costs, number of wells, time of equipment use, volume of service rendered, production volumes or some other reasonable basis. Given the complexity of the required allocation, many companies choose to accumulate these costs in their clearing and apportionment accounts.

Virtually all clearing and apportionment accounts are used to record the depreciation of tangible real and/or personal property. Although ASC 932-360-25-16 states that successful efforts accounting capitalizes the costs of support equipment and facilities used to produce oil and gas, it does not specify the depreciation method; that choice is left to management.

Some companies also consider certain expenses incurred at their central administrative offices as production costs. Management should clearly understand the nature of these expenses and appropriately accumulate and classify them. General corporate overhead is not included in a company's production costs.

Well services and workovers

The accounting treatment for well services and workovers varies from company to company. Workovers are remedial operations undertaken to maintain maximum oil production. Some companies include repairs in this category; others record them in the repairs and maintenance of surface equipment sub account discussed previously.

In the example herein, E-Lease charges its well services and workovers expense subaccount for the costs of repairing wellhead connections, swabbing, performing clean-out, scraping paraffin, and replacing or servicing gas lift valves.

It also charges to this expense subaccount third-party service costs related to reconditioning, repairing or reworking a producing well. In addition, it charges to this expense subaccount third-party service costs for restoring efficient operating conditions, such as re-perforating casing, repairing casing leaks, or acidizing and shooting.

An important determination for workover costs specifically is the classification as an expense or capital cost. Reg. S-X Rule 4-10 notes that workover costs incurred solely to maintain or increase production from an existing completion interval shall be charged to expense as incurred, consistent with the accounting for all other production costs.

However, if workovers increase proved reserves, a company may capitalize the workover costs to oil and gas properties. Common activities which may increase proved reserves include costs incurred to deepen the well to another horizon, attempts to secure production from a shallower horizon (i.e., recompletions), or improved (not restored) access to proved reserves from a producing horizon (e.g., through fracking or lateral drilling).

If the deeper drilling or attempted recompletion at a shallower horizon reaches proved reserves at that horizon, the company would capitalize the costs as development costs. Along these same lines, costs incurred to secure production in a horizon that is not already proved would be recorded as exploratory drilling costs. Regardless of the type of capitalized cost, the key consideration is determining if the effort finds new proved reserves. If it does not, the costs must be expensed.

Saltwater disposal

Saltwater is a frequent byproduct of oil and gas production. Because it is considered waste, it must be disposed of with care. Customarily, saltwater from a well is gathered and reinjected into a subsurface formation.

If only one property is served by a particular saltwater disposal system, these expenses are considered direct costs charged to a lease operating expense account.

When a disposal system serves more than one lease, accountants must apportion the costs. If the ratio of water to oil does not vary significantly among the properties, the costs may be apportioned based on the number of wells served. However, if the oil-to-water ratio varies significantly among the properties, a company may consider basing the charge on the volume of saltwater disposed of.

For example, assume that the oil-to-water ratio is about the same from each well in a reservoir served by a saltwater disposal system. The June 2019 costs for operating the system were $35,000. This system serves Lease 10101, with two producing wells, Lease 10102, with three producing wells, and Lease 10103, with five producing wells.

To apportion the costs based on the number of wells, the company would record the following journal entry:

LOE – saltwater disposal (Lease 10101)	7,000	
LOE – saltwater disposal (Lease 10102)	10,500	
LOE – saltwater disposal (Lease 10103)	17,500	
Accounts payable		35,000
To apportion the June 2019 saltwater disposal expense.		

Lease operating statements

The operator typically prepares monthly lease operating statements (production cost statements) for each well, lease or property. Since individual properties often are used as cost centers for successful efforts accounting, these statements serve as a form of income statement.

Some companies' statements include revenue from production while others show expenses only. Details of all items are reported for the current month along with year-to-date totals. Any additional information included will depend on the entity's needs and circumstances. A portion of E-Lease's operating statement for Lease 24001 (with a one-eighth royalty) is illustrated in Figure 14-2.

Figure 14-2
Illustrative lease operating statement

E-Lease Oil Co.			Lease:	24001
Lease Operating Statement			WI:	73.000%
2019			NRI:	63.875%

	January	February		Year-to-Date
8/8ths volumes sold				
Oil (Bbls)	354	362		4,200
Gas (Mcf)	1,400	1,350		12,000
NGL (Bbls)	–	–		–
E-Lease's sales prices				
Oil $ per Bbl	$50.40	$51.10		$50.00
Gas $ per Mcf	$2.85	$2.53		$2.50
NGL $ per Bbl	$0.00	$0.00		$0.00
Price per BOE	$37.19	$37.33		$38.71
Revenues @ 8/8ths				
Oil	$17,842	$18,498		$210,000
Gas	3,990	3,416		30,000
NGL	–	–		–
Total revenues	21,832	21,914	*10 more monthly columns would exist on a standard lease operating statement.*	240,000
Less royalties and ORRIs	(2,881)	(2,991)		(31,500)
WI revenues @ 100%	18,951	18,923		208,500
WI expenses @ 100%				
Salaries and wages	120	115		1,520
Employee benefits	75	72		950
Contract pumping	225	225		2,700
Other subaccounts	550	895		7,999
Total expenses	970	1,307		13,169
WI net cash flow @ 100%	$17,981	$17,616		$195,331
E-Lease's share:				
Revenues @ 63.875%	$13,945	$13,998		$153,300
Expenses @ 73.000%	(708)	(954)		(9,613)
Cash flow	$13,237	$13,044		$143,687
Revenues per BOE	$37.19	$37.33		$38.71
Expenses per BOE	(1.65)	(2.22)		(2.12)
Cash flow per BOE	$35.54	$35.11		$36.59

• • •

CHAPTER

15

Oil and Gas Reserves

Key concepts

- **SEC reserves definitions**

- **Industry reserves definitions**

- **Reserves estimation**

- **Reserves schedules**

- **Reserves reports**

- **SPE standards**

Photograph by istock.com/Leonid Ikan

Reserves are considered a category of overall oil and gas resources. Reserves estimates usually are made by petroleum reservoir engineers and occasionally by geologists. The emergence of unconventional resource plays has added complexity to reserves estimation (compared with conventional resources).

Proved reserves are a critical component of an E&P company's financial reporting disclosure requirements as demonstrated by the following:

- Under successful efforts accounting, exploratory well costs remain capitalized only if they result in finding proved reserves as discussed in Chapter 6.

- Capitalized costs of proved properties are amortized on a units-of-production basis, calculated as the ratio between volumes currently produced and the sum of those volumes plus remaining proved reserves, as explained in Chapter 16.

- Proved properties' net capitalized costs are limited to certain computations of value based on reserves, including proved reserves, as discussed in Chapters 17 and 18.

- Public companies must disclose certain supplemental unaudited information about proved reserves volumes, as outlined in Chapter 30.

- Reserves are also used to determine the fair value of oil and gas properties in business combinations, as explained further in Chapter 32.

SEC reserves definitions

Financial reporting uses a definition of proved reserves adopted by the SEC in 2008. Prior to 2008, SEC definitions were not consistent with the *Petroleum Resources Management System* (PRMS) definition, discussed in a subsequent section. In 2008, the SEC issued its final rule, *Modernization of Oil and Gas Reporting* (the Final Rule), which revised the SEC definitions to consider the then-current environment, newer technology, market evolution and other factors. As a result, the SEC definitions and the PRMS definitions are now more consistent.

SEC proved reserves

Reg. S-X Rule 4-10(a)(22) defines proved oil and gas reserves as:

> [T]hose quantities of oil and gas, which, by analysis of geoscience and engineering data, can be estimated with reasonable certainty to be economically producible – from a given date forward, from known reservoirs, and under existing economic conditions, operating methods, and government regulations – prior to the time at which contracts providing the right to operate expire, unless evidence indicates that renewal is reasonably certain, regardless of whether deterministic or probabilistic methods are used for the estimation. The project to extract the hydrocarbons must have commenced or the operator must be reasonably certain that it will commence the project within a reasonable time.

Note that the SEC requirement uses the deterministic approach (reasonable certainty) rather than the probabilistic approach (90 percent certainty), as discussed later in the chapter.

The following guidance based on industry practices illustrates how to apply the phrase "existing economic conditions" to proved reserves as of the end of the period (i.e., December 31 for calendar year-end companies):

- Reserves should reflect the 12-month average prices for oil, gas and NGLs calculated as the unweighted arithmetic average of the first day of the month for each month within the 12-month period prior to the end of the reporting period, unless prices are defined by contractual arrangement, excluding escalations for future conditions. The average price should reflect the value of the proved reserves at the physical location, adjusted for quality differences.

  For example, assume for a given field that the average gas price for the 12 months ended December 31 is $2.50 per MMBtu. A contract in December calls for the sale of one Bcf of gas from the field in the next calendar year at a fixed price of $2.75 per MMBtu, while a second contract in the next calendar year calls for the sale of two Bcf of gas at five cents over index prices. In this case, the fixed (and therefore determinable) price of $2.75 per MMBtu is used for the one Bcf of reserves to be produced in the subsequent year, while the average price of $2.50 per MMBtu is used to calculate all other reserves for the field, as the contract price based on index pricing is not fixed and determinable at December 31.

- In the absence of fixed and determinable contract prices, the oil, gas and NGL market average prices for the 12 months ended December 31 should be used, even though these prices may be materially higher or lower than the spot price as of December 31. The SEC rules dictate an average price mechanism, intended to reduce volatility in reserves estimates. However, when prices are rising, reserves estimates will be lower as of period end using the average price rather than the spot price.

- Quality adjustments should reflect those that are actually received by the end of the period. They should not reflect forecast adjustments unless they are fixed and determinable from contracts that exist at the end of the period.

- The production and severance tax rates used to calculate the value of estimated proved reserves should reflect laws enacted as of period end. For example, if a state law enacted in November 2019 raised the severance tax rate from four percent to five percent, effective January 1, 2020, the severance tax rate for estimating the proved reserves recoverable under December 31, 2019, economic conditions would be five percent.

- Future operating costs should reflect cost levels actually incurred as of period-end, applied to all expected future operations, including major maintenance such as capital workovers.

The SEC definition of proved oil and gas reserves continues:

(i)   The area of the reservoir considered as proved includes:

    (A) The area identified by drilling and limited by fluid contacts, if any, and

    (B) Adjacent undrilled portions of the reservoir that can, with reasonable certainty, be judged to be continuous with it and to contain economically producible oil or gas on the basis of available geosciences and engineering data.

(ii) In the absence of data on fluid contacts, proved quantities in a reservoir are limited by the lowest known hydrocarbons (LKH) as seen in a well penetration unless geosciences, engineering, or performance data and reliable technology establishes a lower contact with reasonable certainty.

(iii) Where direct observation from well penetrations has defined a highest known oil (HKO) elevation and the potential exists for an associated gas cap, proved oil reserves may be assigned in the structurally higher portions of the reservoir only if geoscience, engineering or performance data and reliable technology establish the higher contact with reasonable certainty.

(iv) Reserves which can be produced economically through application of improved recovery techniques (including but not limited to, fluid injection) are included in the proved classification when:

    (A) Successful testing by a pilot project in an area of the reservoir with properties no more favorable than in the reservoir as a whole, the operation of an installed program in the reservoir or an analogous reservoir, or other evidence using reliable technology establishes the reasonable certainty of the engineering analysis on which the project or program was based; and

    (B) The project has been approved for development by all necessary parties and entities, including governmental entities.

(v)   Existing economic conditions include prices and costs at which economic producibility from a reservoir is to be determined. The price shall be the average price during the 12-month period prior to the ending date of the period covered by the report, determined as an unweighted arithmetic average of the first-day-of the-month price for each month within such period, unless prices are defined by contractual arrangements, excluding escalations based upon future conditions.

Developed and undeveloped reserves

Reg. S-X Rule 4-10(a)(6) defines <u>developed</u> oil and gas reserves as:

[R]eserves of any category that can be expected to be recovered:

(i)   Through existing wells with existing equipment and operating methods or in which the cost of the required equipment is relatively minor compared to the cost of a new well; and

(ii) Through installed extraction equipment and infrastructure operational at the time of the reserves estimate if the extraction is by means not involving a well.

Reg. S-X Rule 4-10(a)(31) defines <u>undeveloped</u> oil and gas reserves as:

[R]eserves of any category that are expected to be recovered from new wells on undrilled acreage, or from existing wells where a relatively major expenditure is required for recompletion.

(i)   Reserves on undrilled acreage shall be limited to those directly offsetting development spacing areas that are reasonably certain of production when drilled, unless evidence using reliable technology exists that establishes reasonable certainty of economic produciblity at greater distances.

(ii) Undrilled locations can be classified as having undeveloped reserves only if a development plan has been adopted indicating that they are scheduled to be drilled within five years, unless the specific circumstances, justify a longer time.

(iii) Under no circumstances shall estimates for undeveloped reserves be attributable to any acreage for which an application of fluid injection or other improved recovery technique is contemplated, unless such techniques have been proved effective by actual projects in the same reservoir or an analogous reservoir, as defined in paragraph (a)(2) of [Regulation S-X Rule 4-10], or by other evidence using reliable technology establishing reasonable certainty.

The definition of undeveloped reserves includes the concept that they should be recognized only if the adopted development plan schedules the drilling of the reserves within five years, unless specific circumstances support a longer period of time. The SEC published a *Compliance and Disclosure Interpretation* of this definition (Question 131.03), which describes additional factors to consider in determining whether or not circumstances justify recognizing reserves when development may extend beyond five years.

These factors include:

- The company's level of ongoing significant development activities in the area.

- The company's historical record of completing development for comparable long-term projects.

- The length of time the leases have been maintained or reserves have been booked without significant development activities.

- The company's history of following previously adopted development plans.

- Delays in development caused by factors external to the company, specifically related to the physical operating environment.

The interpretation also indicates that no particular type of project justifies a longer time period, and any extensions beyond five years should be the exception and not the rule. Determining when to record undeveloped reserves, and how long to continue recording them, requires careful consideration of all the pertinent facts and circumstances.

Subcategories of proved developed reserves

Proved developed reserves consist of proved developed producing (PDP) reserves and proved developed non-producing (PDNP) reserves. Proved developed producing reserves are those expected to be recovered from completion intervals producing at the time of the estimate. Two types of proved developed non-producing reserves exist: shut-in reserves and behind-pipe reserves.

Shut-in reserves are those expected to be recovered from completion intervals that were open at the time of the reserves estimate but are not producing for one of three reasons:

- The well is shut-in, intentionally, for market conditions such as perceived temporary declines in oil or gas prices.

- The well has not yet begun production from the completed interval, perhaps because production equipment or pipelines are not yet installed.

- Mechanical difficulties were encountered and must be corrected.

Behind-pipe reserves are those expected to be recovered from completion intervals not yet open but that remain behind casing in existing wells. These wells usually are producing but from another completion interval. Additional completion work is needed before behind-pipe reserves can be produced. A requirement for developing behind-pipe reserves is that they can be produced with minimal capital expenditures, compared with the cost of drilling a new well. If the capital costs are large, these reserves should be classified as proved undeveloped (PUD) reserves.

Probable and possible reserves

Reg S-X Rule 4-10 (a)(18) defines probable reserves as:

> [T]hose additional reserves that are less certain to be recovered than proved reserves but which, together with proved reserves, are as likely as not to be recovered.
>
> (i)   When deterministic methods are used, it is as likely as not that actual remaining quantities recovered will exceed the sum of estimated proved plus probable reserves. When probabilistic methods are used, there should be at least a 50% probability that the actual quantities recovered will equal or exceed the proved plus probable reserves estimates.
>
> (ii) Probable reserves may be assigned to areas of a reservoir adjacent to proved reserves where data control or interpretations of available data are less certain, even if the interpreted reservoir continuity of structure or productivity does not meet the reasonable certainty criterion. Probable reserves may be assigned to areas that are structurally higher than the proved area if these areas are in communication with the proved reservoir.
>
> (iii) Probable reserves estimates also include potential incremental quantities associated with a greater percentage recovery of the hydrocarbons in place than assumed for proved reserves.
>
> (iv) See also guidelines in paragraphs (a)(17)(iv) and (a)(17)(vi) [provided below in the definition of possible reserves].

Reg S-X Rule 4-10 (a)(17) defines possible reserves as:

> [T]hose additional reserves that are less certain to be recovered than probable reserves.
>
> (i)   When deterministic methods are used, the total quantities ultimately recovered from a project have a low probability of exceeding proved plus probable plus possible reserves. When probabilistic methods are used, there should be at least a 10% probability that the total quantities ultimately recovered will equal or exceed the proved plus probable plus possible reserves estimates.
>
> (ii) Possible reserves may be assigned to areas of a reservoir adjacent to probable reserves where data control and interpretations of available data are progressively less certain. Frequently, this will be in area where geoscience and engineering data are unable to define clearly the area and vertical limits of commercial production from the reservoir by a defined project.

(iii) Possible reserves also include incremental quantities associated with a greater percentage recovery of the hydrocarbons in place than the recovery quantities assumed for probable reserves.

(iv) The proved plus probable and proved plus probable plus possible reserves estimates must be based on reasonable alternative technical and commercial interpretations within the reservoir or subject project that are clearly documented, including comparisons to results in successful similar projects.

(v) Possible reserves may be assigned where geoscience and engineering data identify directly adjacent portions of a reservoir within the same accumulation that may be separated from proved areas by faults with displacement less than formation thickness or other geological discontinuities and that have not been penetrated by a wellbore, and the registrant believes that such adjacent portions are in communication with the known (proved) reservoir. Possible reserves may be assigned to areas that are structurally higher or lower than the proved area if these areas are in communication with the proved reservoir.

(vi) Pursuant to paragraph (a)(22)(iii) of [Reg S-X Rule 4-10], where direct observation has defined a highest known oil (HKO) elevation and the potential exists for an associated gas cap, proved oil reserves should be assigned in the structurally higher portions of the reservoir above the HKO only if the higher contact can be established with reasonable certainty through reliable technology. Portions of the reservoir that do not meet this reasonable certainty criterion may be assigned as probable and possible oil or gas based on reservoir fluid properties and pressure gradient interpretations.

Industry reserves definitions

Petroleum accountants should note that SEC definitions should be used for financial reporting purposes, although certain professional societies, including the Society of Petroleum Engineers (SPE), have also developed and maintained definitions of reserves. Various definitions of reserves are also used throughout the world, with countries such as Russia, China and Norway using their own definitions.

In June 2018, the SPE, working with the World Petroleum Council (WPC), the American Association of Petroleum Geologists (AAPG), the Society of Petroleum Evaluation Engineers (SPEE), the Society of Exploration Geophysicists, the European Association of Geoscientists and Engineers and the Society of Petrophysicists and Well Log Analysts, updated the PRMS framework originally issued in March 2007 to provide a common framework for reserves definitions. At that time, it replaced the joint industry guidelines previously issued in 1997, 2000 and 2001.

Under the 2018 PRMS framework, reserves of oil and gas are defined as:

> [T]hose quantities of petroleum anticipated to be commercially recoverable by application of development projects to known accumulations from a given date forward under defined conditions. Reserves must further satisfy four criteria: They must be discovered, recoverable, commercial, and remaining (as of the evaluation's effective date) based on the development project(s) applied... Reserves are further categorized in accordance with the range of uncertainty and should be sub-classified based on project maturity and/or characterized by development and production status.

There are two significant attributes of the PRMS framework's definition of reserves: (1) acceptance by four well-respected industry organizations (SPE, WPC, AAPG and SPEE) and (2) inclusion of deterministic and probabilistic methods for expressing reserves estimates. Deterministic methods use known geological, engineering and economic data to calculate a single best estimate of reserves. Probabilistic methods also use known geological, engineering and economic data, but they generate a range of estimates and their associated probabilities.

Several important points to note about reserves follow:

- Reserves are expressed in volumes rather than in dollars or energy content. Some definitions refer to quantities rather than volumes and recognize that reserves may be expressed by weight (i.e., metric tons of oil) or energy content (i.e., MMBtu of gas).

- The amounts of both reserves and recoverable resources change as economic factors change. In general, if the price of oil increases faster than production costs, more oil can be recovered commercially and reserves will increase. If oil prices decline, reserves typically decrease. Reserves are estimated as of a given date (i.e., as of December 31, 2019, not for the year ended December 31, 2019). When reporting reserves estimates, the as-of date should be included.

- The terms estimated reserves, reserves quantities and remaining reserves are redundant because reserves represent estimated remaining volumes. However, the industry generally accepts these terms because they emphasize certain characteristics of reserves.

- The reliability of reserves estimates is subject to the reliability of available underlying geologic and engineering data, as well as the experience, expertise and judgment of the estimator.

- All reserves estimates reflect some degree of uncertainty.

- The SEC rules caution that reserves estimates do not represent fair market value. Instead, they report to investors the relative quantity of reserves that is likely to be extracted, while minimizing any variables that do not apply specifically to reserves.

Figure 15-1 illustrates the industry's resources classification framework.

Figure 15-1

Resources classification framework

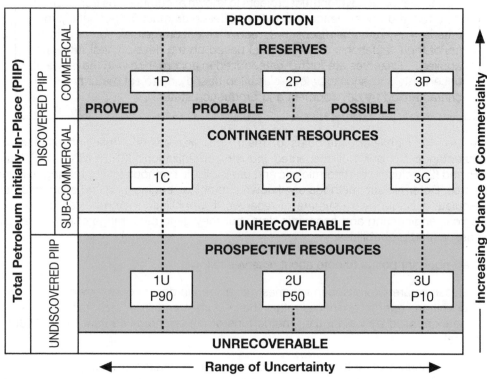

Source: Society of Petroleum Engineers, <www.spe.org>.

Proved reserves

Within the PRMS framework, proved reserves are defined as:

> [T]hose quantities of petroleum, which by analysis of geoscience and engineering data, can be estimated with reasonable certainty to be commercially recoverable, from a given date forward, from known reservoirs and under defined economic conditions, operating methods, and government regulations. If deterministic methods are used, the term "reasonable certainty" is intended to express a high degree of confidence that the quantities will be recovered. If probabilistic methods are used, there should be at least a 90% probability that the quantities actually recovered will equal or exceed the estimate.

As previously discussed, subclassifications of proved reserves include proved developed producing reserves, proved developed non-producing reserves and proved undeveloped reserves.

Unproved reserves

Unproved reserves consist of probable and possible reserves, as defined in the 2018 updated PRMS. Although not required to disclose unproved reserves in publicly filed documents with the SEC, companies may do so. However, for financial accounting and reporting purposes unproved reserves are not used in calculating DD&A. Risk-adjusted unproved reserves, particularly probable reserves, may be used in developing expected cash flows in accounting for impairment of long-lived assets (discussed in Chapter 17) or in calculating fair value for business combinations (discussed in Chapter 32).

Probable reserves refer to additional reserves that likely will become proved with further drilling or successful testing, or implementation of a new enhanced recovery project, while possible reserves have even less certainty of future development.

The 2018 PRMS defines probable reserves as:

> [T]hose additional Reserves which analysis of geoscience and engineering data indicate are less likely to be recovered than Proved Reserves but more certain to be recovered than Possible Reserves. It is equally likely that actual remaining quantities recovered will be greater than or less than the sum of the estimated Proved plus Probable Reserves (2P). In this context, when probabilistic methods are used, there should be at least a 50% probability that the actual quantities recovered will equal or exceed the 2P estimate.

The 2018 PRMS defines possible reserves as:

> [T]hose additional Reserves that analysis of geoscience and engineering data suggest are less likely to be recoverable than Probable Reserves. The total quantities ultimately recovered from the project have a low probability to exceed the sum of Proved plus Probable plus Possible (3P) Reserves, which is equivalent to the high estimate scenario. When probabilistic methods are used, there should be at least a 10% probability that the actual quantities recovered will equal or exceed the 3P estimate.

Reserves estimation

Reserves estimation is a complex, imprecise process requiring a synthesis of diverse data about the geological environment, the structure and other characteristics of the reservoir rock, and engineering analyses of the interrelationships among reservoir fluids, pressure, temperature, operating practices, markets, prices and operating costs. When estimating reserves, an engineer's judgment is influenced by existing knowledge and technology. Engineers also consider economic conditions, applicable statutory and regulatory provisions and the purposes for the reserves information. The development and production of a field results in more geological and engineering data available for estimating reserves.

Common estimation methods

In addition to deterministic and probabilistic methods of estimating reserves, four approaches for estimating reserves are commonly used:

1. Analogy.

2. Volumetric.

3. Performance curves.

4. Material balance analysis.

Analogy. Analogy employs experience and judgment from observing similar situations (i.e., nearby producing wells) and considering hypothetical performance. Engineers use analogy when data is unreliable and/or insufficient to warrant the use of other methods. For example, possible reserves for a proposed well are estimated at 750,000 barrels by analogy to similar nearby producing wells that are known to have ultimately produced an average of 750,000 barrels. Analogy alone is less accurate than other methods. However, all methods employ some degree of analogy.

Volumetric. The volumetric method estimates reserves by using a combination of measured physical data and estimates for certain unmeasured data. This method combines factors such as formation and fluid properties with estimates of the reservoir volume (derived from seismic and/or drilling information) to determine economic recoverability. The percentage of original oil in place that typically can be recovered may vary from less than 10 percent to more than 50 percent, depending on the formation and fluid properties. Recovery factors for natural gas, on the other hand, often range from 50 percent to 90 percent.

The volumetric method is used most commonly for newly developed and/or nonpressure-depleting reservoirs (those undergoing water drive). Overall, this method is not very accurate, but it is more precise when it is used to estimate reserves in uncomplicated reservoirs. Figure 15-2 illustrates a simple example of the volumetric method.

Figure 15-2

Volumetric method – Proved areas of a reservoir

Two exploratory wells, E1 and E2, drilled on 40-acre spacing, have proved reserves. Earlier G&G studies showed the producing structure to be a narrow elipse, so only three offset locations are proved (D1, D2 and D3). The total proved area is 200 acres consisting of five drill spacing units.

Top view

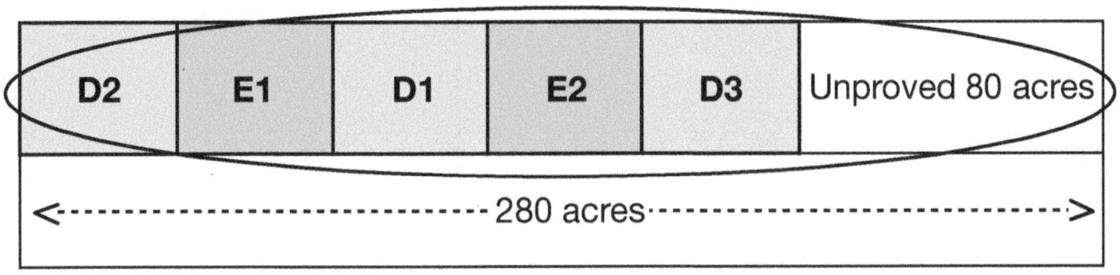

| D2 | E1 | D1 | E2 | D3 | Unproved 80 acres |

<----------------------------- 280 acres ----------------------------->

Side view

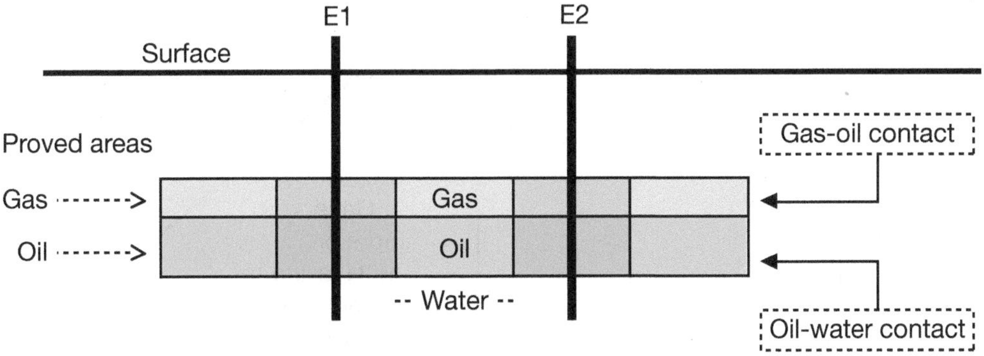

E1   E2

Surface

Proved areas

Gas ------->   Gas   Gas-oil contact

Oil ------->   Oil   Oil-water contact

-- Water --

If the gas-oil and oil-water contacts are 10 feet apart, then the 200-acre proved portion of the oil reservoir has 10 feet of pay and a volume of 2,000 acre-feet. If such volume is 90 percent rock, 2 percent water, 5 percent unrecoverable oil and 3 percent recoverable oil (with 7,758 barrels in an acre-foot), then the proved oil reserves approximate 465,000 barrels [2,000 x 3% x 7,758 barrels]. Fluid properties could be used to estimate the change in volume as the oil moves from reservoir temperature and pressure to the surface.

Performance curves. At many properties, production rates and reservoir pressures decline in patterns or curves that can be extrapolated to estimate future production. Figure 15-3 shows a decline curve for a property that has been producing for four years. The graphed historical production reveals a trend. Engineers often use logarithmic graph scales to identify these trends, which they can extrapolate to estimate future production. The engineer ends the curve extrapolation, and future production, when the production rate declines to the property's economic limit, that is, when the monthly cash inflow from production is lower than the cash outflow for operating costs.

Figure 15-3
Exponential production decline graph

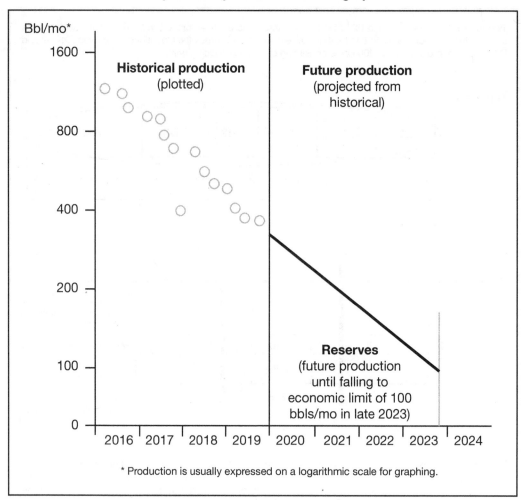

* Production is usually expressed on a logarithmic scale for graphing.

The performance curve approach generally produces more precise estimates than analogy or volumetric methods. Most commonly used after production is established, its accuracy generally improves as production data accumulates. The analysis of decline curves (plotting the log of producing rates versus time) requires special attention when:

- Wells are not producing at capacity due to a number of factors which may include seasonal curtailments, regulatory constraints and operational problems.

- The number of producing wells is changing.

- Operating practices change.

- Completion zones are not consistent over time.

In some circumstances, engineers combine several types of performance curves: cumulative, pressure, water production or even the ratio of oil to gas.

In general, production declines in one of two patterns:

- Exponentially, with a relatively constant percentage decline each year.

- Hyperbolically, with the percentage of the decline decreasing during the well's productive life.

When production is plotted on a logarithmic scale, an exponential decline appears as a straight line, as in Figure 15-3, whereas a hyperbolic decline drops steeply initially then curves or flattens to an almost horizontal line. The historical production pattern and analogy with older wells in the same or similar reservoirs help indicate the applicable curve and the likely annual decline rate(s).

Material balance analysis. This method uses complex calculations that analyze the relationship of production and pressure to well performance. It recognizes that reservoir pressure declines as fluid (oil, gas and water) is produced from the reservoir.

Essentially, material balance sets up an equation: the mass of all material (oil, gas and water) produced from the reservoir must equal the difference between the initial material and the material remaining.

From this simple equation, the engineer develops more complex relationships based on reliable pressure and temperature data, production data, fluid analysis and knowledge of reservoir characteristics. The accuracy of this method is related directly to the quantity and quality of relevant data, and obtaining the data necessary to justify such a detailed study is relatively expensive.

A simple variation of this method generates a p/z decline curve, in which a gas reservoir's pressure (p) is divided by a gas compressibility factor (z). Total cumulative gas production and gas reserves can be estimated by extrapolating this pattern or curve. It requires shutting in wells for several days at a time to periodically measure bottom hole pressure (BHP), or pressure at the bottom of the well.

Analyzing curves that show declining reservoir pressure versus cumulative production requires special attention to ensure estimates are not unreasonably high if:

- Wells are not properly tested.

- Several wells produce from the same reservoir.

- The reservoir had greater than normal original pressure.

- The reservoir is suspected of water drive (as opposed to pressure depletion).

A more complex example of material balance analysis involves the use of reservoir simulators that create a mathematical model of the reservoir. Using measurements of formation and fluid properties obtained from drilled wells and a volumetric model, the simulator subdivides the reservoir into thousands, or perhaps millions, of cells. As the field is produced, production declines and actual field pressures are compared with those predicted by the model. This history matching is used over time to refine the model and improve its accuracy. Although output from reservoir simulators is seldom sufficient for assigning proved reserves early in the life of a field, it can become an important tool as its accuracy improves.

Supporting data

In addition to the geological and engineering data described herein, other important data for quantifying reserves includes:

Production records. These historical records of daily or monthly production (as opposed to sales) are kept in production files and updated periodically by engineering assistants. These records are kept for both operated and nonoperated properties. Engineers use them to establish production decline curves.

Ownership records. For ownership interests (before and after payout), the reporting entity's net share of reserves is the only one reported. These interests come from the lease records of the company maintained by the land department and must agree with the interests used for revenue and joint interest billing in the company's accounting records. Ownership interests can change over time based on a number of factors, including a sale by the company of its ownership interest(s) or other changes as dictated by agreements among the owners. When these ownership changes occur after all well costs have been recovered, the ownership interests are called "before payout" and "after payout."

Gas imbalance records. Imbalances occur when owners of production do not sell quantities in proportion to their ownership interests. See further explanation of imbalances in Chapter 13.

Current price and operating cost records. For proved reserves that are, by definition, based on current economic and operating conditions, engineers use current prices and operating costs to determine the economic limit. Prices based on all available sales contracts and lease operating costs usually are available from lease operating statements. However, a thorough analysis of lease operating costs is necessary to identify fixed and variable portions. This analysis is useful for projecting costs in the later years of a field as the number of wells and daily production rates decline.

Reserves schedules

Reserves estimation normally includes developing schedules of how the reserves are expected to be produced. Timing is affected by market conditions, producer decisions and the availability of capital to develop proved undeveloped reserves. Both historical conditions and future plans are important for reasonable projections. The schedules also may contain estimates of federal income taxes and after-tax cash flow, both undiscounted and discounted.

In practice, reserves schedules include much more extensive information than shown in Figure 15-4 and Figure 15-5, including:

- Production and cash flow, in columnar form for each year (typically 10 to 20 years) along with a grand total.

- Production columns, showing gross and net production of oil, gas and NGLs as well as the ownership percentages for revenues and expenses.

- Cash flow columns, reflecting prices, combined revenues, severance taxes, lease operating costs, net operating cash flow, capital expenditures, abandonment costs, salvage value, net cash flow and net cash flow discounted to a present value.

Figure 15-4 is a simplified production schedule for proved reserves, while Figure 15-5 illustrates a simplified future cash flow estimate for a 10 percent net revenue interest in the gross revenue reflected in Figure 15-4. Schedules may be prepared for each well, field, state, country and reserves classification.

Figure 15-4
Simplified reserves production schedule

(as of 12/31/2019, assuming 10% annual decline in production rate)	
Past	**Oil (bbl)**
2015	10,000
2016	9,000
2017	8,100
2018	7,290
2019	6,561
Cumulative to 12/31/2019	**40,951**
Future	
2020	5,904
2021	5,314
2022	4,782
2023	4,304
2024	3,874
2025	3,486
Reserves at 12/31/2019	**27,664**
Estimated ultimate recovery	**68,615**

Figure 15-5
Simplified future cash flow estimate

Year	Gross oil (bbl)	Net oil (bbl)	Revenues ($50/bbl)	Operating costs	Net cash flow	PV 10
2020	5,904	590	$ 29,500	$10,000	$19,500	$18,593
2021	5,314	531	26,550	10,000	16,550	14,346
2022	4,782	478	23,900	10,000	13,900	10,953
2023	4,304	430	21,500	10,000	11,500	8,239
2024	3,874	387	19,350	10,000	9,350	6,089
2025	3,486	349	17,450	10,000	7,450	4,410
Total	27,664	2,765	$138,250	$60,000	$78,250	$62,630

Reserves reports

Reserves reports are prepared by company employees, independent third party engineering firms or both. Management should communicate with the internal or external engineer(s) for a better understanding of how the report was prepared and for an assessment of any data used.

Reserves reports are designed to meet SEC disclosure requirements with respect to reserves quantities; however, they also have many other uses, including:

- Historical financial and income tax reporting for amortization of certain costs.

- Determining impairment of proved properties in accordance with ASC 360 (discussed in Chapter 17) and calculating the full cost ceiling test (discussed in Chapter 18).

- Developing long-range plans and budgets.

- Management decisions regarding field development and reservoir management.

- Supporting bank loans and lines of credit collateralized by future production.

- Valuing developed oil and gas properties, or valuing a company being considered for acquisition or divestment.

- Regulatory hearings or litigation.

Different purposes may require different definitions, assumptions and methods, which may lead to very different results. Yet each can be a perfectly correct and valid report for its stated purpose. In all cases, the report should include a letter identifying who requested the report, its purpose, effective date, description of properties evaluated, sources of data, significant assumptions, reserves definitions employed, summary results, a statement of the evaluator's independence and the framework used for proved reserves (such as the SEC definition required for financial reporting). The letter typically contains statements of the estimator's limited responsibility for the accuracy of underlying data, as well as remarks about the imprecise nature of the estimates. If the estimator is a registered professional engineer, he or she usually will affix a seal to the letter.

The report can include summary reserves schedules and schedules organized by property. One type of summary ranks all properties according to the total present value, with the most valuable property listed first. Production decline curves and P/Z curves also may be included, as well as maps with locations of existing wells and proved undeveloped areas.

Financial auditors read reserves reports and cover letters in compliance with applicable auditing standards, including AS 1210,[1] AS 2705 and related Interpretation 2705 (supplementary information). The cover letter provides most of the information needed for compliance and may reveal areas that should be investigated more thoroughly. For example, a letter may describe inconsistencies in the assumptions or methods used, such as the use of prices other than the market prices on the date of the reserves estimate.

AS 1210, *Using the Work of a Specialist*, provides "guidance to the auditor who uses the work of a specialist in performing an audit in accordance with the standards of the PCAOB." According to the standard, a financial auditor may conclude that the work of a specialist is needed for certain matters, such as valuations, technical interpretations or determination of physical characteristics related to the quantity or condition of minerals or mineral reserves.

AS 2705, *Required Supplementary Information*, provides guidance on "the nature of procedures to be applied to supplementary information required by the FASB, GASB, or FASAB..." The auditor must consider whether or not supplementary information is required by the FASB or GASB. If it is required, then the auditor must follow the standard's specific procedures.

AI 19, *Required Supplementary Information*: *Auditing Interpretations of AS 2705*, interprets the supplemental guidance in AS 2705 specifically for oil and gas reserves as follows:

> Estimating oil and gas reserves is a complex process requiring the knowledge and experience of a reservoir engineer. In general, the quality of the estimate of proved reserves for an individual reservoir depends on the availability, completeness, and accuracy of data needed to develop the estimate and on the experience and judgment of the reservoir engineer. Estimates of proved reserves inevitably change over time as additional data become available and are taken into account. The magnitude of changes in these estimates is often substantial. Because oil and gas reserve estimates are more imprecise than most estimates that are made in preparing financial statements, entities are encouraged to explain the imprecise nature of such reserve estimates.

SPE standards

In June 2019, the SPE adopted amended standards for estimating and auditing oil and gas reserves information (SPE Standards).[2] The SPE Standards are not binding on petroleum engineers but they provide guidance for estimation and reporting. Many petroleum engineering consulting firms will not issue reserves estimation reports that purport to comply with the SPE Standards, since compliance is not mandatory, and purported compliance might expose the firms to unnecessary legal liabilities.

Although the SPE Standards can guide engineers in their evaluation of reserves estimates by another party, the SEC and FASB do not require the inclusion of this data in audited footnotes to the financial statements. This data appears as unaudited supplemental information as explained in Chapters 30 and 31. Nevertheless, the reserves audit is a popular service offered by independent petroleum engineering firms because it can be less expensive than an independent reserves determination. Reserves prepared or audited by an independent petroleum engineering firm may appear in the unaudited information supplementing the audited financial statements.

Many public companies hire independent petroleum engineers to prepare or conduct audits of proved reserves. In these cases, the engineering firm must consent to the use of its reports in SEC filings. In addition, companies must file reports from the petroleum engineer as exhibits to the relevant registration statement or 1934 Act filing with the SEC. Unlike an audit report under AICPA or PCAOB standards, a petroleum engineer's reserves audit report can express positive assurance without requiring the engineer to test or verify the accuracy and completeness of underlying data. However, the engineer's report should disclose the lack of this testing or verification.

● ● ●

1 Amendments to the entirety of this standard (including retitling) have been adopted by the PCAOB and approved by the SEC. The standard as amended will be effective for audits of financial statements for fiscal years ending on or after December 15, 2020. See PCAOB Release No. 2018-006 and SEC Release No. 34-86270.

2 A copy of the SPE Standards is available on the SPE website: < www.spe.org/industry/docs/Reserves_Audit_Standards_June%202019_Final.pdf >.

Key concepts

- **Unit-of-production method**

- **Aggregation of properties**

- **Computing amortization expense**

- **Equivalent unit-of-production**

- **Unit-of-production equation**

- **Revisions of estimates**

- **Special considerations**

Depreciation, depletion and amortization (DD&A) is not a concept unique to the oil and gas industry. However, whereas in many other industries the calculation involves little more than estimating a useful life and performing a straight-line calculation, the calculation of DD&A in the oil and gas industry involves much more complexity.

Acquisition costs and well and development costs of proved properties are amortized by the unit-of-production method. This method matches amortization expense with related oil and gas production. Both types of capitalized costs are amortized, however amortization is calculated based on different categories of proved reserves under successful efforts. Acquisition costs are depleted (amortized) over total proved reserves. Costs of wells and related equipment and facilities are depreciated (amortized) <u>only</u> over the proved developed reserves associated with those capitalized costs. If a property is fully developed, proved reserves and proved developed reserves are equal. When a property is only partially developed, proved developed reserves are a subset of total proved reserves, as discussed in Chapter 15.

DD&A may be computed for each individual property. Alternatively, properties may be aggregated by common geological feature or stratigraphic condition, such as a reservoir or field. Royalty interests and other nonoperating interests also may provide an alternative basis for property aggregation. See Chapter 18 for considerations under the full cost method of accounting.

Unit-of-production method

Oil and gas often are found together on a property or group of properties. In these cases, the amortization per unit should be calculated according to estimated total equivalent units of oil and gas reserves based on energy content. Unit-of-production rates may be revised whenever the need is indicated but must be revised at least annually.

Computing unit-of-production amortization uses either of two essentially identical formulas:

$$\frac{\text{Net unamortized costs at end of period}}{\text{Reserves at end of period + Production for period}} \times \text{Production for period}$$

or

$$\frac{\text{Production for period}}{\text{Reserves at end of period + Production for period}} \times \frac{\text{Net unamortized costs at}}{\text{end of period}}$$

To illustrate both computations, assume the following at the end of an accounting period:

Capitalized costs at end of period	$1,200,000
Amortization taken in prior periods	$300,000
Estimated reserves at end of period	950,000 Bbls
Production for period	50,000 Bbls

Amortization expense for the period is calculated as follows using either of the two previously illustrated formulas:

$$\frac{\$1,200,000 - \$300,000}{950,000 \text{ bbls} + 50,000 \text{ bbls}} \quad \times \quad 50,000 \text{ bbls} \quad = \quad \$45,000$$

or

$$\frac{50,000 \text{ bbls}}{950,000 \text{ bbls} + 50,000 \text{ bbls}} \quad \times \quad (\$1,200,000 - \$300,000) \quad = \quad \$45,000$$

The remaining examples in this chapter use the second formula above; however, both are acceptable computations of amortization expense.

Aggregation of properties

As noted previously, proved properties with a common geological feature may be combined to compute DD&A. ASC 932-360-35-6 states, in part:

> Under the unit-of-production method, amortization (depletion) may be computed either on a property-by-property basis or on the basis of some reasonable aggregation of properties with a common geological structural feature or stratigraphic condition, such as a reservoir or field.

As a general rule, a cost center is either an individual property or an aggregation of properties. Combining properties by well can be difficult, since a property often encompasses acreage greater than the well's spacing unit.

Of the 24 successful efforts respondents to the *2019 PricewaterhouseCoopers Survey of U.S. Petroleum Accounting Practices* (Question E6), approximately 38 percent of companies using the successful efforts method aggregated the capitalized costs of oil and gas producing properties into cost centers by field. The responses by level of aggregation were as follows:

Level of aggregation	Percentage of successful efforts respondents
Field	38
District or regional aggregation of properties or fields	29
Reservoir or resource play	17
Well	13
Other method	3

To illustrate an aggregation of proved properties, assume that four leases overlying a reservoir are drilled and developed in the current period.

End of period balances	Lease				
	A	B	C	D	Total
Net unamortized costs	$1,000,000	$1,500,000	$700,000	$3,000,000	$6,200,000
Estimated proved reserves (bbls)	190,000	470,000	380,000	190,000	1,230,000
Production (bbls)	10,000	30,000	20,000	10,000	70,000

If amortization is computed for each property individually, the amortization for the period is calculated as follows:

Property A $\dfrac{10,000 \text{ bbls}}{200,000 \text{ bbls}}$ x $1,000,000   = $ 50,000

Property B $\dfrac{30,000 \text{ bbls}}{500,000 \text{ bbls}}$ x $1,500,000   =   90,000

Property C $\dfrac{20,000 \text{ bbls}}{400,000 \text{ bbls}}$ x $ 700,000   =   35,000

Property D $\dfrac{10,000 \text{ bbls}}{200,000 \text{ bbls}}$ x $3,000,000   =   150,000

                              Amortization for the period*   **$325,000**

*Example shows the effect on depletion associated only with the leasehold acquisition costs.

Alternatively, if the properties are aggregated into a single group, amortization for the period is calculated as follows (using amounts from the previous example):

$\dfrac{70,000 \text{ bbls}}{1,300,000 \text{ bbls}}$ x $6,200,000   = $333,846

Costs of unproved properties are not subject to depletion but are subject to an impairment test. Unproved properties whose costs are not individually significant may be aggregated and their costs may be amortized based on the company's experience. In this instance, the company's history of recording write-offs related to unproved property should be considered, among other factors. If impairment of unproved properties has been recorded on an aggregated basis, and the properties have since been proved, the proved properties account contains the gross cost of the formerly unproved properties.

However, if impairment of an unproved property was recorded on an individual basis, the proved properties account shows the net impaired cost (original cost less the impairment allowance) once the property is reclassified to proved. Chapter 7 discusses the recognition of impairment of unproved properties; Chapter 17 offers a more detailed explanation of recognizing impairment of long-lived assets.

Computing amortization expense

To illustrate the application of ASC 932-360-35-6 when a single proved property is treated as a cost center, assume the following data:

Property acquisition cost initially transferred from unproved properties	$400,000	
Depletion taken prior to beginning of period	$60,000	
Production during period	120,000	Mcf
Revised estimate of proved reserves at end of period	6,800,000	Mcf

Amortization expense for the period is calculated as follows:

$$\frac{120,000 \text{ Mcf}}{6,800,000 \text{ Mcf} + 120,000 \text{ Mcf}} \quad \times \quad (\$400,000 - \$60,000) \quad = \quad \$5,896$$

Amortization expense for the period would be recorded as:

DD&A expense – proved properties acquisition costs	5,896	
Accumulated DD&A – proved properties acquisition costs		5,896
To record amortization expense for the period.		

When calculating by individual cost center, a detailed record of amortization should be maintained for each property. Amortization (depletion) for a group of properties should be calculated in the same manner as shown above, except that the data for all properties in the group would be aggregated.

Well and development costs

The capitalized costs of wells and related facilities include both tangible and intangible costs. ASC 932-360-35-7 suggests that the term "depreciation" may be applied to the amortization of these costs, although many companies still call the amortization of intangibles "depletion." This terminology likely stems from the fact that, if capitalizing intangible drilling costs (IDC) for federal income tax, they are subject to depletion.

ASC 932-360-35-7 states that capitalized costs of wells and related facilities should be amortized over <u>only</u> proved developed reserves, whereas acquisition costs should be amortized over total proved reserves:

> Capitalized costs of exploratory wells and exploratory-type stratigraphic test wells that have found proved reserves and capitalized development costs shall be amortized (depreciated) by the unit-of-production method... on the basis of the total estimated units of proved developed reserves, rather than on the basis of all proved reserves, which is the basis for amortizing acquisition costs of proved properties.

For example, assume that a group of partially developed leases in a field has been combined in a single amortization pool:

Proved property acquisition costs	$220,000	
Proved property intangible costs	$4,100,000	
Proved property tangible costs	$700,000	
Accumulated amortization of acquisition costs	$30,000	
Accumulated amortization of intangible costs	$800,000	
Accumulated amortization of tangible costs	$130,000	
Proved developed reserves at year-end	980,000	Bbls
Proved reserves at year-end	1,500,000	Bbls
Production during period	120,000	Bbls

Amortization expense for the period is calculated as follows based on the classification of capitalized costs:

$$\textbf{Acquisition costs} \quad \frac{120,000 \text{ bbls}}{1,500,000 \text{ bbls} + 120,000 \text{ bbls}} \times (\$220,000 - \$30,000) = \$14,074$$

$$\textbf{Intangible costs} \quad \frac{120,000 \text{ bbls}}{980,000 \text{ bbls} + 120,000 \text{ bbls}} \times (\$4,100,000 - \$800,000) = \$360,000$$

$$\textbf{Tangible costs} \quad \frac{120,000 \text{ bbls}}{980,000 \text{ bbls} + 120,000 \text{ bbls}} \times (\$700,000 - \$130,000) = \$62,182$$

The corresponding journal entry is recorded as follows:

DD&A expense – proved properties acquisition costs	14,074	
DD&A expense – intangible costs of wells	360,000	
DD&A expense – tangible costs of wells	62,182	
Accumulated DD&A – proved properties acquisition costs		14,074
Accumulated DD&A – intangible costs of wells		360,000
Accumulated DD&A – tangible costs of wells		62,182
To record amortization expense for the period.		

Significant development projects

Development costs are amortized as the related proved developed reserves are produced. However, to prevent distortions in the amortization rate, the amortization formula should be adjusted for substantial development costs related to both proved developed and proved undeveloped reserves.

To illustrate, assume that an offshore platform is constructed at a cost of $80 million to drill 10 development wells, which are expected to extract an estimated 50 million barrels of proved reserves. Prior to platform construction, two successful stratigraphic evaluation wells are drilled at a cost of $19 million. At the end of the current period, only two development wells have been drilled, at a cost of $6 million ($3 million each). During the current period, 500,000 barrels were produced, and at the end of the period the remaining proved developed reserves from the two wells are estimated to be 6.5 million barrels.

Dividing total capitalized costs of $105 million by the 7 million barrels of beginning proved developed reserves results in an inflated current amortization rate of $15 per barrel. If all 10 wells were drilled at a cost of $3 million per development well, total capitalized costs would be $129 million, all 50 million barrels of proved reserves would be classified as developed and the amortization rate would be calculated as $2.58 per barrel.

To better match DD&A expense with revenue and production, a portion of the $105 million in capitalized costs should be excluded from the amortization formula until all proved reserves are developed. Consistent with ASC 932-360-35-7, "If significant development costs (such as the cost of an offshore production platform) are incurred in connection with a planned group of development wells before all of the planned wells have been drilled, it shall be necessary to exclude a portion of those development costs in determining the unit-of-production amortization rate until the additional development wells are drilled."

ASC 932 does not specify the method used to determine the portion of platform and stratigraphic well costs to exclude from the calculation. Presumably, the excluded costs are based on either:

- The portion of total proved reserves estimated to be recoverable from wells already producing.

- The ratio of wells already productive to the total number of wells projected.

In the first approach, using the figures herein, the amortization rate would be:

$$\text{Amortization rate} = \frac{\left[\$99{,}000{,}000 \times \dfrac{7{,}000{,}000 \text{ bbls}}{50{,}000{,}000 \text{ bbls}}\right] + \$6{,}000{,}000}{6{,}500{,}000 \text{ bbls} + 500{,}000 \text{ bbls}} = \$2.84$$

In the second approach, the amortization rate would be:

$$\text{Amortization rate} = \frac{\left[\$99{,}000{,}000 \times \dfrac{2 \text{ wells}}{10 \text{ wells}}\right] + \$6{,}000{,}000}{6{,}500{,}000 \text{ bbls} + 500{,}000 \text{ bbls}} = \$3.69$$

Capitalized costs that are temporarily excluded from amortization eventually become part of the amortization base as additional wells are drilled. Costs of development wells are included in the amortization calculation as incurred and the related reserves are transferred to proved developed reserves. Also, exclusion from the amortization base applies not only to the platform costs but also to the capitalized costs of stratigraphic test wells that led to the platform's construction.

ASC 932-360-35-7 also offers guidance for situations in which companies have proved developed reserves that may incur additional costs before the reserves can be produced, noting "it shall be necessary to exclude, in computing the amortization rate, those proved developed reserves that will be produced only after significant additional development costs are incurred, such as for improved recovery systems."

However, this problem should be uncommon because Reg. S-X Rule 4-10(a)(6) defines developed oil and gas reserves as:

> [R]eserves of any category that can be expected to be recovered: (i) Through existing wells with existing equipment and operating methods or in which the cost of the required equipment is relatively minor compared to the cost of a new well; and (ii) Through installed extraction equipment and infrastructure operational at the time of the reserves estimate if the extraction is by means not involving a well.

In addition, Reg. S-X Rule 4-10(a)(31) includes a definition of undeveloped oil and gas reserves:

> [R]eserves of any category that are expected to be recovered from new wells on undrilled acreage, or from existing wells where a relatively major expenditure is required for recompletion.

Furthermore, Reg. S-X Rule 4-10 (a)(22)(iv) details the criteria whereby reserves which can be produced economically through improved recovery techniques may be considered proved reserves:

> (iv) Reserves which can be produced economically through application of improved recovery techniques (including, but not limited to, fluid injection) are included in the proved classification when:
>
> (A) Successful testing by a pilot project in an area of the reservoir with properties no more favorable than in the reservoir as a whole, the operation of an installed program in the reservoir or an analogous reservoir, or other evidence using reliable technology establishes the reasonable certainty of the engineering analysis on which the project or program was based; and
>
> (B) The project has been approved for development by all necessary parties and entities, including governmental entities.

To summarize, the goal of these rules is to reasonably match revenue and production with applicable costs. Unit-of-production computations, although useful, can present problems for future production, as described briefly at the end of this chapter.

Dismantlement, restoration and abandonment costs

The future cost of dismantlement, restoration and abandonment (DR&A) is included in the current amortization base to increase DD&A. Chapter 19 addresses accounting for these costs under existing standards.

Equivalent unit-of-production

If oil and gas are found together on a property (or a group of properties forming an amortization group), the amortization basis is the estimated total equivalent units of oil and gas. Equivalent units are expressed by relative energy content such as Btu. An equivalent unit based on revenues is specifically prohibited for companies using successful efforts, although it is allowed for full cost accounting.

The energy content of both oil and gas varies from reservoir to reservoir and even within a single reservoir. As explained in Chapter 1, many companies use a rule-of-thumb formula: one barrel of oil contains six times as much energy content as 1,000 cubic feet (Mcf) of gas. Other companies use the actual equivalent energy content in an attempt to be more precise in their calculations.

To illustrate this concept, assume for a fully developed property:

Capitalized costs	$7,000,000
Amortization in prior periods	$280,000
Estimated oil reserves, end of period	650,000　Bbls
Estimated gas reserves, end of period	3,600,000　Mcf
Oil production during period	80,000　Bbls
Gas production during period	420,000　Mcf

Amortization for the period is calculated by converting gas volumes to barrels of oil equivalent (BOE):

Reserves, end of period	(in BOE)
Oil (650,000 bbls)	650,000
Gas (3,600,000 Mcf ÷ 6 Mcf per bbl)	600,000
Total equivalent bbls, end of period	1,250,000
Production for period	
Oil (80,000 bbls)	80,000
Gas (420,000 Mcf ÷ 6 Mcf per bbl)	70,000
Total equivalent bbls produced	150,000
Total BOE, beginning of period	**1,400,000**

Amortization is computed as follows:

$$\frac{150,000 \text{ BOE}}{1,400,000 \text{ BOE}} \quad \times \quad (\$7,000,000 - \$280,000) \quad = \quad \$720,000$$

Some companies, especially gas-producing companies, may wish to convert oil to gas equivalents (Mcfe), which does not change the amortization expense for the period:

Reserves, end of period	(in Mcfe)
Oil (650,000 bbls x 6 Mcf per bbl)	3,900,000
Gas (3,600,000 Mcf)	3,600,000
Total Mcfe, end of period	7,500,000
Production for period	
Oil (80,000 bbls x 6 Mcf per bbl)	480,000
Gas (420,000 Mcf)	420,000
Total Mcfe produced	900,000
Total Mcfe, beginning of period	8,400,000

Amortization is computed as follows:

$$\frac{900,000 \text{ Mcfe}}{8,400,000 \text{ Mcfe}} \quad \times \quad (\$7,000,000 - \$280,000) \quad = \quad \$720,000$$

ASC 932-360-35-5 presumes that if both oil and gas are found in a property or group of properties, amortization is based on the cost per equivalent unit. However, two exceptions are also noted in the guidance:

> ... However, if the relative proportion of gas and oil extracted in the current period is expected to continue throughout the remaining productive life of the property, unit-of-production amortization may be computed on the basis of one of the two minerals only; similarly, if either oil or gas clearly dominates both the reserves and the current production (with dominance determined on the basis of relative energy content), unit-of-production amortization may be computed on the basis of the dominant mineral only.

The first exception is illustrated using data from the preceding example. Since oil comprises 52 percent of the minerals in the reservoir at the end of the period and 53 percent of the production during the current period, the relative production of oil and gas in the current period is assumed to be approximately the same as it will be in future periods.

Therefore, the calculation uses production and reserves of only one mineral: oil. Considering only oil production and reserves, amortization for the period is:

$$\frac{80{,}000 \text{ bbls}}{730{,}000 \text{ bbls}} \quad \text{x} \quad (\$7{,}000{,}000 - \$280{,}000) \quad = \quad \$736{,}438$$

Determining the appropriate circumstances for calculating depletion using a dominant mineral requires significant judgment.

Unit-of-production equation

The unit-of-production equation or formula may be expressed for a given cost center as follows:

Amortization expense = [(B x S) ÷ (S+R)], where:

B = amortization base (defined below).

S = volumes sold during the period (equivalent barrels or Mcf or volumes of the dominant hydrocarbon).

R = volumes of proved reserves at end of period, using proved developed reserves for well costs and equipment DD&A, and using total proved reserves for property acquisition DD&A.

Amortization base (B) = C – A – E , where:

C = incurred capitalized costs of mineral property interests or of wells and development.

A = prior accumulated amortization.

E = capitalized development costs excluded from the amortization base (as allowed by ASC 932-360-35-7).

The formula for full cost accounting (addressed in Chapter 18) is very similar to this example, but is calculated country by country. The full cost equation uses total proved reserves and adds a new factor to the amortization base for estimated future development costs (F) for properties in the amortization base.

Volumes sold (S) arguably could be replaced with units produced because the two volumes are typically equal over quarterly or annual periods. However, in some instances, units sold are significantly less than units produced, with the difference being "shrinkage." Shrinkage can arise from natural gas usage on the lease, gas volumes lost in the extraction of NGLs, removal of impurities and BS&W and even theft or pipeline leaks. If shrinkage is significant, amortization should be calculated using units produced or sold (S) and proved reserves (R) determined consistently (i.e., both before shrinkage or both after shrinkage), to reasonably allocate costs over the reserves' productive life.

The *2019 PricewaterhouseCoopers Survey of U.S. Petroleum Accounting Practices* (Question E2) indicates that when volumes sold differ from volumes produced, volumes sold are more commonly used to calculate amortization under both successful efforts and full cost accounting. Of the 33 respondents, 18 (or 55 percent) use volumes sold, 14 (or 42 percent) use volumes produced and one respondent uses another basis for volumes when calculating amortization.

The unit-of-production method mandated by ASC 932-360-35 is far from perfect. During the economic life of an oil or gas field, as production declines, net cash flow per barrel declines to zero while amortization per barrel may remain relatively constant. The unit-of-production method mandated in ASC 932-360-35 results in a general decline in net income per barrel during the life of the field, or even a loss in later years.

The example property below is expected to produce for seven years:

Year	Net sold (bbls)	Revenue ($50/bbl)	Oper. costs	Cash flow per bbl	DD&A per bbl	Income per bbl	Net income	Net unamortized cost	Future cash flow
								$30,000	$30,000
1	1,000	$ 50,000	$ 20,000	$30.00	$5.00	$25.00	$ 25,000	25,000	33,400
2	890	53,400	20,000	$37.53	$5.00	32.53	28,950	20,550	26,800
3	780	46,800	20,000	$34.36	$5.00	29.36	22,900	16,650	21,400
4	690	41,400	20,000	$31.01	$5.00	26.01	17,950	13,200	16,000
5	600	36,000	20,000	$26.67	$5.00	21.67	13,000	10,200	11,800
6	530	31,800	20,000	$22.26	$5.00	17.26	9,150	7,550	10,600
7	510	30,600	20,000	$20.78	$5.00	15.78	8,050	5,000	
Total	5,000	$290,000	$140,000	$30.00	$5.00	$25.00	$125,000		

For simplicity, this example assumes future cash flows based on a constant oil price of $50 per barrel and constant fixed operating costs of $20,000 annually. The property generates $125,000 of net income (an average of $25 per barrel) during its seven-year life. Arguably, to better match revenue and expense, DD&A expense should reflect the $25 per barrel of net income every year. However, the example illustrates that unit-of-production amortization tends to overstate net income per barrel early in the life of a producing property and understate it in later years.

For an ongoing oil and gas producing company, the understated amortization of capitalized costs in new fields compensates, to some degree, for its overstated amortization in old fields. A company that is not adding new fields will find that its net income per barrel declines over time.

Mismatching of revenues and expenses over time also impairs capitalized costs for any single field. This necessitates impairment write-offs under ASC 360 to prevent losses in the field's future productive life.

Accounting for long-lived asset impairment under ASC 360 (discussed in Chapter 17) and the full cost ceiling test (discussed in Chapter 18) mitigate the risk of significantly mismatching revenues and expenses when applying the unit-of-production amortization method.

Revisions of estimates

ASC 932-360-35-6 requires amortization rates to "be revised whenever there is an indication of the need for revision but at least once a year." Rates may need revision due to: (1) major discoveries, (2) other reserves additions or declines, (3) price changes that affect the volume of proved reserves, (4) property expenditures or (5) acquisition or divestiture. Management should exercise caution when using predetermined DD&A estimates by default.

A change in estimated reserves is considered a change in accounting estimate under ASC 250, *Accounting Changes and Error Corrections*, and therefore is treated prospectively. This requirement has been interpreted differently in practice. Two general approaches were reported in the *2019 PricewaterhouseCoopers Survey of U.S. Petroleum Accounting Practices*. The following example illustrates both methods.

Facts. Assume that amortization (depreciation) is being recorded quarterly and reported in quarterly financial statements. On January 1, 2019, the first day of the fiscal year, undepreciated costs of wells and facilities on a property are $7 million and estimated proved developed reserves are 1 million barrels.

During the first quarter, 30,000 barrels are produced; during the second quarter, 15,000 barrels are produced; and during the third quarter, 25,000 barrels are produced. Therefore, the amortization recorded in the first three quarters was $210,000 [($7,000,000 ÷ 1,000,000 barrels) x 30,000 barrels], $105,000 and $175,000, respectively.

In October, 9,000 barrels are produced; in November, 8,000 barrels are produced. In December, a revised estimate of proved developed reserves is calculated showing that on December 1 estimated proved developed reserves are 493,000 barrels. The revised estimate as of October 1 is 510,000 barrels. Production during December is 6,000 barrels.

Analysis – Approach A. In the first approach, the "period" refers to the last quarter in which reserves are revised. Amortization for the year is the sum of the four quarterly amortization amounts.

Using this approach and the previous assumptions:

Amortization for first three quarters	$490,000

Amortization for the fourth quarter

$$\frac{23,000 \text{ bbls}}{510,000 \text{ bbls}} \quad \times \quad (\$7,000,000 - \$490,000) \quad = \quad \underline{293,588}$$

Total amortization for the year	**$783,588**

Analysis – Approach B. In the second approach, the total proved developed reserves used to compute amortization expense are updated for future periods only (i.e., for December, since the reserves estimates were revised December 1).

Using this approach and the previous assumptions:

Amortization for first three quarters	$490,000

Amortization for October and November

$$\frac{17,000 \text{ bbls}}{930,000 \text{ bbls}} \quad \times \quad (\$7,000,000 - \$490,000) \quad = \quad 119,000$$

Amortization for December

$$\frac{6,000 \text{ bbls}}{493,000 \text{ bbls}} \quad \times \quad (\$7,000,000 - \$609,000) \quad = \quad \underline{77,781}$$

Total amortization for the year	**$686,781**

Public companies are required to give effect to any change in proved reserves prospectively, following the ASC 250 guidance for a change in accounting estimate. However, after following the first approach, if there is a proved reserves change at year-end, public companies may give effect to the change in the quarter for which the financial statements have not yet been issued (in the example above, the fourth quarter of the reporting year). and should be consistent in their approach from year to year.

Special considerations

ASC 932-360 provides guidance to companies in considering the appropriate DD&A method to apply in various circumstances.

Nonoperating interests amortization

The costs of nonoperating interests, like those of operating interests, generally should be depleted or amortized by unit of production. ASC 932-360-35-6 states that in certain circumstances other methods of computing amortization may be appropriate:

> ... When an entity has a relatively large number of royalty interests whose acquisition costs are not individually significant, they may be aggregated, for the purpose of computing amortization, without regard to commonality of geological structural features or stratigraphic conditions; if information is not available to estimate reserves quantities applicable to royalty interests owned (see paragraph ASC 932-235-50-4), a method other than the unit-of-production method may be used to amortize their acquisition costs.

Two significant challenges arise when implementing the unit-of-production method for nonoperating interests:

- Many nonoperating interests may be quite small in both cost and value, making them individually immaterial.

- Operating interest owners may refuse to provide information to nonoperating interest owners concerning the proved reserves for a particular property or field, especially when the royalty interest is small and the royalty owner is not an operating oil and gas company.

ASC 932-360-35-6 implies that if a single royalty interest is significant, its capitalized costs should be amortized over the property's related proved reserves. Royalty interests in a field or reservoir also may be combined without regard to geological commonality and amortized as the related proved reserves are produced.

More commonly, however, when lacking the information to compute unit-of-production amortization, petroleum accountants may combine royalty costs and amortize them on a straight-line basis over a period based on the average reserves life observed for similar fields or regions. In other instances, the royalty owner may be able to estimate reserves by projecting the property's production decline curve based on past production history.

Although ASC 932-360-35-6 refers specifically to royalties, including overriding royalties, the same basic concepts apply to net profits interests. Conceptually, the unamortized costs of a net profits interest are depleted by: (1) the production on which the net profit for the period is determined and (2) the fractional share of reserves represented by the net profits interest. However, working interest owners may be reluctant to inform a net profits interest owner of the estimated proved reserves underlying the property or properties. Therefore, amortization using the straight-line method may be logical for computing depletion.

The holder of a production payment payable in product amortizes costs by production received if there is reason to believe the payment will be satisfied. For example, an entity obtained for $2 million a production payment of one million Mcf of gas and received the first 250,000 Mcf during the current period. With reasonable assurance that it will receive the remaining 750,000 Mcf, the entity records depletion of $500,000, calculated as $2,000,000 x (250,000 Mcf ÷ 1,000,000 Mcf), matched against the value of the gas received.

If receipt is doubtful, but it is possible to estimate the amount of product that could be received, a portion of the costs is amortized based on the ratio of units delivered versus total expected delivery (assuming that an impairment is not required). For example, if: (1) $6 million is paid, to be satisfied by delivery of one million Mcf of gas, (2) the first 200,000 Mcf of gas is received in the current period and (3) it is expected that only 400,000 additional Mcf will be received, then depletion is $2 million, calculated as $6,000,000 x (200,000 Mcf ÷ 600,000 Mcf).

Other allowable methods

Although ASC 932-360-35-7 specifies the unit-of-production method to deplete the costs of wells and related facilities and equipment, other methods may be used in limited situations. ASC 932-360-35-7 mentions one exception:

> ... It may be more appropriate, in some cases, to depreciate natural gas cycling and processing plants by a method other than the unit-of-production method.

Presumably, if a gas cycling or processing plant serves only one lease (or one group of leases combined for amortization purposes), the unit-of-production method should be used. However, when a gas cycling or processing plant serves a number of properties, each subject to individual amortization, or when the plant contracts to process gas for other operators, another depreciation method (e.g., the straight-line method) may be more appropriate. This supports the fact that many companies consider processing plants as more akin to refineries than to oil and gas producing assets.

A depreciation method other than unit-of-production might also be appropriate when high-cost assets have a productive life that differs substantially from the life of the reserves of the property where the assets are located. However, this approach is not addressed specifically in Reg. S-X Rule 4-10 or ASC 932.

Support equipment and facilities

Support facilities such as warehouses, camps, trucks, communication equipment and office buildings frequently serve two or more functions including exploration, acquisition, development and production. For example, a district warehouse serves all four functions.

Even when support equipment is used for only one activity, such as production, it may be impossible to identify the asset with only a single property or group of properties in a single amortization base. Therefore, the unit-of-production method may not be appropriate. Instead, the straight-line method, the unit-of-output method (based on a factor such as miles driven for trucks) or another acceptable method should be used.

Depreciation and other costs of owning and using support equipment are allocated to operating activities by usage and consequently are expensed or capitalized as appropriate. For example, to the extent that an asset is used for development, its depreciation and operating costs are capitalized, whereas depreciation and operating costs for its use in production are charged to expense.

• • •

Key concepts

- **Impairment indicators**

- **Adjustments to asset carrying amounts**

- **Assessing and measuring impairment**

- **Application issues**

ASC 360-10-35, *Impairment or Disposal of Long-Lived Assets*, addresses the measurement of long-lived assets, including related impairment issues. For successful efforts companies, these impairment provisions apply to proved properties and their related equipment and facilities. Unproved properties fall under the impairment provisions of ASC 932-360-35 and Reg. S-X Rule 4-10, as described in Chapter 7. When assessing impairment for full cost companies, the full cost ceiling provisions in Reg. S-X Rule 4-10 apply.

ASC 360-10-35 specifies a two-step approach:

Step 1. Whenever events or changes in circumstances indicate that the asset's carrying amount may not be recoverable, the entity estimates the expected undiscounted future cash flows from the asset's use and ultimate disposal. If the asset's carrying amount exceeds such cash flows (undiscounted and without interest charges), the entity must recognize an impairment loss as calculated in Step 2. This comparison is usually based on pre-tax cash flows.

Step 2. The impairment loss is measured as the amount by which the asset's carrying amount exceeds its fair value.

Impairment indicators

ASC 360-10-35 requires management to review the carrying value of long-lived assets if events or changes in circumstances indicate that the carrying value may no longer be recoverable. To ensure that these events or changes are identified in a timely fashion, companies should have processes and controls to identify possible triggering events, such as:

- Lower expected oil and gas prices (e.g., prices used by management to evaluate whether or not to develop or acquire properties).

- Significant changes in actual or expected future development or operating costs for a group of properties (e.g., significant development cost overruns or higher oil field or other service costs, with no significant upward revision in reserves estimates).

- Significant downward revision to a field's reserves estimates.

- Significant increases in capitalized asset-retirement costs.

- Significant adverse changes in the legislative or regulatory climate.

If an impairment indicator exists, the recoverability of the asset's carrying value should be assessed. If an asset's expected undiscounted future cash flows (as calculated in Step 1) are less than its carrying value, the carrying value may be unrecoverable and the company should compare the carrying value to the fair value of the assets to determine if an impairment loss should be recorded.

Adjustments to asset carrying amounts

ASC 360-10-35 does not define a long-lived asset's carrying amount. Generally, however, this is the asset's net book value, or cost less accumulated DD&A. Deferred income taxes are usually excluded from this calculation.

To appropriately compare the net book value with expected undiscounted future cash flows, other balance sheet accounts, such as deferred income taxes, asset retirement obligations (AROs) and volumetric production payment (VPP) deferred revenues, should be considered, as described below.

Deferred income taxes

Unlike their treatment in the full cost ceiling test, deferred income tax assets and liabilities are typically excluded from an asset group's carrying value for comparison to the related expected undiscounted future net cash flows, which also typically are prepared on a pre-tax basis. This is because the results of the undiscounted cash flow test generally will produce the same result on both a pre-tax and after-tax basis. For example, if an asset's carrying value is $1 million, and the expected future cash flow is $1 million, the related future income taxes will equal or closely approximate the related deferred income taxes.

ARO liabilities

As described in Chapter 19, ASC 410-20, *Asset Retirement Obligations*, requires that AROs be recorded as a liability when incurred. The amount of the liability can be calculated at the time a field is explored and developed. The initial liability accrual increases the carrying value of the asset. When determining whether to recognize an impairment of an asset, ASC 360-10-35-18 requires the inclusion of capitalized retirement costs in the asset's carrying amount. However, if the ARO is recognized on the balance sheet, the estimated cash outflows associated with the liability must be excluded from both the cash flows used to test recoverability and those used to determine the asset's fair value, in order to avoid double counting.

VPP deferred revenue

The conveyance of a VPP from a proved property is considered the sale of a mineral interest which reduces reserves, according to ASC 932-360-55. For successful efforts companies, cash proceeds are typically credited to deferred revenue rather than to oil and gas properties (as would be the case under full cost). To apply ASC 360 for measuring impairment loss, the asset's carrying amount should be reduced by any related VPP deferred revenue for comparison to the asset's fair value.

Assessing and measuring impairment

ASC 360-10-35 offers only general measurement guidelines. This example demonstrates how a successful efforts company typically applies ASC guidance to its proved properties, based on the following assumptions:

- Proved oil and gas properties and related equipment are grouped by field.

- The company has 10 proved fields.

- During the current reporting period, given significant declines in oil prices and the outlook for forward pricing, management significantly reduced its previously planned development of three nonoperated fields (Field A, Field B and Field C). Accordingly, it also revised downward its proved crude oil reserves estimates for these fields.

Given these impairment indicators, the company performed the recoverability test for the three fields, as illustrated in Figure 17-1 below.

Figure 17-1
Recoverability test

	Field A	Field B	Field C
Calculation of net book value[1]		(in millions)	
Capitalized cost of proved properties	$5	$20	$10
Asset retirement costs	0	2	1
Accumulated DD&A	(2)	(12)	(5)
Deferred revenue for VPP on Field C	0	0	(3)
Net book value	$3	$10	$ 3
Comparison to future cash flows			
Future undiscounted expected cash flows[2]	$4	$8	$8
Recoverable?	Yes	No	Yes

[1] Deferred income taxes are excluded in determining net book value subject to impairment.
[2] Calculated before taxes and excluding cash outflows for AROs included on the balance sheet.

Based on the recoverability test calculation for each field, the company compares the net book value of Field B to its fair value to determine if an impairment loss should be recorded, as illustrated in Figure 17-2 below.

Figure 17-2
Impairment calculation

	Field B
	(in millions)
Net book value	$10
Fair value	5
Impairment loss	$ 5

The measurement of impairment is considered a pre-tax amount. Net book value is not reduced by related deferred income taxes, and fair value should reflect a market price for the asset, which may or may not include taxes (see Chapter 33 for further explanation of fair value). Impairment loss does not include income tax expenses or benefits resulting from selling the asset at fair value. Therefore, the adjusting journal entry to record the impairment loss is like that of any pre-tax expense: its effect on the income tax provision must be separately computed and recorded.

Continuing the previous example:

- The impairment loss account is debited $5 million and the impaired asset's accumulated DD&A account is credited $5 million. This reduces the asset's net book value by the impairment amount.

- If the effective income tax rate is 25 percent, an additional entry debits the deferred income tax liability account for $1.25 million and credits the deferred income tax benefit account for $1.25 million.

- Net income is reduced by $3.75 million (impairment of $5 million, less the deferred tax benefit of $1.25 million).

By contrast, a full cost company calculates impairment as a ceiling write-down (under the ceiling test), which includes the effect of taxes (see Chapter 18).

ASC 360-10-45-4 requires entities with multi-tier income statements to report impairment losses as a component of income from continuing operations, before income taxes. Furthermore, if presenting a subtotal, such as income from operations, it should include the impairment charge.

A company's policy for assessing and measuring impairment of its long-lived assets should be disclosed in the notes to the financial statements. In addition, for each period in which an impairment loss is recognized, ASC 360-10-50-2 requires the following disclosures in the financial statements:

- A description of the impaired assets (e.g., type of assets, location, fields) and the facts and circumstances leading to the impairment.

- The method(s) selected to determine fair value (e.g., whether based on a quoted market price, prices for similar assets or another valuation technique).

- The amount of impairment loss, disclosed either on the face of the income statement or in a note to the financial statements identifying the income statement caption that includes the loss.

- If applicable, the segment (determined under Topic 280) affected by the loss.

Application issues

When applying ASC 360-10-45 to proved properties, including wells and facilities, several issues may arise, including:

- Impairment under unit-of-production amortization.

- Asset groupings (discussion herein).

- Determining expected undiscounted future cash flows (Step 1).

- Determining fair value (Step 2).

- Assets held for sale.

- Discontinued operations.

Impairment under unit-of-production amortization

ASC 360-10-35-22 notes that an impairment assessment may prompt a company's review of its depreciation policies. However, for successful efforts companies, ASC 932-360-35-6 permits only the unit-of-production amortization method. Consequently, the likelihood of impairment increases with time as an asset group's production declines to its economic limit. This is due to the nature of calculating unit-of-production amortization and the fact that operating costs tend to be fixed, rather than variable.

For example, if reserves are acquired at $5 per BOE, the expected DD&A rate is $5 per BOE produced. However, as production declines over time, net cash flows per BOE will also decline, eventually to zero.

This situation occurs because fixed operating costs are spread over fewer units of production. Therefore, in the asset group's later years, cash flow per BOE is less than the $5 needed to recover the asset group's unamortized carrying costs. Upward reserve revisions during the asset group's productive life may help restore value, but the problem may still exist with this amortization method.

Additionally, the method by which a company groups its costs for DD&A purposes (such as by property) may differ from the method used to group assets for ASC 360-10-35 impairment tests. According to the *2019 PricewaterhouseCoopers Survey of U.S. Petroleum Practices* (Question E7), of the 24 respondents using the successful efforts method, 13 respondents perform impairment tests using the same grouping of properties as for DD&A, two use a less aggregated grouping and the remaining respondents use a grouping of two or more depletable units or another basis of aggregation.

Asset groupings

ASC 360-10-35-23 states "... assets shall be grouped with other assets and liabilities at the lowest level for which identifiable cash flows are largely independent of the cash flows of other assets and liabilities."

The *2019 PricewaterhouseCoopers Survey of U.S. Petroleum Accounting Practices* (Question D1) found that, of the 24 respondents using the successful efforts method, 16 group assets by field, three group by resource play, three group by district or other regional aggregation of fields and two group on another basis for purposes of assessing impairment.

Wells within a given field generally share production facilities. This kind of cost sharing implies that the cash flows from a given well or lease are not largely independent. Furthermore, well operations typically fall within the field's operational and regulatory constraints. Grouping proved properties by field is also generally appropriate due to sales arrangements with purchasers who contract for a specific quantity of hydrocarbons.

Most sales arrangements include production from several wells within a given field, and production from a well can be dedicated to several purchasers. Sales proceeds from intermingled production of several wells are allocated based on each well's adjusted production volumes.

Grouping certain proved fields, or grouping proved fields with downstream activities, may be appropriate for assessing impairment – if the cash flows from these operations depend on each other. However, these asset groupings should be considered the exception, not the norm.

Step 1: Determining expected undiscounted future cash flows

ASC 360-10-35-29 defines expected future cash flows as "the future cash flows (cash inflows less associated cash outflows) that are directly associated with and that are expected to arise as a direct result of the use and eventual disposition of the asset (asset group). Those estimates shall exclude interest charges that will be recognized as an expense when incurred."

ASC 360-10-35-30 further states:

> Estimates of future cash flows used to test the recoverability of a long-lived asset (asset group) shall incorporate the entity's own assumptions about its use of the asset (asset group) and shall consider all available evidence. The assumptions used in developing those estimates shall be reasonable in relation to the assumptions used in developing other information used by the entity for comparable periods, such as internal budgets and projections, accruals related to incentive compensation plans, or information communicated to others. However, if alternative courses of action to recover the carrying amount of a long-lived asset (asset group) are under consideration or if a range is estimated for the amount of possible future cash flows associated with the likely course of action, the likelihood of those possible outcomes shall be considered. A probability-weighted approach may be useful in considering the likelihood of those possible outcomes. See Example 2 (paragraph 360-10-55-23) for an illustration of this guidance.

ASC 932 requires oil and gas companies to disclose their estimated future cash flows associated with proved oil and gas reserves. This standardized measure disclosure in ASC 932-235-50-30 and 31 (addressed in Chapter 31) is required to be based on proved reserves calculated using the 12-month, first-of-month, arithmetic average prices and year-end costs.

However, using the ASC 932 standardized measure cash flows for the ASC 360-10-35 two-step impairment calculation is not appropriate, as expected future cash flows under ASC 360-10-35 should be based on expected costs and expected future production. Furthermore, expected future production might include risk-weighted probable and possible reserves. Note, however, that ASC 932 successful efforts and Reg. S-X Rule 4-10 full cost accounting rules specifically require DD&A calculations to be based on proved reserves.

The determination of expected future cash flows for Step 1 impairment purposes should incorporate entity-specific assumptions, which generally include the following inputs.

Reserves. Note that unproved properties are assessed for impairment under ASC 932-360-35, which does not factor in reserves. However, for proved property impairment assessments, companies should consider proved, probable and possible reserves (appropriately risk-weighted) when estimating future cash flows.

ASC 360-10-35-30 requires considering the likelihood of possible outcomes, which permits companies to consider probable and possible reserves. However, the likelihood of possible reserves may be so remote that the incremental effect on expected future cash flows is nominal.

As explained in Chapter 15, probable reserves are defined in the updated 2018 PRMS as follows:

- Additional reserves which analysis of geological and engineering data suggests are less likely to be recovered than proved reserves, but are more certain to be recovered than possible reserves.

- When probabilistic methods are used, those having at least a 50 percent probability that the quantities recovered will equal or exceed the sum of estimated proved plus probable reserves.

For expediency, a company might use only proved reserves to quickly eliminate many properties from the list of those that are potentially unrecoverable. That is, properties with undiscounted cash flows that exceed the related carrying amount considering only cash flows from proved reserves would also be recoverable considering additional cash flows from probable and/or possible reserves.

For the remaining properties, a more refined estimate of future undiscounted cash flows should be made using: (1) proved reserves, (2) risk-adjusted probable reserves and (3) risk-adjusted possible reserves. Companies should consider the impact of all three categories of reserves (appropriately risk-weighted) in determining the appropriate fair value to use in measuring any impairment loss to be recorded.

Prices. Forecasted prices used in reserves estimates should be consistent with those used by management to operate the business, including its capital allocations. These price estimates typically are derived from a variety of sources, including but not limited to: customer contracts, future strip prices, analyst reports, government publications, internally developed estimates, etc.

Fixed and determinable contractual arrangements to which the company already is a party on the valuation date may help establish or reflect short-term expected prices, adjusted for basis differential(s). Prices should reflect the value of hydrocarbons at the wellhead or point of transfer from the asset group (e.g., at the gas plant tailgate, if the plant is grouped with the producing wells for ASC 360-10-35 purposes). Therefore, incremental profits or losses from subsequent downstream activities, and some risk management activities, should be excluded when determining future prices for asset groups.

According to the *2019 PricewaterhouseCoopers Survey of U.S. Petroleum Accounting Practices* (Question D5), 67 percent of the successful efforts respondents use externally published strip pricing as a primary input to compute expected undiscounted future cash flows when assessing impairment under ASC 360-10-35, while only 17 percent use internal expectations as reflected in capital budgeting models, with the remaining companies using other pricing inputs.

Costs. Future cost projections should reflect management's best estimates of the future capital expenditures and operating costs directly associated with the asset group. These costs also should correlate with the future capital and operating expenditure assumptions used by management for long-term budgeting.

When estimating future costs, current costs should be escalated by anticipated inflation factors, consistent with using oil and gas sales prices in nominal dollars. Like risk-weighted reserve quantities (described previously), capital expenditures should be risked at a level based on the risking applied to projected reserve quantities.

G&A overhead. Overhead costs should be considered to the extent they directly relate to operations of the asset group (e.g., operating personnel and project support staff working in district offices).

Taxes. Taxes in foreign jurisdictions should be evaluated as to whether they are more appropriately classified as royalties or production taxes, both of which reduce future pre-tax cash flows.

Plugging and abandonment costs. Because AROs are already shown as liabilities on the balance sheet, the future cash outflows for plugging and abandonment (P&A) costs are excluded from the fair value calculation even though, as discussed previously, the asset retirement costs (the asset side of the ARO entry) are included in the net book value of the asset. Including the asset retirement costs in the net asset carrying value and including the P&A cash outflows in the reserves cash outflows would inappropriately result in double counting the effects of the P&A costs on the impairment calculation.

Step 2: Determining fair value

ASC 360-10-35-17 states that the impairment loss associated with an asset group is "the amount by which the carrying amount of a long-lived asset (asset group) exceeds its fair value." ASC 820-10-20 defines fair value as, "The price that would be received to sell an asset or paid to transfer a liability in an orderly transaction between market participants at the measurement date." Market participants are defined as:

> Buyers and sellers in the principal (or most advantageous) market for the asset or liability that have all of the following characteristics:
>
> a. They are independent of each other, that is, they are not related parties, although the price in a related-party transaction may be used as an input to a fair value measurement if the reporting entity has evidence that the transaction was entered into at market terms
>
> b. They are knowledgeable, having a reasonable understanding about the asset or liability and the transaction using all available information, including information that might be obtained through due diligence efforts that are usual and customary
>
> c. They are able to enter into a transaction for the asset or liability
>
> d. They are willing to enter into a transaction for the asset or liability, that is, they are motivated but not forced or otherwise compelled to do so.

An asset's fair value is, preferably, indicated by a quoted market price in the asset's principal market. Otherwise, it is based on the best information available, such as the price of a similar asset or the result of valuation techniques. Chapter 33 describes the application of these techniques to the oil and gas industry, including whether or not to consider income taxes.

Assets held for sale

ASC 360-10-35 also provides guidance to petroleum accountants in recognizing and measuring the impairment of long-lived assets that have been identified for disposal. Furthermore, ASC 205-20-45 requires reporting discontinued operations separately from continuing operations. It extends the reporting requirement to any component of an entity that has either been disposed of or is classified as "held for sale."

For proved oil and gas properties that management has identified as held for sale, ASC 360-10-35-43 directs accountants to record them at the lower of: (1) carrying value or (2) fair value, less costs to sell. Assets held for sale must be presented separately from the company's other proved properties, either on the balance sheet or in the notes to the financial statements. Furthermore, a plan must exist for asset disposal, which generally should occur within one year of the plan date.

For asset disposal, fair value is the amount of expected future net realizable value from sale, discounted to present value on the appraisal date. Fair value excludes estimated future oil and gas revenues and related operating expenses during the period prior to sale.

ASC 360-10-35-38 states that, if the sale is expected to occur more than one year from the date held for sale classification was achieved, the cost to sell should be discounted (implying that the cost to sell is not discounted otherwise). ASC 360-10-35-43 notes that a long-lived asset identified as held for sale should not be depreciated (amortized). Therefore, oil and gas revenues and related operating expenses from assets held for sale are recognized, but no corresponding DD&A is recorded.

This treatment is appropriate since the carrying value of an asset held for sale is recovered from its disposal, not from its use. When the fair value (less costs to sell) is subsequently revised, the carrying value of the asset held for sale should be adjusted, provided the revised fair value does not exceed the asset's carrying value before the decision to dispose.

For example, assume that an E&P company signs a letter of intent on February 15, 2019, to sell its Texas properties for $100 million, less an estimated $5 million in operating cash flows through the expected closing date of September 20, 2019. Selling costs total $3 million. Expected sales proceeds are $95 million and expected net sales proceeds are $92 million. Assuming that all criteria in ASC 360-10-35 have been met, the Texas properties should be treated as long-lived assets to be disposed of (held for sale).

On February 28, 2019, the properties are carried at whichever is lower, carrying value or fair value, less the costs to sell. Assuming a four percent discount rate for six months, the expected $95 million in sales proceeds is discounted to $91.3 million in fair value as of February 28, 2019. The fair value, less the undiscounted costs to sell, equals $88.3 million. If the properties' total carrying value on February 28, 2019 is $90 million, the company will write-down the asset's carrying value to $88.3 million and will not depreciate that amount during the six-month pre-sale holding period.

If the property's fair value subsequently recovers, the increase in fair value would be recorded, but only up to the original carrying value of $90 million. If the total carrying value is $85 million, the company will not take the write-down or any depreciation during the pre-sale holding period.

Disclosure requirements for impairment losses on assets held for sale are similar to disclosures for assets held and used; however, the following additional disclosures may also be required:

- Facts and circumstances leading to the expected disposal.

- Expected manner and timing of the disposal and the associated carrying amount.

- Any gains or losses that result from asset remeasurement, if material.

- Results of operations included in the income statement, if identifiable.

Discontinued operations

To qualify as discontinued operations under ASC 205-20-45-1B, a disposal or planned disposal must represent a strategic shift that has or will have a major effect on a company's operations and financial results. ASC 205 does not define "strategic shift" or "major effect;" however, it does include examples of strategic shifts that have or will have a major effect on a company's operations and financial results, as outlined below. Therefore, applying the guidance depends on each company's individual facts and circumstances.

The following examples of strategic shifts are included in ASC 205:

- The sale of a product line that represents 15 percent or more of a company's total revenues.

- The sale of operations in a geographical area that represents 20 percent or more of a company's total assets.

- The sale of an equity method investment that represents 20 percent or more of a company's total assets.

- The sale of 80 percent or more of a product line that accounts for 40 percent or more of total revenue but the seller retains 20 percent or more of its ownership interest.

The above examples are not intended to be all-inclusive and companies should consider other financial benchmarks appropriate to the industry. For example, an E&P company might consider the significance of a disposal to its reserves. Refining, chemical and certain midstream businesses might look at throughput capacity or gross margin. When relevant, companies should also consider the effect of a disposal on operating cash flows or non-GAAP measures such as EBITDA.

• • •

Key concepts

- Cost center definition

- Capitalized costs

- Amortization of capitalized costs

- Full cost ceiling

- Sales and abandonments

- ARO settlements

- Other special considerations

- Limitations under IFRS

Photograph by istock.com/baona

Oil and gas companies used some variation of the successful efforts method of accounting prior to the development of the full cost method in the late 1950s. Many publicly held oil and gas companies, especially small, newly formed companies, subsequently adopted the full cost method in the 1960s. However, as discussed in Chapter 4, significant regulatory controversy, combined with harsh criticism from registrants, continued through the 1980s as the SEC and FASB attempted to define the provisions of each accounting method.

Under current rules, both methods are accepted for financial accounting and reporting purposes, although successful efforts is the preferred method of the SEC, such that the SEC does not require an independent auditor's letter of preferability from a registrant that wants to change to the successful efforts method of accounting for oil and gas properties.

As used today, the full cost accounting method considers all costs of acquisition, exploration and development activities as necessary for the ultimate production of reserves, even though many costs do not directly relate to finding and developing reserves. Oil and gas companies using the full cost method expect the benefits obtained from prospects that prove to be successful, together with the benefits from past discoveries, will be adequate to recover the costs of all activities, both successful and unsuccessful, and to yield a profit. Figure 18-1 (identical to Figure 4-2) summarizes the major full cost accounting concepts explained in this chapter.

Cost center definition

Under SEC full cost accounting rules, "Cost centers shall be established on a country-by-country basis." A strict interpretation of this rule prohibits combining or grouping countries in a geographical area. For example, it would be improper to combine a company's North Sea operations with its Norwegian and British territorial areas. Reg. S-X Rule 4-10(c)(6)(ii) provides a rare exception to the countrywide cost center:

> Purchases of reserves. Purchases of oil and gas reserves in place ordinarily shall be accounted for as additional capitalized costs within the applicable cost center; however, significant purchases of production payments or properties with lives substantially shorter than the composite productive life of the cost center shall be accounted for separately.

An example of this exception could occur in an acquisition of a short-lived proved property such as a volumetric production payment (VPP), a term net profits interest, a term overriding royalty interest or any working interest in a rapidly depleting property. In this acquisition scenario, the property may have to be amortized separately from other proved properties located in the same country. However, an acquisition of a short-lived property does not necessarily require the property to be amortized separately; instead, the property must be significant and have a life substantially shorter than the composite productive life of the cost center.

The terms "significant" and "substantially shorter" are not clearly defined. Separate amortization of a large, short-lived property may, or may not, have a significant effect on amortization. This topic is further discussed later in this chapter.

Figure 18-1

Classification of costs – Full cost

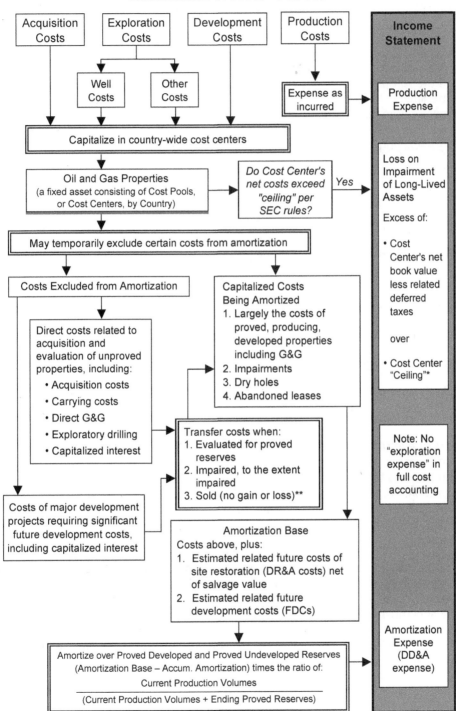

*   Prescribed in Reg. S-X Rule 4-10 (see Appendix I).

** See discussion herein of related considerations.

Capitalized costs

Reg. S-X Rule 4-10(c)(2) specifies the costs to be capitalized under the full cost method:

> **Costs to be capitalized.** All costs associated with property acquisition, exploration, and development activities... shall be capitalized within the appropriate cost center. Any internal costs that are capitalized shall be limited to those costs that can be directly identified with acquisition, exploration, and development activities undertaken by the reporting entity for its own account, and shall not include any costs related to production, general corporate overhead, or similar activities.

Qualifying costs

Under these rules, the following costs would be capitalized, as depicted in Figure 18-1:

- All geological and geophysical costs.

- Carrying costs such as delay rentals and maintenance of land and lease records.

- Dry hole and bottom hole contributions.

- Costs of exploratory wells (both dry and successful).

- Costs of stratigraphic tests wells.

- Costs of acquiring properties.

- All development costs.

Accordingly, even after leases are surrendered or abandoned, their costs remain capitalized in the cost center, as do costs of dry holes and other unsuccessful exploration activities. Companies using the full cost method may also capitalize overhead costs related directly to exploration, acquisition and development activities, although the amount to capitalize is dependent on management's judgment. Determining the amount of interest to be capitalized by full cost companies may also present a challenge, as described later in this chapter.

Since all capitalized costs incurred in each country are recorded in a cost center with the other mineral assets held within that country, individual properties and assets conceptually lose their identities. A single oil and gas assets account (or similar title) for each country typically accumulates the costs in that country. For example, a company with operations in the U.S. (onshore and offshore), Canada and Norway might maintain accounts in three cost centers, one for each country in which it operates. Even though all oil and gas assets in a cost center are combined into a single account, certain detailed records must be maintained for federal income tax and other regulatory purposes.

In addition, companies can exclude, temporarily, certain unevaluated costs from the amortization base. Thus, companies using the full cost method should maintain subledgers for individual proved properties and individual unproved properties. Furthermore, the method of accounting chosen does not alter the need for management and internal control of operations. Basic accounting procedures, such as the use of an AFE, are not affected by the choice of successful efforts accounting versus full cost accounting. For these reasons, most companies use general ledger accounts similar to those used in successful efforts accounting.

Interest capitalization

Chapter 9 addresses the requirements of ASC 835-20 for capitalization of interest during a construction period. Interest should not be capitalized on assets "that are in use or ready for their intended use in the earning activities of the business."

ASC 932-835-25 clarifies the interest capitalization rules for oil and gas companies using the full cost method. The FASB concluded that full cost companies should capitalize interest only on assets that have been excluded from the full cost amortization pool. Assets being amortized are deemed to relate to reserves being produced and thus are part of the earnings process; interest on those assets should not be capitalized. Capitalized interest becomes a part of the cost of the related properties or projects and is subject to amortization when the asset costs are transferred to the amortization pool.

Amortization of capitalized costs

Full cost accounting differs significantly from the successful efforts method when calculating amortization, primarily driven by differences in the reserves volumes and capitalized costs used in the amortization calculations under the two methods.

Costs subject to amortization

All capitalized costs within a cost center are amortized on the unit-of-production basis, using total proved oil and gas reserves, with certain temporary exceptions from amortization provided by Reg. S-X Rule 4-10. Oil and gas reserves are converted to a common unit of measure based on energy content, with a single exception related to the gross revenue method of amortization, as described later in this chapter. Conversion to an equivalent barrel or Mcf is the same as illustrated in Chapter 16.

Reg. S-X Rule 4-10(c)(3)(i) contains the basic description of costs to be amortized, although paragraph (ii) provides two exceptions to this general rule:

> Costs to be amortized shall include (A) all capitalized costs, less accumulated amortization, other than the cost of properties described in paragraph (ii) below; (B) the estimated future expenditures (based on current costs) to be incurred in developing proved reserves; and (C) estimated dismantlement and abandonment costs, net of estimated salvage values.

Costs excluded from amortization

As provided in Reg. S-X Rule 4-10 (c)(3)(ii), "The cost of investments in unproved properties and major development projects may be excluded from capitalized costs to be amortized," subject to additional provisions of the rule, as discussed below.

Costs of unproved properties. The first permissible exclusion from amortization is the cost of acquisition and exploration directly related to unproved properties. Paragraph (A) of Reg. S-X Rule 4-10 (c)(3)(ii) states:

> (A) All costs directly associated with the acquisition and evaluation of unproved properties may be excluded from the amortization computation until it is determined whether or not proved reserves can be assigned to the properties, subject to the following conditions:
>
> (1) Until such a determination is made, the properties shall be assessed at least annually to ascertain whether impairment has occurred. Unevaluated properties whose costs are individually significant shall be assessed individually. Where it is not practicable to individually assess the amount of impairment of properties for which costs are not individually significant, such properties may be grouped for purposes of assessing impairment. Impairment may be estimated by applying factors based on historical experience and other data such as primary lease terms of the properties, average holding periods of unproved properties, and geographic and geologic data to groupings of individually insignificant properties and projects. The amount of impairment assessed under either of these methods shall be added to the costs to be amortized.
>
> (2) The costs of drilling exploratory dry holes shall be included in the amortization base immediately upon determination that the well is dry.
>
> (3) If geological and geophysical costs cannot be directly associated with specific unevaluated properties, they shall be included in the amortization base as incurred. Upon complete evaluation of a property, the total remaining excluded cost (net of any impairment) shall be included in the full cost amortization base.

Note that the rules for determining impairment of unevaluated properties and related costs are similar to those described in Chapter 7 for determining impairment of unproved properties by successful efforts companies. In many instances, the SEC has adapted the rules for successful efforts accounting to specific problems in applying the full cost method.

Under the full cost method, companies may (but are not required to) exclude from their amortization pool the acquisition and exploration costs directly related to unevaluated properties. If such costs are excluded, the entity is required to begin immediate amortization of any amount of impairment.

Similar to successful efforts accounting, unproved properties must be impaired on a property-by-property basis (for individually significant properties). The SEC has stated that for full cost companies, the term "individually significant" identifies a property or project with costs in excess of 10 percent of the net capitalized costs of the cost center. Individual impairment also is allowed for insignificant properties. Note that impairment of unproved properties does not give rise to an expense or loss for a full cost company; it merely moves the impaired amounts to the pool of costs that is subject to amortization.

Exclusion from amortization is permitted to prevent distortion in the amortization per unit that could result if the cost of unevaluated properties, with no proved reserves attributed to them, were to be included in the amortization base. This guidance is intended to match proved reserves in the countrywide cost center with associated costs, including unsuccessful exploration costs.

Figure 18-2 illustrates how the costs of unevaluated properties are excluded from a hypothetical cost center's amortization base.

Figure 18-2
Amortization base calculation – Full cost

Capitalized costs as of period-end		$150,000,000
Less: amortization in prior periods		(40,000,000)
Net book value prior to current amortization		110,000,000
Plus: estimated future development costs		20,000,000
Total capitalized costs		130,000,000
Less: costs related to unproved properties		
Unproved properties costs	$35,000,000	
Less: cumulative impairments	(15,000,000)	(20,000,000)
Amortization base		**$110,000,000**

Major Development Projects. The second permissible exclusion of capitalized costs from the amortization pool is also stated in Reg. S-X Rule 4-10(c)(3)(ii):

(B) Certain costs may be excluded from amortization when incurred in connection with major development projects expected to entail significant costs to ascertain the quantities of proved reserves attributable to the properties under development (e.g., the installation of an offshore drilling platform from which development wells are to be drilled, the installation of improved recovery programs, and similar major projects undertaken in the expectation of significant additions to proved reserves). The amounts which may be excluded are applicable portions of (1) the costs that relate to the major development project and have not previously been included in the amortization base, and (2) the estimated future expenditures associated with the development project. The excluded portion of any common costs associated with the development project should be based, as is most appropriate in the circumstances, on a comparison of either (i) existing proved reserves to total proved reserves expected to be established upon completion of the project, or (ii) the number of wells to which proved reserves have been assigned and the total number of wells expected to be drilled. Such costs may be excluded from costs to be amortized until the earlier determination of whether additional reserves are proved or impairment occurs.

> (C) Excluded costs and the proved reserves related to such costs shall be transferred into the amortization base on an ongoing (well-by-well or property-by-property) basis as the project is evaluated and proved reserves established or impairment determined. Once proved reserves are established, there is no further justification for continued exclusion from the full cost amortization base even if other factors prevent immediate production or marketing.

To illustrate the exclusion of major development project costs from the amortization calculation, assume that the capitalized costs of a discovery well, two evaluation wells and a platform related to a major offshore project total $50 million.

Two producing wells have been drilled from the platform at a cost of $3.5 million per well and eight more wells are expected to cost $3.5 million each. They will be drilled to formations containing an estimated 10.2 million barrels of probable reserves. It is projected that a total of 12 million barrels ultimately may be proved, although only 1.2 million have been proved by the first two development wells. In computing amortization for the year, reserves not yet proved are omitted from the proved reserves amount. That portion of the $50 million of common costs related to the excluded reserves is also appropriately excluded from the amortization base.

Figure 18-3 presents the calculations of the excluded portion of major development projects using two possible allocation methods based on: (1) number of wells or (2) reserves quantities:

Figure 18-3
Costs excluded from amortization base – Major development projects

Allocation based on number of wells

Direct costs of the eight wells to be drilled at $3.5 million each	$28,000,000
Plus: common costs of $50 million x 80%*	40,000,000
	$68,000,000

Allocation based on reserves quantities

Direct costs of the eight wells, at $3.5 million each	$28,000,000
Plus: common costs of $50 million x 85%**	42,500,000
	$70,500,000

* 8 wells remaining to be drilled divided by 10 total wells to be drilled.

** 10.2 million bbls of probable reserves divided by 12 million bbls of total expected proved reserves.

Disclosure requirements. Reg. S-X Rule 4-10(c)(7)(ii) requires several disclosures of costs excluded from the amortization base. An E&P company is required to state separately, on the face of the balance sheet, the aggregate capitalized costs of unproved properties and major development projects excluded from capitalized costs being amortized. In addition, the footnotes to the financial statements must include a description of the current status of the significant properties or projects involved, including the anticipated timing of when costs will be included in the amortization base.

A table should be presented showing, by category of cost (acquisition, exploration, development and capitalized interest): (1) total costs excluded as of the most recent fiscal year and (2) the amount of excluded costs incurred: (a) in each of the three most recent fiscal years and (b) in the aggregate for any earlier fiscal years in which the costs were incurred. Excluded costs do not have to be disclosed by cost center, nor does the disclosure need to indicate the status of all properties and projects with excluded costs.

For example, the balance sheet could show the following:

Oil and gas properties, on the basis of full cost accounting:	
Proved properties	$50,000,000
Unproved properties and development costs not being amortized	15,000,000
Less: accumulated amortization and impairment	(10,000,000)
Net oil and gas properties	$55,000,000

A financial statement footnote might read as follows:

The Company excludes from amortization the costs of unproved properties, exploratory wells in progress and major development projects in progress. The costs of oil and gas properties not being amortized as of December 31, 2019, are as follows, by the year in which such costs were incurred (in millions):

	Total	2019	2018	2017	Prior
Acquisition costs	$ 6.3	$3.0	$2.5	$0.5	$0.3
Exploration costs	1.2	0.9	0.2	0.1	–
Development costs	8.5	4.0	4.5	–	–
Capitalized interest	1.0	0.5	0.4	0.1	–
Costs excluded from amortization	**$17.0**	**$8.4**	**$7.6**	**$0.7**	**$0.3**

The excluded costs include: (1) $4.9 million for the Nymeria offshore field expected to be included in the amortization base in 2020 and (2) $2.5 million for the unproved, unevaluated JSB Ranch lease expected to be evaluated in 2020.

Calculating amortization expense

The full cost unit-of-production amortization formula is similar to the one shown in Chapter 16 for successful efforts accounting, except:

- The cost center is country-wide.

- The amortization calculation is based on <u>total proved</u> reserves.

- The amortization base includes estimated future development costs related to undeveloped proved reserves.

The full cost amortization formula is expressed as follows:

Amortization expense = B x [S ÷ (S + R)], where:

B = amortization base, as defined in the next paragraph.

S = volumes sold during the period (BOE, Mcfe or the volume of the dominant hydrocarbon).

R = volume of total proved reserves at period-end.

B (the amortization base) = C – A – V – E + F + D, where:

C = capitalized costs incurred for acquisition, exploration and development activities, including ARCs for all AROs resulting from exploration and development activities completed to date.

A = accumulated amortization at prior period end.

V = estimated undiscounted future salvage value of well equipment (see Chapter 19).

E = excluded unproved property costs and certain capitalized development costs (i.e., costs excluded from the amortization base, as allowed by Reg. SX Rule 4-10(c)(3)(ii).

F = undiscounted estimated future expenditures (based on current cost rates) to develop proved reserves.

D = undiscounted cash flows related to abandonment activities created by future development activities (which are not currently accrued under ASC 410).

Figure 18-4 illustrates an amortization expense computation for a public company's oil and gas assets in a given cost center:

Figure 18-4

Amortization expense calculation

C:	Capitalized costs	$280,000,000	
Less A:	Prior accumulated amortization	(44,000,000)	
Less V:	Estimated equipment salvage value	(10,000,000)	
Less E:	Costs excluded from amortization	(8,000,000)	
Plus F:	Estimated future development costs	16,000,000	
Plus D:	Estimated ARCs on future development activities	12,000,000	
Equals B:	**Amortization base**	**$246,000,000**	
Times S:	Units sold in the year	x 5,000,000	BOE
Divided by (S+R)	S = 5 MBOE; R = 33 MBOE	÷ 38,000,000	BOE
Equals:	**Amortization expense**	**$32,368,421**	

Notice that the formula adds the units sold in the period (S) to reserves at the end of the amortization period (R) to calculate the best current estimate of proved reserves as of the beginning of the period (S+R), in order to correspond to the amortization base (B) prior to the current period amortization.

As noted in Chapter 16, the figure for units sold (S) could arguably be replaced with units produced; however, the two volumes will normally be equivalent over a three-month or 12-month period. In some instances, units sold are significantly less than units produced due to shrinkage. Shrinkage arises from natural gas used on a lease, gas volumes lost in processing for extraction of NGL, removal of impurities and BS&W, or even theft or pipeline leaks.

If shrinkage is significant, the amortization calculation should use units sold (S) and proved reserves (R), both calculated either before or after shrinkage, so that costs are allocated reasonably over the productive life of the reserves.

Gross revenue method of amortization

Paragraph (c)(3)(iii) of Reg. S-X Rule 4-10 allows the computation of amortization using units of revenue when appropriate due to economic circumstances arising from oil or gas price regulations. Staff Accounting Bulletin (SAB) Topic 12.F also clarified that the gross revenue method may be more appropriate to use, even when production is not subject to price regulation in the following circumstances:

> [W]henever oil and gas sales prices are disproportionate to their relative energy content to the extent that the use of the units of production method would result in an improper matching of the costs of oil and gas production against the related revenue received. The method should be consistently applied and appropriately disclosed within the financial statements.

SAB Topic 12.F further states that factors other than price regulation, such as changes in typical contract lengths and methods of marketing natural gas, may also cause oil and natural gas prices to be disproportionate to their relative energy content.

Reg. S-X Rule 4-10(c)(3)(iii) directs the computation of unit-of-revenue amortization based on current gross revenues from production in relation to future gross revenues based on current prices from estimated production of proved oil and gas reserves. As used herein, the term "gross revenue" means revenue net of royalty and net profit disbursements but not reduced by production costs. Changes in existing prices are considered only when provided by contractual arrangements. SAB Topic 12.F further states that "current prices" is consistent with the definition provided in Reg. S-X Rule 4-10(c)(8).

Other considerations for amortization

Consolidation. Reg. S-X Rule 4-10(c)(3)(v) states that amortization "shall be made on a consolidated basis, including investees accounted for on a proportionate consolidation basis. Investees accounted for under the equity method shall be treated separately."

As indicated in SAB Topic 12, reporting entities that follow the full cost method shall apply the method to all operations, including the operations of their subsidiaries; however, conformity of accounting methods between a registrant and its equity investees, although desirable, is not required, unless the registrant proportionately consolidates its equity investees.

Gas processing plants. Reg. S-X Rule 4-10(c)(3)(iv) permits depreciation of natural gas processing plants by a method other than the unit-of-production method. Presumably, this exception applies in instances where a processing plant treats, on a contract basis, not only the plant owner's gas, but also gas belonging to others.

Purchases of reserves. As previously mentioned, Reg. S-X Rule 4-10(c)(6)(ii) states, "Purchases of oil and gas reserves in place ordinarily shall be accounted for as additional capitalized costs within the applicable cost center; however, significant purchases of production payments or properties with lives substantially shorter than the composite productive life of the cost center shall be accounted for separately."

Separate accounting of significant acquired production payments and short-lived properties usually increases the following year's total amortization, as illustrated below:

Properties	Unamortized costs	Production	Opening reserves	Amortization
Existing	$20.0 million	300,000 BOE	3,000,000 BOE	$2.0 million
Purchased	$ 5.0 million	50,000 BOE	250,000 BOE	$1.0 million
Aggregate	$25.0 million	350,000 BOE	3,250,000 BOE	$2.7 million

In the above scenario, separate accounting for the properties would result in amortization expense of $3.0 million ($2.0 million plus $1.0 million), whereas aggregating the properties results in amortization expense of $2.7 million.

Further, as illustrated above, the purchased properties' unamortized costs of $5.0 million represent 20 percent of the aggregate unamortized costs, while their productive life is approximately one-half of the existing properties' average productive life based on the amortization rate calculated as production divided by opening reserves. Yet the change in the first year's total amortization only results in a $300,000, or 11 percent, increase when calculated separately versus in the aggregate.

A question arises as to whether or not the purchased property is "significant", as well as whether or not it has a substantially shorter life. Although no clear guidance exists in this area, the SEC has addressed significance in two closely-related situations:

- The SEC states in section 406.01.c.i of its Financial Reporting Policies (FRP) that, "in general individual properties or projects would be expected to be individually significant if their costs exceed 10 percent of the net capitalized costs of the cost center."

- S-X Rule 4-10(c)(6)(i) calls for gain/loss recognition on the sale (but not the purchase) of property from the full cost pool when deferring the gain or loss would alter the cost pool's amortization rate significantly. Section (c)(6)(i) adds that a significant alteration is not expected to occur for sales involving less than 25 percent of the reserves in the full cost pool.

The guidance previously described would seem to suggest that, in deciding when to separately compute amortization expense for a significant purchase, the combined amortization expense should change by more than 10 percent immediately after the acquisition. A purchase similar to the example previously provided should be closely evaluated to determine if it is appropriate to separately compute amortization expense for the acquired properties.

Full cost ceiling

One of the principal criticisms of the full cost method is that capitalizing costs such as dry holes, exploration costs and surrendered leases creates a risk that unamortized capitalized costs in a cost center may exceed the underlying value of the associated oil and gas reserves. This concern led the SEC to call for the establishment of a cost ceiling for each cost center.

Ceiling calculation

The ceiling calculation is complicated and may be difficult to compute in some cases. The details are enumerated in Reg. S-X Rule 4-10(c)(4) below and clarified in SAB Topic 12.D:

Limitation on capitalized costs:

(i) For each cost center, capitalized costs, less accumulated amortization and related deferred income taxes, shall not exceed an amount (the cost center ceiling) equal to the sum of:

   (A) the present value of estimated future net revenues computed by applying current prices of oil and gas reserves (with consideration of price changes only to the extent provided by contractual arrangements) to estimated future production of proved oil and gas reserves as of the date of the latest balance sheet presented, less estimated future expenditures (based on current costs) to be incurred in developing and producing the proved reserves computed using a discount factor of ten percent and assuming continuation of existing economic conditions; plus

   (B) the cost of properties not being amortized pursuant to paragraph (i)(3)(ii) of this section; plus

   (C) the lower of cost or estimated fair value of unproven properties included in the costs being amortized; less

   (D) income tax effects related to differences between the book and tax basis of the properties referred to in paragraphs (i)(4)(i)(B) and (C) of this section. [The SEC has offered helpful interpretive guidance for Part D, as explained later in this chapter.]

(ii) If unamortized costs capitalized within a cost center, less related deferred income taxes, exceed the cost center ceiling, the excess shall be charged to expense and separately disclosed during the period in which the excess occurs. Amounts thus required to be written off shall not be reinstated for any subsequent increase in the cost center ceiling.

If the cost center's unamortized capitalized costs, less related deferred income taxes, exceed the ceiling, the net capitalized costs must be written down to the ceiling amount. A corresponding charge is made against income as of the balance sheet date. The write-down cannot be reversed in a subsequent reporting period.

Oil and gas properties that are accounted for using the full cost method of accounting as prescribed by Rule 4-10 are specifically scoped out of the impairment guidance in ASC 360. Furthermore, the ceiling test is calculated differently than the ASC 360 impairment calculation, since the ceiling is based on discounted future cash flows. ASC 360 does not recognize impairment unless capitalized costs exceed undiscounted expected future cash flows.

Rule 4-10(c)(4)(i)(A): Discounted cash flows. The present value of future net revenues is essentially the discounted present value of future net cash flows from proved reserves. Future net cash flows are based on current oil and gas prices and current production cost rates applied to the projected production of the company's proved reserves. Costs include estimated future development, production and asset retirement costs. The calculation requires a scheduling of production, revenues and costs, by year, in order to apply the 10 percent annual discount rate.

Discounted cash flows are computed according to these guidelines:

- Estimated future gross revenues ("future revenues") are determined by multiplying expected future net production, for each year, by the current price in effect at the end of the current fiscal quarter. Price changes are considered only to the extent provided by contractual arrangements, including hedging arrangements pursuant to SAB Topic 12.D(3)(b).[1] Rule 4-10(c)(8) of Regulation S-X defines current price as "the average price during the 12-month period prior to the ending date of the period covered by the report, determined as an unweighted arithmetic average of the first-day-of-the-month price for each month within such period, unless prices are defined by contractual arrangements, excluding escalations based upon future conditions."

- Estimated future expenditures to develop and produce the proved reserves each year are deducted from gross revenues. Estimates of future expenditures are based on current cost levels and cost rates.

- A fixed discount rate of 10 percent per annum is used to compute the present value of net revenues (gross revenues less costs) in order to arrive at the net present value of proved reserves.

In practice, a company's present value of its oil and gas reserves is the sum of present values computed well by well, property by property or field by field using petroleum engineering software. This is because prices and operating cost rates vary widely from one property or field to another due to differences in the quality of reserves, the existence of contractual sales prices and numerous other factors.

As an example, assume the following:

- LW Oil Co. owns a single proved field in a cost center.

- The unweighted arithmetic average of the first-day-of-the-month price during the 12-month period prior to the ending date of the period covered by the report is $65 per barrel.

- Severance taxes are four percent of revenue.

- Other production costs are currently $2 million per year.

- Additional development costs of $9 million will likely be incurred in 2020 to develop the current proved reserves.

Net cash flow and discounted net cash flow from production of proved reserves are shown in Figure 18-5. In computing the cost center ceiling, the value assigned to proved reserves is $87,492,991.

Figure 18-5
Calculating discounted cash flows

Year	Future production (bbls)	Gross revenue	Costs	Net cash flow	Discount factor*	Discounted cash flows
2020	800,000	$52,000,000	$13,080,000	$ 38,920,000	0.9535	$37,110,220
2021	560,000	36,400,000	3,456,000	32,944,000	0.8668	28,555,859
2022	320,000	20,800,000	2,832,000	17,968,000	0.7880	14,158,784
2023	160,000	10,400,000	2,416,000	7,984,000	0.7164	5,719,738
2024	80,000	5,200,000	2,208,000	2,992,000	0.6512	1,948,390
Total				**$100,808,000**		**$87,492,991**

*See Chapter 31.

Rule 4-10(c)(4)(i)(B): Cost of properties not being amortized. The costs of both unevaluated properties and significant development projects being withheld from the amortization calculation are included in the ceiling at the current carrying cost (i.e., cost less any impaired costs included in the amortization base). Due to the nature of such costs and the impairment requirement, it is not necessary to consider the fair value of such assets.

Rule 4-10(c)(4)(i)(C): Unproved properties being amortized. When the exclusion option under Rule 4-10(c)(3)(ii) is adopted, the costs being amortized are the worthless impaired costs and worthless costs of "evaluated unproved property." These properties are evaluated as having no proved reserves and are also considered worthless under normal circumstances, which would indicate that the estimated fair value is zero. As a result, the lower of cost or estimated fair value in these cases would be zero. Reg. S-X Rule 4-10 does not indicate whether to apply this valuation to all unproved properties in the base or on a property-by-property basis.

Rule 4-10(c)(4)(i)(D): Income tax effects. Subsection (c)(4)(i)(D) refers to "book basis," denoting the future net revenues (or alternatively, the present value of such future net revenues) cited in section (c)(4)(i)(A) and the values cited in (c)(4)(i)(B) and (C), as indicated in SAB Topic 12.D.

However, the ceiling amount mandated for proved properties in (c)(4)(i)(A) may differ substantially from the actual book basis of those properties. Hence, the related income tax effects may differ substantially from recorded deferred taxes that reflect the difference between actual book and tax bases.

Based on the guidance in SAB Topic 12.D and informal commentary from SEC staff, companies treat the amended (c)(4)(i)(D) as if it were corrected to read income tax effects related to differences between:

- The future net revenues and values referred to in Reg. S-X Rule 4-10 (c)(4)(i)(A), (B), and (C), and

- The tax bases of the related assets.

Note that if this calculation results in an income tax benefit instead of income tax expense, the benefit should be ignored when calculating the ceiling. This treatment is consistent with SAB Topic 12.D, Question 1.

Although this guidance relates specifically to the treatment of net operating losses, investment tax credits and foreign tax credit carryforwards in computing the income tax effects to deduct from estimated future net revenues, it implies that the consideration of tax attributes should not reduce the total tax effects below zero.

Income tax effect calculations

Theoretically, the income tax effect of future net revenue from proved properties is calculated on a future year by future year basis using the future cash flows determined under Rule 4-10 (c)(4)(i)(A). These future taxes, calculated year by year, are discounted to a present value. The income tax effects related to the values in (c)(4)(i)(B) and (C) are the taxes on the difference (often minimal) between the values in (B) and (C) and the properties' tax bases as of the effective date of the ceiling test, as if the properties relating to (B) and (C) were sold on that date for the values used in (B) and (C).

The calculated income tax effects are then combined to determine the ceiling component for (c)(4)(i)(D). These calculations are, collectively, called a "year-by-year approach" because the largest component reflects income taxes on future net revenues calculated future year by future year and discounted to a present value.

A year-by-year approach to calculating the income tax effect has an acceptable alternative allowed under SAB Topic 12.D. Known as the "short-cut approach," it is similar in many ways to assuming that all of the oil and gas properties, including proved properties, are sold as of the balance sheet date at the values determined in Reg. S-4 Rule 4-10(c) (4)(i)(A), (B) and (C). The short-cut approach calculates related income taxes as those due on the hypothetical "gain" from the "sale." However, statutory depletion (percentage depletion) can be used in the calculation. Therefore, this method is truly a short-cut to the year-by-year calculation and not an approach that assumes immediate sales of proved properties.

In both approaches, income tax calculations consider the current tax bases of the oil and gas assets, as well as any related net operating loss carryforwards and tax credits.

Assume the previous facts for LW Oil Co., as well as the following information:

- $7.5 million of 2020 development costs include $5.1 million immediately deductible as IDC and $2.4 million of equipment costs depreciable for tax purposes on a unit-of-production basis.

- $5 million tax basis of proved property is deductible.

- LW Oil Co. will have additional percentage depletion deductions of $901,000.

- The combined federal and state income tax rate is 25 percent.

- On average, taxes are paid midway through the year, using the same discount factors as shown in Figure 18-5.

- LW Oil Co. has the following income tax credit carryforwards and a net operating loss carryforward:

    - $1 million foreign tax credit carryforward.

    - $500,000 other credit carryforwards.

    - $40,000,000 net operating loss carryforward.

Figure 18-6

Income tax effects relating to future net revenue

	2020	2021	2022	2023	2024	Total
Net cash flow	$38,920,000	$32,944,000	$17,968,000	$ 7,984,000	$2,992,000	$100,808,000
Add back 2020 equipment costs	2,400,000	–	–	–	–	2,400,000
Depreciate 2020 equipment costs	(1,000,000)	(700,000)	(400,000)	(200,000)	(100,000)	(2,400,000)
Deduct 12/31/19 tax bases	(1,825,000)	(2,138,000)	(550,000)	(425,000)	(62,000)	(5,000,000)
Deduct additional % depletion	(200,000)	(300,000)	(200,000)	(200,000)	(1,000)	(901,000)
Taxable income	**38,295,000**	**29,806,000**	**16,818,000**	**7,159,000**	**2,829,000**	**94,907,000**
NOL carryforwards	(38,295,000)	(1,705,000)				(40,000,000)
	–	28,101,000	16,818,000	7,159,000	2,829,000	54,907,000
Income tax at 25%	–	7,025,250	4,204,500	1,789,750	707,250	13,726,750
Foreign tax credit carryforward	–	(1,000,000)	–	–	–	(1,000,000)
Other credit carryforwards	–	(500,000)	–	–	–	(500,000)
	–	5,525,250	4,204,500	1,789,750	707,250	12,226,750
x Discount factor	0.9535	0.8668	0.7880	0.7164	0.6512	
Income tax present value	$ -	$ 4,789,287	$ 3,313,146	$1,282,177	$ 460,561	$ 9,845,171

As illustrated in Figure 18-6, under the year-by-year approach, the income tax effect relating to the future net revenues is $9,845,171. The income tax effects relating to the values in (c)(4)(i)(B) and (C) are much smaller and are computed as follows:

	(c)(4)(i)(B)	(c)(4)(i)(C)
Value	$10,000,000	$4,700,000
Less: tax basis	(8,000,000)	(0)
Difference	$ 2,000,000	$4,700,000
Tax effect at 25%	**$ 500,000**	**$1,175,000**

For costs excluded from amortization, the corresponding tax basis typically is smaller because some of those costs may be tax-deductible when incurred, such as intangible drilling and development costs and delay rentals. For example, the combined income tax effect under the year-by-year approach is $9,845,171 plus $500,000 and $1,175,000 (as calculated above), for a total of $11,520,171.

Under the short-cut approach, Figure 18-7 calculates the income tax effect, assuming the present value of the additional percentage depletion is $700,000:

Figure 18-7
Income tax effect – Short-cut approach

Present value of future net revenues (Figure 18-5)		$ 87,492,991
Costs of properties not being amortized		10,000,000
Lower of cost or estimated fair value of unproved properties included in costs being amortized		4,700,000
Ceiling limitation before income tax effects		$102,192,991
Less: tax bases and other deductions		
Tax basis of proved properties to be amortized	$5,000,000	
Tax basis of unproved properties being amortized	–	
Tax basis of unproved properties not being amortized	8,000,000	
Present value of statutory depletion	700,000	
Net operating loss carryforwards*	40,000,000	(53,700,000)
Future taxable income		$48,492,991
Short-cut approach calculation		
Income tax effect at 25%		$12,123,248
Foreign tax credit carryforward*		(1,000,000)
Other credit carryforwards*		(500,000)
Estimated preference tax		200,000
Income tax effect		**$10,823,248**

* All carryforward amounts represent amounts that are available for tax purposes and that relate to oil and gas operations.

In the short-cut approach example, the $10,823,248 income tax effect is approximately six percent less than the $11,520,171 calculated using the year-by-year approach. Generally, the short-cut approach calculates tax effects slightly lower because it assumes the proved properties tax basis is immediately deductible.

The ceiling test calculations using both income tax calculation approaches are summarized as follows:

	Year-by-year	Short-cut
Ceiling, pre-tax	$102,192,991	$102,192,991
Less: income tax effect	(11,520,171)	(10,823,248)
Ceiling	90,672,820	91,369,743
Less: net book basis to be recovered	(63,275,000)	(63,275,000)
Excess ceiling (no write-down)	**$ 27,397,820**	**$ 28,094,743**

Since SAB Topic 12.D states that the short-cut approach is acceptable, companies using it may not need to record a write-down. However, if a write-down is recorded, it should adjust both the gross asset carrying value and related deferred income taxes. When a write-down is required, the ceiling shortfall amount must be grossed up for the tax effects. Otherwise, a ceiling test proof will result in costs that exceed the ceiling on an after-tax basis.

Assuming a ceiling shortfall of $24 million and a 25 percent income tax rate, the journal entry recorded would be as follows:

Impairment expense – proved properties	32,000,000	
Deferred income tax provision	8,000,000	
Accumulated impairment – proved properties		32,000,000
Income tax expense		8,000,000
To record impairment of carrying value of oil and gas properties.		

Note that if there is a deferred tax asset related to the net book basis to be recovered, this asset should be ignored for purposes of the ceiling test. For example, if the related net deferred income tax was an asset rather than a liability (i.e., an increase to the net book basis to be recovered rather than a decrease), the tax effect would not be included in the ceiling test computation.

This approach preserves the premise under Reg. S-X Rule 4-10 that the ceiling is not intended to assess the recognition or recoverability of any deferred tax assets resulting from the tax basis in excess of future net revenues. The recoverability of deferred tax assets should, instead, be assessed under ASC 740, *Income Taxes*.

Furthermore, if the recording of a write-down results in a deferred tax asset related to the net book basis to be recovered within a subsequent ceiling test calculation, this asset also should be ignored within the calculation. Otherwise, it would produce costs that exceed the ceiling. To arrive at the appropriate write-down amount, the company should add the excess of the net book basis to be recovered over future net revenues to the deferred tax liability related to the net book basis to be recovered, if any, prior to the write-down.

Net book basis to be recovered

The full cost ceiling is compared to capitalized costs less accumulated amortization and related deferred income taxes. The net book basis to be recovered by LW Oil Co. is shown in Figure 18-8 as of December 31, 2019.

ASC 410 considerations

ASC 410 brings unique challenges for full cost companies because it is silent in regard to the ceiling test. Under ASC 410, ARCs: (1) represent the fair value that AROs had on the date the liabilities were recognized and (2) are additional historical costs of the related assets, which are included in the full cost pool for oil and gas companies that follow Reg. S-X Rule 4-10.

Figure 18-8
Net book basis to be recovered

Costs of proved properties being amortized	$69,000,000
Plus: lower of cost or estimated fair value of unproved properties being amortized	4,700,000
Amortization base	73,700,000
Plus: costs of properties not being amortized	10,000,000
Less: accumulated amortization	(15,000,000)
Net book basis of oil and gas properties	$68,700,000

Related deferred income taxes

Net book basis of oil and gas properties	$68,700,000	
Less: tax basis of proved properties to be amortized	(5,000,000)	
Less: tax basis of unproved properties being amortized	–	
Less: tax basis of properties not being amortized	(8,000,000)	
Book-tax difference	55,700,000	
Less: NOL carryforward*	(28,000,000)	
	27,700,000	
25% effective tax rate	x 25%	
Related deferred income taxes	6,925,000	
Less: foreign tax credit carryforward*	(1,000,000)	
Less: other credit carryforwards*	(500,000)	(5,425,000)
Net book basis to be recovered		**$63,275,000**

* All carryforward amounts represent amounts that are available for tax purposes and that relate to oil and gas operations.

The interaction of ASC 410 and Rule 4-10 includes ARCs in capitalized costs, while reducing the ceiling limit on those costs by including the future cash outflows required to settle the related AROs. This would appear to result in double-counting of the effect of asset retirement activities in the ceiling test.

This double-counting issue was addressed in SAB Topic 12.D(4), which requires a company to increase the full cost ceiling by excluding the cash outflows (discounted at 10 percent in accordance with Rule 4-10) that are required to settle the AROs accrued on the balance sheet. If an obligation for expected asset retirement costs has not been accrued under ASC 410 for certain ARCs that must be included in the full cost ceiling calculation under Rule 4-10 (c)(4) (i.e., for proved undeveloped reserves), those cash outflows should continue to be included in the full cost ceiling calculation.

SAB Topic 12.D(4) is consistent with ASC 360-10-35 guidance regarding impairments for companies following the successful efforts method of accounting. The total capitalized costs of the full cost pool (recorded on the balance sheet) are tested for impairment by referencing the future discounted net revenues to be realized from those oil and gas reserves, excluding cash outflows related to the settlement of AROs already reflected on the balance sheet.

Purchased proved property

Companies may purchase proved property at a cost that exceeds the related increase in the full cost ceiling. The property's cost generally is based on fair value using expected prices, while the ceiling test requires the use of historical prices, as defined, which may be different. This potentially could result in a ceiling test write-down due to the recent purchase of a property at its fair value.

SEC Accounting Series Release No. 258 (ASR 258) addressed this issue. A registrant may request an exemption from the ceiling test when: (A) the write-down is attributable to recently purchased proved property and (B) the registrant believes the fair value of its properties exceeds the net book value.

SAB Topic 12.D, Question 3 explains how to obtain the ASR 258 ceiling exemption. The registrant should request a temporary waiver from the ceiling test for the purchased property, excluding the cost and ceiling value of the purchased property from the ceiling computation. Registrants should be prepared to demonstrate that the additional value exists, beyond a reasonable doubt. Therefore, the purchased property's fair value on the ceiling test date should be at least sufficient to eliminate the need for a write-down.

Subsequent events

SAB Topic 12.D, Question 3 also allows a write-down to be avoided if the ceiling test considers additional reserves that are transferred to proved properties owned at year-end and occurring after the ceiling test date (the balance sheet date) but before the date of the auditor's report on the affected financial statements.

If the ceiling were recomputed giving effect to the additional reserves (both cost and ceiling adjustments), and no write-down is calculated, a company may elect not to record a write-down. By analogy, an interim ceiling test write-down could be avoided if the subsequent event occurred prior to issuance of the unaudited quarterly financial statements.

Financial statements should disclose that "capitalized costs exceeded the limitation at [the balance sheet date]" and explain why the excess was not charged against earnings. The registrant's supplemental disclosures of proved reserves (see Chapter 30) and the related standardized measure (see Chapter 31) should not reflect the subsequent event(s). However, the effects could be disclosed separately with appropriate explanation. Property acquisitions after the balance sheet date may not be considered.

Price changes after the balance sheet date should not be considered in the ceiling test, although substantial declines may warrant disclosure as a material subsequent event.

Sales and abandonments

Under the full cost method, all oil and gas properties in each country are combined into a common pool. Conceptually, each property loses its separate cost identity. Thus, sales and abandonments of properties are treated, generally, as adjustments of capitalized costs, with no recognition of gains or losses. Reg. S-X Rule 4-10 (c)(6) includes these rules:

> Other transactions. The provisions of paragraph (h) of this section, "Mineral property conveyances and related transactions if the successful efforts method of accounting is followed," shall apply also to those reporting entities following the full cost method except as follows:
>
> (i)   Sales and abandonments of oil and gas properties. Sales of oil and gas properties, whether or not being amortized currently, shall be accounted for as adjustments of capitalized costs, with no gain or loss recognized, unless such adjustments would significantly alter the relationship between capitalized costs and proved reserves of oil and gas attributable to a cost center. For instance, a significant alteration would not ordinarily be expected to occur for sales involving less than 25 percent of the reserve quantities of a given cost center. If gain or loss is recognized on such a sale, total capitalization costs within the cost center shall be allocated between the reserves sold and reserves retained on the same basis used to compute amortization, unless there are substantial economic differences between the properties sold and those retained, in which case capitalized costs shall be allocated on the basis of the relative fair values of the properties. Abandonments of oil and gas properties shall be accounted for as .adjustments of capitalized costs, that is, the cost of abandoned properties shall be charged to the full cost center and amortized (subject to the limitation on capitalized costs in paragraph (b) of this section). [The limitation on capitalized costs appears in Reg. S-X Rule 4-10(c)(4).]

In evaluating whether a significant alteration has occurred, petroleum accountants should refer to the above guidance, which indicates that recognizing gains and losses generally is not appropriate for sales involving less than 25 percent of reserve quantities for a given cost center.

Substantial economic differences occur between the properties sold and those retained when the fair value per BOE of reserves sold differs substantially from the corresponding value for those retained. Such differences can arise when:

- Production life is substantially different.

- Expected prices differ because of quality or location.

- The development of the reserves sold versus those retained is not comparable.

- Production costs differ widely.

In these cases, capitalized costs should be allocated according to the relative fair values of the properties sold versus those retained. However, this requirement may require a complex calculation to arrive at a fair value for the properties retained.

The following example illustrates the concepts of "significant alteration" and "substantial economic differences" as referred to in Reg. S-X Rule 4-10(c)(6)(i).

Hoosier Energy is a full cost company with $300 million in gross capitalized costs, $100 million in accumulated amortization, and 25 million BOE of reserves as of December 31, 2019. For simplicity, both future development costs and future net amortization are estimated at zero. The current amortization rate is $8 per BOE [($300 million less $100 million) ÷ 25 million BOE].

On December 31, 2019, Hoosier Energy sells certain of its U.S. properties to Aggie Petroleum for $75 million. The divested properties contain an estimated 10 million BOE of reserves. The fair value of the remaining properties in Hoosier Energy's U.S. cost center is $150 million. In this example, Hoosier would calculate a gain or loss on the property sale because a significant alteration has occurred – the sale of 40 percent of its reserves for its U.S. cost center (10 million BOE ÷ 25 million BOE).

In calculating the gain or loss on sale, Hoosier Energy would conclude that substantial economic differences exist between the properties sold and those retained, as evidenced by the $7.50 per BOE value of the properties sold versus the $10 per BOE value of the properties retained. Therefore, Hoosier Energy would allocate 33.3 percent of the net book value to the divested properties ($66.7 million) and recognize an $8.3 million gain on sale, based on the relative fair values of the properties sold and those retained.

Changing the assumptions slightly, consider that the value of the retained properties also is $7.50 per BOE, which would allow for an allocation based on reserves. In this instance, Hoosier Energy would allocate 40 percent of the net book value to the divested properties ($80 million) and recognize a $5 million loss on the sale.

Note that a deferral of the indicated gain or loss is not allowed under either of the scenarios outlined above, based on the SEC staff's view that a significant alteration has occurred (as evidenced by the sale of more than 25 percent of the cost center reserves).

Sales proceeds should not be simply credited to the accumulated amortization account. To illustrate, assume that Lucas Energy, a full cost company, operates only in the U.S. Total capitalized costs are $364 million and accumulated amortization of these costs is $120 million as of December 31, 2019. In January 2020, Lucas Energy enters into the following transactions:

- Unproved leases with a cost of $4 million are surrendered.

- Proved leases with a historical cost of $600,000 are abandoned; IDC originally incurred on abandoned leases totaled $3.9 million.

- Related equipment with a cost of $380,000 is also sold; salvage proceeds are $20,000.

Under the full cost method, it is not necessary to record adjustments to specific leases, nor is it even possible in some cases. The only entry required is to reduce the carrying value of the cost pool by the salvage proceeds by either crediting a capitalized cost account or crediting the accumulated amortization account for $20,000. Obviously, the above approach, applied over many years, would create a continuing increase in the capitalized cost accounts and the accumulated amortization account, because acquisition costs are never reduced for salvaged equipment no longer owned by the company.

In practice, most companies remove the asset costs from the asset account and charge these amounts, less any net salvage, against the accumulated amortization account. The summarized journal entry below reflects the previous transaction, based on the facts provided:

Cash	20,000	
Accumulated DD&A – proved properties	8,860,000	
Proved properties acquisition costs		600,000
Unproved properties acquisition costs		4,000,000
Intangible costs of wells		3,900,000
Tangible costs of wells		380,000

To record the January 2020 disposition of proved and unproved properties and well costs.

Multiple divestitures

Reg. S-X Rule 4-10 is silent as to whether or not full cost registrants should aggregate multiple divestitures of oil and gas properties in determining whether to recognize gains or losses. Registrants should apply careful judgment to each set of facts and circumstances.

The first key consideration is whether or not the registrant has publicly announced a divestiture program under which it will make multiple divestitures. If so, all divestitures occurring under that program could be aggregated for purposes of the gain or loss test, even if they occur with different purchasers.

When multiple divestitures occur in a given reporting period (e.g., annual or interim) with different counterparties, such divestitures generally should not be aggregated for the gain or loss test, as long as there are no contingencies or linkage between the transactions. Conversely, if multiple transactions occur with the same counterparty, the transactions could be aggregated for purposes of determining gain or loss, unless the registrant can demonstrate clearly that the transactions are not contingent upon each other or linked in some way.

When sales to the same counterparty extend across reporting periods, accounting treatment should be considered carefully. If gain or loss is to be recognized when sales of oil and gas properties extend across reporting periods, registrants must use care in allocating gain or loss to the respective reporting periods because of uncertainty about the likelihood of the divestitures closing in subsequent reporting periods.

Other conveyance types

Reg. S-X Rule 4-10(c)(6) stipulates that, in general, the conveyance rules found in ASC 932-360-40-4 apply not only to successful efforts companies but also to companies using full cost. However, Reg. S-X Rule 4-10(c)(6)(iii) adds that, under the full cost method, no income is recognized from the sales of properties or participation in various forms of drilling arrangements, except for amounts that represent reimbursement of certain expenses that are identifiable with the transaction.

Considerations relating to the formation and operation of partnerships are described in Chapter 23.

Accounting for production payments under full cost is similar to that for successful efforts, with two notable exceptions. Since a VPP conveyance is regarded as a sale of a mineral interest, Reg. S-X Rule 4-10(c)(6)(i) applies, whereby "sales of oil and gas properties... shall be accounted for as adjustments of capitalized costs." Generally, no gain or loss is recognized "unless such adjustments would significantly alter the relationship between capitalized costs and proved reserves... attributable to the cost center."

Reg. S-X Rule 4-10(c)(6) requires that (6)(i) supersede the conveyance rules of ASC 932-360-55, including the VPP rules of ASC 932-360-55-2. When a significant alteration occurs, a gain or loss should be recognized.

Held for sale considerations

Many accountants argue that an E&P company can participate in two distinct businesses: (1) oil and gas production in which it acquires unproved properties for drilling purposes and (2) lease brokerage for the purpose of promoting properties to limited partnerships. Reg. S-X Rule 4-10 clarifies that full cost companies cannot record gains or losses on the sales or promotion of unproved properties. Reg. S-X Rule 4-10(c)(6)(iii)(A) states:

> Except as provided in subparagraph (i)(6)(i) of this section, all consideration received from sales or transfers of properties in connection with partnerships, joint venture operations, or various other forms of drilling arrangements involving oil and gas exploration and development activities (e.g., carried interest, turnkey wells, management fees, etc.) shall be credited to the full cost account, except to the extent of amounts that represent reimbursement of organization, offering, general and administrative expenses, etc., that are identifiable with the transaction, if such amounts are currently incurred and charged to expense.

Subparagraph (c)(6)(iii)(A) contains extremely minor exceptions to the basic rule. Thus, even though a full cost company acquires an unproved property for the specific purpose of resale or transfer to a drilling fund (or partnership) operated by the company, any gain or loss resulting from a sale or transfer is treated as an adjustment of the full cost pool. Costs of all mineral properties owned by a full cost company, including those acquired for resale or promotion, are treated alike and included in a single, countrywide cost center.

Discontinued operations

Oil and gas properties that are accounted for using the full cost method of accounting as prescribed by Reg. S-X Rule 4-10 are specifically scoped out of the discontinued operations guidance per ASC 205-20-15-3 as follows:

> The guidance in this Subtopic does not apply to oil and gas properties that are accounted for using the full-cost method of accounting as prescribed by the U.S. Securities and Exchange Commission (SEC) (see Regulation S-X, Rule 4-10, Financial Accounting and Reporting for Oil and Gas Producing Activities Pursuant to the Federal Securities Laws and the Energy Policy and Conservation Act of 1975).

ARO settlements

ARO settlements, either through sale of oil and gas properties or satisfaction of an obligation, represent another unique circumstance for full cost companies for which diversity in practice exists within the industry. According to the *2019 PricewaterhouseCoopers Survey of U.S. Petroleum Practices* (Question F9), of the nine respondents following full cost, a majority of companies record settlements of AROs as adjustments to the full cost pool while other respondents recognize a gain or loss on settlement.

While the predominant view is that a gain or loss should not be recorded in either type of settlement scenario, both views are provided herein for reference. Careful consideration should be given to the specific facts and circumstances, including the potential need to initiate informal discussions or pre-clearance with the SEC related to the proper accounting treatment when contemplating recording a gain or loss on ARO settlement. In all cases, the accounting treatment should be carefully evaluated and applied consistently.

Adjustment to full cost pool

Under Reg. S-X Rule 4-10(c)(6)(i), companies following the full cost method of accounting for oil and gas properties recognize sales or abandonments of oil and gas properties as adjustments to capitalized costs, unless such adjustments would significantly alter the relationship between capitalized costs and proved reserves of oil and gas. No gains or losses are recorded on sales of insignificant properties.

Similarly, proponents of this view believe that companies following the full cost method of accounting should not recognize any gains or losses from the settlement of AROs related to oil and gas properties. Any variance between the ARO liability accrued and the actual cost incurred by an entity to settle the ARO should be recorded as an adjustment to accumulated amortization of the full cost pool. This is consistent with the overall theoretical basis of full cost accounting: that transactions related to individual properties within the full cost pool should not result in gains or losses except in limited circumstances prescribed by Reg. S-X Rule 4-10. Proponents of this view also believe that the nature of settling an ARO is consistent with the nature of the services covered in Reg. S-X Rule 4-10(c)(6)(iv), and therefore its guidance applies.

Gain or loss recorded on settlement

ASC 410 recognizes an ARO at its fair value, defined as the amount at which that liability could be settled in a current transaction between willing parties. ASC 410-20 explains that when estimating an ARO by the most common method of using a present value technique, estimates of future cash flows should include all costs and expenses, including overhead, profit margin and other costs that would be incurred to settle the ARO. ASC 410 explains why the FASB chose a market participant based fair value as the appropriate measure of AROs, even though it could result in the recognition of a gain on settlement by entities that settle these obligations internally in a more efficient manner.

Proponents of this view believe to the extent that internal resources are used to settle an ARO, the amounts representing profit margin ultimately will be derecognized upon the complete settlement of the liability, resulting in a gain. Alternatively, some AROs could result in a loss upon settlement, due to unplanned operational difficulties. For example, when decommissioning an offshore platform, any number of unforeseen variables could affect the total cost of removing the platform.

Accordingly, companies following this view should estimate the fair value of the ARO on the settlement date or at the date the transaction closes, with any gain or loss recognized regardless of whether or not the liability was settled directly by the registrant or assumed by a third party as part of a sales transaction. The difference between the fair value of the ARO at the transaction date and the amount accrued is recognized in the statement of operations in accordance with ASC 410.

Note in the case of an insignificant sale, any difference in the fair value of the oil and gas properties and the cost basis would still be recorded as an adjustment to the full cost pool in accordance with Reg. S-X Rule 4-10(c)(6)(i).

Other special considerations

The appropriate accounting treatment and financial reporting requirements for a variety of other issues are specific to companies that apply the full cost method of accounting.

Equipment costs

Some full cost companies have historically classified the costs for certain types of equipment and other depreciable assets as "unproved properties" that are not subject to amortization. They believe this grouping is consistent with the provision in Reg. S-X Rule 4-10 (c)(3)(ii)(A) that "all costs directly associated with the acquisition and evaluation of unproved properties" should be put in one bucket and excluded from amortization, as the equipment and leasehold cost are considered components of the acquisition cost.

However, this view does not appear to be consistent with "acquisition of properties" as defined in Reg. S-X Rule 4-10 (a)(1), which does not indicate that such equipment is a component of acquisition costs.

Goodwill

When performing an impairment test of goodwill in accordance with ASC 350, full cost companies should first complete the ceiling test calculation and record any ceiling test impairment. Failure to consider a ceiling test impairment prior to completing the goodwill impairment test could lead to overstating the reporting unit carrying amount and an inappropriate write-off of goodwill.

Because the unit of account under the full cost accounting method is the countrywide cost center, the reporting unit for purposes of the goodwill impairment test generally would not be below the level of the countrywide cost center.

Management fees

Companies using the full cost method should look to Reg. S-X Rule 4-10(c)(6)(iii) and (iv) when accounting for management fees and other income received for contractual services (e.g., drilling, well service or equipment supply services) performed by the registrant or an affiliate in connection with any property in which the registrant or an affiliate holds an ownership or other economic interest. Paragraph (iv) does not distinguish between proved producing properties and unproved properties; the prohibition on income recognition applies to all properties.

The rule's general prohibition of income recognition reflects the SEC's view that current recognition of income for services rendered in connection with an owned property would be inconsistent with the full cost concept, under which income is recognized only when reserves are produced. The SEC indicated that income should be recognized only to the extent it exceeds a company's costs in connection with the contract and the properties, except for the limited circumstances described in Reg. S-X Rule 4-10(c)(6) paragraph (iii) (B) and paragraphs (iv)(A) and (B).

Accordingly, registrants must treat management and service fees as reimbursements of costs, offsetting the costs incurred to provide the services, with any excess of fees over costs credited to the full cost pool and recognized through lower cost amortization only as production occurs. An example in Chapter 23 illustrates how to account for drilling services provided to properties owned through a partnership.

Statement of cash flows

Because a full cost company capitalizes geological and geophysical costs in the full cost pool, it is unclear how to treat these costs in the statement of cash flows (i.e., as either operating or investing activities). Companies applying the successful efforts method of accounting, however, are precluded from classifying such costs as investing activities in the statement of cash flows given the requirement under ASC 932-720-25-1, which specifies that geological and geophysical costs should be charged to expense.

Cash expenditures for exploratory wells, however, are appropriately classified within investing activities in the statement of cash flows for successful efforts companies. Thus, while there is no specific guidance in this area for full cost companies, common industry practice is to classify them with the other additions to oil and gas properties within investing activities in the statement of cash flows.

Limitations under IFRS

The unit of account used under the full cost accounting method for oil and gas properties is not supported by current IFRS. Under IFRS 1, *First-time Adoption of International Financial Reporting Standards* (IFRS 1), full retrospective restatement is required, which may be a difficult and costly undertaking for most companies.

Prior to July 2009, this situation was not addressed by the IASB for two principal reasons: (1) the IASB historically has preferred to limit its industry-specific guidance and (2) most oil and gas companies outside of North America followed a form of the successful efforts method of accounting.

With the conversion of Canadian oil and gas companies to IFRS, the issue gained more attention because many Canadian upstream companies followed the full cost accounting model. This was an urgent transition issue for these companies when Canada's conversion became effective in 2011.

At that time, the key area of concern was the recognition and measurement of oil and gas assets on the opening IFRS balance sheet at the transition date. Applying IFRS 1 would have required full cost companies to retrospectively restate: (1) historical full cost pools, allocating values to appropriate units of account under IFRS and (2) DD&A expense.

At the time, changing the unit of account and retrospectively restating would create difficulties in obtaining the necessary historical data. In addition, companies would incur significant costs in order to generate the necessary information for the retrospective allocation of the full cost pool.

Recognizing the issues faced by full cost companies adopting IFRS and applying the retrospective provisions of transitioning to IFRS, the IASB issued amendments to IFRS 1 to address the measurement of exploration and evaluation (E&E), as well as development and production assets upon transition for full cost companies.

The guidance states:

> A first-time adopter using such accounting under previous GAAP may elect to measure oil and gas assets at the date of transition to IFRS on the following basis:
>
> a. Exploration and evaluation assets at the amount determined under the entity's previous GAAP; and
>
> b. Assets in the development or production phases at the amount determined for the cost centre under the entity's previous GAAP. The entity shall allocate this amount to the cost centre's underlying assets pro rata using reserve volumes or reserve values as of that date.
>
> The entity shall test exploration and evaluation assets and assets in the development and production phases for impairment at the date of transition to IFRSs in accordance with IFRS 6 Exploration for and Evaluation of Mineral Resources or IAS 36 respectively and, if necessary, reduce the amount determined in accordance with (a) or (b) above.

Exploration and evaluation assets

Following the provision of paragraph a. above, upon transition a full cost company has the option in its opening IFRS balance sheet to measure its E&E assets (unproved properties) either at the amounts: (1) determined under the company's previous GAAP (full cost) or (2) determined under the successful efforts method.

Most full cost companies transitioning to IFRS choose to use the "soft landing" exemption included in the amendments. Similar to IFRS 6, which provided relief for full cost companies to continue to aggregate costs in large countrywide cost centers, the amendments allow this practice to continue during the E&E phase.

Development and production assets

The amendments also allow initial measurements of assets in the development and production phases (proved properties) at the amounts determined for the cost center under the company's previous GAAP, but they require allocation of the assets to a level that complies with the conceptual framework. For a full cost entity transitioning to IFRS, this likely will be a much lower level.

The amendments therefore allow allocation of the total costs of the cost center (full cost pool) at the transition date to the underlying assets (fields or wells) on a pro rata basis, using reserves volumes or reserves values as of the transition date.

Allocation of the full cost pool to underlying assets is an important focus area for management during the transition to IFRS. This process requires considerable judgment and estimates and likely will require experts to determine reserves volumes and reserves values. The judgment and rationale applied by management also must be disclosed in the company's financial statements prepared under IFRS.

Overall, the allocation of cost to the underlying assets in the company's opening balance sheet is time-consuming and requires a great deal of management involvement.

Impairment

The full cost pool under prior GAAP may include amounts that would not have been capitalized under IFRS, such as unsuccessful exploration costs (dry hole costs), overhead costs and other costs that were incurred before an entity obtained the legal right to explore a particular area. Thus, the costs allocated to the underlying individual assets (fields) may include amounts that will not be recoverable.

The amendments require the testing of both E&E assets and development and production assets for impairment to comply with IFRS 6 and International Accounting Standard 36 (IAS 36), *Impairment of Assets*, respectively, at the transition date.

Other amendments

Due to the exemption for full cost companies' cost pools, the IASB also revised its transition provisions related to oil and gas decommissioning and restoration liabilities. The guidance requires full cost companies that apply the cost pool allocation exemption to measure the related liability for oil and gas assets in the development or production phase at the date of transition (under IAS 37, *Provisions, Contingent Liabilities and Contingent Assets*), and recognize directly in retained earnings any difference between that amount and the carrying amount of those liabilities at the date of transition to IFRS (as determined under the entity's previous GAAP).

In addition, the amendments clarify that if a first-time adopter made the same decision about whether or not an arrangement contains a lease according to previous GAAP as those required by International Financial Reporting Interpretations Committee No. 4 (IFRIC 4), but at a date other than that required by IFRIC 4, the adopter need not reassess that decision when it adopts IFRS.

• • •

1 SAB Topic 12.D.3.b states that derivative contracts which qualify as a hedging instrument in a cash flow hedge and are accounted for as such pursuant to FASB ASC Topic 815 represent the type of contractual arrangements for which consideration of price changes should be given under the existing rule.

Asset Retirement Obligations

An asset 'retirement obligation (ARO) is the cost of retiring a long-lived asset that arises from either the asset's normal operation or its acquisition. Asset retirement is a permanent removal from service at the end of an asset's useful economic life. The term "retirement" includes sale, abandonment, recycling and any manner of disposal.

In the oil and gas industry, these obligations include: (1) future dismantling and removal of production equipment and facilities and (2) restoring and reclaiming the field's surface (or subsurface, in offshore activities) to an ecological state similar to its condition before oil and gas extraction began. Usually required by government regulations or lease contracts, these costs typically are paid when oil and gas reserves are depleted and production is no longer economically feasible.

Much like estimating oil and gas reserves, estimating the cost of future abandonment and reclamation is an inexact science. Those responsible often must revise their assumptions to reflect changes in reserves lives, costs, technology and the regulatory environment. They must also consider factors such as future contract labor rates, equipment rental costs and expected inflation rates. Furthermore, contiguous production areas often reach the end of their operational life at essentially the same time, placing excess demand on local abandonment services and further complicating the estimation of AROs.

Regulatory and operational environment

Regulations governing lease and well abandonment depend on the jurisdiction, with the most common practices discussed herein. Because E&P companies often operate in multiple jurisdictions, they frequently maintain a compliance department to monitor changing regulatory environments.

Permitting

A producer's first step before beginning any dismantlement, restoration or reclamation is to obtain permits from local regulatory authorities. Well logs or test flow data usually are required to confirm that the well is no longer capable of producing economic quantities of oil and gas. Regulators also may request detailed work plans, as well as assurances that plugging and abandonment will not jeopardize nearby wells or pose an environmental hazard.

In the U.S., onshore permitting generally follows state and local regulations. Operators typically are required to commence plugging and abandonment after a well is determined to be dry or after the well is inactive, with no production, for a specified time. In Texas, for example, plugging must begin within one year after drilling or operations cease. Before beginning, the operator must obtain approval for its proposed plugging procedures from the Railroad Commission of Texas. Within 30 days after completing the process, the operator must file a verified plugging record.

U.S. offshore permitting is regulated by the BSEE. In mature producing areas, such as the Gulf of Mexico's Outer Continental Shelf, abandonment procedures are firmly established. However, recent years have marked the advent of greater regulatory oversight and more restrictive regulations.

In September 2010, BOEMRE issued Notice to Lessees and Operators (NTL) No. 2010-G05, *Decommissioning Guidance for Wells and Platforms* (sometimes referred to as the Idle Iron policy), which clarified existing regulations regarding wells or platforms that are "no longer useful for operations" and need to be plugged (wells) or removed (platforms and other structures).

Effective September 2016, the BOEM issued NTL No. 2016-N01 to clarify the procedures and criteria used to determine when additional security is required from the lessee or operator to protect taxpayers from shouldering any liability for decommissioning. A permit can be readily obtained, as long as the operator follows accepted procedures.

Obtaining permits in less developed areas of the world can be onerous. Because of a general lack of production history and ongoing regulatory and scientific debates regarding which techniques qualify as environmentally friendly, producers in frontier areas may be required to perform detailed scientific and environmental impact studies. Alternative abandonment plans may be required before a permit is granted. In evaluating options, regulations consider many factors:

- The technical and engineering aspects of the plan.

- Potential reduced consumption of natural resources due to reuse and recycling contemplated in the plan.

- Potential environmental impact on biological habitations, the atmosphere, groundwater, soil, the ocean and/or surface fresh water.

- Potential interference with other legitimate uses of the physical environment, such as shipping and commercial fishing.

- Safety.

- The company's plans to mitigate any adverse consequences of the plan.

- The party responsible for future environmental monitoring associated with the plan.

- The party liable for satisfying any damage claims spurred by the abandonment.

- Plans to notify appropriate authorities about modified or moved structures.

Abandonment techniques

A technique known as toppling is one of several acceptable methods for abandoning offshore production facilities. Toppling uses explosive or nonexplosive cutting to remove the upper section of a platform (i.e., decks, jackets and facilities). In most cases, it requires clearing at least 50 to 75 meters below the water's surface. The removed sections are towed either to shore, where they are scrapped or placed on the adjacent seabed, or to designated reef sites, where they are sunk. Because environmental impact studies show that they can benefit local ecology, offshore subsea structures often are permitted to remain in place. Since its establishment in the 1980s, Rigs to Reefs (the BSEE federal program encouraging this practice) has dramatically reduced removal costs in the Gulf of Mexico.

In other geographic areas, both in the U.S. and elsewhere, offshore regulations for abandoning production facilities can be much more stringent, such as requiring restoration of the ocean floor to its predrilling state. This requires removing the entire platform, including the subsurface casing, wellhead equipment and pilings, to a specified depth below the ocean floor. Associated flow lines generally can be flushed, cleaned of all hydrocarbon-bearing parts, plugged and left in place. In most cases, the salvage values of these lines do not justify the costs of bringing them to the surface.

Scope of accounting guidance

An ARO is a legal obligation. It can be established by agreement between two or more parties, be imposed by a government unit, or arise due to promissory estoppel (i.e., through third-party reliance on a promise, even absent consideration in exchange for that promise). Considerable judgment, possibly with assistance from legal counsel, may be required to determine whether or not an obligation should be recorded due to promissory estoppel. AROs also can be recognized in a business combination or asset acquisition.

The FASB issued guidance in 2001, codified in ASC 410, *Asset Retirement and Environmental Obligations*, which addresses recognizing, measuring and disclosing AROs.

The ARO guidance applies to the following transactions and activities stated in ASC 410-20-15-2:

a. Legal obligations associated with the retirement of a tangible long-lived asset that result from the acquisition, construction, or development and (or) the normal operation of a long-lived asset, including any legal obligations that require disposal of a replaced part that is a component of a tangible long-lived asset.

b. An environmental remediation liability that results from the normal operation of a long-lived asset and that is associated with the retirement of that asset.

c. A conditional obligation to perform a retirement activity; uncertainty about the timing of settlement of the asset retirement obligation does not remove that obligation from the scope of this subtopic but will affect the measurement of a liability for that obligation.

d. Obligations of a lessor in connection with leased property that meet the provisions in (a).

e. The costs associated with the retirement of a specified asset that qualifies as historical waste equipment as defined by EU Directive 2002/96/EC.

For an obligation to fall within the scope of ASC 410-20, it must be unavoidable; associated with retiring a tangible, long-lived asset; and result from the acquisition, construction, or development and/or normal operation of that asset. Because the liability is associated with the acquisition, construction, or development and/or normal operation of the asset, any plans to dispose of or transfer the asset prior to paying for remediation is irrelevant. If the asset is sold, the asset retirement obligation is transferred to the buyer absent a negotiated arrangement with the seller; the buyer's assumption of liability is typically considered when establishing the sales price.

ASC 410-20 specifically excludes certain lease obligations, environmental remediation liabilities and obligations that arise solely from an asset-disposal plan. However, most leases for oil and gas properties lie within the scope of ASC 410-20.

Prior to the guidance issued in 2001, accounting for AROs that resulted from onshore development and production was relatively simple. Most operators assumed that salvage values equalled the cost of dismantling facilities and performing cleanup and reclamation and net dismantlement costs typically were not significant.

However, global expansion of the industry into more remote and environmentally sensitive areas and the continued evolution of federal, state and local regulations have dramatically increased these costs. Today, the costs can exceed those of the original construction and installation.

Recognition and measurement

AROs are initially recognized as liabilities at fair value, with a corresponding asset retirement cost (ARC) recorded as part of the related asset.

Figure 19-1 highlights various accounting considerations from initial recognition to retirement.

Figure 19-1

Effect of ARCs and AROs on financial statements

Phase	Balance sheet	Income statement	Statement of cash flows
Liability incurred	Record ARO at the fair value of the legal obligation. Record the ARC as an increase to the carrying value of the related asset.	No immediate effect.	No immediate effect.
Passage of time	Increase the ARO through periodic accretion expense and assess for short-term vs. long-term classification. Allocate ARC to expense, using a systematic and rational method over the related asset's useful life.	Record accretion expense as a component of operating expenses. Depreciate ARC as a component of oil and gas properties.	Classify accretion expense and depreciation expense as noncash adjustments to net income within operating cash flows.
Changes in expected cash flows	Adjust the ARO for the effect of the change. Record corresponding change in the ARC.	No immediate impact. Reflect changes in accretion expense and depreciation expense in the period of change (if applicable) and in future periods.	No immediate impact. Classify accretion expense and depreciation expense as noncash adjustments to operating cash flows.
Retirement/ settlement (see Chapter 18 for full cost considerations)	Derecognize ARO as costs are incurred. Derecognize any unamortized ARC.	Record a gain or loss for the difference between the cost of settling the ARO and the recorded ARO liability. Record a loss for any unamortized ARC.	Classify cash outflows for settlement of the ARO within operating cash flows. Any settlement difference is a noncash adjustment to net income within operating cash flows.

Recognition

ASC 410-20 requires recognizing the fair value of an ARO liability, in the period incurred, when: (1) an existing legal obligation is associated with the retirement of a tangible long-lived asset (ASC 410-20-15-2) and (2) the liability can be reasonably estimated (ASC 410-20-25-4). The manner in which an ARO is incurred affects the timing and pattern of liability recognition:

- Obligations that arise upon acquiring, constructing or developing a long-lived asset are recognized when the asset's cost is first incurred.

- Obligations that arise (either ratably or nonratably) during the asset's operating life are recognized concurrent with the events that create the obligations.

- Obligations resulting from (a) a change in law, statute or contract provisions or (b) an entity's assumption of a duty or responsibility to another entity (or several entities) are recognized when the obligating event occurs. Obligations for past operations are recorded when the new law is enacted, whereas those for future operations are recorded when the obligations are created.

Even if an oil and gas company intends to retire an asset with internal resources, it must recognize an ARO when an obligating event takes place, provided it can reasonably estimate the fair value, or at the earliest date when it can make a reasonable estimate.

Initial measurement

ASC 410-20-30-1 states, "An expected present value technique will usually be the only appropriate technique with which to estimate the fair value of a liability for an asset retirement obligation." Accordingly, asset retirement obligations should be measured, initially, at fair value determined in accordance with ASC 820, *Fair Value Measurement*.

The expected present value (PV) technique requires explicit assumptions about the amount and timing of costs under varying future scenarios, as well as calculation of their relative probability. ASC 410-20-25-7 indicates that the measurement should assign probabilities to address any uncertainty about the timing of cash flows.

ASC 410-20-25-8 states that a reporting entity has sufficient information to apply expected present value if either of these conditions exists:

- The settlement date and method of settlement have been specified by others.

- The information is available to reasonably estimate all of the following: (1) the settlement date or range of settlement dates; (2) the method, or potential methods, of settlement; and (3) the probabilities associated with the potential settlement dates and methods.

The reporting entity should establish a reasonable basis for assigning probabilities. However, according to ASC 410-20-25-8(b)(3), it may determine, instead, that the time range is too narrow and/or that for each potential settlement method the associated cash flows are so similar that assigning probabilities without a reasonable basis would have no material effect on the ARO's fair value.

A common technique uses current, third-party cost experience multiplied by an inflation factor to determine present value. The resulting expected future cash flows are then discounted back to present value, using a company-specific credit adjusted risk-free interest rate. This expected cash flow approach should apply multiple scenarios to reflect the range of possible outcomes.

Although some reporting entities may possess the expertise needed to settle an ARO using internal resources, and may intend to do so, ASC 820 still requires the use of market-participant assumptions to measure fair value. This is true even if the entity believes that its assumptions about profit margin, overhead and other costs (based on third-party costs) could produce a gain when the asset is retired. Excluding certain costs, assuming no profit margin, or assigning a low or zero probability to a third-party scenario does not meet the requirements of ASC 410-20.

According to ASC 410-20-55-15, calculating expected present value requires discounting the estimated cash flows, using a credit adjusted risk-free rate. The required "risk-free rate" is the interest rate on monetary assets that are essentially risk-free (e.g., in the United States, zero coupon U.S. Treasury instruments), with maturity dates that coincide with the expected timing of the estimated cash flows required to satisfy the ARO. The risk-free rate should then be adjusted to reflect the reporting entity's risk profile, which is its "credit adjusted risk-free rate" (CARFR). For example, a company would use a five-year credit adjusted risk-free interest rate when five years remain until payment of the ARO.

Figure 19-2 poses two probability-weighted scenarios for settlement on December 31, 2029:

Figure 19-2
Probability-weighted present value

	Probability	Timing (one-time cost)	Estimated third-party cost	CARFR	PV	Probability-weighted present value
Low-cost scenario	50%	2029	$100,000	5%	$61,391	$30,695
High-cost scenario	50%	2029	120,000	5%	73,670	36,835
Expected value						**$67,530**

The corresponding journal entry would be as follows:

Asset retirement costs (ARC)	67,530	
Asset retirement obligations (ARO)		67,530

To record the initial measurement of the ARO on December 31, 2019, based on the expected fair value of the ARO.

Subsequent measurement

Companies should use a systematic and rational method to expense the related ARC over its useful life, which is commonly achieved using unit-of-production amortization for producing oil and gas properties. ARO liabilities must be accreted over time so that the balance initially recognized is adjusted to reflect the passage of time. Oil and gas companies accrete the beginning-of-period liability, using the credit adjusted risk-free interest rate that existed when the liability (or a portion of it) was first measured. Accretion increases the ARO liability account on the balance sheet and also increases accretion expense in the income statement.

Figure 19-3 illustrates the 2020 accretion expense calculation:

Figure 19-3

Calculation of accretion expense

ARO at December 31, 2019 (Figure 19-2)	$67,530
Discount rate when ARO incurred	× 5%
2020 accretion expense	**$ 3,377**

The resulting journal entry is reflected below:

Accretion expense	3,377	
Asset retirement obligations (ARO)		3,377
To record accretion expense for 2020.		

Companies that follow the successful efforts method of accounting include capitalized asset retirement costs as a cost of the related wells, equipment and facilities; they usually amortize them over the remaining proved developed reserves. Undeveloped reserves, by definition, require new wells or major expenditures before they can be classified as proved developed reserves. The construction of these new wells, and the associated transfer of reserves from undeveloped to developed, typically creates new obligations to eventually retire these assets.

However, companies should consider carefully whether or not it makes sense to amortize asset retirement costs over proved developed or total proved reserves, considering if the asset retirement cost relates to the entire asset or a component of the entire asset (e.g., an individual well).

Revisions

Changes in estimated timing and cost to settle the obligation (from continued use of the asset, changes in available technology or other factors) should be recognized as an increase or decrease in the carrying amount of the ARO and ARC. The adjustment will not affect the income statement at the time of change; however, it will affect future recognition of amortization and accretion expense. The discount rate for calculating the new ARO and ARC depends on whether there is an upward or downward revision in estimated cash flows. In this regard, ASC 410-20-35-8 states:

... Upward revisions in the amount of undiscounted estimated cash flows shall be discounted using the current credit-adjusted risk-free rate. Downward revisions in the amount of undiscounted estimated cash flows shall be discounted using the credit- adjusted risk-free rate that existed when the original liability was recognized. If an entity cannot identify the prior period to which the downward revision relates, it may use a weighted-average credit-adjusted risk-free rate to discount the downward revision to estimated future cash flows...

Continuing with the previous example, assume that on December 31, 2020: (1) the cash outflow is revised to occur in 2025, (2) the expected amount of the ARO increases and (3) the CARFR for the remaining five-year term increases to six percent.

ASC 410-20-35-4 requires recognizing accretion expense for 2020 at the beginning of the period prior to adjusting for revised timing or amounts. Accretion is calculated at the five percent CARFR used when the ARO was first booked (see Figure 19-3).

On December 31, 2020, the revised timing and amount of cash flows is recognized as an increase in the carrying amount of the ARO and the ARC. The ARO, using the current CARFR applied to all cash flows (both original and incremental), should be remeasured. The revised ARO's present value calculation is illustrated in Figure 19-4; the additional ARO calculation is illustrated in Figure 19-5.

Figure 19-4

Calculation of revised ARO present value

	Probability	Timing (one time cost)	Estimated third-party cost	CARFR	PV	Probability-weighted present value
Low-cost scenario	60%	2025	$130,000	6%	$97,144	$ 58,286
High-cost scenario	40%	2025	$150,000	6%	112,089	44,836
Expected value						**$103,122**

Figure 19-5

Calculation of additional ARO

Revised ARO balance, to be recognized as of December 31, 2020	$103,122
Current ARO balance, after recognizing 2020 accretion expense ($67,530 + $3,377)	(70,907)
Additional ARO, to be recognized on December 31, 2020	**$ 32,215**

The resulting journal entry would be as follows:

Asset retirement costs (ARC)	32,215	
Asset retirement obligations (ARO)		32,215

To record additional asset retirement costs on December 31, 2020, associated with revised estimated timing and amount calculated in Figure 19-4.

As a result of the entries above, Figure 19-6 illustrates the ARO liability rollforward as of December 31, 2020:

Figure 19-6
ARO liability rollforward

ARO recognized at inception	$ 67,530
Plus: 2019 accretion recognized	3,377
Plus: additional ARO recognized in 2019	32,215
Carrying value of ARO as of December 31, 2020	**$103,122**

When a revision occurs in the timing, but not the amount, of cash flows, ASC 410-20 is not clear about how to account for the change or which specific credit adjusted risk-free rate should be used to remeasure the ARO (either the current rate or the rate used in the original estimate).

Some believe that like upward revisions due to increased estimated cash flows, timing changes in expected cash flows should be discounted using the current credit adjusted risk-free rate at the time of the revision, regardless of whether the expected settlement timing has increased or decreased. This rate applies to all cash flows associated with the ARO because it only changes their timing. However, it also is acceptable to use the credit adjusted risk-free rate from the original estimate. Whichever method is chosen, it should be applied consistently.

ASC 410-20 also is not clear about how to account for a revision due to changes in both timing and amount. When possible, follow the specific guidance of ASC 410-20-35-8 for an upward or downward revision.

For example, if there is a downward revision in estimated cash flows and the retirement will occur further in the future ("timing increase"), it is appropriate to use the credit adjusted risk-free rate used in the original estimate, consistent with guidance for downward revisions.

Alternatively, if there is an upward revision in estimated cash flows and a timing increase or decrease, all future cash flows should be remeasured, using the current credit adjusted risk-free rate. This is considered appropriate because it represents: (1) a change in timing, but not amount, for the original portion of cash flows (current credit adjusted risk-free rate applied to all cash flows when the timing, but not the amount, changes) and (2) an upward revision in amount (current credit adjusted risk-free rate applied to incremental cash flows, consistent with ASC 410-20-35-8).

Because guidance is not clear, alternative approaches also are acceptable. For example, if there is a timing change and an upward revision to the amount, it also may be acceptable to treat the incremental amount as a separate layer, discounted at the current credit adjusted risk-free rate, while continuing to use the original credit adjusted risk-free rate on the original amount. Once again, whichever method is chosen, consistent application should be followed.

Retirement

Accretion is calculated separately for each component of the ARO, using the discount rate employed when respective portions of the ARO balance were recognized. Figure 19-7 illustrates expected accretion expense for 2021 through 2025 from the previous example. The example uses a single calculation because the same discount rate of six percent has been applied to all cash flows.

Figure 19-7
Expected accretion expense

ARO balance as of December 31, 2020	**$103,122**
Accretion expense recognized in:	
2021	6,187
2022	6,559
2023	6,952
2024	7,369
2025	7,811
Total ARO balance, as of settlement	**$138,000**

Assume that, on December 31, 2025, the company settles its ARO by hiring an outside contractor. The company incurs actual costs of $146,000 to settle this liability, recognizing an $8,000 loss. According to ASC 410-20-45-3, the cash payment to settle the ARO would be classified as an operating cash outflow in the statement of cash flows.

The following entry is required on December 31, 2025:

Asset retirement obligations (ARO)	138,000	
Loss on settlement of ARO	8,000	
Accounts payable		146,000
To record the settlement of the ARO on December 31, 2025.		

Application issues

While AROs are not unique to the oil and gas industry, there are a number of application issues specific to the ARO and the corresponding ARC included within the carrying value of oil and gas properties which should be carefully considered.

Asset impairment

ASC 360 includes all cash inflows and outflows for the asset group in both the undiscounted cash flows used to test the group for recoverability and the discounted cash flows used to determine fair value. Although ASC 360-10-35-18 includes capitalized asset retirement costs in the carrying value of the asset when testing for impairment, it excludes the estimated ARO cash outflows recognized in the financial statements from both the asset recoverability test and the determination of fair value to avoid double-counting.

Estimated useful lives

When measuring an ARO's fair value, the timing of future cash outflows should be based on the asset's estimated economic life. Most petroleum accountants use a reserves report that assumes market-participant pricing, such as NYMEX strip pricing. A reserves report based on SEC pricing may not be appropriate in determining the end of the economic life of a producing well.

Due to volatile commodity prices, a well's estimated economic life fluctuates, which may create upward and downward ARO revisions. Therefore, most companies periodically assess the appropriateness of the remaining estimated useful lives, among other inputs.

Capitalized interest

ARO accretion expense does not qualify for interest capitalization because it is not considered an interest cost under ASC 835-20-15-7. Conversely, accretion expense is reflected in the income statement as part of operating income. Companies may show it as a separate line within operating expenses if it is material, while others may group it with DD&A expense.

ASC 932-235 disclosures

In February 2004, the SEC clarified its positions on ARO disclosures for oil and gas producing companies as follows:

- Asset retirement costs should be included with the costs incurred disclosures in the year in which the liability is incurred, rather than on a cash basis.

- Accretion of the ARO liability should be included in the results of operations disclosure, either as a separate line item, if material, or in the same line item where presented on the statement of operations.

- Future cash flows for the ARO settlement should be included in the standardized measure disclosure.

- The reported carrying value of oil and gas properties should include the related asset retirement costs, and accumulated depreciation, depletion and amortization should include the accumulated allocation of the asset retirement costs since the beginning of the respective property's productive life.

Contractual arrangements

Various contractual arrangements that are unique to the oil and gas industry raise a question of whether they meet the ASC 410-20 criteria for recognizing a liability.

For example, in a reversionary interest arrangement, an entity returns its economic interest in a property to the former owner after it (1) produces a predetermined amount of production, (2) meets a specified income threshold or (3) generates a required rate of return. If a company owns a 60 percent working interest in a field, but expects to lose one-fourth of that interest to a reversion upon payout, it will bear only 45 percent of future AROs.

Depending on how contracts are written, other arrangements such as net profits interests, rights to VPPs, production-sharing contracts or other foreign concessions may create assets without corresponding AROs. Determining whether or not an ARO is created requires a careful reading of these contracts.

Offsetting amounts

Salvage value is not included in the cash flows used to estimate the ARO's fair value.

However, estimated salvage value helps determine the unit-of-production depletion rate of the related asset: the capitalized costs in the numerator of the DD&A calculation are reduced by the expected salvage value. The salvage value remains in the property account at the end of the asset's productive life, to be offset by salvage proceeds.

Some entities provide assurances (typically, to regulators) of their ability to satisfy AROs. These assurances include surety bonds, insurance policies, letters of credit, guarantees by other entities, and trust funds or other dedicated assets. These assurances do not satisfy or extinguish the ARO, and they do not affect or offset its recognition. However, they may affect the choice of a credit adjusted risk-free interest rate used to measure the ARO.

Conditional AROs

ASC 420-20-25-7 through 25-15 addresses accounting for a legal obligation to perform an asset retirement activity when the settlement timing and/or method are conditional upon a future event that may not be controlled by the entity.

Although the settlement timing and/or method may depend upon a future event, the obligation to perform the activity is unconditional. Therefore, the entity must recognize a liability for a conditional ARO's fair value if it can be estimated reasonably. This fair value is recognized when incurred, generally upon acquisition, construction, or development and/or through normal asset operation. Any uncertainty about the settlement timing and/or method should be factored into the liability measurement if sufficient information exists.

"Sufficient information" exists in both of the following cases:

1. The settlement date and method are specified by others. Therefore, the only uncertainty is whether the obligation will be enforced (i.e., whether or not performance is required). Uncertainty about the performance requirement does not defer the recognition of an ARO. A legal obligation still exists to perform the retirement activities. The uncertainty regarding whether the performance will be required does not prevent a reasonable estimation of fair value.

2. Information is available to reasonably estimate and associate probabilities with the potential settlement dates and methods.

Examples of information that can serve as a basis for the estimates include information derived from the entity's past practice, industry practice, management's intent and the asset's estimated economic life.

Environmental remediation

ASC 410-20 does not apply to obligations created by improper asset operation, such as those subject to ASC 410-30. Guidance in ASC 410-20-15-3(b) distinguishes between obligations that are subject to ASC 410-20 and those to be accounted for within an environmental remediation reserve.

Determining whether an obligation falls under ASC 410-20 or other appropriate literature (such as ASC 410-30) requires judgment. It may be helpful to consider the timing of remediation activities. Any environmental damage that is extensive enough to require immediate remediation generally arises from improper or abnormal operation of an asset (e.g., an oil spill, pipeline leak or hurricane damage to production platforms). This type of environmental liability should be accounted for according to ASC 410-30. The ability to delay remediation until asset retirement suggests that the damage arose from normal operations and was inherent in operating the asset. This kind of damage is subject to ASC 410-20.

● ● ●

Conveyances

A mineral conveyance transfers an ownership interest from one entity to another. In an initial lease agreement, a lessor conveys a 100 percent working interest (WI) in the mineral rights to a lessee and the lessor retains a royalty interest. Later, the lessee may convey all or part of the WI to a third party and the lessor likewise may do so with the royalty interest.

For example, the lessee can sell all or a fractional share of its WI. It can assign the WI and retain a nonoperating interest (a sublease). It also can carve-out and transfer an overriding royalty interest (ORRI), net profits interest (NPI) or production payment. Likewise, the holder of a royalty or other nonoperating interest may convey all or a portion of the interest to another party. Owners, especially WI owners, convey their mineral interests for many reasons: to obtain financing, to share ownership risks and costs, to operate more efficiently or to realize tax benefits. Therefore, conveyance contracts can be quite complex and may burden one of the parties with extra obligations and commitments.

Additionally, while the concepts within this chapter may be relevant to full cost companies in certain instances, the primary applicability is to conveyances accounted for under the successful efforts method of accounting.

Accounting principles

ASC 932 offers general guidelines for mineral conveyance accounting. In Reg. S-X Rule 4-10, the SEC adopted conveyance accounting rules found in ASC 932-360-40-4 through 40-9 for all publicly held oil and gas production companies, including (with some modifications) those using full cost accounting.

ASC 932 and Reg. S-X Rule 4-10 offer the following guidelines:

- Some conveyances are, in substance, borrowings repayable in cash or its equivalent. These should be accounted for as borrowings.

- In general, gain or loss should not be recognized at the time of the conveyance in a pooling of assets in a joint undertaking intended to find, develop, or produce oil or gas from a particular property or group of properties.

- A gain should not be recognized (although a loss may be)[1] at the time the following types of conveyances are transacted:

  - Part of an interest is sold and substantial uncertainty exists about recovery of the cost applicable to the retained interest.

  - Part of an interest is sold and the seller has a substantial obligation for future performance, such as an obligation to drill a well or to operate the property without proportional reimbursement for that portion of the drilling or operating costs applicable to the interest sold.

- Gain or loss should generally be recognized by successful efforts companies on other types of conveyances unless GAAP would prohibit such recognition.

- With limited exceptions, no gain or loss should be recognized by a full cost company on a mineral conveyance. The major exception is a situation in which the conveyance is so large that to treat the proceeds as a cost recovery would significantly distort the prospective amortization of assets in the full cost pool.

Conveyance topics span three chapters in this book. Conveyances that are classified as sales and subleases, in which the sole consideration is cash or cash equivalent, are described in this chapter, along with nonmonetary exchanges accounted for in accordance with ASC 845. Chapter 21 addresses conveyances in the form of production payments, while Chapter 22 addresses conveyances in which the sole consideration is an agreement by the transferee to perform specified exploration or development work (sharing arrangements).

Conveyance agreements may refer to transferred interests in various ways, using terms such as overrides, royalties or term overrides, when in fact the conveyed nonoperating interest is an NPI or production payment. Accountants must be careful to record the substance of the conveyance, regardless of the terms used by the seller or buyer.

Sales and subleases of unproved properties

When unproved properties are sold or exchanged for cash or cash equivalent, the accounting treatment depends on the answers to the following questions.[2]

- Is the impairment of unproved properties recorded individually or on a group basis?

- Is the conveyance an entire interest or only a partial interest?

Sale of an entire WI in unproved properties

If the entire interest in an unproved property is sold, the recognition of gain or loss depends on the method used to determine lease impairment. If impairment was assessed individually, ASC 932-360-55-8 requires recognition of a gain or loss as the difference between the proceeds received and the property's net carrying value.

Individually significant properties. For example, assume that an unproved property originally cost $700,000. An individual $150,000 impairment allowance was recorded. The property is subsequently sold for $600,000. A gain of $50,000 would be recognized as follows:

Cash	600,000	
Allowance for impairment – unproved properties	150,000	
Unproved properties acquisition costs		700,000
Gain on property sales		50,000
To record the sale of unproved property.		

Grouped properties. However, if the unproved property's impairment was determined as part of a group, the accounting outcome is different. ASC 932-360-55-8 states:

> ... For a property amortized by providing a valuation allowance on a group basis, neither gain nor loss shall be recognized when an unproved property is sold unless the sales price exceeds the original cost of the property, in which case gain shall be recognized in the amount of such excess.

Continuing the previous example, if such property was grouped with other properties when determining impairment, no gain or loss would be recognized because the $600,000 sales proceeds are less than the $700,000 original cost. In that case, the journal entry would reflect a $600,000 credit to the unproved properties acquisition costs account.

Alternatively, if a lease originally costing $700,000 was subject to group impairment and was later sold for $800,000, a gain would be recorded.

Cash	800,000	
Unproved properties acquisition costs		700,000
Gain on property sales		100,000
To record the sale of unproved property.		

Sale of a share of a WI in unproved properties

If a company sells only part of an interest in an unproved property, whether undivided or divided, no gain should be recognized. However, if sales proceeds for a partial interest exceed the entire original cost of a property assessed for impairment within a group, or if such proceeds exceed the carrying amount of a property assessed for impairment individually, a gain should be recorded. Any loss on the sale is recognized by using the impairment test, whether the partial share is assessed for impairment individually or on a group basis. According to ASC 932-360-55-9:

> If a part of the interest in an unproved property is sold, even though for cash or cash equivalent, substantial uncertainty usually exists as to recovery of the cost applicable to the interest retained. Consequently, the amount received shall be treated as a recovery of the cost. The carrying amount of the interest retained shall continue to be subject to the assessment for impairment as required by paragraph 932-360-35-11. However, if the sales price exceeds the carrying amount of a property whose impairment has been assessed individually in accordance with that paragraph, or exceeds the original cost of a property amortized by providing a valuation allowance on a group basis, gain shall be recognized in the amount of such excess.

Assume that a successful efforts company owns Lease 15074 originally costing $1 million with a $600,000 individual impairment allowance. The company sells an undivided three-fourths interest with a $300,000 net book value [($1 million x 3/4) minus ($600,000 x 3/4)] for $380,000. No gain or loss should be recorded because the sales proceeds are less than the entire property's $400,000 net book value, such that the $380,000 proceeds are treated as a recovery of capital, recorded as follows:

Cash	380,000	
Unproved properties acquisition costs		380,000
To record the sale of a three-fourths interest in Lease 15074.		

However, if the three-fourths interest in the property is sold for $820,000, a gain of $420,000 should be recorded, as reflected in the journal entry below.

Cash	820,000	
Allowance for impairment – unproved properties	600,000	
Unproved properties acquisition costs		1,000,000
Gain on property sales		420,000
To record the sale of a three-fourths interest in Lease 15074.		

As mentioned, losses on sales of unproved property should be recognized, either directly or indirectly, by applying the ASC 932-360-35-11 impairment test. If recording the loss directly, companies may also consider reducing the remaining net book value to account for additional impairment implied by the loss on the property sold.

For example, assume the same facts as provided previously herein for Lease 15074, except in this case the three-fourths WI with a $300,000 net book value is sold for $180,000 (i.e., the remaining $100,000 of net capitalized costs has an indicated value of only $60,000, assuming the sales price for the entire WI would have been $240,000), implying an impairment of $40,000 on the retained one-fourth WI. Accordingly, the loss on sale and impairment of the retained WI in the lease are recorded as follows:

Cash	180,000	
Allowance for impairment – unproved properties	450,000	
Loss on property sales	120,000	
Unproved properties acquisition costs		750,000
To record the sale of three-fourths interest in Lease 15074.		

Impairment expense – unproved properties	40,000	
Allowance for impairment – unproved properties		40,000
To recognize additional impairment on the retained WI in Lease 15074.		

However, if impairment was determined on a group basis, no additional impairment may be necessary because the total indicated value of the grouped properties may exceed their net book value.

Sale of a nonoperating interest in unproved properties

Journal entries illustrated in this chapter so far deal with sales of unproved WIs. The same general rules apply when selling nonoperating interests, including royalties, ORRIs, NPIs and production payments (if classified as mineral interests). A complicating factor arises when selling a nonoperating interest that is carved out from the WI, as discussed in the next section.

Sale of an entire unproved nonoperating interest. When selling the entire nonoperating interest in an unproved property, the WI rules previously discussed regarding the sale of an entire WI should be applied. If the property is subject to individual impairment, successful efforts companies should treat the difference between the interest's net book value and its sales price as a gain or loss. However, if the nonoperating interest is grouped with other properties when determining impairment, any sales proceeds lower than the interest's original cost should be treated as a recovery of cost, such that the credit to unproved property is equal to the sale price. If proceeds exceed the original cost, the difference is recognized as a gain.

Suppose that an unproved ORRI with an original cost of $16,000 is part of a group of properties for which impairment has been recorded. The ORRI is a one-eighth interest in a 640-acre lease that is sold for $15,200. The journal entry to record the sale would be as follows:

Cash	15,200	
Unproved royalties and overriding royalties		15,200
To record the sale of a one-eighth ORRI.		

As noted above, no gain or loss is recorded, as the sales proceeds amount is less than the ORRI's original cost. However, if the interest sells for $30,000, the company would recognize a gain of $14,000.

Sale of a portion of an unproved nonoperating interest. ASC 932-360 does not distinguish between the accounting treatment for: (1) selling a portion of a nonoperating interest share of a WI or a carved-out nonoperating interest in an unproved property and (2) selling a portion of a WI in an unproved property. In both cases, a successful efforts company should treat the proceeds as cost recovery up to the property's net book value (or original cost, if using group impairment); any excess is treated as a gain.

A loss may also be recognized when selling a share of a nonoperating interest in an unproved property to the extent the sales proceeds are less than the book value and the unproved property is subject to individual impairment, similar to the previous discussion of the sale of a partial WI in an unproved property.

Sale of a WI with a retained nonoperating interest

Conveyance to pool assets. ASC 932-360-55-3 states that retaining a nonoperating interest, such as an override, when assigning a WI in an unproved property in return for the assignee taking on drilling and development costs and operation of the property is a pooling of assets in a joint undertaking. The assignor recognizes no gain or loss and its original lease cost becomes the cost basis of the retained nonoperating interest.

Sublease of unproved properties. A sublease occurs when the WI owner transfers operating rights to another party for cash or cash-equivalent consideration, while retaining an ORRI, NPI or production payment that is considered to be equivalent to an overriding royalty (see Chapter 21 for additional discussion on production payments). A sublease is treated like selling part of an unproved property interest under ASC 932-360-55-9. That is, the WI's unrecovered book value (or, if using group impairment, the unrecovered original cost) is assigned to the retained nonoperating interest.

For example, assume that ABC Oil Co. (ABC) receives $300,000 to assign to another party an undeveloped lease's WI that originally cost $1 million. ABC previously established an individual impairment allowance of $600,000. ABC retains an ORRI of one-sixteenth of total production. The journal entry to record the sublease would be as follows:

Cash	300,000	
Allowance for impairment – unproved properties	600,000	
Unproved royalties and overriding royalties	100,000	
Unproved properties acquisition costs		1,000,000
To record a sublease of unproved property.		

The retained unproved ORRI is subject to the impairment test prescribed in ASC 932-360-35-11. A question arises when the overriding royalty from a property with individual impairment recorded is to be placed in a group of unproved properties for impairment with respect to whether further impairment should be recorded before transferring the ORRI to the group. If the ORRI's value is clearly and substantially less than the assigned residual book value, then a write-down to its fair value should take place on the sublease date.

When subleasing an unproved WI that was impaired on a group basis while retaining an ORRI, presumably the retained interest should be included in an unproved royalties and overriding royalties account. If the proceeds are less than the WI's original cost, the amount received should be treated as a recovery of capital and any unrecovered original cost should be transferred to the unproved royalties and overriding royalties account. Conversely, if the proceeds exceed the original cost, a gain should be recognized.

To further explore these concepts, assume that ABC assigns an unproved lease's WI to another operator for cash consideration of $16,000, retaining a one-sixteenth override. Originally costing $14,000, the lease is within a group of unproved properties with a total cost of $2.1 million and total impairment of $1.4 million. As such, ABC would record the journal entry for the assignment of the WI as follows:

Cash	16,000	
Unproved properties acquisition costs		14,000
Gain on property sales		2,000
To record gain on sublease of unproved property.		

However, if the cash consideration was only $6,000, ABC would record the journal entry as follows:

Cash	6,000	
Unproved royalties and overriding royalties	8,000	
Unproved properties acquisition costs		14,000
To record sublease of unproved property, with no gain or loss.		

Figure 20-1

Creation of nonoperating interests from a working interest

1. Party A owns a mineral interest.

A
Mineral interest (MI)

2. Party A leases the property to Party B, retaining a 1/8 royalty interest (RI).

1/8	1/8	1/8	1/8	1/8	1/8	1/8	1/8
A	**B**						
1/8	100% WI, with 7/8 net revenue interest (NRI)						
RI							

3. Party B transfers the WI to Party C, retaining a 1/8 ORRI.

A	B	C
1/8	1/8	100% working interest (WI), with 6/8 NRI
RI	ORRI	

4. Party C carves out to Party D a VPP of X quantity, payable out of 2/3 of Party C's 75% NRI.

A	B	D	C
1/8	1/8	VPP volumes delivered out of	100% WI and 2/8 NRI
RI	ORRI	4/8 NRI; after payout (APO)	before payout (BPO)
		of X volume, the 4/8 NRI	
		proceeds go to C	

5. Party C sells one-half of the WI to Party E, subject to the ORRI and VPP.

A	B	D	C	E
1/8	1/8	VPP volumes delivered out	4/8 WI and	4/8 WI and
RI	ORRI	of 4/8 NRI; APO of X volume,	1/8 NRI BPO	1/8 NRI BPO
		the 4/8 NRI proceeds		
		go to C and E		

6. After VPP volumes have been delivered to Party D and payout is achieved.

A	B	D	C	E
1/8	1/8	VPP satisfied.	4/8 WI and	4/8 WI and
RI	ORRI		3/8 NRI APO	3/8 NRI APO
		4/8 NRI reverts to C and E.		

Retained ORRI with a reversionary WI. The holder of a retained ORRI may have the right to convert the ORRI to a future WI at an agreed-upon time or event, such as after the WI owner recovers its drilling and completion costs from production. The right to convert the ORRI to a WI, contingent upon some future event, does not change the accounting for the initial conveyance of the WI for which the ORRI was retained. Figure 20-1 summarizes the creation of different types of nonoperating interests from the WI.

Sales of proved properties

Selling a proved property is similar to selling any other plant or equipment for successful efforts companies. Similar to disposals of unproved properties, the determination of whether the lease is amortized individually or within a group is a critical factor in assessing the appropriate accounting treatment.

Sale of an entire proved property

For example, assume that ABC individually amortizes the cost of a proved 480-acre lease. The property balances on January 1, 2019 are as follows:

Proved leasehold costs	$200,000	
Less: accumulated DD&A	(40,000)	
		$160,000
Intangible costs of wells	800,000	
Less: accumulated DD&A	(160,000)	
		640,000
Tangible costs of wells	160,000	
Less: accumulated DD&A	(40,000)	
		120,000
Net book value		**$920,000**

If ABC sells the entire interest, all balances related to the lease are closed out and a gain or loss is recorded based on the difference between the consideration received and the net book value conveyed. For instance, if the above lease sold for $3 million, a gain of $2.08 million would be recognized.

Sale of an undivided portion of a proved property

If ABC sells only a portion of a property, the accounting treatment can be more complex. ASC 932-360-55-11 offers general guidelines as follows: "The sale of a part of a proved property, or of an entire proved property constituting a part of an amortization base, shall be accounted for as the sale of an asset, and a gain or loss shall be recognized, since it is not one of the conveyances described in paragraphs ASC 932-360-40-7 through 40-8. The unamortized cost of the property or group of properties a part of which was sold shall be apportioned to the interest sold and the interest retained on the basis of the fair values of those interests.

However, the sale may be accounted for as a normal retirement under the provisions of paragraph 932-360-40-3 with no gain or loss recognized if doing so does not significantly affect the unit-of-production amortization rate."

Continuing from the previous example, assume that ABC sells an undivided interest in a proved property that has been individually amortized. A proportionate share of each related account should be removed and the gain or loss should be recognized as the difference between the net book value sold and the consideration received. Assume the sale by ABC for $3 million represents an undivided three-fourths share of the WI in the 480-acre lease. ABC's journal entry to record the sale is as follows:

Cash	3,000,000	
Accumulated DD&A – proved properties acquisition costs	30,000	
Accumulated DD&A – intangible costs of wells	120,000	
Accumulated DD&A – tangible costs of wells	30,000	
Proved properties acquisition costs		150,000
Intangible costs of wells		600,000
Tangible costs of wells		120,000
Gain on property sales		2,310,000
To record gain on sale of an undivided three-fourths interest in a proved lease.		

Sale of a divided portion of a proved property

A difficulty arises when a successful efforts company sells a divided interest in a proved property (e.g., 320 acres of a 480-acre tract). If the portion sold is undeveloped, and the portion retained is developed, the cost of equipment or IDC should not be removed from the accounts. Theoretically, the unamortized mineral property cost is allocated, based on relative fair values, between the acreage conveyed and the acreage retained.

Some practitioners may interpret the ASC 932 term "cost of the property" as including not only the mineral leasehold cost but also the cost of wells and related facilities and equipment. In measuring the cost to be "apportioned to the interest sold and the interest retained," those practitioners believe the unamortized cost of all property assets should be included, even though the sold portion is undeveloped and the retained portion is developed. Following this approach, the sold interest's fair value is presumably the sales price, and the retained interest's fair value is the total fair value for the developed lease, including equipment.

This interpretation may seem unusual when a company sells the entire WI in a proved undeveloped property within an amortization group. For example, assume that eight properties in a field, some developed and some undeveloped, are grouped for amortization purposes. No production or amortization has occurred yet. The group's unamortized costs are as follows:

- Proved leasehold: $800,000

- IDC: $6,000,000

- Equipment: $1,000,000

An undeveloped lease in the group sells for $2 million and the remaining seven leases are valued at $18 million on a combined basis. To allocate costs according to relative fair value, the following journal entry would be recorded:

Cash	2,000,000	
Proved properties acquisition costs		80,000
Intangible costs of wells		600,000
Tangible costs of wells		100,000
Gain on property sales		1,220,000
To record gain on sale of an divided interest in a proved lease.		

This treatment is justified because once an amortization group is formed, the individual leases lose their identities and one combined property replaces them.

Sale treated as a normal retirement

ASC 932-360-55-11 notes that the sale of a portion of a proved property or group of properties can be treated as a normal retirement by successful efforts companies, "with no gain or loss recognized if doing so does not significantly affect the unit-of-production amortization rate." Presumably, this treatment applies only when selling an immaterial quantity of reserves (compared to total reserves retained) or when the sales price per unit of reserves does not differ significantly from the amortization cost per unit (i.e., when the deferred gain or loss is immaterial).

To illustrate this distinction, assume that a property (or group of properties) has an unamortized balance of $10 million and the related reserves are 2.0 million BOE. If a portion of the property containing 600,000 BOE of reserves sells for $3.6 million, with no recognition of gain or loss, the remaining cost is $6.4 million and the remaining reserves are 1.4 million BOE. Thus, the amortization rate for the retained properties is $4.57 per BOE ($6,400,000 ÷ 1,400,000). Furthermore, assume that the portion retained has a fair value of $14.4 million ($10.29 per barrel).

Conversely, if the sale is not treated as a normal retirement, the $10 million unamortized balance is allocated to the portion sold and the portion retained based on the relative fair values of $3.6 million and $14.4 million, respectively. The portion sold would be allocated $2 million of value [$10,000,000 x $3,600,000/($3.6 million + $14.4 million)] and the portion retained would have a book value of $8 million. In this case, the portion retained would have an amortization rate of $5.71 per BOE ($8 million ÷ 1.4 million BOE).

As evidenced from this example, treating the sale like a normal retirement dramatically reduces the new unit-of-production amortization rate for the retained properties, from $5.71 per barrel to $4.57 per barrel (a 20 percent decrease).

Note that the critical comparison to make for purposes of evaluating the amortization effect of applying normal retirement treatment to a sale is the amortization rate assuming a gain or loss is recorded, as compared to the amortization rate assuming the sale is treated as a normal retirement. The comparison should not take into account the pre-sale amortization rate of $5 per BOE ($10 million ÷ 2 million BOE) or the amortization rate based on the fair value of the portion retained of $10.29 per BOE ($14.4 million ÷ 1.4 million BOE).

Retirements of proved properties

For successful efforts companies, if surrendering an unproved property on which individual impairment has been recorded, the property's net book value should be written off as an abandonment loss. Alternatively, if an unproved property is within an amortized group, the relinquished property's cost is charged to an allowance for impairment account, with no loss recognized.

ASC 932-360-40-3 treats the abandonment of proved mineral interests within a proved cost center like the normal retirement of equipment or wells:

> Normally, no gain or loss shall be recognized if only an individual well or individual item of equipment is abandoned or retired or if only a single lease or other part of a group of proved properties constituting the amortization base is abandoned or retired as long as the remainder of the property or group of properties continues to produce oil or gas. Instead, the asset being abandoned or retired shall be deemed to be fully amortized, and its costs shall be charged to accumulated depreciation, depletion, or amortization. When the last well on an individual property (if that is the amortization base) or group of properties (if amortization is determined on the basis of an aggregation of properties with a common geological structure) ceases to produce and the entire property or property group is abandoned, gain or loss shall be recognized. Occasionally, the partial abandonment or retirement of a proved property or group of proved properties or the abandonment or retirement of wells or related equipment or facilities may result from a catastrophic event or other major abnormality. In those cases, a loss shall be recognized at the time of abandonment or retirement.

Abandonments

For example, assume the following costs and accumulated DD&A for a field:

Proved leasehold costs	$ 1,000,000
Less: accumulated DD&A	(600,000)
	$ 400,000
Intangible costs of wells	$12,000,000
Less: accumulated DD&A	(7,200,000)
	$ 4,800,000
Tangible costs of wells	$ 600,000
Less: accumulated DD&A	(360,000)
	$ 240,000

Equipment costing $20,000, currently valued at $200, is retired from the lease and transferred to warehouse salvage inventory. The following journal entry would be recorded:

Inventory – materials, supplies and equipment	200
Accumulated DD&A – tangible costs of wells	19,800
Tangible costs of wells	20,000
To record retirement of equipment on lease.	

Similarly, if abandoning an entire lease within an amortization group, no gain or loss should be recognized. Suppose the company abandons a lease from the previous group. Original costs are $32,000 for leasehold, $980,000 for IDC and $63,000 for equipment. Cash salvage totals $1,000:

Cash	1,000	
Accumulated DD&A – proved properties acquisition costs	32,000	
Accumulated DD&A – intangible costs of wells	980,000	
Accumulated DD&A – tangible costs of wells	62,000	
Proved properties acquisition costs		32,000
Intangible costs of wells		980,000
Tangible costs of wells		63,000
To record abandonment of lease in amortization group.		

Conceptually, if the properties within a common geological structure are combined to compute amortization, the individual assets lose their identities. In practice, however, this does not occur because the IRS, federal regulators and some state agencies require separate cost reports.

However, if it is impossible to determine which costs apply to individual properties, a credit can be recorded to net the salvage proceeds against the tangible costs of wells or an accumulated DD&A of tangible costs of wells account. This achieves the same net result as removing the costs from asset accounts and charging them to accumulated amortization accounts.

When abandoning the last well on the last lease of an amortization base or when abandoning the last well on an individually amortized lease, all of the property's asset accounts should be closed and a loss should be recorded for the net book values (less any salvage proceeds).

Catastrophic events

ASC 932-360-40-3 addresses the recognition of gains or losses from catastrophic events or other abnormalities. Fires, floods, earthquakes, hurricanes or unusual governmental actions are considered abnormalities, but routine items such as well blowouts, well abandonments due to excess saltwater intrusion and other inherent industry risks are not.

For example, assume that a flood in the Smith field destroys equipment that cost $250,000. Leases are combined for amortization purposes and net equipment salvage proceeds are $28,000. The field's total capitalized equipment costs are $750,000 and $375,000 in amortization has accumulated. A loss of $97,000 should be calculated as follows:

Cost of equipment destroyed	$250,000
Less: accumulated DD&A [($375,000 ÷ $750,000) X $250,000]	(125,000)
Imputed book value	125,000
Less: salvage proceeds	(28,000)
Net loss	**$ 97,000**

The corresponding journal entry is:

Cash	28,000	
Accumulated DD&A – tangible costs of wells	125,000	
Casualty loss	97,000	
Tangible costs of wells		250,000
To record flood loss of equipment at Smith field.		

ORRI conveyances

Overrides and other types of ORRI conveyances may involve multiple ORRI conveyances, even for single transactions. Accepted accounting methods for single transactions that involve multiple types of ORRI conveyances require bifurcation and separate accounting for each conveyance.

Sale of an override

Override sale from an unproved property. Accounting for the sale of nonoperating interests from unproved properties (such as overrides) was covered earlier in this chapter. In general, such a sale is treated as cost recovery until the book value of the original property (or original cost, if using group impairment) has been recovered; any excess should be treated as a gain.

Override sale from a proved property with no retained WI. When selling an override (or a portion of an override) without retaining a WI, the accounting is the same as when selling a WI in a proved property. For successful efforts companies, the sale of an entire override is treated like the sale of an entire proved property interest, with gain or loss recognized. When selling an undivided portion of an override, a gain or loss is recognized by allocating the override's book value between the portion sold and the portion retained, based on their relative fair values.

Override sale carved-out from a WI in a proved property. ASC 932 is unclear about how to account for the sale of an ORRI (or other nonoperating interest) carved from a working (operating) interest. Consider the following guidance:

- ASC 932-360-40-8 does not permit recognizing gain for partial interest sales, if the seller retains a substantial obligation for future performance (i.e., to operate the property without proportional reimbursement for the associated costs).

- ASC 932-360-55-11 requires accounting for the partial sale of a proved property like the sale of an asset, with gain or loss recognized. Companies should measure the gain or loss by assigning book value to both the asset sold and the asset retained, in proportion to their relative fair values.

- ASC 932-360-55-11 (including its reference to ASC 932-360-40-8) adds that a partial sale of a proved property is not defined as an interest for which the seller retains a substantial obligation for future performance (e.g., to operate the property without proportional reimbursement for the associated costs). However, selling an ORRI carved from the WI leaves the seller with a substantial obligation for future performance (e.g., paying 100 percent of the related costs in return for a reduced share of revenues).

- ASC 932-360-55-12 requires the same accounting specified in ASC 932-360-55-11 for selling a WI and retaining an ORRI.

- ASC 932-360-55-2, which addresses conveying a VPP carved from a retained WI, does not permit recognizing a gain because the seller retains a sizable obligation for future performance (i.e., to operate the property without proportional reimbursement for operating costs).

Consider the following when applying the above ASC-932 guidance to overrides or other types of ORRI conveyances:

- An outright sale, for cash, of an ORRI carved from a WI is considered the partial sale of a mineral interest.

- The buyer has purchased an interest in the WI owner's reserves. The reserves pertaining to the ORRI are no longer included in the seller's reserves base.

- The WI owner has an obligation for substantial future performance to operate the property and bear all associated costs related to the sold ORRI.

ASC 932-360-40-8 seems to be the most applicable to these transaction types, whereby a loss is recognized upon conveyance, but not a gain. Gain or loss is measured to determine whether: (1) a loss has occurred and must be recognized or (2) the sales proceeds simply can be credited to the cost of the asset. ASC 932-360-55-11 specifies measuring gain or loss by apportioning book value to the asset sold and the asset retained, in proportion to their relative fair values.

To illustrate the apportioning method, assume ABC owns a WI with a book value of $100,000. It sells a 10 percent ORRI for $40,000 cash. The remaining WI has a fair market value of $120,000. The 10 percent ORRI is valued at 25 percent of the property's total fair value [$40,000 ÷ ($40,000 + $120,000) = 25 percent]. A difference of $15,000 [$40,000 − (0.25 x $100,000)] between the cash proceeds and relative book value of the asset sold is calculated.

As noted above, it would be inappropriate to record this amount as a gain; accordingly, it should be recorded as a credit against the asset cost. Alternatively, if the cash price is $20,000 and the fair market value of the remaining WI is $60,000, the ORRI's allocated cost is $25,000, and ABC would recognize a loss of $5,000. The retained WI would be subject to ASC 932-360-35 impairment guidance (see Chapter 17).

Override sale treated as a normal retirement. As explained earlier in this chapter, ASC 932-360-55-11 allows the "sale of a part of a proved property, or of an entire proved property constituting a part of an amortization base... [to] be accounted for as a normal retirement under the provisions of paragraph ASC 932-360-40-3 with no gain or loss recognized if doing so does not significantly affect the unit-of-production amortization rate." The rule does not preclude this accounting treatment for the sale of an override in a proved property. However, the option to account for the override as a normal retirement has limited application in practice for the following reasons:

- The option produces no positive income effect if the override sells at a gain.

- The income effect does not differ if the gain is deferred because a WI is retained.

- Using the option to defer a loss (by charging it to the cost of the retained interest) is of little or no value since ASC 932-360-35 impairment accounting rules require a write-down to fair value of the retained interest's cost.

- In many cases, deferring the loss greatly affects the unit-of-production amortization rate to the point that normal retirement accounting would not be allowed.

Note that normal retirement accounting (deferring gain or loss) is not available when selling a WI while retaining an override.

Conveying an override to a key employee

Some companies hold a carried WI or NPI on behalf of key employees. Although they are conveyed in substance, title may not transfer until triggered by specified future events. Frequently, these conveyances occur before the property is proved and their value usually is nominal. In theory, the conveyance should be recorded at fair value by debiting wage expense and applying the rules for unproved property conveyances.

Retaining an override when conveying a WI

Override retention in unproved properties. ASC 932-360-55-3 defines the retention of a nonoperating interest when a WI is assigned in return for drilling, development and operation as a pooling of assets in a joint undertaking. The assignor does not recognize gain or loss and its lease cost becomes the cost of the retained nonoperating interest.

If a WI is sold for cash or cash equivalent and an ORRI is retained, the conveyance is considered a sublease in which recovery of the assigned cost is uncertain. Subleases are treated like the sale of part of an unproved property interest under ASC 932-360-55-9, as previously discussed in this chapter.

Override retention in a proved properties. ASC 932-360-55-12 defines the sale of a WI with retention of a nonoperating interest as an asset sale and requires that "any gain or loss shall be recognized." The seller measures the gain or loss by allocating the property's book value between the portion sold and the portion retained based on their relative fair values. ASC 932-360-55-12 mirrors 55-11, except that it does not mention the option for normal retirement. The language of 55-11 and 55-12 suggests that normal retirement is not available for these sales.

Term overrides

Certain types of overrides do not extend to the end of the property's economic life (i.e., they have a shorter duration than the underlying WI). Often referred to as term overrides, they can be limited in terms of either quantity or time. Generally, term overrides are construed to be production payments. If so, they are accounted for as either VPPs or loans. Chapter 21 further addresses this topic.

Nonmonetary exchanges

Companies may agree to acquire an interest in one or more oil and gas properties in exchange for an interest in other properties owned by others. Exchanges of leases on mineral properties are an example of a nonmonetary exchange as defined by ASC 845-10-05-6, and they can result in gain or loss recognition. Note that certain exceptions in ASC 845-10-15-4 can exclude transactions from the nonmonetary exchange guidance in ASC 845-10.

ASC 845-10-25-1 provides a basic principle about reciprocal transfers of nonmonetary assets: These transfers are considered exchanges only if the transferors retain no substantial continuing involvement in the transferred assets (i.e., the usual risks and rewards of asset ownership are transferred). If a transaction meets the definition of a nonmonetary exchange, ASC 845-10-30-1 requires valuing the assets acquired and surrendered at fair value, as follows: "In general, the accounting for nonmonetary transactions should be based on the fair values of the assets (or services) involved, which is the same basis as that used in monetary transactions. Thus, the cost of a nonmonetary asset acquired in exchange for another nonmonetary asset is the fair value of the asset surrendered to obtain it, and a gain or loss shall be recognized on the exchange. The fair value of the asset received shall be used to measure the cost if it is more clearly evident than the fair value of the asset surrendered."

However, a nonmonetary exchange is measured according to the recorded amount of the relinquished nonmonetary asset and not according to the exchanged assets' fair values if any of the following ASC 845-10-30-3 conditions apply:

a. The company cannot reasonably determine the fair value of either the asset(s) received or those relinquished.

b. The transaction exchanges a product or property that is held for sale, in the ordinary course of business, for a product or property to be sold in the same line of business to facilitate sales to customers other than the parties to the exchange.

c. The transaction lacks commercial substance.

ASC 845-10-30-4 notes that a nonmonetary exchange has commercial substance if it creates a significant change in the entity's future cash flows; it also defines "significant change."

● ● ●

1   A loss effectively is recognized when the remaining capitalized cost is subject to impairment analysis (ASC 932-360-35). For example, if a company sells 50 percent of an unproved property for $2,000 that originally cost $10,000, it seems unreasonable not to recognize an impairment loss (i.e., to carry the unsold 50 percent interest at $8,000, when the sale demonstrates a value of only $2,000 and an impairment of $6,000). The loss recognized due to impairment depends, in part, on whether the unproved property is assessed for impairment individually or within a group.

2   Companies using full cost accounting treat the sale or abandonment of properties as described in Chapter 18. Furthermore, Chapter 18 describes settling AROs under full cost.

CHAPTER 21

Production Payments and Net Profits Interests

Photograph by istock.com/spooh

From time to time, oil and gas companies seek alternatives to traditional markets for necessary capital. Historically, common structures for raising money have included production payments and net profits interests (NPI). Accounting for these structures varies, depending on the risks transferred to the buyer (capital provider) and those retained by the seller. The underlying economics of these structures also do not always result in an intuitive accounting treatment.

Attributes of ownership

Accounting for a conveyance follows the transaction's economic substance rather than terminology used by the parties or within a sales contract. Sellers and buyers retain or assume certain risks when they transfer a property, including production risk, reserves risk and price risk.

Below are the four principal means of conveying oil and gas properties, which are also summarized in Figure 21-1.

Production loan. The seller retains substantially all production, reserves and price risks. The contractual interest is expressed in dollars, and either: (1) the underlying expected cash flow for repayment is significantly greater than the contractual obligation or (2) the seller guarantees the obligation. In substance, the owner is not selling the property but is, instead, borrowing funds.

Prepaid commodity sale (prepaid). The seller retains all, or substantially all, production and reserves risks, whereas the buyer assumes all, or most, price risks given that it pays the seller before delivery of the underlying oil or gas. A seller sells oil or gas in advance and buys it, if necessary, to meet its delivery commitments under the terms of the prepaid agreement. The seller records the transaction in accordance with ASC 606, *Revenue from Contracts with Customers*. The seller's proved reserves are unaffected and the transaction is not considered the sale of a mineral interest.

Volumetric (volume) production payment (VPP). The buyer assumes significant production and reserves risks and assumes all, or substantially all, price risks. VPPs differ from prepaids because the VPP buyer receives agreed-upon quantities from specified future production; however, if production is inadequate to meet the agreed-upon delivery targets, the seller is not obligated to make up the shortfall.

A VPP is considered the sale of a mineral interest, whereby the seller debits cash, credits deferred revenue and excludes the related reserves from its disclosures of reserves estimates and production data. Chapter 18 discusses the accounting for a VPP under the full cost method of accounting. Additionally, VPPs entered into in connection with a business combination can have a different accounting impact, as discussed in Chapter 32.

Sale of a mineral interest. A buyer assumes all, or substantially all, of the seller's ownership risks. The seller debits cash, credits oil and gas properties and recognizes gain or loss to the extent allowed under successful efforts accounting. See Chapter 20 for further discussion of sales of oil and gas properties.

Conveyance types based on transfer of ownership risks

Conveyance type	Assumption of risks		
	Production	**Reserves**	**Price**
Production loan	Seller	Seller	Seller
Prepaid commodity sale	Seller	Seller	Buyer
VPP	Buyer, primarily	Buyer	Buyer
Sale of a mineral interest	Buyer	Buyer	Buyer

Production payments

Production payment transactions obligate the grantor to pay the holder for a specified portion of production proceeds or deliver a specific amount of oil or gas before production ceases. The holder is not obligated to pay operating costs. The holder looks to specified production for a limited period to receive either cash or marketable production.

Accounting for this type of transfer depends, in part, on whether the company conveyed the production payment or, instead, conveyed a working interest with a retained production payment.

Conveyed production payments

Commonly, production payments are conveyed in return for cash. The transaction resembles a financing arrangement whereby the mineral owner pledges production, or proceeds from production, as collateral for the repayment of the funds that were advanced.

Accounting complexities arise because financial and legal advisors have become more creative in designing ways to provide capital to E&P companies. The funds advanced may be equivalent to production loans, or they may be advance payments to purchase future production or sales of oil and gas interests. Subtle wording differences in contracts can alter the nature of these transactions, even when the transactions appear to be similar and may use similar terminology.

Furthermore, in some agreements vendors provide services instead of cash (i.e., drilling services) in exchange for a production payment in the form of a net profits interest (NPI) or overriding royalty interest (ORRI). These arrangements should be carefully evaluated in the context of the guidance below to determine where the transaction's substance falls on the continuum of accounting treatments (e.g., from a loan to a sale).

Although the classification (debt versus sale) depends on the transaction's specific facts and circumstances, ASC 470-10-25-2 states that the presence of any one of the following factors independently creates a rebuttable presumption that the proceeds should be classified as debt:

> a. The transaction does not purport to be a sale (that is, the form of the transaction is debt).
>
> b. The entity has significant continuing involvement in the generation of the cash flows due the investor (for example, active involvement in the generation of the operating revenues of a product line, subsidiary, or business segment).
>
> c. The transaction is cancellable by either the entity or the investor through payment of a lump sum or other transfer of assets by the entity.
>
> d. The investor's rate of return is implicitly or explicitly limited by the terms of the transaction.
>
> e. Variations in the entity's revenue or income underlying the transaction have only a trifling impact on the investor's rate of return.
>
> f. The investor has any recourse to the entity relating to the payments due the investor.

The overarching premise is that advances for future production are considered debt, unless conditions justify otherwise. Although some conveyed production payments are, in substance, borrowings, conveying a VPP (in which the grantor pledges to deliver certain quantities out of future production, free and clear to the seller) is considered the sale of a mineral interest. These sales proceeds are recorded as deferred revenue by successful efforts companies if certain criteria are met, as illustrated later in this chapter.

Four general types of financing arrangements common in the oil and gas industry are discussed in this section:

- Production loans.

- Guaranteed recoupable exploration advances.

- Production payments conveyed as security for loan repayments.

- Conveyed production payments payable in product.

Production loans

A basic financing arrangement is the production loan whereby E&P companies obtain funds from banks or other financing institutions which are repaid (including interest) out of production proceeds from specified properties. If production proceeds are insufficient to repay the advance, other funds must be used by the operator to repay the lending institution, effectively assuring repayment.

A production loan transaction has no effect on an E&P company's revenue accounting. Payments made on the loan are treated in the same way as any other debt. The E&P company includes its entire working interest's share of reserves in computing DD&A and disclosing its reserves quantities because the lender does not own an actual mineral interest in the underlying oil and gas properties.

Guaranteed recoupable exploration advances

Historically, a pipeline company needing natural gas supplies might advance funds to an operator for exploration or development, in return for the right to purchase all, or part, of the natural gas produced from specific properties. The pipeline company bought production from the properties at either a set price per unit or the prevailing market price at the time of production. Any advances were offset against the purchase price of the gas.

Furthermore, if the advance was not recouped within a specified period, it could be repaid from the operator's general assets, as well as from production of other properties specifically pledged, such that the advance was guaranteed to be repaid by the operator.

Given the abundant supplies of natural gas available today, this type of advance is extremely rare in current industry practice. However, it illustrates a financing arrangement described in ASC 932-470-25-1(a), which stipulates accounting for a recoupable advance as a receivable by the company advancing funds and as a payable by the operator.

> Entities seeking supplies of oil or gas sometimes make cash advances to operators to finance exploration in return for the right to purchase oil or gas discovered. Funds advanced for exploration that are repayable by offset against purchases of oil or gas discovered, or in cash if insufficient oil or gas is produced by a specified date, shall be accounted for as a receivable by the lender and as a payable by the operator.

When computing DD&A and disclosing its reserves estimates, the operator includes its entire working interest's share of reserves because the company advancing the funds does not own the mineral interests. This type of transaction also has no effect on an E&P company's revenue accounting. In these ways, a guaranteed recoupable exploration advance is accounted for similarly to a production loan as discussed above.

Production payments conveyed as security for loan repayments

One variation of the above arrangement is treated as a true production payment. The operator carves out an interest in the minerals from one or more properties and transfers it to a financing institution as security for a loan.

Production payments become the source for repayment of the loan. The portion of production that applies to the production payment is a specified fractional share of production proceeds, until the principal and interest are recovered. Repayment is reasonably assured and the lender bears little risk of nonpayment due to production or price declines.

This form of production payment is distinct from a traditional production loan in several ways. Most important, the loan is repaid when, if and as the production occurs. This means the arrangement is "nonrecourse;" the advance is repaid only from the specified production from named properties. Neither other assets nor the operator's general credit serves as collateral.

A financial institution generally lends money under these circumstances only if: (1) the property has a good production history, (2) the loan represents a small part of the value of the property's estimated total reserves; and (3) interest rates are favorable.

In this transaction, the intention of the operator is to obtain financing, not to sell future production. As in a traditional production loan, the operator (seller) retains substantially all risks of ownership of the reserves, although price risk is transferred to the lender (buyer). As a result, a production payment carved out of a producing property is recorded as a receivable by the lender and as a payable by the operator.

ASC 932-470-25-1(b) states:

> Funds advanced to an operator that are repayable in cash out of the proceeds from a specified share of future production of a producing property, until the amount advanced plus interest at a specified or determinable rate is paid in full, shall be accounted for as a borrowing. The advance is a payable for the recipient of the cash and a receivable for the party making the advance. Such transactions... are commonly referred to as production payments.

In this scenario, the operator reports all production proceeds as revenue (subject to the requirements in ASC 606) and includes the entire working interest's share of reserves in computing both DD&A and reserves estimates, because the lender does not own a mineral interest.

Production payments, by nature, are generally long-term obligations, although they should be classified as either short-term or long-term in the same way as other debt. Accordingly, ASC 210-10-45-11 suggests classifying as a current liability the accrued amount as of the balance sheet date which coincides with any current period production that will be used to satisfy the production payment over the next 12 months; the remainder of the payable should remain classified as a long-term liability.

The above guidance could also apply when a vendor advances services (rather than cash) in exchange for payment from a specified property's future production.

Conveyed production payments payable in product

Customarily, production payments payable in product are created from a proved developed producing property. These transactions typically take two forms:

- Payable in product from specified production, with no recourse for the holder for payment.

- Payable in product, but not limited to specific production, whereby the holder has recourse for payment through other means available to the E&P company.

The first form is a VPP, as described in ASC 932-360-55-2:

Some production payments differ from those described in paragraph 932-470-25-1 in that the seller's obligation is not expressed in monetary terms but as an obligation to deliver, free and clear of all expenses associated with operation of the property, a specified quantity of oil or gas to the purchaser out of a specified share of future production. Such a transaction is a sale of a mineral interest for which gain shall not be recognized because the seller has a substantial obligation for future performance. The seller shall account for the funds received as unearned revenue to be recognized as the oil or gas is delivered. The purchaser of such a production payment has acquired an interest in mineral property that shall be recorded at cost and amortized by the unit-of-production method as delivery takes place. The related reserve estimates and production data shall be reported as those of the purchaser of the production payment and not of the seller (see paragraphs 932-235-50-4 through 50-11).

The second type is a prepaid commodity sale, described earlier in this chapter. It is not a mineral interest sale, since the delivery obligation is not solely dependent on specific production or reserves, such that delivery of product to the holder is essentially guaranteed.

Since a VPP obligation is satisfied solely from specified future production, the seller has a substantial obligation for future performance (i.e., to produce the product and pay the related production costs).[1] While a VPP is considered the sale of a mineral interest, the seller does not recognize a gain when executing the conveyance contract. As previously mentioned, successful efforts companies record proceeds from the sale as deferred revenue, which is recognized as the oil and gas is delivered and the revenue recognition criteria is met according to ASC 606. However, the oil or gas reserves that correspond to the unearned revenue are excluded from those reported by the operator (seller). The VPP purchaser also reports revenue according to ASC 606. Both the seller and the purchaser should consider the appropriate recognition of revenues on a gross or net basis depending on each entity's determination that it is the principal or agent to any sales agreements for the volumes subject to the VPP.

As an example, on January 2, 2019. Carolina E&P (CEP) carves out a production payment of 500,000 Mcf from its working interest in a producing lease and assigns it to Charlotte Co. in exchange for $2.5 million. The obligation will be satisfied by delivery from the first 80 percent of CEP's share of production. The lease's net book value is $7.1 million. CEP allocates a net book value of $1.2 million to the production payment and $5.9 million to the remaining portion of the property. During 2019, CEP's share of production is 450,000 Mcf, of which 360,000 Mcf is delivered to Charlotte Co., which sells the gas to a third-party for $2 per Mcf. On December 31, 2019, CEP's share of proved reserves is 2,500,000 Mcf, of which 140,000 Mcf (500,000 Mcf assigned less 360,000 Mcf delivered in 2019) belongs to the production payment owner, Charlotte Co.

CEP records the following journal entries for the transaction as the seller:

Cash	2,500,000	
Deferred revenues		2,500,000
To record the sale of the VPP.		

Deferred revenues	1,800,000	
Gas revenues		1,800,000
To record earned revenues applicable to the VPP [(360,000 Mcf ÷ 500,000 Mcf) x $2,500,000].		

As the buyer, Charlotte Co. records the following journal entries:

Proved production payments	2,500,000	
Cash		2,500,000
To record the purchase of the VPP.		

DD&A expense – proved production payments	1,800,000	
Accumulated DD&A – proved production payments		1,800,000
To record amortization of VPP costs [(360,000 Mcf ÷ 500,000 Mcf) x $2,500,000].		

For the year ended December 31, 2019, Charlotte Co. records gas revenues as follows:

Accounts receivable – oil and gas sales	720,000	
Gas revenues		720,000
To record earned revenues applicable to the VPP (360,000 Mcf x $2 per Mcf).		

In its supplemental disclosures as of December 31, 2019, CEP includes 2,360,000 Mcf (2,500,000 Mcf – 140,000 Mcf) of proved reserves and 90,000 Mcf (450,000 Mcf – 360,000 Mcf) of produced gas. Because the company deferred the production payment revenue, and the property's capitalized costs and corresponding DD&A were unaffected (i.e., there was no credit to oil and gas properties for the VPP conveyance), the 140,000 Mcf of reserves and 360,000 Mcf of production applicable to the VPP, as well as the property burdened by the VPP, must be included in the computation of DD&A for 2019.

Total recorded DD&A in 2019 for the lease is $1,080,735 (see Figure 21-2), which considers both VPP and non-VPP reserves, as well as the property's production.

Figure 21-2

Calculating DD&A – VPP and property burdened by VPP

VPP

$$\frac{360,000\ \text{Mcf}}{140,000\ \text{Mcf} + 360,000\ \text{Mcf}} \quad x \quad \$1,200,000 \quad = \quad \$864,000$$

Property burdened by VPP

$$\frac{90,000\ \text{Mcf}}{2,360,000\ \text{Mcf} + 90,000\ \text{Mcf}} \quad x \quad \$5,900,000 \quad = \quad \$216,735$$

The resulting journal entry recorded by CEP is as follows:

DD&A expense – proved production payments	864,000	
DD&A expense – proved properties acquisition costs	216,735	
Accumulated DD&A – proved production payments		864,000
Accumulated DD&A – proved properties acquisition costs		216,735
To record DD&A expense for 2019 related to the VPP.		

The allocation of those costs to expense through DD&A should be based on the VPP owner's share of production and reserves. However, in accordance with ASC 932-360-55-2, the VPP reserves and production of the VPP holder (Charlotte Co.) must be excluded from CEP's reported reserves and production data as of December 31, 2019.

Comparatively, in its disclosure of proved reserves as of December 31, 2019, Charlotte Co. includes 140,000 Mcf of gas that remains to be received under the VPP.

Prepaid price swaps

In one variation of the VPP, an oil and gas producer receives an advance from a financial institution in exchange for the revenue relating to a set volume of production for a specified time period. The producer sells its production in the normal course of business at market prices and remits the proceeds to the financial institution.

This arrangement differs from a traditional VPP because the producer sells the product first and then delivers the proceeds to the financing institution. This variation has been characterized in practice as a prepaid price swap.

Given that both price and production risks are transferred to the financial institution, the economics of a typical prepaid price swap are the same to the producer as a VPP. Therefore, successful efforts accounting requires proceeds from the advance to be recorded as deferred revenue, with revenue recognized in accordance with ASC 606 as the oil or gas is delivered over the agreement term.

Conveyed production payment examples

Five examples of conveyed production payments are described below. In each case, upon conveyance, the grantor and holder reasonably expect the production payment to be fully satisfied before the underlying property ceases production.[2]

1. **Borrowing.** For cash received, a production payment is conveyed that entitles its holder to $5,000 per month for four years from production proceeds (net of production taxes) of the grantor's 20 percent working interest in a lease.

2. **Borrowing.** For cash received, a production payment is conveyed that entitles its holder to 75 percent of oil production proceeds attributable to the grantor's 20 percent working interest in a lease, until the holder has received $100,000, plus related interest of 12 percent annually.

3. **VPP.** For cash received, a production payment is conveyed that entitles its holder to 75 percent of oil production attributable to the grantor's 20 percent working interest in a lease, until the holder has received 20,000 barrels of oil.

4. **VPP.** For cash received, a production payment is conveyed that entitles its holder to 75 percent of oil production attributable to the grantor's 20 percent working interest in two leases for 10 years.

5. **Prepaid.** For cash received, a production payment is conveyed that entitles its holder to 300 barrels per month for five years attributable to the grantor's 20 percent working interest in a lease. If production is insufficient to satisfy 300 barrels in any given month, the grantor will make up the difference by delivering other oil of similar grade and quality.

In the first example, the production payment proceeds are fixed in terms of amount and timing, and the holder assumes virtually no production, reserves or price risks. Therefore, the conveyance is, in substance, a borrowing. The second example calls for the holder to be repaid $100,000 at 12 percent interest. The holder's production and price risks are similar to those of a loan, with the property serving as collateral.

The third and fourth examples meet the VPP requirement to repay a specific quantity from specific reserves, with the holder assuming price risk and some production risk. The grantor must record the proceeds as deferred revenue and reduce its reserves by the specific quantity that is due the holder.

In the fifth example, the conveyance also calls for a specific quantity from specific reserves but contains a safety net clause: if production is insufficient, the grantor must make up the difference – even if it has to buy oil in the open market to deliver to the holder. The holder assumes price risk but no production or reserves risks. In substance, the conveyance is a prepaid and the grantor records the initial proceeds as deferred revenue but continues to own the underlying reserves.

Three accounting concepts for production payments are expressed in ASC 932-470-25-1 and ASC 932-360-40-8:

- Some conveyances are, in substance, borrowings repayable in cash or its equivalent and should be accounted for as borrowings.

- If part of an interest is sold and substantial uncertainty exists about the seller's recovery of costs that apply to the retained interest, the seller does not recognize a gain upon conveyance.

- Similarly, if part of an interest is sold and the seller continues its major obligation for future performance, no gain should be recognized at the time of conveyance.

Proper accounting for production payments depends on the facts of the contract that created the parties' rights and obligations. Individual circumstances will cause the arrangement to be accounted for under one of these accounting concepts, as discussed further herein.

Retained production payments

A retained production payment is created when the owner of a working interest transfers its interest to a purchaser but retains an oil or gas payment that will be satisfied when, if, and as oil or gas is produced out of the assigned working interest.

This type of production payment may be created from a group of properties rather than from a single property. Also, it is a non-recourse transaction: Only production can satisfy the obligation. Retained payments can arise when the lessee of a mineral property assigns its working interest to another operator. They also can be created by the original lease contract between the mineral rights owner and the lessee.

For example, a company wants to sell a producing property for $1 million. Another company is willing to purchase the property for that price but lacks the necessary financing. The seller sells the property to the buyer for $1 million. The buyer pays $200,000 in cash and the seller retains a production payment of $800,000, plus interest, payable out of 90 percent of the working interest's share of revenues that otherwise would go to the buyer.

Accounting for conveyances subject to retained production payments depends, in part, on whether the underlying property is proved or unproved. Additional consideration then takes into account whether the retained production payment is:

- Expressed in monetary terms and reasonably assured.

- Expressed in monetary terms but not reasonably assured (similar to an override).

Retained payments carved from proved properties

Expressed in monetary terms and reasonably assured. For a conveyance transaction that creates a retained production payment expressed in monetary terms, the appropriate accounting treatment depends on whether or not the payment's satisfaction is reasonably assured. Reasonable assurance of satisfaction from a proved property exists only when the estimated reserves needed to satisfy the payment are significantly less than the total working interest share of proved reserves in the particular property.

ASC 932 is explicit in describing the accounting rules for retained payments expressed in monetary terms arising from the conveyance of proved properties. ASC 932-360-55-13(a) specifies the treatment by a successful efforts company:

> The sale of a proved property subject to a retained production payment that is expressed as a fixed sum of money payable only from a specified share of production from that property, with the purchaser of the property obligated to incur the future costs of operating the property, shall be accounted for as follows:
>
> a. If satisfaction of the retained production payment is reasonably assured, the seller of the property, who retained the production payment, shall record the transaction as a sale, with recognition of any resulting gain or loss. The retained production payment shall be recorded as a receivable, with interest accounted for in accordance with the provisions of Subtopic 835-30 [Imputation of Interest]. The purchaser shall record as the cost of the assets acquired the cash consideration paid plus the present value of the retained production payment, which shall be recorded as a payable. The oil and gas reserve estimates and production data, including those applicable to liquidation of the retained production payment, shall be reported by the purchaser of the property (see paragraphs 932-235-50-4 through 50-11).

As indicated, if satisfaction is reasonably assured, the retained production payment is, in substance, a note receivable. It is measured and recorded according to ASC 835-30-25. In general, these receivables are recorded at the discounted present value of the payments due. If the contract provides for a market interest rate, the payment's face amount is its appropriate measure.

For example, assume ABC Co. (ABC) conveys to Tiger Co. the working interest in a producing leasehold with the following capitalized costs and accumulated amortization:

Figure 21-3
Capitalized costs – ABC Co.

	Leasehold	Intangibles	Tangibles
Cost	$60,000	$480,000	$90,000
Less: accumulated DD&A	(20,000)	(160,000)	(30,000)
Net book value	**$40,000**	**$320,000**	**$60,000**

The consideration is $1 million cash and a production payment of $1.6 million, bearing interest at 12 percent (assumed to be a market interest rate), payable from the first 75 percent of the working interest's share of production. Satisfaction of the production payment is reasonably assured. ABC records the following journal entry:

Cash	1,000,000	
Accumulated DD&A – proved properties acquisition costs	20,000	
Accumulated DD&A – intangible costs of wells	160,000	
Accumulated DD&A – tangible costs of wells	30,000	
Notes receivable – proved production payments	1,600,000	
Proved properties acquisition costs		60,000
Intangible costs of wells		480,000
Tangible costs of wells		90,000
Gain on property sales		2,180,000
To record sale of lease.		

Assuming an equipment value of $70,000, Tiger Co. records the transaction as follows:

Tangible costs of wells	70,000	
Proved properties acquisition costs	2,530,000	
Cash		1,000,000
Notes payable – proved production payments		1,600,000
To record purchase of lease.		

As the purchaser, Tiger Co. would subsequently record all of the property's revenues and expenses. Payments due to ABC would first be allocated to interest expense in the manner specified in the contract, with the balance treated as a reduction of the principal amount. Similarly, ABC would record the proceeds earned as interest income first, with any remaining proceeds treated as recovered principal.

Expressed in monetary terms but not reasonably assured. ASC 932-360-55-13(b) addresses the sale of a proved property that is subject to a production payment expressed as a fixed sum of money but without reasonable assurance of repayment, noting, "If satisfaction of the retained production payment is not reasonably assured, the transaction is in substance a sale with retention of an overriding royalty that shall be accounted for in accordance with [paragraph ASC 932-360-55-12]."

The satisfaction of a retained production payment expressed in monetary terms that is not reasonably assured is similar in substance to the sale of a proved property subject to a retained production payment that is expressed as a right to a specified quantity of oil or gas out of specified future production, as is described in ASC 932-360-55-14 (see further discussion in Chapter 20). Both the operating interest sold and the nonoperating interest retained should be accounted for in accordance with ASC 932-360-55-12 as described below:

> The sale of the operating interest in a proved property for cash with retention of a nonoperating interest is not one of the types of conveyances described in paragraphs 932-360-40-7 through 40-8. Accordingly, it shall be accounted for as the sale of an asset, and any gain or loss shall be recognized. The seller shall allocate the cost of the proved property to the operating interest sold and the nonoperating interest retained on the basis of the fair values of those interests. A retained production payment denominated in money is not a mineral interest (see paragraphs 932-360-25-4 and 932-470-25-1).

As described in this guidance, the sale of an operating interest in proved property subject to a retained production payment not reasonably assured should be accounted for as a sale with a gain or loss recognized. Book value should be allocated to the interest sold and interest retained based on relative fair values. This is similar to accounting for the sale of an undivided portion of an operating interest in proved property, also described in Chapter 20.

To illustrate, assume from the preceding example that satisfaction of the $1.6 million production payment is not reasonably assured. Based on known reserves, the production schedule, selling prices, costs and appropriate discount rates, the production payment's fair value is $600,000.

Sales proceeds allocated to the equipment, based on its $70,000 fair value, will result in a gain of $10,000 ($70,000 less $60,000). ABC allocates the remaining unrecovered cost ($360,000 for leasehold cost and IDC) based on the relative fair values of the interest sold and the interest retained as illustrated in Figure 21-4:

Figure 21-4

Allocation of unrecovered costs based on relative FV

Value of interest sold (cash proceeds)	$1,000,000	− $70,000	=	$ 930,000
Value of production payment retained				600,000
Total				**$1,530,000**
Costs allocated to interest sold:	$\dfrac{\$930,000}{\$1,530,000}$	x $360,000	=	$218,824
Costs allocated to production payment retained:	$\dfrac{\$600,000}{\$1,530,000}$	x $360,000	=	$141,176

The gain on the sale of the mineral interest and IDC is $711,176 ($1,000,000 less $70,000 less $218,824). Total gain is $721,176 ($711,176 on mineral interest and IDC and $10,000 on equipment), as shown in the journal entry below:

Cash	1,000,000	
Proved production payments	141,176	
Accumulated DD&A – proved properties acquisition costs	20,000	
Accumulated DD&A – intangible costs of wells	160,000	
Accumulated DD&A – tangible costs of wells	30,000	
Proved properties acquisition costs		60,000
Intangible costs of wells		480,000
Tangible costs of wells		90,000
Gain on property sales		721,176
To record the sale of property.		

As is illustrated from the two previous examples, the reasonable assurance that a retained production payment will be satisfied has a profound effect on its accounting treatment, especially if the payment is large compared to the cash consideration received. However, the determination of reasonable assurance is highly subjective. If satisfaction is reasonably assured, the payment is, in effect, a monetary asset (or note receivable); however, if satisfaction is not reasonably assured, the retained production payment is equivalent to an overriding royalty interest.

Retained payments carved from unproved properties

A production payment retained on the assignment of an unproved property is likely to be expressed in terms of barrels of oil or Mcf of gas. ASC 932-360-55-13 does not specifically address payments retained from unproved properties. However, by their very nature, these payments have no assurance of satisfaction. It is logical to conclude that these payments are equivalent to overriding royalties and should be treated as such.

This type of transaction should be treated as a sublease, with cash proceeds recorded as a return of book value, or of the property's original cost if using a group impairment approach (see Chapter 20). The production payment's carrying value is the unrecovered book value (or unrecovered cost). The unproved production payment will be subject to an impairment test.

Conceptually, ASC 932-360-55-13 identifies a production payment expressed in a monetary amount as a cash equivalent. However, ASC 932-360-55-13(b) severely limits that concept by concluding that, if satisfaction from proved properties is not reasonably assured, the payment takes on characteristics of a mineral interest rather than a monetary asset.

Net profits interests

A net profits interest (NPI) is a production interest governed by contract and created from a property's working interest, measured using a stated percentage of the net profits from the property.[3] NPI holders are never obligated to pay a share of losses; however, net profits may be considered cumulative and, therefore, may incorporate losses from prior periods. An NPI is similar to an ORRI but it is measured against net profits, not revenue. The holder is not liable for net costs or losses.

Accounting for an NPI conveyance

ASC 932 conveyance rules are silent with respect to accounting for an NPI conveyance. Because an NPI is classified as a nonoperating interest, it can most closely be compared to the override conveyance guidance described in Chapter 20. However, the accounting differs when the NPI is conveyed with the retention of a working interest.

Unlike the sale of an ORRI carved from a retained working interest, accounting for the sale of an NPI on proved property allows for immediate recognition of any gain (under successful efforts). When the NPI share is based on cumulative net profits, the retained working interest holder may assume a very limited future obligation to bear a cumulative loss (i.e., a disproportionate share of future development and operating costs).

Absent a cumulative loss, the NPI indirectly bears the costs, since the costs determine cumulative net profit. The computation of the gain itself (reflecting fair value in excess of allocated cost) indicates that overall fair value exceeds overall book value, whereby future cumulative loss to the WI holder is not expected. Under some circumstances, such as an NPI based on periodic, noncumulative net profit, the WI holder may have substantial future obligations that preclude its immediate recognition of a gain.

For example, on January 1, 2019, ABC conveys an NPI (20 percent of net profits from its 50 percent working interest) in ABC field. The agreement defines net profits as follows: revenue less severance taxes and other direct exploration and development costs, as well as direct operating costs. Usually, NPI contracts treat exploration and development outlays as deductible expenses. Amortization, indirect administration costs, interest expense and income taxes generally are ignored in computing net profits. Net profits are specified to be cumulative.

If in January 2019 ABC did not earn any revenue or incur any operating expenses in the field but incurred $50,000 in development costs, there were no net profits that month. The NPI holder receives nothing for its interest in the property.

However, if ABC's share of operations in February 2019 consisted of $100,000 in revenue, $10,000 in severance taxes and $30,000 in other direct operating expenses, February net profits would be $60,000, while cumulative net profits would be $10,000. ABC would then pay the NPI holder 20 percent of $10,000.

Industry use of NPIs

An E&P company should record net profits received or paid, and assign reserves to such net profits, on a consistent basis.

NPIs are not commonly used by E&P companies, and accounting for them varies, as noted in the *2019 PricewaterhouseCoopers Survey of U.S. Petroleum Accounting Practices*. Of 33 survey respondents, 16 of them addressed NPIs, with 9 responding affirmatively to including proved reserves associated with an NPI owned in their DD&A calculations. The responses (Questions K1 through K5) are summarized below:

Figure 21-5

2019 PwC Survey of U.S. Petroleum Accounting Practices – NPIs

Treatment of related revenues and expenses	NPI owned	NPI obligation
As a financing arrangement[1]	N/A	0%
Report both revenues and costs as though a WI	15%	15%
Record net as though a royalty interest	33%	27%
Record net as an operating expense[1]	N/A	0%
Other	52%	58%
	100%	100%

Calculation of proved reserves volumes	NPI owned	
Treat the NPI as though a WI	33%	
Treat the NPI as though a royalty interest	56%	
Treat the NPI as additional operating expense	0%	
Other	11%	
	100%	

1 While no survey respondents responded affirmatively to applying this type of treatment for an NPI obligation, the option of selecting this response has been included herein for reference.

Term NPIs

Term NPIs are limited to a specified time period, net profits amount or underlying production volume. They are similar to production payments because their economic life is limited. Term NPIs, like VPPs, are attractive partly because their sales may be treated as borrowings for federal income tax purposes. For financial reporting purposes, they sometimes are treated as sales, which results in deferred revenue or a reduction to the full cost pool. The accounting treatment for specific NPIs varies, depending on the contract.

For example, a term NPI most closely resembles a VPP if it meets all of the following criteria:

- It is limited to a stated quantity.

- It is unlikely to extend to the full productive life of the underlying producing properties.

- It does not require the operator to deliver products to the holder.

- It does not put the holder at risk for cash payments to the operator if expenses exceed revenues at any time during the life of the agreement.

Alternatively, if a term NPI does not require quantities to be delivered and its conveyance is not, in substance, a borrowing, it could be considered the sale of a portion of a property, whereby:

- For a proved property, gain (or loss) is calculated and any gain must be deferred if the seller has a substantial obligation for future performance.

- For an unproved property (which would be rare), the proceeds simply reduce associated capitalized costs before any gain is recognized.

Therefore, proper accounting would depend on the transaction's substance, as addressed in the agreement.

Accounting for other property conveyances

E&P companies and financial markets commonly use oil and gas reserves as the basis to create securities or financial instruments for investor purchases. Today's E&P companies may seek new ways to raise capital in traditional markets, often due to their inability to raise capital quickly and at an acceptable price. An operator's desire to monetize its reserves in unconventional ways often leads to unique financing methods and corresponding accounting questions.

Accounting for unusual conveyances and financing methods requires careful consideration of the mineral conveyance accounting rules found in ASC 932-360-55-2 through 55-14, as described in this chapter and Chapter 20. Another source of guidance is ASC 470-10-25, which is discussed in the production payments section of this chapter.

● ● ●

1 This differs from an operator's sale of a working interest, in which the operator maintains a fiduciary obligation to manage future operations (i.e., to produce, but not to pay for, the new owner's working interest share of production costs).

2 In that sense, the production payment is similar to a limited override that will cease, or likely will cease, before the working interest ceases.

3 The contract should also address the NPI holder's right for accounting and right to audit the accounting as briefly discussed in COPAS *Accounting Guideline No. 13* (AG-13).

Farmouts, Carried Interests and Unitizations

Key concepts

- **Farmouts**

- **Free wells**

- **Carried interests**

- **Promoted versus promoting**

- **Unitizations**

- **Creation of joint ventures**

The pooling of capital concept has long been a part of accounting theory, as well as an essential element in the federal taxation of extractive industries. Commonly, an entity acquires an interest in a mineral property through the contribution of money, property or services and assumes all or part of the risk and burden of developing and operating it.

In joint operations, one party may contribute cash to the venture, another may contribute a leasehold and another may provide equipment or drilling and other services. The venture's members agree that they are contributing to a common pool of capital. Thus, each is viewed as investing in a venture or adding to the venture's capital reservoir in return for an ownership interest in the venture as a whole.

ASC 932-360-40-7 states that no gain or loss is recognized at the time of conveyance in a pooling of assets in a joint undertaking intended to find, develop or produce oil or gas from a particular property or group of properties.

This chapter examines common applications of these concepts by successful efforts companies. Although many of the same rules apply, special considerations for full cost companies are discussed in Chapter 18.

Farmouts

The owner of a working interest may transfer all or part of the operating rights to another party in exchange for the transferee assuming some portion of the cost of exploring or developing the property. This transaction is referred to as a farmout. One type of farmout is essentially a sublease without cash consideration. The original lessee assigns the working interest but retains an overriding royalty or a net profits interest in return for the assignee's agreement to perform and pay for specified drilling and development activities.

For example, assume High West Company (HWC) assigns the working interest in the Durham Bull Lease to River Bandit Company (RBC), subject to a retained overriding royalty interest of one-eighth of total production from the unproved property. As consideration, RBC agrees to drill a well to a depth of 5,000 feet or to a specific formation, if less than 5,000 feet. RBC completes the well and pays all equipment installation costs. It spends $350,000 for intangible drilling costs (IDC) and $70,000 for lease and well equipment (tangible costs). HWC's original lease cost was $85,000.

ASC 932-360-55-3 specifies the accounting by the two parties:

> An assignment of the operating interest in an unproved property with retention of a nonoperating interest in return for drilling, development, and operation by the assignee is a pooling of assets in a joint undertaking for which the assignor shall not recognize gain or loss. The assignor's cost of the original interest shall become the cost of the interest retained. The assignee shall account for all costs incurred as specified by Sections 932-360-25 and 932-360-35 and shall allocate none of those costs to the mineral interest acquired. If oil or gas is discovered, each party shall report its share of reserves and production (see paragraphs 932-235-50-4 through 50-11).

In this example, both companies have contributed capital. Each party benefits from this arrangement, yet neither party recognizes a gain or loss. Assuming no previous impairment has been recorded for the property on an individual lease basis, HWC's leasehold cost of $85,000 becomes its cost for the overriding royalty interest retained and is recorded as follows:

Proved royalties and overriding royalties	85,000	
Unproved properties acquisition costs		85,000
To record farmout of Durham Bull Lease and retention of a one-eighth override.		

If an allowance for impairment was previously recorded for the lease, the net book value of the lease is assigned to the overriding royalty interest retained. Assuming an individual impairment of $30,000 had been recorded on the lease in the preceding example, HWC's journal entry to record the farmout is as follows:

Proved royalties and overriding royalties	55,000	
Allowance for impairment – unproved properties	30,000	
Unproved properties acquisition costs		85,000
To record farmout of Durham Bull Lease and retention of a one-eighth override.		

RBC classifies its investment based on the type of expenditures made. No part of the costs incurred is allocated to the mineral rights obtained and no gain or loss is recorded. The journal entry made by RBC is as follows:

Intangible costs of wells	350,000	
Tangible costs of wells	70,000	
Accounts payable		420,000
To record drilling and equipment costs on the Durham Bull Lease.		

If the well is dry, RBC would charge the costs incurred (less net salvage value) to the unsuccessful exploratory wells account. HWC would record impairment of the overriding royalty.

Free wells

When a working interest owner assigns a fractional share of its working interest in return for the assignee drilling and equipping one or more wells without cost to the assignor, the result is a free well. The term free well is used because the assignor retains a portion of the working interest and receives an interest in the well and equipment without paying any part of the initial drilling and equipment costs. The assignor also shares in production from the well.

A free well is considered a sharing arrangement under the pooling of capital concept, and no gain or loss is recognized by either party to the transaction. ASC 932-360-55-4 provides the following guidance:

An assignment of a part of an operating interest in an unproved property in exchange for a free well with provision for joint ownership and operation is a pooling of assets in a joint undertaking by the parties. The assignor shall record no cost for the obligatory well; the assignee shall record no cost for the mineral interest acquired. All drilling, development, and operating costs incurred by either party shall be accounted for as specified by this Topic. If the conveyance agreement requires the assignee to incur geological or geophysical expenditures instead of, or in addition to, a drilling obligation, those costs shall likewise be accounted for by the assignee as specified by this Topic. If reserves are discovered, each party shall report its share of reserves and production (see paragraphs 932-235-50-4 through 50-11).

To illustrate a free well scenario, assume HWC owns several unproved leases in the same general area. In January 2019, it contracts with Freedom to drill and equip a well on the property at Freedom's cost. In return, HWC assigns an undivided one-half working interest in a lease to Freedom.

HWC's original cost of the lease is $38,000. Freedom spends $135,000 on IDC and $20,000 on equipment for the property, which is considered proved after the well is completed. Each party receives one-half of the production revenues, beginning with the first production, and each pays one-half of operating expenses and further developmental costs. Although HWC will pay one-half of the well's operating costs, the well is still considered a free well since Freedom paid all of the well's initial drilling and equipment costs. Since the transaction comes under the pooling of capital concept, the accounting treatment for both parties is essentially the same as the accounting for farmouts. Assuming the group impairment method is used, the journal entry recorded by HWC is:

Proved properties acquisition costs	38,000	
Unproved properties acquisition costs		38,000
To transfer cost of lease to proved leaseholds.		

Similarly, the entry recorded by Freedom is:

Intangible costs of wells	135,000	
Tangible costs of wells	20,000	
Accounts payable		155,000
To record costs of a free well drilled for a fractional interest in HWC lease.		

In this example, HWC assigns no cost to IDC or equipment and Freedom assigns no cost to the mineral interest. Each party reports only its share of production and proved reserves.

In another type of free well arrangement, the lessor retains all of the working interest and assigns the driller a nonoperating interest in the property in return for drilling and equipping the well. Using data from the preceding example, assume HWC retains the entire working interest in the lease and assigns Freedom an overriding royalty interest of one-fourth of total production from the property in return for Freedom's drilling and equipping the well. This transaction also represents a pooling of capital because each party contributes property, cash or services to a joint venture in return for some type of ownership interest. Thus, no gain or loss is recognized by either party.

As the holder of a nonoperating interest, Freedom has no ownership in either the IDC or equipment. It might appear that the entire $155,000 spent by Freedom should be treated as the acquisition cost of the overriding royalty interest. However, since ASC 932-360-55-4 specifically prohibits classifying a portion of well costs to an earned mineral interest, it is appropriate under ASC 932 conveyance rules for Freedom to treat the entire $155,000 as well costs.

Carried interests

Carried interests arrangements have been widely used in the oil and gas industry for many years. While various forms exist, such as the carried interests arrangement illustrated in the example provided below, all achieve the same economic result.

Rhubarb, the carried party, owns a working interest in unproved Lease A57. It assigns its entire interest to Developco, the carrying party. Developco agrees to pay all costs of drilling, equipping and operating the property until it recovers all costs from its working interest revenue (i.e., until it achieves payout). Developco then reassigns one-half of the working interest to Rhubarb (which has a 50% reversionary interest). Subsequent to the reversion, Rhubarb and Developco share equally in further revenues and production expenses and any additional expenditures for drilling or development.

For purposes of this example, Rhubarb's lease cost is $20,000. Developco spends $100,000 for IDC and $32,000 for lease equipment. The well is completed and production begins on November 1, 2019. Working interest revenues are $32,500 per month for 650 barrels beginning with first production and expenses are $6,500 per month. Developco has determined that it is an agent of the other working interest owners with respect to the sales agreement with the ultimate purchaser. As such, Developco records its revenues on a net basis, as required under ASC 606, based on the working interest share of the production it was assigned by Rhubarb. On December 31, 2019, proved reserves attributable to the working interest are 390,000 barrels.

Based on these facts, Developco receives $26,000 per month of net revenue ($32,500 of net revenues less $6,500 of expenses) to apply toward recoupment of drilling and development costs. At the end of 2019, Developco has received $52,000 (two months at $26,000 per month) and is entitled to recover an additional $80,000 ($132,000 less $52,000) before Rhubarb begins to share in production.

ASC 932-360-55-5 addresses carried interests as follows:

> A part of an operating interest in an unproved property may be assigned to effect an arrangement called a carried interest whereby the assignee (the carrying party) agrees to defray all costs of drilling, developing, and operating the property and is entitled to all of the revenue from production from the property, excluding any third party interest, until all of the assignee's costs have been recovered, after which the assignor will share in both costs and production. Such an arrangement represents a pooling of assets in a joint undertaking by the assignor and assignee. The carried party shall make no accounting for any costs and revenue until after recoupment (payout) of the carried costs by the carrying party. Subsequent to payout the carried party shall account for its share of revenue, operating expenses, and (if the agreement provides for subsequent sharing of costs rather than a carried interest) subsequent development costs... [continued on next page]

> [continued from previous page] ...During the payout period the carrying party shall record all costs, including those carried, as specified by this Topic and shall record all revenue from the property including that applicable to the recovery of costs carried. The carried party shall report as oil or gas reserves only its share of proved reserves estimated to remain after payout, and unit-of-production amortization of the carried party's property cost shall not commence prior to payout. Prior to payout the carrying party's reserve estimates and production data shall include the quantities applicable to recoupment of the carried costs (see paragraphs 932-235-50-4 through 50-11).

The accounting treatment specified by ASC 932-360-55-5 is summarized as follows:

- Neither party recognizes a gain or loss at the time of conveyance.

- Each party making the expenditure or contribution accounts for the expenditure or contribution in a proper manner.

- All revenues and cash expenses belong or apply to the carrying party until payout.

- Except for the entry to transfer the property's cost to proved properties, no entries are necessary by the carried party until payout has occurred.

Since neither party records a gain or loss for the conveyance transaction, Rhubarb transfers the leasehold cost of $20,000 (or net book value, if impairment has been recorded on an individual lease basis) to a proved properties leasehold account when the property becomes proved, as illustrated in the following journal entry.

Proved properties acquisition costs	20,000	
Unproved properties acquisition costs		20,000
To transfer cost of lease to proved leaseholds.		

Since Developco is considered to own the full working interest until payout, its costs of drilling and equipping the well are recorded in the following journal entry:

Intangible costs of wells	100,000	
Tangible costs of wells	32,000	
Accounts payable		132,000
To record drilling and equipment costs on Lease A57.		

As mentioned, Developco is entitled to recover its costs related to the property. If cash proceeds from the property are inadequate, Rhubarb has no liability for unrecovered amounts. Developco receives $26,000 per month ($32,500 of net revenues less $6,500 of expenses), which is $40 for each working interest barrel ($26,000 ÷ 650 barrels) to apply toward recoupment of drilling and equipment costs.

Accordingly, in November and December of 2019, assuming all revenue recognition criteria have been met in accordance with ASC 606, Developco includes all revenues and expenses in its income statement as summarized for the two months in the following journal entries:

Accounts receivable – oil and gas sales	65,000	
Crude oil revenues		65,000
To record production revenues from Lease A57.		

Lease operating expenses	13,000	
Accounts payable		13,000
To record production expenses on Lease A57.		

Since all working interest production up until payout belongs to the carrying party, its reserves disclosures should include all working interest production expected until payout plus the carrying party's share of reserves at payout. The reserves quantities to be reported by the carried party prior to payout (and used in computing DD&A after payout) is the carried party's share of reserves at payout.

The calculation of proved reserves attributed to each party at December 31, 2019, is shown in Figure 22-1:

Figure 22-1

Illustrative proved reserves – Carried interest

	Bbls
December 31, 2019, total working interest share of proved reserves	390,000
Less: barrels expected to be produced from December 31 to date of payout attributed to the carrying party ($80,000 ÷ $40 per barrel)	(2,000)
Expected proved reserves at date of payout	**388,000**
Reserves attributable to carrying party (Developco)	
Barrels to be produced until payout	2,000
Plus: one-half of reserves at payout (388,000 x 50%)	194,000
Expected total to carrying party	196,000
Reserves attributable to carried party (Rhubarb)	
Expected total to carried party	194,000

For 2019, Rhubarb has no revenue from production and records no DD&A for the year. Developco does not record leasehold costs; however, IDC and equipment amortization are computed as follows and recorded in 2019 (assume net ARO costs such as dismantling, removal and abandonment are zero):

		IDC	Equipment
[1,300 ÷ (1,300 + 196,000)] x $100,000	=	$659	
[1,300 ÷ (1,300 + 196,000)] x $ 32,000	=		$211

Once payout has been reached, each party reports its share of revenues, lifting costs and additional drilling and development costs. Continuing the preceding example, assume the following data for the year ended December 31, 2020, for Lease A57:

Production and sales (working interest share)	
January – November 2020	500 Bbls per month
December 2020	750 Bbls
Sales price per barrel for 2020	$50 per Bbl
Lifting costs	
January – November 2020	$5,000 per month
December 2020	$7,500
Additional well costs*	
IDC	$120,000
Tangible equipment	30,000
Reserves as of December 31, 2020**	
Proved developed	562,500 Bbls
Proved undeveloped	– Bbls

* Completed in November 2020.
** Represents 100% working interest.

Figures 22-2 through 22-5 illustrate ASC 932 computations of revenues, production expenses and amortization to be reported by each party in 2020:

Figure 22-2
ASC 932 computations – Revenues

Developco	Bbls	Price	
January 1 through April 30 (payout)	2,000	$50	$100,000
May 1 through November 30	1,750	$50	87,500
December	375	$50	18,750
Total – carrying party	**4,125**		**$206,250**
Rhubarb			
January 1 through April 30 (payout)	–	$ –	$ –
May 1 through November 30	1,750	$50	87,500
December	375	$50	18,750
Total – carried party	**2,125**		**$106,250**

Figure 22-3

ASC 932 computations – Production expenses

Developco

January 1 – April 30	$5,000 per month x 4 months	x	100% WI	=	$20,000
May 1 – November 30	$5,000 per month x 7 months	x	50% WI	=	17,500
December	$7,500	x	50% WI	=	3,750
Total – carrying party					**$41,250**

Rhubarb

January 1 – April 30	–		–		$ –
May 1 – November 30	5,000 per month x 7 months	x	50% WI	=	17,500
December	$7,500	x	50% WI	=	3,750
Total – carried party					**$21,250**

Figure 22-4

ASC 932 computations – Amortization of mineral interest cost

Developco				$ –
Rhubarb	$\dfrac{2{,}125 \text{ bbls}}{2{,}125 \text{ bbls} + (50\% \text{ WI} \times 562{,}500 \text{ bbls})}$	x	$20,000	= **$150**

Figure 22-5

ASC 932 computations – Amortization of IDC and equipment*

Developco (assuming an annual computation)			IDC	Equipment
$\dfrac{4{,}125 \text{ bbls}}{4{,}125 \text{ bbls} + (50\% \times 562{,}500 \text{ bbls})}$	x	[$100,000 – $659 + (50% x $120,000)]	$2,303	
$\dfrac{4{,}125 \text{ bbls}}{4{,}125 \text{ bbls} + (50\% \times 562{,}500 \text{ bbls})}$	x	[$32,000 – $211 + (50% x $30,000)]		$676
Rhubarb				
$\dfrac{2{,}125 \text{ bbls}}{2{,}125 \text{ bbls} + (50\% \times 562{,}500 \text{ bbls})}$	x	50% x $120,000	$450	
$\dfrac{2{,}125 \text{ bbls}}{2{,}125 \text{ bbls} + (50\% \times 562{,}500 \text{ bbls})}$	x	50% x $30,000		$112

* Assume net DR&A costs are zero.

The information ultimately reflected in the accounts of the two companies for 2020 is summarized in the following journal entries:

	Developco		Rhubarb	
Intangible costs of wells	60,000		60,000	
Tangible costs of wells	15,000		15,000	
Accounts payable		75,000		75,000
To record additional development costs on the A57 Lease.				
Accounts receivable – oil and gas sales	206,250		106,250	
Crude oil revenues		206,250		106,250
To record 2020 production revenues from Lease A57.				
Lease operating expenses	41,250		21,250	
Accounts payable		41,250		21,250
To record 2020 production expenses on Lease A57.				
DD&A expense – intangible costs of wells	2,303		450	
DD&A expense – tangible costs of wells	676		112	
Accumulated DD&A – intangible costs of wells		2,303		450
Accumulated DD&A – tangible costs of wells		676		112
To record 2020 amortization on wells and facilities on Lease A57				
DD&A expense – proved acquisition costs	–		150	
Accumulated DD&A – proved acquisition costs		–		150
To record 2020 depletion on Lease A57 acquisition costs.				

As noted previously, contract terms for carried interests can vary. For example, a nonconsent clause in a joint venture operating agreement may also give rise to a carried working interest. Rhubarb might propose drilling an additional well to fully exploit a reservoir. If Developco elects not to participate, it has gone nonconsent in the well.

Consequently, the terms of the operating agreement typically entitle Rhubarb to drill and produce the well, receive all working interest revenues and pay all operating costs until it recovers a specified multiple (i.e., 300 percent) of all costs of drilling and equipping the well. When the specified multiple is achieved, payout occurs. From this point forward, Developco participates in the well's revenues and costs based on its working interest as though it had never nonconsented.

For additional guidance, refer to COPAS Accounting Guideline No. 13 (AG-13), *Accounting for Farmouts/Farmins, Net Profits Interests, Carried Interests.*

Promoted versus promoting

In most joint ventures, the venturers share both revenues and costs in proportion to their ownership interests in the properties. For example, assume joint venture partners A and B each have a 50 percent working interest and a 45 percent net revenue interest in a venture (the lessor has a 10 percent net revenue interest in the form of a royalty interest). Since the parties share revenues and costs in the same proportions, this type of joint venture is sometimes referred to as a straight-up arrangement.

In some cases, revenues and costs are not shared in the same ratios. A joint venture agreement may call for joint venture partners X and Y to each receive 45 percent of the net revenue (the other 10 percent going to the royalty holder), but X pays 40 percent of the costs and Y pays 60 percent of the costs. In this situation, X is said to be the promoter or promoting party and Y the promoted party. Such an arrangement might occur if X originally owned 100 percent of the working interest in an attractive property and agreed to let Y have one-half of the working interest's 90 percent share of revenues in return for Y paying 60 percent of the costs.

Unitizations

Another important type of sharing arrangement is known as a unitization. In this case, all owners of operating and nonoperating interests pool their property interests in a producing area (normally a field) to form a single operating unit. In return, they receive participation factors, which are undivided interests in the total unit, which are either operating or non-operating based on the properties contributed.

Unitizations are intended to achieve the most efficient and economic exploitation of reserves in an area by allowing operators to maximize the amount of resources extracted from the unit. The arrangement can be voluntary or it may be required by federal or state regulatory bodies. Unitizations are common in fields with primary production and are even more widely utilized for reservoir-wide enhanced recovery operations (as discussed in Chapter 25).

Unitizations are also popular on offshore properties where costs are high and development of reserves may not be justified on an individual basis. Joint development of an area can make a unit more economically feasible as the parties can share in common facilities such as platforms and pipelines. Units involve more than one lease and have diverse ownerships of various mineral interests and reservoirs that cross lease boundaries.

Shares in the unit that participating owners receive (participation factors) are based on acreage, reserves or other criteria with respect to each lease to be placed in the unit.[1] Participation factors do not usually give weight to the stage of development of properties. Leases are often in different phases of development with some leases being fully drilled and equipped, others being partially developed and some completely undeveloped. Percentages are subject to revision within a specified subsequent period as additional information about the reserves becomes available. Accounting challenges resulting from subsequent adjustments are discussed later in this chapter.

Equalizations

Unit participants with undeveloped leases in the unit are normally required to pay cash to participants with fully or partially developed leases in order to equalize the capital contributions of wells and equipment.

For example, assume the 600 acre Autumn lease is 100 percent owned by Company A. It will be unitized with an adjoining 400 acre tract known as the Brown lease, which is owned 100 percent by Company B. Unit participation factors are based on acreage.

Thus, Company A receives a 60 percent participation factor and Company B is allotted a 40 percent participation factor for both unit revenues and unit costs. Company A pays the Autumn lease royalty based on A's share of revenues. Company B pays the Brown lease royalty based on B's share of revenues. Note that both Company A and Company B should evaluate the proper recognition of unit revenues on a gross versus net basis with respect to the royalty revenues, based on a determination of whether they are a principal or an agent in any production sales agreements in accordance with ASC 606.

Prior to unitization, Company A spent $700,000 on two wells and Company B spent $300,000 on one well. Terms of the unitization agreement require that $1,000,000 of prior well costs be reallocated so that the sharing of prior well costs equals the sharing of post-unitization revenues and costs. As a result, Company B pays $100,000 to Company A at the time of unitization so that Company A's adjusted well cost is $600,000 (60 percent of total well costs) and Company B's adjusted well cost is $400,000. Such adjustments are called equalizations.

Equalizing pre-unitization costs. In new fields where development is not completed, it is common for an equalization agreement to be based on expenditures for exploration and drilling that occurred prior to the date of unitization. Four steps are involved in the unitization process:

1. Identifying pre-unit contributions to be allowed in computing equalization.

2. Accumulating or collecting contributions from each pre-unit working interest owner.

3. Calculating the obligation of each working interest owner for pre-unit costs.

4. Determining the settlement for underspent and overspent amounts.

Generally, expenditures made for wells and facilities that directly benefit the unit are accepted for equalization; costs that relate to other wells and facilities that do not benefit the unit are not equalized. Costs to be equalized almost always include direct costs such as labor, employee benefits, taxes, construction charges, costs of special studies and other expenditures that can be specifically identified with individual wells and equipment. In addition, geological and geophysical costs, permits and environmental study costs may be considered direct charges.

Overhead that is not directly related to individual wells and facilities may also be equalized. These costs include such items as offsite labor, administrative charges and the costs of operating district or regional offices. Parties frequently limit overhead to a percentage of direct costs or a specified fixed annual fee. Actual time worked by personnel on the properties may also be equalized. In addition to direct costs and overhead, unitization agreements may permit an equalization of risk charges or imputed risk charges.

For example, insurance costs incurred in transporting equipment and facilities or the imputed costs of insurance to cover facilities prior to unitization may be considered for equalization. Finally, equalization agreements may provide for an inflation factor to reimburse parties for changes in purchasing power between the time of the original investment and ultimate recovery from other owners.

Cash equalization. The unitization process is a pooling of capital to achieve a common benefit for all parties. No gain or loss is typically recognized by any party to the unitization. A party making a cash equalization payment increases its recorded investment in wells and related equipment and facilities. Conversely, a participant who receives a cash equalization payment reduces the recorded investment in the wells and related equipment.

ASC 932-360-55-7 contains the following accounting guidelines for unitizations:

> In a unitization all the operating and nonoperating participants pool their assets in a producing area (normally a field) to form a single unit and in return receive an undivided interest (of the same type as previously held) in that unit. Unitizations generally are undertaken to obtain operating efficiencies and to enhance recovery of reserves, often through improved recovery operations. Participation in the unit is generally proportionate to the oil and gas reserves contributed by each. Because the properties may be in different stages of development at the time of unitization, some participants may pay cash and others may receive cash to equalize contributions of wells and related equipment and facilities with the ownership interests in reserves. In those circumstances, cash paid by a participant shall be recorded as an additional investment in wells and related equipment and facilities, and cash received by a participant shall be recorded as a recovery of costs. The cost of the assets contributed plus or minus cash paid or received is the cost of the participant's undivided interest in the assets of the unit. Each participant shall include its interest in reporting reserve estimates and production data (see paragraphs 932-235-50-4 through 50-11).

The following simplified example in Figure 22-6 on the next page demonstrates the accounting treatment required by ASC 932-360-55-7 at the time of unit formation.

Assume three E&P companies are involved in a unitization of their respective properties, all of which have been developed. Based on several factors, each company is allocated a one-third interest in the unit. In order to give each company credit for IDC and tangible equipment, cash equalization calculations are made.

In the example illustrated in Figure 22-6, assume the following facts:

- Column (2) shows the unamortized balances of well costs on each company's books.

- Column (3) represents the agreed-upon values of the well costs contributed by each company based on current costs to drill the wells contributed by each company.

- Column (4) reflects the share of the agreed-upon values of well costs belonging to each company after the unitization.

- Column (5) shows how cash is contributed or received to equalize the value of well costs received and contributed by each company.

Note that for newly developed fields, the agreed-upon value is usually considered to be equal to allowable costs incurred by each company for exploration and development prior to the unitization.

Figure 22-6

Cash equalization calculations

		Equalization for IDC		
(1)	(2)	(3)	(4)	(5)
Company	Unamortized balance	Value contributed	Value received	Cash equalization
A	$300,000	$ 550,000	$ 400,000	$ 150,000
B	260,000	375,000	400,000	(25,000)
C	320,000	275,000	400,000	(125,000)
Total		$1,200,000	$1,200,000	$ –

		Equalization for equipment		
(1)	(2)	(3)	(4)	(5)
Company	Unamortized balance	Value contributed	Value received	Cash equalization
A	$20,000	$ 50,000	$ 60,000	$ (10,000)
B	70,000	65,000	60,000	5,000
C	65,000	65,000	60,000	5,000
Total		$180,000	$180,000	$ –

Company A receives $150,000 in cash as equalization for IDC. Under ASC 932-360-55-7, the cash received is treated as a reduction of investment as follows:

Cash	150,000	
Intangible costs of wells		150,000
To record receipt of cash on IDC equalization.		

Since the unamortized balance of Company A's IDC contribution is greater than the amount of cash received, the equalization payment merely reduces its investment. Both Company B and Company C must make cash payments to equalize Company A for the IDC. Under ASC 932-360-55-7, these payments will be capitalized by Company B and Company C as additional investment in IDC. Both Company B and Company C receive cash in equalization of equipment contributions. In each case, the amount of cash received is less than the value of equipment contributed; therefore, the full amount received is credited to a tangible costs of wells account.

Equalization in excess of costs. Due to the process in which valuations are made and current pricing is taken into account, it may be possible to receive equalization credit in excess of cost. After equalization, the carrying value of a well may be negative for book purposes, but individual asset carrying values within a proven property asset pool are generally not important for purposes of determining DD&A under either successful efforts or full cost accounting methods.

Mineral rights equalization. Monetary entries are not necessary to record the exchanges of mineral rights in property transferred to the unit for a share of minerals in return. Parties treat the book value of their contributed property as their investment in the mineral interest in the unit. Most unitization agreements, especially when some of the properties have not been fully developed, call for one or more subsequent evaluations and readjustment of participation factors. This topic is discussed later in this chapter.

Disproportionate spending equalization. Certain parties may strive to avoid cash equalization. In this case, equalization occurs by adjusting the amount of future expenditures to be paid by each party to compensate for disproportionate contributions. This technique is especially common in new fields where there has been little drilling activity up to the time of unitization.

To illustrate a cost-equalization program involving disproportionate spending, Figure 22-7 shows the working interest ownership of each party, pre-unitization costs, costs to be paid by each party, and over/under-spend positions of each:

Figure 22-7

Disproportionate spending equalization

Company	WI % ownership	Pre-unitization costs incurred	Proportionate share	Over (under) spend
Acorn	15	$ 200,000	$ 225,000	$ (25,000)
Bayou	35	300,000	525,000	(225,000)
Canary	50	1,000,000	750,000	250,000
Total		**$1,500,000**	**$1,500,000**	**$ −**

Since actual expenditures incurred by Canary prior to unitization exceed its proportionate share of the $1,500,000 in total costs, Canary pays no part of costs after unitization until the other companies have overspent their shares by the same amount. Subsequent over-spending by the two under-spent parties is shared in the ratio of the proportionate interest of the shortfall.

Accordingly, in the example above, Bayou will absorb 90 percent ($225,000 ÷ $250,000), and Acorn will absorb 10 percent ($25,000 ÷ $250,000), of the first $250,000 of future expenditures to bring the parties back in balance to their proportionate working interests. A reasonable interpretation of the provisions of ASC 932-360-55-7 relating to sharing arrangements suggests that each party should account for its actual expenditures.

Equalization resulting from redetermination of interests. As previously noted, unitization agreements often contain provisions requiring the ownership to be redetermined and adjusted at dates subsequent to the date of unitization. These adjustments are based on revised estimates of recoverable reserves that result from improved technical knowledge of the reservoir as the field is developed and oil and gas are produced.

Between the dates of the unitization and subsequent readjustment, production revenues as well as operating expenses and development costs are allocated on the basis of the percentages of ownership interest in effect.

When a redetermination is made, it may be retroactively applied to the date the unit was formed. In other cases, the effective date occurs later such as when a discovery changes the size and extent of the proved portion(s) of reserves. As a result, an equalization computation is made at the date of redetermination to equalize production proceeds and costs incurred during the period. It is customary for equalization of production revenues to be handled through under-takes and over-takes of subsequent production rather than through cash settlements. Equalization of post-unitization costs incurred is handled through disproportionate spending equalization as previously described.

For example, assume a unitization agreement becomes effective January 1, 2019, at which time equalization for prior expenditures is made through a cash settlement. The initial agreed-upon ownerships are 30 percent to Company X, 50 percent to Company Y and 20 percent to Company Z. The agreement calls for a redetermination of ownership interests on January 1, 2022, based on revised estimates of oil and gas reserves contributed to the unit by the parties. During the three-year period prior to redetermination, production totalled 10 million barrels at an average price of $50 per barrel. Development expenditures of $30 million for drilling costs and $10 million for equipment and facilities were incurred. Operating expenses were $10 million. All revenues and costs were shared in the original agreed-upon ratio of 30 percent, 50 percent and 20 percent.

On January 1, 2022, a redetermination is made and working interests are readjusted as follows: X receives 27 percent; Y receives 55 percent; Z receives 18 percent. Equalization for the over/under-take of production prior to the redetermination is accomplished by offsetting over/under-takes of production over the two-year period following redetermination per the terms of the agreement. Equalization of over-expenditures and under-expenditures for development costs and operating expenses is accomplished through an adjustment of costs incurred after the redetermination of interests.

As illustrated in Figure 22-8 below, during each month of the two-year period following redetermination, Company Y will receive 20,833 barrels in excess of its normal share of production, and production volumes of Company X and Company Z will be reduced by 12,500 barrels and 8,333 barrels per month, respectively, in order to correct the allocation of prior production.

Figure 22-8

Redetermination of interest equalization

Company	Initial allocation of production	Redetermined allocation of production	Over (under) produced	Monthly equalization over 24 months
		(in bbls)		
X	3,000,000	2,700,000	300,000	(12,500)
Y	5,000,000	5,500,000	(500,000)	20,833
Z	2,000,000	1,800,000	200,000	(8,333)

Assuming that production in the first month following redetermination is 300,000 barrels, it would be allocated as shown in Figure 22-9:

Figure 22-9
Equalization adjustment of production at January 31, 2022

Company	WI %	Normal allocation of production	Equalization adjustment	Total share of production
		(in bbls)		
X	27	81,000	(12,500)	68,500
Y	55	165,000	20,833	185,833
Z	18	54,000	(8,333)	45,667
Total	**100%**	**300,000**	–	**300,000**

Figures 22-8 and 22-9 illustrate equalization of production quantities but not revenues. Equalization of development costs and operating expenses are accomplished through disproportionate spending equalization in the manner illustrated previously. It is appropriate for each owner to report revenues in accordance with ASC 606 and for each party to account in the customary way for all costs incurred. Reserves disclosures should reflect readjusted amounts, and future depreciation, depletion and amortization calculations should be based on the revised estimates.

Unitization on federal lands

Unitizations on federal lands have unusual features that complicate the related accounting treatment. Federal unitization is a two-step process. First, lessees of federal mineral rights in a large prospective area of perhaps several thousand acres (the unit area) sign an exploratory unit agreement and a unit operating agreement to "adequately and timely explore and develop all committed lands within the unit area without regard to the internal ownership boundaries."[2] Second, as proved areas within the unit become known, leaseholders within the areas (called a participating area or PA) are required to form a joint venture to develop and operate the participating area and share in revenues and costs.

The PA expands as new wells extend the proved area, or it may contract as dry holes and uneconomic wells are drilled and define the productive area. Two or more PAs may combine into one large PA as new wells demonstrate the continuity of the underlying reservoir. A large unit area may have more than one PA when the unit area is ultimately developed.

Often, a PA interest is determined by relative acreage of the lease areas within the PA. A company's 100 percent working interest in a 320-acre lease with one well may become a 50 percent working interest in a two-well or three-well 640-acre PA. As the PA expands to 3,200 acres and 15 wells, the company's PA interest may fall to 10 percent. In this case, the company pays 10 percent of all 15 wells' costs and receives 10 percent of the PA revenues after royalties, assuming uniform royalty rates. Any PA formation, expansion or contraction must be approved by the U.S. Department of the Interior and is generally effective with, and retroactive to, the completion date of the well that justified the PA change. As a result, a company's working interest in a PA will vary as the PA expands or contracts.

Figure 22-10
Illustrative post-unitization redetermination

The Prudhoe Bay Unit

The Prudhoe Bay field (the Field) is located on the North Slope of Alaska, 250 miles north of the Arctic Circle and 650 miles north of Anchorage. The Field extends approximately 12 miles by 27 miles and contains nearly 150,000 gross productive acres. The Field, which was discovered in 1968 by BP and others, has been in production since 1977. The Field is the largest producing oil field in North America. As of December 31, 2019, approximately 12.6 billion barrels of oil and condensate had been produced from the Field.

Since several oil companies besides BP Alaska hold acreage within the Field, as well as several contiguous oil fields, the Prudhoe Bay Unit was established to optimize field development. The Prudhoe Bay Unit Operating Agreement specifies the allocation of production and costs to the working interest owners. It also defines operator responsibilities and voting requirements and is unusual in its establishment of separate participating areas for the gas cap and oil rim. Since July 1, 2000, BP Alaska has been the sole operator of the Prudhoe Bay Unit.

The ownership of the Prudhoe Bay Unit by participating area as of December 31, 2018 is shown below:

	Oil rim	Gas cap
BP Alaska	26.36%(a)	26.36%(b)
ExxonMobil	36.40	36.40
ConocoPhillips	36.08	36.08
Chevron	1.16	1.16
Total	**100.00%**	**100.00%**

a. The Trust's share of oil production and condensate is computed based on BP Alaska's ownership interest in the oil rim participating area of 50.68% as of February 28, 1989. Subsequent decreases in BP Alaska's participation in oil rim ownership do not affect calculation of Royalty Production from the 1989 Working Interests and have not decreased the Trust's Royalty Interest.

b. The Trust's share of condensate production is computed based on BP Alaska's ownership interest in the gas cap participating area of 13.84% as of February 28, 1989. Subsequent increases in BP Alaska's gas cap ownership do not affect calculation of Royalty Production from the 1989 Working Interests and have not increased the Trust's Royalty Interest. Under the terms of an Issues Resolution Agreement entered into by the Prudhoe Bay Unit owners in October 1990, produced condensate (defined as the Original Condensate Reserve in the agreement) from the gas cap participating area was allocated to that participating area until a cumulative limit of 1,175 million barrels was reached. This cumulative limit was reached in June 2014, and beginning at that time and continuing thereafter, the condensate is allocated to the oil rim participating area.

A company can elect to go nonconsent and not participate in future wells within the PA or the unit, subject to a nonconsent penalty.[3] However, accounting for nonconsent interests is difficult and has been the subject of litigation due to internally inconsistent language in at least three versions of a standard unit operating agreement form used from 1954 through the early 1990s. Further discussion of this issue is beyond the scope of this book but it is indicative of the complexity of accounting for PA interests.

An example of post-unitization redetermination is described in the excerpt in Figure 22-10 from the forepart of the 2019 Form 10-K of BP Prudhoe Bay Royalty Trust. The trust has a net profits interest akin to a 16.4246 percent ORRI (royalty interest) in BP's first 90,000 barrels per day of production from the Prudhoe Bay Unit.[4]

Creation of joint ventures

Prior chapters have noted that E&P joint ventures are common in the U.S. Chapter 10 addresses joint venture operations, billing for joint venture costs and day-to-day accounting for joint interests. ASC 932-360-55-6 describes joint ventures and indicates how the formation of a joint venture is to be accounted for:

> A part of an operating interest owned may be exchanged for part of an operating interest owned by another party. The purpose of such an arrangement, commonly called a joint venture in the oil and gas industry, often is to avoid duplication of facilities, diversify risks, and achieve operating efficiencies. No gain or loss shall be recognized by either party at the time of transaction. In some joint ventures, which may or may not involve an exchange of interests, the parties may share different elements of costs in different proportions. In such an arrangement, a party may acquire an interest in a property or in wells and related equipment that is disproportionate to the share of costs borne by it. As in the case of a carried interest or a free well, each party shall account for its own cost under the provisions of this Subtopic. No gain shall be recognized for the acquisition of an interest in joint assets, the cost of which may have been paid in whole or in part by another party.

Two major points from ASC 932-360-55-6 are illustrated in the following example.

Assume two operators own contiguous unproved properties. For the sake of efficiency, they form a joint venture, with PermianWestCo owning a two-thirds interest and South Company (South) owning a one-third interest. The two parties decide to cross-assign interests: PermianWestCo assigns to South a one-third undivided interest in a property (which had a book value of $120,000 and was being impaired individually), and South assigns a two-thirds interest in each of three leases (which had a cost of $260,000 and are part of a group subject to impairment on a group basis).

Neither party recognizes a gain or loss on the exchange. PermianWestCo removes one-third of the cost of the lease in which it gives up an interest and one-third of the allowance for impairment of that lease. The net book value ($40,000) of the one-third interest is assigned to the two-thirds interest in the three leases acquired from South. A $40,000 allocation is made to individual leases (in which interests were acquired) based on the relative fair values of the interests. Similar entries are recorded by South.

The second point involves disproportionate sharing arrangements. In a different scenario, PermianWestCo, a successful efforts company, owns a lease which cost $30,000 and for which no impairment has been recorded. It retains one-fourth of the working interest and assigns three equal interests equivalent to three-fourths of the working interest to other parties, which will bear the entire cost of drilling the first well.

If the first well is to be completed, all parties, including PermianWestCo, are to pay for a proportionate share of completing the well. This type of arrangement is a "third for a quarter" deal that was common years ago when oil prices escalated rapidly. The drilling cost on this well amounts to $600,000, which will be paid in equal shares by the other three parties.

PermianWestCo retains $30,000 as its leasehold cost but has no IDC and would record its share of tangible equipment costs when the costs are incurred. Each assignee accounts for the $200,000 contributed to the venture as IDC, and each would properly account for its share of equipment costs subsequently incurred. The assignees do not treat any part of their contributions as leasehold costs.

● ● ●

---

1 A participant's fractional interest (or participation factor) may be based on any number of reasonable factors – acreage, estimated reservoir thickness under a given acreage, estimated reserves under a given acreage, number of producing wells on the acreage and even prior production history for the acreage.

2 See the Unitization section of the U.S. Department of the Interior Bureau of Land Management's Handbook for further discussion of this topic.

3 The concept of nonconsent and nonconsent penalty is addressed briefly in Chapter 10.

4 The trust's share in revenue is reduced for certain chargeable costs of several dollars per barrel.

Accounting for Partnership Interests

Photograph by istock.com/kodda

A partnership is a business entity comprising two or more parties that share in profits and losses. Partnerships are legal organizations that differ from contractual joint operations discussed in Chapter 10. E&P companies often form partnerships for tax purposes. Regardless of whether they are sole proprietors or corporations, operators may buy into these entities which usually are formed as general or limited partnerships.

Accounting challenges are similar across the structures, as accountants prepare financial statements, file tax returns and supply tax information to the partners for their own returns. Special allocations to the partners of revenues, expenses and costs can lead to accounting complexities.

Many limited partnerships use the income tax basis of reporting to partners because the limited partners are individually responsible for paying taxes on their partnership income. Partnerships also may fall under SEC jurisdiction. Discussion of the legal requirements for exemption from SEC registration is outside the scope of this book.

Overview of partnerships

In a general partnership (GP), each partner has the right to participate in management and is subject to unlimited personal liability. When an E&P company invests in a general partnership, it enters into a joint operation, usually with one or more other E&P companies. For tax or other reasons, the partners do not follow the more common approach to joint operations, which is to operate as undivided interest holders.

In a limited partnership, one or more general partners has unlimited personal liability, and one or more limited partners has limited liability without the right to participate in management. Limited partnerships typically are formed to finance business activities, and almost all of them designate a single operator as the sponsor and managing partner, with individual investors as limited partners.

The managing partner maintains business records, files tax returns and provides both financial accounting and tax information to the other partners. The managing partner also determines the fiscal year, method of accounting (cash vs. accrual) and whether to use full cost or successful efforts. However, to the extent the partnership is consolidated, it must apply the same accounting policies as the parent upon consolidation, including the method used to account for oil and gas properties.

In a master limited partnership, the partnership's income (or loss) is passed through to the investors. Chapter 29 discusses master limited partnerships.

Organizing the partnership

ASC 720-15, *Start-up Costs,* guides accountants to expense the costs of organizing partnerships. These costs include legal services (e.g., attorney fees for drafting and filing articles of partnership, filing fees and other state charges) and the work of promoters and organizers.

Limited partnerships typically pay syndication fees, which are essentially broker commissions for selling limited partnership interests. These commissions customarily are paid from the proceeds of the limited partners' contributions; they range from five percent to 10 percent of the subscription price of the limited partnership interests.

Syndication fees also include the cost of a prospectus or private placement memorandum, unless paid by the general partner. These upfront costs are treated as offsets against the partners' capital accounts in the same way that corporations treat the costs of issuing capital stock.

In limited partnerships, the managing partner (or its affiliate) generally is reimbursed by the other partners for costs incurred and also charges them a fee for management services. The partnership records acquisition, exploration and development costs based on the chosen accounting method, while management fees and production costs are charged to current expense. Management fees may be paid to the managing partner in advance by a partnership. These prepaid costs are deferred to asset accounts and expensed as the general partner performs the related services.

Limited partnership interests are sold in units. A limited partner either pays for an interest upfront or makes capital commitments throughout the enterprise's life. In the latter case, the managing partner can call for capital contributions up to the total capital commitment amount, which usually requires large sums in the first year or two to fund acquisition, exploration and development activities.

Accounting complexities

Both general and limited partnership investments present two major challenges: (1) accounting and reporting for the partnership investment and (2) accounting for transactions between the partners and the partnership, each of which is described in further detail below.

Accounting and reporting considerations

Whenever a reporting entity has a financial relationship with a legal entity, it should evaluate whether the entity should be consolidated or accounted for under the equity method. In accounting for an investment by a partner for its partnership interest, one of four methods is appropriate, depending on the facts and circumstances of the partnership arrangement:

- Consolidation, under ASC 810, *Consolidation.*

- Equity method, under ASC 323, *Investments – Equity Method and Joint Ventures.*

- Proportionate consolidation.

- Fair value under ASC 321, *Investments – Equity Securities.*

Consolidation

If a reporting entity has a controlling financial interest in another entity, it should consolidate that entity. In the context of consolidation, a reporting entity must have a variable interest in the other entity to assess whether consolidation is required.

A partnership investment generally is considered a variable interest because it typically represents a financial relationship that exposes the investor to the risks and/or rewards of (variability in) the partnership's assets and operations.

Variable interest entities. The first step to determine the accounting for a partnership interest is to assess whether the partnership is a variable interest entity (VIE). An entity is a VIE if it meets any one of the following characteristics in ASC 810-10-15-14:

- **The entity is thinly capitalized.** The total equity investment at risk is not sufficient to finance the entity's expected activities without additional subordinated financial support. ASC 810-10-15-14(a) notes that at-risk equity has all of the following characteristics:

    1. Participates significantly in profits and losses, regardless of voting ability.

    2. Excludes equity interests issued in exchange for subordinated interests in other VIEs (i.e., the equity investment cannot be used to capitalize two entities at the same time).

    3. Excludes amounts provided to the equity investor directly or indirectly by the legal entity or by other parties involved with the legal entity, unless the provider is a parent, subsidiary or affiliate of the investor in a consolidated group.

    4. Excludes amounts financed for the equity investor (e.g., loans or guarantees) directly by the legal entity or other parties involved with the legal entity, unless the financing party is a parent, subsidiary or affiliate of the investor within a consolidated group.

    ASC 810-10-25-45 states that if the equity investment at risk is less than 10 percent of the entity's total assets, it is not considered sufficient to permit the entity to finance its activities without additional subordinated financial support unless the equity investment can be demonstrated to be sufficient. This rebuttable presumption does not mean that at-risk equity of more than 10 percent is automatically deemed to be sufficient. No matter the amount of at-risk equity, both qualitative and quantitative factors should be considered to determine whether the amount of equity investment at risk is sufficient.

    ASC 810-10-20 defines subordinated financial support as variable interests that will absorb some or all of a VIE's expected losses. Examples include: certain subordinated or other noninvestment-grade debt, funding commitments, preferred interests and other investments that do not qualify as at-risk equity.

    Many partnerships are capitalized through stepped funding arrangements (equity or debt infusions) that occur over time, rather than at the entity's formation. As a result, a thinly capitalized partnership at inception may not have sufficient at-risk equity and, therefore, would be considered a VIE under ASC 810-10-15-14.

- **Equity holders as a group lack decision-making rights**. If the at-risk equity investors as a group lack the power to direct the activities that have the most significant impact on the entity's economic performance, it can be inferred that a party other than the equity investor(s) most likely controls the entity. The application of this characteristic to entities other than limited partnerships centers on whether the holders of equity at risk, as a group, have rights (through their equity interests) to direct the activities of the entity that most significantly impact its economic performance.

Determining which activities most significantly impact the entity's economic performance requires judgment. When an entity's operations are straightforward or one-dimensional, determining whether or not the holders of the equity investment at risk meet this criterion may not require significant judgment.

In some circumstances, a holder of equity at risk may have the ability to make decisions through another variable interest (i.e., a decision-making arrangement, such as a management contract) as opposed to an at-risk equity investment. If these decisions are made through another variable interest as opposed to the decision-maker's at-risk equity investment, then depending on the facts those rights may not be attributed to the group of at-risk equity investors for purposes of assessing whether this characteristic is present. Consequently, the entity may be considered a VIE.

Because of their unique purpose and design as compared to corporations and general partnerships, limited partnerships must follow specific rules in evaluating this criterion. ASC 810-10-15-14(b)(1)(ii) states that, in a limited partnership, if the limited partners do not hold substantive kick-out rights that can be exercised through a simple majority vote (or less than majority), or they do not have substantive participating rights, the equity holders as a group would not have the power to direct the significant activities of the entity that impact economic performance, and the entity would be a VIE.

A kick-out right is the ability of the limited partners to remove (or kick out) the general partner. The mere existence of kick-out rights does not necessarily demonstrate that the limited partnership (or similar entity) is a VIE. Instead, the kick-out rights must be substantive in order to demonstrate that the group of at-risk equity investors (i.e., the limited partners) has power. Kick-out rights are considered substantive only when they can be exercised by a simple majority vote of the entity's limited partners (excluding the general partner, parties under common control with the general partner and others acting on behalf of the general partner), or a lower exercise threshold (as low as a single limited partner), based on the limited partners' relative voting rights. Limited partners' voting rights often are determined by their relative capital account balance.

Unlike a kick-out right, a participating right does not convey power, since it does not allow the holder to initiate the action or decision, but rather it prevents another party from exercising power over a decision or significant activity of the potential VIE. Participating rights are not substantive unless the limited partners can block at least one major operating or financial decision made in the ordinary course of business.

- **Equity holders as a group are not obligated to absorb economic losses**. The entity qualifies as a VIE if the equity holders as a group are directly or indirectly protected from expected losses or are guaranteed a return by the entity itself or by other parties involved with the entity. This characteristic may be present if a potential VIE is designed such that its equity interests do not fully absorb the entity's expected losses on a first-dollar loss basis. If other variable interests begin sharing in the entity's expected losses before the equity investment at risk is fully depleted, and that sharing arrangement is part of the entity's design, then the entity may be a VIE. An entity may also be a VIE under this characteristic if it issued equity with puttable characteristics that are embedded in the terms of the interest.

- **Equity holders as a group do not receive expected residual returns**. The entity qualifies as a VIE if the expected residual returns to the equity holders as a group are capped by the legal entity's governing documents or arrangements with other variable interest holders, or by the legal entity itself. This characteristic may be present if a potential VIE is designed to issue equity interests that do not provide the holder with the ability to receive an entity's expected residual returns. If an entity was designed to issue equity interests that do not allow the holder to participate in the entity's expected residual returns (i.e., the equity interests have embedded fixed-price callable features), the entity may be a VIE.

- **Equity holders as a group possess nonsubstantive voting rights**. This characteristic identifies entities that confer nonsubstantive voting rights to another party to prevent consolidation under the voting interest model. In essence, this provision is meant to nullify potential abuses of the voting interest model which seek to avoid consolidation in cases where the investors' voting rights are not useful in identifying the party with a controlling financial interest in the entity being evaluated for consolidation. The voting interest model is discussed in a subsequent section within this chapter.

An entity is considered a VIE under this characteristic if both of the following criteria are met:

- Some investors' voting rights are disproportionate to their economic interests (i.e., obligations to absorb the entity's expected losses and rights as compared to expected residual returns).

- Substantially all of the entity's activities either involve, or are conducted on behalf of, the investor(s) with disproportionately fewer voting rights.

Under the first criterion, each equity investor must be evaluated individually to determine whether its obligation to absorb the entity's expected losses and/or receive the entity's expected residual returns are proportional to that investor's voting rights. To be proportional, the investor's voting rights and economics are not required to be identical, but they should generally be similar.

When an investor's economic and voting interests straddle 50 percent (i.e., 48 percent voting rights and 52 percent economics), its voting and economic interests typically are not considered proportional. Generally, an investor's ability to exercise voting rights over an entity changes dramatically when its voting interest crosses the 50 percent threshold. Partnerships frequently meet this criterion because the equity investors typically have other variable interests in the entity that create economics which are disproportionate to their voting rights. Judgment should be applied based on the facts and circumstances.

Under the second criterion, essentially all of an entity's activities must involve or be conducted on behalf of the investor (and its related parties) with disproportionately fewer voting rights. This assessment should be primarily qualitative.

Facts. Oil Co. holds a 65 percent equity interest in Shale Co., and Water Co. holds the remaining 35 percent. Oil Co. and Water Co. share in Shale Co.'s profits and losses in proportion to their relative equity investments. Shale Co.'s governing documents include specific provisions providing Water Co. with approval rights over the substantive operating decisions of Shale Co. (i.e., joint control with a 50 percent vote in key operating decisions). In addition, Shale Co. sells substantially all of its production to Oil Co. under long-term contracts.

Question. Is this characteristic met?

Analysis. Yes. Given that Oil Co. has a 50 percent vote in key operating decisions of Shale Co., in relation to its 65 percent economic interest, the first criterion of this characteristic is met. If Oil Co.'s voting rights equaled its 65 percent economic interest, its right to govern Shale Co. would differ substantively.

Shale Co. also meets the second criterion of this characteristic because substantially all of its activities either involve, or are conducted on behalf of, Oil Co., which has disproportionately fewer voting rights.

Therefore, both criteria of this characteristic are present and Shale Co. would be considered a VIE.

Primary beneficiary considerations. Once a reporting entity determines that it has a variable interest in a VIE, the second step is to determine the primary beneficiary: that is, the reporting entity that holds the VIE's controlling financial interest and, thus, is required to consolidate it.

A reporting entity is considered the VIE's primary beneficiary if it meets both criteria below:

- It has the power to direct activities that most significantly impact the VIE's economic performance.

- It has the obligation to absorb losses from the VIE or the right to receive benefits of the VIE that potentially could be significant to the VIE.

Only one reporting entity, if any, should be identified as a VIE's primary beneficiary. Although more than one reporting entity could meet the losses/benefits criterion, only one reporting entity, if any, will have the power to direct the VIE activities that most significantly impact the VIE's economic performance.

If the power to direct a VIE's most significant activities is shared, the partners in the partnership should consider whether or not they are related parties, which include de facto agents as defined in ASC 810-10-25-43. If the parties are deemed to be related, a qualitative analysis is required to determine which party within the related party group is most closely associated with the VIE. The party within the related party group that is most closely associated with the VIE is the primary beneficiary and is required to consolidate and disclose the impact of the VIE.

In certain situations, the power to direct a VIE's most significant activities may be shared among unrelated parties. In those situations, no party is considered the VIE's primary beneficiary.

Judgment may be required to determine whether the losses/benefits of a VIE that are absorbed/received by a reporting entity are potentially significant to the VIE. When the variable interest(s) being evaluated potentially expose the holder to benefits and losses between five percent and 10 percent, this could potentially be significant depending on facts and circumstances.

As noted previously, for a limited partnership to be considered a VIE, the limited partners must lack either substantive kick-out rights or participating rights. Furthermore, in a limited partnership, the general partner usually is designated to manage the partnership's operations. Because it usually meets both the power criterion and the losses/benefits criterion, the general partner typically is considered the primary beneficiary of a limited partnership, and thus it consolidates the VIE. However, all individual facts and circumstances should be considered.

Voting interest entities. The voting interest entity model applies to all entities that are not VIEs. That is, the voting interest model applies after an investor considers whether it has a variable interest in a VIE and determines that the investee is not a VIE. The voting interest entity model requires the reporting entity to consolidate any entity in which it has a controlling financial interest.

A controlling financial interest generally means that the reporting entity has the unilateral right to make the significant financial and operating decisions for an entity without regard to probability. For corporations and general partnerships, the usual condition for a controlling financial interest is owning more than 50 percent of the outstanding voting shares. ASC 810-10-15-10(a) requires consolidation of all majority-owned subsidiaries (i.e., all companies in which a parent has a controlling financial interest through direct or indirect ownership of a majority voting interest) unless control does not rest with the majority owner.

A limited partnership can only be a voting interest entity if the limited partners have kick-out rights (including liquidation rights) and/or substantive participating rights. If the limited partners do not have these rights, the limited partnership is a VIE. Therefore, under the voting interest model for limited partnerships, only a limited partner can consolidate a limited partnership. Said differently, if a general partner consolidates a limited partnership, the limited partnership is a VIE.

ASC 810-10-15-8A notes special considerations under the voting interest model for limited partnerships as follows:

> Given the purpose and design of limited partnerships, kick-out rights through voting interests are analogous to voting rights held by shareholders of a corporation. For limited partnerships, the usual condition for a controlling financial interest, as a general rule, is ownership by one limited partner, directly or indirectly, of more than 50 percent of the limited partnership's kick-out rights through voting interests. The power to control also may exist with a lesser percentage of ownership, for example, by contract, lease, agreement with partners, or by court decree.

For purposes of assessing a controlling financial interest in a limited partnership under the voting interest model, one must evaluate whether kick-out rights (including liquidation rights) are held by limited partners, since these rights may be the equivalent of voting interests held by shareholders of a corporation.

Therefore, a limited partner with a majority of kick-out rights through voting interests would usually control and consolidate the limited partnership. If none of the individual limited partners are able to exercise the kick-out right unilaterally, no partner would have a controlling financial interest in the limited partnership.

The guidance states that kick-out rights are exercised "through voting interests," which refers to the voting interest that a limited partner has in the kick-out right. The voting interest that a limited partner has in the kick-out right is generally equal to its economic interest in the limited partnership.

For example, assume a limited partnership has a general partner with a 20 percent ownership interest and four limited partners each having a 20 percent ownership interest. The four limited partners each have an equal vote in the kick-out right based on their ownership interest; thus, each limited partner would have a 20 percent voting interest in deciding whether to exercise the kick-out right to remove the general partner. The general partner does not have a voting interest in the kick-out right.

In this example, a simple majority of the voting interests in the kick-out right held by the limited partners would be 41 percent of the voting interests in the kick-out right, calculated as 51 percent of the 80 percent voting interest held by the limited partners.

Noncontrolling shareholder rights. ASC 810-10-25-2 through 25-14 addresses the issue of whether consolidation is appropriate when one shareholder or partner has a majority voting interest in another entity, but the majority shareholder's or partner's power to control the investee's operations or assets is restricted, in certain respects, by approval or veto rights granted to the noncontrolling interest holder(s). A similar concept applies to limited partnerships.

Some partnership agreements may allow limited partners to participate in decisions that could have a significant impact on the partnership's business (i.e., significant financial and operating decisions), thereby limiting the rights of the general partner or a limited partner with majority kick-out rights through voting interests. If limited partners are able to exercise substantive participating rights over the general partner based on their voting interests, the limited partnership would not be considered a VIE based on the guidance in ASC 810.

Assuming none of the other VIE criteria are met, the limited partnership would be considered a voting interest entity. Under the voting interest model, similar to noncontrolling shareholder participating rights in corporations, if limited partners have substantive participating rights, neither the general partner nor the limited partner with a majority of kick-out rights through voting interests would control the limited partnership.

The assessment of whether noncontrolling shareholder rights should preclude a majority shareholder from consolidating is a matter of judgment that depends on facts and circumstances. The framework under which such facts and circumstances are judged should be based on whether the noncontrolling shareholder rights, individually or in the aggregate, provide for the noncontrolling shareholder to effectively participate in significant decisions that would be expected in the "ordinary course of business." A limited partner's veto right to block actions that are not made in the ordinary course of business are protective rights which do not preclude consolidation by a limited partner with majority kick-out rights through voting interests. ASC 810-10-25-11 addresses substantive participating rights as follows:

> Noncontrolling rights (whether granted by contract or by law) that would allow the noncontrolling shareholder or limited partner to effectively participate in either of the following corporate or partnership actions shall be considered substantive participating rights and would overcome the presumption that the investor with a majority voting interest or limited partner with a majority of kick-out rights through voting interests shall consolidate its investee. The following list is illustrative of substantive participating rights, but is not necessarily all-inclusive:
>
> a. Selecting, terminating, and setting the compensation of management responsible for implementing the investee's policies and procedures
>
> b. Establishing operating and capital decisions of the investee, including budgets, in the ordinary course of business.

This assessment should be made at the time a majority voting interest is obtained and should be reassessed if there is a significant modification to the terms of the rights of the noncontrolling shareholder.

Equity method

Once an investor has determined that it does not have a controlling financial interest in an investee, it should determine if the equity method of accounting applies. Many investments in oil and gas partnerships are subject to the equity method of accounting. ASC 323, *Investments – Equity Method and Joint Ventures*, requires use of the equity method when an investor can exert significant influence over the investee's operating and financial plans.

The presumed levels of ownership that enable an investor to exercise significant influence over the operating and financial policies of the investee vary depending on the nature of the investee (e.g., a corporation versus a partnership). Absent contrary evidence, an investor has the ability to exercise significant influence when it owns (directly or indirectly) 20 percent or more of the investee's outstanding voting securities. This includes investments in common stock, in-substance common stock and limited liability companies (LLCs) that have characteristics of a corporation.

Investments in limited partnerships and similar entities (e.g., an LLC that maintains a specific ownership account for each investor) should generally be accounted for under the equity method of accounting unless the investment is so minor that the limited partner may have virtually no influence over the partnership's operating and financial policies. In practice, limited partnership investments of more than three to five percent are viewed as more than minor. This threshold is different than the level applied for an investment in a corporation as discussed above.

The determination of whether an investor has the ability to exercise significant influence over the operating and financial policies of an investee is not limited to the evaluation of voting interests and the level of ownership interest it holds. An investor must consider all relationships and interests (voting and nonvoting) in an investee, including any means through which an investor might influence the operating and financial policies of an investee, such as board representation, veto rights, or voting rights conveyed by a security other than voting common stock. An investor should also consider the capitalization structure of the investee, how significant its investment is to the investee's capitalization, and the rights and preferences of other investors.

An investment of less than the thresholds noted previously leads to the presumption that an investor does not have the ability to exercise significant influence over the operating and financial results of the investee, unless such ability can be demonstrated. ASC 323-10-15-6 provides a list of indicators that an investor should consider when evaluating whether or not it has the ability to exercise significant influence over the operating and financial policies of an investee.

> Ability to exercise significant influence over operating and financial policies of an investee may be indicated in several ways, including the following:
>
> a. Representation on the board of directors
>
> b. Participation in policy-making processes
>
> c. Material intra-entity transactions
>
> d. Interchange of managerial personnel
>
> e. Technological dependency
>
> f. Extent of ownership by an investor in relation to the concentration of other shareholdings (but substantial or majority ownership of the voting stock of an investee by another investor does not necessarily preclude the ability to exercise significant influence by the investor).

ASC 323 does not apply when an investor owns more than 50 percent of the investee's stock. A full consolidation of the investee's financial statements is normally required in this case.

Under the equity method, a partner's initial investment is recorded at cost in an account with a caption such as "Investment in partnership." At the end of each fiscal period, the partner's share of the partnership's income or loss is recorded as an increase or decrease in the investment account and appears as a single amount under a caption such as "Income (loss) from partnership interest" in the income statement. Any distributions received from the partnership are recorded as a reduction of the investment account. The balance in the investment account is shown as a single amount on the partner's balance sheet.

If a reporting entity's financial statements include investments that are accounted for under the equity method, the investees' results of operations for oil and gas producing activities are not included gross in the reporting entity's statement of operations. However, the reporting entity's share of the investees' results should be disclosed separately for the year in the aggregate and by each geographic area for which reserves quantities are disclosed.

Under the equity method, neither the share of the investee's reserves nor the share of the investee's oil and gas assets enter into the investor's DD&A calculation under either the successful efforts or full cost methods.

However, ASC 932 requires entities to disclose separately significant oil and gas producing activities conducted by their equity method investees at the same level of detail as consolidated investments. The disclosures include:

- Reserve quantity information.

- Capitalized costs relating to oil and gas producing activities.

- Costs incurred in oil and gas property acquisition, exploration and development.

- Results of operations from producing activities.

- Standardized measure of discounted cash flows.

- Changes in the standardized measure of discounted cash flows.

In addition to these disclosures, the entity may present a combined total for its consolidated entities and for the entity's share of equity method investees for reserve quantity information, results of operations from producing activities (excluding corporate overhead and interest costs), the standardized measure of discounted cash flows and changes in the standardized measure of discounted cash flows. However, presenting a combined total for the three other items listed above is not permitted.

The ASC also clarifies that, when determining if the company has significant oil and gas producing activities, it should include its equity earnings or losses and the related investment balance from the oil and gas producing activities of its equity method investees. These requirements are described further in Chapters 30 and 31.

A major shortcoming of the equity method is that the investor's financial statements do not fully disclose all pertinent financial information related to the investee. Accordingly, ASC 323-10-50 indicates that disclosure of summarized financial information of such equity investees may be appropriate for material investments.

Proportionate consolidation

The term "proportionate consolidation" means presenting an investor's pro rata share of a venture's assets and liabilities in each applicable line item of the investor's balance sheet, and pro rata results of a venture's operations in each applicable line item in its income statement. This presentation may be used in two situations, if certain conditions are met.

Undivided interest. In this situation, the investor does not have an ownership interest in a legal entity but rather has an undivided ownership interest in assets and is proportionately liable for each liability. In this case, the reporting entity is outside the scope of equity method accounting (ASC 323) and proportionate consolidation is appropriate. Ownership of oil and gas is usually through a mineral interest, which is an economic interest in underground minerals. Such an arrangement does not involve a separate legal entity, and each party holds an individual interest in the asset and is proportionately liable for any liabilities. As a result, these arrangements are typically accounted for using proportionate consolidation.

Equity method in the construction and extractive industries. In this situation, the investor has an ownership interest in an unincorporated legal entity. An investor that holds a noncontrolling ownership interest in an unincorporated legal entity within the construction or extractive industries, and which qualifies for the equity method of accounting, may elect proportionate consolidation in accordance with ASC 810-10-45-14.

In determining whether a legal entity is an unincorporated entity, the reporting entity should consider the governance attributes and economic characteristics of the legal entity to determine whether it is more akin to a corporation or a partnership. For example, if the legal entity has governance attributes that are more representative of a corporation (e.g., a board of directors as opposed to a general partner or managing member), it generally would not be considered an unincorporated legal entity. Therefore, it would be precluded from using proportionate consolidation.

To qualify as an extractive industry, activities of the investee must be limited to extraction of mineral resources, such as oil and gas exploration and production. A reporting entity with a noncontrolling investment in an unincorporated legal entity engaged in activities such as refining, marketing or transporting extracted mineral resources would not qualify to elect proportionate consolidation. In that case, the presentation and disclosure requirements of the equity method of accounting (ASC 323) would apply.

Illustrative examples

Figure 23-1 and Figure 23-2 illustrate the equity and proportionate consolidation methods, respectively, for C Corp.'s share of LH Partnership's loss assuming that both C Corp. and LH Partnership use the successful efforts method of accounting.

Figure 23-1
Equity method – Successful efforts

Financial statement line item	LH Partnership	C Corp. Pre-entry	C Corp. Entry	C Corp. Post entry
		(in thousands)		
Cash	$ 480	$ 1,000	$ –	$ 1,000
Receivables	400	4,000	–	4,000
Oil and gas properties	4,760	20,000	–	20,000
Investment in LH Partnership	–	1,500	(500)	1,000
Other assets	360	2,000	–	2,000
Total assets	**$ 6,000**	**$28,500**	**$(500)**	**$28,000**
Liabilities and deferred taxes	$ 2,000	$10,000	$(105)	$ 9,895
Partners' capital	4,000	–	–	–
Stockholders' equity	–	18,500	(395)	18,105
Total liabilities and equity	**$ 6,000**	**$28,500**	**$(500)**	**$28,000**
Revenues	$ 2,000	$40,000	$ –	$40,000
Production expense	(400)	(12,000)	–	(12,000)
Exploration expense	(3,000)	(10,000)	–	(10,000)
DD&A	(400)	(8,000)	–	(8,000)
G&A expense	(200)	(2,800)	–	(2,800)
25% share of LH loss	–	–	(500)	(500)
Income tax (provision) benefit	–	(1,512)	105	(1,407)
Net income (loss)	**$(2,000)**	**$ 5,688**	**$(395)**	**$ 5,293**

Assume that C Corp. owns a one-fourth interest in LH Partnership. C Corp. invested $1.5 million for its interest on January 2, 2019. For 2019, LH Partnership has a $2.0 million net loss. C Corp.'s one-fourth interest is $500,000, which results in a $105,000 income tax benefit. Note that C Corp.'s final net income is the same under the equity method in Figure 23-1 and the proportionate consolidation method in Figure 23-2. This is true under successful efforts, but not under the full cost method, as discussed below.

If the investor uses full cost, the proportionate share of the partnership's assets and proved reserves for investees accounted for using proportionate consolidation must be included with those owned directly by the partner when computing DD&A for each cost center per Reg. S-X Rule 4-10(c)(3)(v). However, investees accounted for under the equity method are treated separately.

Figure 23-2

Proportionate consolidation method – Successful efforts

Financial statement line item	LH Partnership	C Corp. Pre-entry[1]	C Corp. Entry	C Corp. Post entry
		(in thousands)		
Cash	$ 480	$ 1,000	$ 120	$ 1,120
Receivables	400	4,000	100	4,100
Oil and gas properties	4,760	20,000	1,190	21,190
Investment in LH Partnership	–	1,000	(1,000)	–
Other assets	360	2,000	90	2,090
Total assets	$ 6,000	$28,000	$ 500	$28,500
Liabilities and deferred taxes	$ 2,000	$10,000	$ 395	$10,395
Partners' capital	4,000	–	–	–
Stockholders' equity	–	18,000	105	18,105
Total liabilities and equity	$ 6,000	$28,000	$ 500	$28,500
Revenues	$ 2,000	$40,000	$ 500	$40,500
Production expense	(400)	(12,000)	(100)	(12,100)
Exploration expense	(3,000)	(10,000)	(750)	(10,750)
DD&A	(400)	(8,000)	(100)	(8,100)
G&A expense	(200)	(2,800)	(50)	(2,850)
25% share of LH loss	–	(500)	500	–
Income tax (provision) benefit	(201)	(1,512)	105	(1,407)
Net income (loss)	$(2,000)	$ 5,188	$ 105	$ 5,293

[1] Assumes that the $(2,000) net loss of LH Partnership has been closed out to stockholders' equity by C Corp. for illustrative purposes of showing C Corp.'s financial statements on a proportionate consolidation basis.

Note: This example assumes that LH Partnership's properties are in separate cost centers from C Corp.'s.

Figure 23-3

Proportionate consolidation method – Full cost

		Partner's direct holding	Partner's share in partnership	Consolidated
A	Cost basis	$10,000,000	$2,000,000	$12,000,000
B	Production (bbls)	200,000	40,000	240,000
C	Reserves (bbls)	1,800,000	160,000	1,960,000
D	Ratio of B ÷ (B + C)	10.0%	20.0%	10.91%
	Amortization (A x D)	$ 1,000,000	$ 400,000	$ 1,309,200
	Amortization rate per bbl	$5.00	$10.00	$5.45

As shown in Figure 23-3, the computed amount of DD&A for a cost center with a proportionately consolidated investee will likely cause the consolidated net income to differ from that of a cost center with an investee accounted for under the equity method, because the ratio of production to reserves will likely change.

Assuming no other items of profit or loss, the total net loss using the equity method is $1.4 million ($1.0 million of partner direct amortization plus its equity pickup of the $400,000 loss of the partnership), whereas the consolidated net loss is $1,309,200 (using the proportionate consolidation of cost basis, production and reserves).

Impact to combined financial information

The oil and gas accounting method (successful efforts versus full cost) affects the impact of proportionate consolidation on combined financial information as follows:

- If both the investee and the investor use the successful efforts accounting method (as shown in Figure 23-1 and Figure 23-2), it is a simple matter to combine the investor's separate statements with those of the investor's proportionate interest in the investee's financial statements.

- When both the investee and the investor use full cost, and the investee has applied a ceiling test with a resulting write-down of capitalized costs, the investor's share of the write-down must be added back, and the ceiling test should be applied to the total cost and total value of the combined assets in the cost center.

- If the investee uses full cost and the investor uses successful efforts accounting, it may be difficult for the investor to accurately convert all investee financial statement line items to the successful efforts method.

Necessary data for proportionate consolidation is obtained from financial reports provided by the partnership at the end of the fiscal period (assuming the partnership and the partner use the same accounting method and have the same fiscal year). If special allocations have been made of revenues or expenses, or if the accounting method used by the partnership differs from that of the partner, a reconstruction or reconciliation is required based on the periodic reports of partnership revenues and expenditures prepared by the managing partner.

As demonstrated herein, the primary advantage of proportionate consolidation compared to the equity method of accounting is greater transparency in the financial statements, as the investor will show its share of investee assets, liabilities, revenues, expenses and oil and gas reserves quantities.

Fair value

If the partnership investment does not qualify for either consolidation or the equity method of accounting as described above and the investor has not applied proportionate consolidation, the investment in the partnership should initially be recorded at fair value in accordance with ASC 321, *Investments – Equity Securities*. The investment should be measured at fair value in subsequent periods with unrealized holding gains and losses recorded in earnings.

Partner and partnership transactions

Transactions with the general partner can create complex accounting challenges, especially in limited partnerships. When recording transactions between general and limited partners, consideration should be given as to whether or not common control (carryover basis) is appropriate.

Management and service fees

In general, full cost companies do not recognize income from management and service fees. Promoters of income funds may qualify for certain exceptions. Reg. S-X Rule 4-10(c)(6)(iii)(B) states:

> Where a registrant organizes and manages a limited partnership involved only in the purchase of proved developed properties and subsequent distribution of income from such properties, management fee income may be recognized provided the properties involved do not require aggregate development expenditures in connection with production of existing proved reserves in excess of 10% of the partnership's recorded cost of such properties. Any income not recognized as a result of this limitation would be credited to the full cost account and recognized through a lower amortization provision as reserves are produced.

For example, assume CPF Oil Co. (CPF), a full cost company, organizes a limited partnership in which it is the general partner and manager. The total cost of the proved properties, most of which have been developed, is $28.0 million. Estimated costs to complete development of the properties are $5.0 million. During the year, CPF receives management fees of $800,000 from the limited partnership and related expenses are $320,000.

Since the additional development costs of $5.0 million are greater than 10 percent of the partnership's total costs related to the properties (10 percent of $28.0 million, or $2.8 million), CPF will treat the $480,000 excess of fees over expenses as a reduction of capitalized costs in the full cost pool. If additional development costs had been only $2.0 million, net income of $480,000 ($800,000 less $320,000) would be recognized as management fee income.

Reg. S-X Rule 4-10(c)(6)(iv)(C) states that if a full cost company manages the properties involved, then generally no income can be recognized from rendering contractual services such as drilling:

> [N]o income may be recognized for contractual services performed on behalf of investors in oil and gas producing activities managed by the registrant or an affiliate. Furthermore, no income may be recognized for contractual services to the extent the consideration received for such services represents an interest in the underlying property.

Continuing with the previous example, assume that during the year the limited partnership contracts CPF to drill a well to the casing point for a fixed fee of $320,000. CPF's share of these costs is 25 percent and the limited partners' share is 75 percent.

Total costs incurred on the project are $280,000, resulting in a $40,000 drilling profit. The intercompany profit of $10,000 is credited to the full cost pool to eliminate CPF's 25 percent share of the $40,000 drilling profit. Additionally, in accordance with Reg. S-X Rule 4-10(c)(6)(iv)(C), the additional $30,000 is also credited to the pool to avoid recognizing a drilling profit on the investors' well costs.

When a company maintains a separate contract drilling division, segment income statements are normally prepared. In the preparation of a consolidated income statement, the intercompany profit on the drilling contract would be eliminated. As demonstrated for CPF's transactions in Figure 23-4, any profit resulting from that portion of the drilling contract applicable to its limited partners would be offset against the full cost pool.

Figure 23-4
Consolidation by the general partner – Full cost

Financial statement line item	Drilling segment	Intercompany elimination	CPF Oil Co. consolidated
Contract drilling revenues	$320,000	$(80,000)	$240,000
Contract drilling expenses	(280,000)	70,000	(210,000)
Net income on contract	$ 40,000	$(10,000)	30,000
Less: full cost pool credit			(30,000)
Consolidated net income from drilling			$ –

Reg. S-X Rule 4-10(c)(6)(iv)(A) permits recognizing income when acquiring an interest in connection with a service contract. However, the income can be recognized only to the extent that the cash consideration exceeds all related contract costs, plus the partner's share of costs incurred (and estimated to be incurred) in connection with the properties, and only if neither the partner nor an affiliate manages the oil and gas activity.

To illustrate these concepts, assume that EJA Oil Co. (EJA) performs drilling services and receives cash of $640,000 from the partnership. EJA's total drilling expenses are $560,000. EJA contributes cash of $64,000 for its 10 percent share of drilling costs, pays $10,000 for leasehold costs based on its 10 percent working interest in the lease and pays $10,000 to an outside service company for its share of completion costs. Contract costs of $560,000, plus $84,000 ($10,000 plus $64,000 plus $10,000) to be capitalized to the full cost pool, exceed the $640,000 cash received by $4,000 ($560,000 plus $84,000 less $640,000). No income would be recognized and the full cost pool would be charged for a net $4,000.

The following schedules reflect EJA's income statement and balance sheet after eliminating intercompany profit on the 10 percent share of drilling costs.

Figure 23-5
Intercompany profit elimination – Income statement presentation

Financial statement line item	Drilling segment	Intercompany elimination	EJA Oil Co. consolidated
Drilling revenues	$640,000	$(64,000)	$576,000
Drilling expensess	(560,000)	56,000	(504,000)
Net drilling income	$ 80,000	$ (8,000)	72,000
Less: full cost pool credit			(72,000)
Recognized profit			$ –

Figure 23-6
Intercompany profit elimination – Balance sheet presentation

Financial statement line item	E&P segment	Elimination Intercompany profit[1]	Elimination Drilling profit[2]	EJA Oil Co. consolidated
Leasehold costs	$10,000	$ –	$ (6,000)	$4,000
Drilling costs	64,000	(8,000)	(56,000)	–
Completion costs	10,000	–	(10,000)	–
	$84,000	$(8,000)	$(72,000)	$4,000

[1] Intercompany profit (see income statement schedule).

[2] Total drilling profit = $72,000 (eliminated first against drilling costs of $56,000, then against completion costs of $10,000, then against leasehold costs of $6,000).

If total profit attributed to the other partners had been $9,000 greater (i.e., $81,000 instead of $72,000), a profit of $5,000 could have been recognized (as long as EJA or an affiliate did not manage the property) because cash proceeds would have exceeded all related costs by that amount. Before the partner can recognize a profit on service contracts involving properties where it has an economic interest or serves as manager, the consideration received must exceed: (1) costs already incurred and (2) those estimated to be incurred by the partner. By contrast, if an E&P company operates as an independent drilling contractor, performing services for other entities in which it has no economic interest and it is not the manager of the venture, then profit on drilling or other services may be recognized.

Reg. S-X Rule 4-10(c)(6)(iv)(B) allows the recognition of profit, even though the E&P company has an interest in the properties, provided: (1) the interest was obtained at least one year before the date of the service contract and (2) the interest is unaffected by the service contract. Income from such a contract may be recognized, subject to the GAAP provisions for eliminating intercompany profits.

For example, assume that for three years EPZ Oil Co. (EPZ) has owned a 25 percent ownership interest in a partnership that holds a working interest in a prospect operated by another company. EPZ's share of the leasehold interest cost totals $180,000.

During the current year, EPZ contracts to drill a well on the prospect for a contract price of $800,000. The well is successful and total drilling costs are $680,000. As shown in Figure 23-7 below, EPZ recognizes $90,000 of drilling profit in its consolidated financial statements.

Figure 23-7
EPZ's consolidated financial statements

Income statement	Drilling segment	Intercompany elimination	EPZ Oil Co. consolidated
Contract drilling revenues	$800,000	$(200,000)	$600,000
Contract drilling expenses	(680,000)	170,000	(510,000)
Net drilling income	**$120,000**	**$ (30,000)**	**$ 90,000**
Balance sheet – full cost			
Leasehold costs	$180,000	$ –	$180,000
IDC	$200,000	$ (30,000)	$170,000

The special rules in Reg. S-X Rule 4-10(c) address partnerships, joint ventures, drilling arrangements, management fees and service income for full cost companies. These limitations on income recognition do not appear to apply to managing partners using the successful efforts method of accounting. Under successful efforts, management fees should be accounted for in accordance with ASC 606.

General and administrative reimbursement

Most limited partnership agreements permit reimbursement of G&A expenses. Reimbursement may cover specific G&A expenses, which should be reported by the general partner as a reduction of expenses. The reimbursement may be a specified monthly amount, but it normally is computed as a percentage of partnership revenues or as a percentage of specified costs incurred. Frequently, the rate is higher during the drilling phase of the partnership than during production.

Similar legal entities

Consolidation guidance for limited partnerships also applies to other similar legal entities. These entities are functionally equivalent to limited partnerships in terms of their governing provisions and economic characteristics. They include entities such as limited liability companies (LLCs), limited liability partnerships (LLPs) and others.

LLCs can have governing provisions that are the functional equivalent of either a limited partnership or a corporation. As a result, a reporting entity with an interest in an LLC will need to determine whether the LLC has governing provisions that are the functional equivalent of a limited partnership or a corporation in order to determine whether it has a controlling financial interest in the LLC. A detailed analysis of the LLC's formation and governing documents should be performed to determine whether it is the functional equivalent of a limited partnership or a corporation.

For LLCs with managing and nonmanaging members, ASC 810-10-05-3 defines a managing member as the functional equivalent of a general partner and a nonmanaging member as the functional equivalent of a limited partner. A reporting entity with an interest in an LLC (which is not a VIE) would likely apply the consolidation model for limited partnerships if the managing member has the right to make the significant operating and financial decisions of the LLC.

Alternatively, some LLCs are governed by a board of members which makes all significant operating and financial decisions. In this case, a reporting entity with an interest in an LLC (which is not a VIE) would follow the consolidation model for majority-owned subsidiaries (analogous to a corporation).

In other cases, an LLC has both a managing member and a board of members. A reporting entity would need to assess the rights of both the managing member and the board of members to determine who is responsible for making the significant operating and financial decisions of the LLC.

• • •

International Operations

- **Risks of international E&P operations**

- **Concessions**

- **Joint ventures**

- **Production sharing contracts**

- **Service contracts**

- **Additional considerations**

Entering a new market can bring appealing benefits to international E&P companies, including higher growth rates and returns, diversified investment and access to significant unexploited reserves. That said, operating outside of the U.S. presents a diverse set of legal, operational, accounting and financial reporting challenges. This chapter provides an overview of the variety of arrangements governing international E&P activities, as well as commentary on challenges faced.

These arrangements form the basis of shared economic benefit among the host government (or royalty owner) and the international E&P participants. The most common arrangements are summarized below and described in greater detail in the remainder of this chapter:

- **Concessions.** Concessions are much like leases in the U.S. An E&P company typically owns the discovered reserves and has title to equipment and any oil and gas produced. Bonuses, royalties, production taxes and income taxes flow into government coffers.

- **Joint ventures.** Usually similar to those found in the U.S., international joint ventures typically involve the host government, often through a national oil company (NOC), participating as a nonoperating working interest owner. E&P companies generally agree to pay 100 percent of upfront costs, with the NOC considered a carried working interest – through the exploration phase. If the operator finds commercial reserves, the NOC can opt to participate in development and production as a working interest owner at predetermined rates. When exercising this option, the NOC typically agrees to share in all future drilling, development and production costs.

- **Production sharing contracts (PSCs).** In these arrangements, the host government owns the reserves; it contracts with an E&P company to perform or manage specific activities. The key element to a PSC is cost recovery: the E&P company (or companies) is reimbursed for its investments through assignment of future hydrocarbon production. The E&P company typically is also entitled to a share of production which represents a return on its investment.

- **Service contracts.** Under a service contract, the host government also owns the reserves and signs a contract with an E&P company to perform specific activities. Service contracts differ from PSCs in that the fee typically is paid in cash rather than as a share of future production. Service contracts require an assessment of whether the operations are defined as exploration and production or financing and contracting. The answer depends on the E&P company's assumption of risks and rewards.

Risks of international E&P operations

Beyond the inherent risks of oil and gas operations, investing in international E&P bears additional risks to those common in domestic operations. Understanding the risks of working in a particular country requires careful consideration by management of the various risks and impacts to the business.

Political instability

The stability of a country's political regime is an important consideration. Instability is an increasing concern in certain regions, often times fueled by internal conflicts, civil wars, polarization of religious and ethnic groups, and terrorism. Instability can lead to significant uncertainty, which can make it difficult to plan, invest in and operate international E&P activities. Instability can affect E&P activities in several major ways, including: government-enforced revisions to agreements and contracts; changes to or revised interpretation of tax legislation; changes to a broader regulatory regime governing investments; and, in extreme cases, expropriation of the E&P investment.

Sanctity of contract

Even in territories with a stable political regime, existing contracts and arrangements are often subject to reinterpretation by the host government or statutory authorities, which can then be applied either retrospectively or prospectively. Typically, contracts will allow for international arbitration to mitigate this risk; however, the uncertainty combined with the effort required to resolve disputes can result in delayed investments, additional costs and other burdens to E&P companies.

Fraud and corruption

Corruption, including bribery, preferential treatment for foreign officials and other behaviors or relationships deemed inappropriate, can damage a company's reputation, legal standing and ability to maintain its license to operate. International E&P companies should fully understand and properly mitigate the exposures and associated risks in those foreign countries where they operate.

Furthermore, international E&P companies should develop and maintain anti-fraud and anti-bribery policies and processes, including training their employees in the Foreign Corrupt Practices Act of 1977 (FCPA). In recent decades, both within and outside the industry, numerous companies with international operations have been found to be non-compliant with FCPA guidelines and subjected to significant fines and penalties.

Accounting and compliance

In some developing countries, accounting and compliance departments may have to work with limited logistical support, inadequately trained personnel, high staff turnover and limited or unreliable communication and data processing. They may spend considerable time in the early stages of a project establishing back-office operations which can then be challenging to sustain.

International E&P companies increasingly use regional shared service centers to support compliance and back-office functions such as accounting, human resources (HR) and information technology (IT), which helps to mitigate the risks as well as the burden of sustaining local operations.

Societal pressures

Social activism is another challenge sometimes faced by international E&P companies. Typically led by a nongovernmental organization (NGO), social activism can exert pressure on E&P companies to increase their transparency about the nature of their international operations and the associated effects on the host countries' economies, environment and political system. Social activism also may lead to demands on E&P companies to exit their operations in certain countries. Responding to social activism can be challenging in terms of cost, reputation and maintenance of host country relationships.

Concessions

The U.K. sector of the North Sea is an example of a concessionary system. In a concession, a government grants a permit to an E&P company (the concessionaire) to explore for and produce oil and gas within a strictly defined geographic area. These grants are based primarily on development plans submitted by the E&P company to the host government and are awarded in consideration for some type of bonus or license fee.

Concessionaires assume all of the risks of exploration, development and exploitation of reserves beneath government-owned lands, just as they do in the U.S. Revenues are typically shared with the host government through royalties, taxes on production and/or income taxes on company operations.

For example, assume that an E&P entity, Bullco, operates in a concessionary area. The contract between Bullco and the host government requires Bullco to pay an 8 percent royalty based on gross revenues. Bullco is responsible for all costs of exploration, development and production.

Bullco incurred $40 million in exploration and development costs from 2018 to 2019. At the beginning of 2020, the property began producing, earning gross revenues of $30 million.

Local income tax laws allow Bullco to deduct the total $15 million incurred in 2020 for operating expenses, as well as to amortize 20 percent of the exploration and development costs incurred (amortized over five years). None of the exploration and development costs were deducted from the local taxable income in 2018 and 2019.

Figure 24-1 shows the share of net proceeds accruing to the host government and Bullco in 2020, assuming an income tax rate of 25 percent.

Joint ventures

In a joint venture, the host government participates as a working interest owner through an NOC with an international E&P company in the exploration, development and production of hydrocarbons.

In many cases, E&P companies will agree to pay 100 percent of upfront costs and the NOC is considered to be a carried working interest owner through the exploration phase. If the company finds commercial reserves, the NOC has the option to participate in development and production as a working interest owner at predetermined rates.

Figure 24-1

Allocation of net proceeds – Concession arrangement

	Government	Bullco
Gross revenues		$30,000,000
8% royalty	$2,400,000	(2,400,000)
Net revenues		27,600,000
Less: operating expenses		(15,000,000)
Less: 20% of prior costs		(8,000,000)
Taxable income		4,600,000
Income taxes at 25%	1,150,000	(1,150,000)
Net to the parties	**$3,550,000**	**$ 3,450,000**

Depending on contract terms, an E&P company may be allowed to recover all or a portion of its exploration expenditures, typically through: (1) direct payment by the NOC to the E&P entity, or more commonly, (2) E&P retention of the NOC's share of production until it has recovered its expenses. However, recoveries can be subject to annual limitations and may take years.

Once production begins, the NOC shares in production and costs just like any other working interest owner that elected to participate in the well. This arrangement does not alter the host government's entitlement to royalty and income taxes; however, customs duties on imported materials and supplies, and export duties on production, often are exempt.

In many joint ventures, several participating E&P companies collectively deal with the host government. In these circumstances, the parties may execute a joint operating agreement appointing an operator and establishing governance. Operator responsibilities to the host government and nonoperating participants introduce additional layers of administrative accounting and compliance-related requirements.

A nonoperator in a joint venture can face additional challenges, such as obtaining timely and high-quality financial and operating information from the operator. This can affect a company's assessment of hydrocarbon reserves and its accounting for results of its investment in the venture. In addition, a nonoperator should consider its influence on managing costs and deciding where, and to what extent, to drill, produce or develop. The challenges to operator/nonoperator arrangements are not limited to joint ventures; the operator/nonoperator model also can be found in concessions and PSCs.

Production sharing contracts

Production sharing contracts (PSCs) are one of the most common forms of agreement between host governments and international E&P companies. Under a PSC, the host government owns the hydrocarbons. Typically, the government, through an NOC, actively participates in exploration, development and production, while the E&P company acts as the operator, such that it earns an interest in the hydrocarbons to recover costs and provide for a return on its investment.

Principal concepts

Several principal concepts are contained within PSCs, including:

- Upfront and periodic bonus payments to the host government.

- Periodic royalty payments to the host government.

- Recovery of investments and operating costs by the E&P company.

- Profit-sharing (profit-splitting) between the host government and E&P company.

- Taxation by the host government.

- Infrastructure development for the host government.

Common terms

While PSCs are used across a diverse group of countries, there are typically common terms and conditions found in each contract.

Duration. The agreement's term is divided into consecutive phases: exploration and, if applicable, production. The operator undertakes exploration activities, such as seismic surveys and drilling, and proceeds to the production phase to extract the resources if it discovers commercial quantities of oil or gas. Production phase duration varies but generally includes an option for the operator to extend it for at least one additional term.

Operation and control. When multiple E&P companies are party to the PSC, they usually appoint one company as operator. The operator's responsibilities often are described separately in a joint operating agreement (JOA), which also governs the relationship between the operator and other working interest owners. The operator's responsibilities are generally very broad: they include preparing work programs and budgets, research, appraisal and development, and maintaining necessary insurance. The operator's exploration and production operations must meet annual work programs and budgets approved by a management committee and/or the host government.

Capital uplift. Often times, host governments offer incentives for capital investments in exploration, drilling and development, which may be part of the PSC terms or result from other negotiations. Sometimes called "investment credit," capital uplift represents compensation from the host government for the investment risk, as it encourages E&P companies to maximize their capital spending by providing cost recovery on capital expenditures beyond the actual amount spent.

For example, if an E&P company spends $1 million in capital expenditures, and the PSC terms provide for a 10 percent capital uplift, the E&P company will be able to recover 110 percent of the actual expenditures, or $1.1 million.

Sharing production and profit. Cost recovery is fundamental to PSCs. As stated earlier, E&P companies typically pay 100 percent of exploration costs and some or all of development and production costs. In cost recovery, oil (or gas) or other consideration accruing to the parties with respect to cost recovery is called "cost oil." Gross revenue accruing to the parties after cost recovery or as a result of applying a profit factor is called "profit oil."

Cost recovery. Typically, the contractor is entitled to recover exploration, development and production costs from oil and gas revenues, net of royalties owed to the host government. Recoverable costs usually are determined by the contract's prescribed accounting procedures and are deductible from the operator's taxable income.

The percentage of costs that can be recovered varies from country to country; it may extend to full recovery or be restricted to a certain level. Agreements also determine the order of cost recovery. Although each contract is different, below is a common order:

- Current year operating costs.

- Unrecovered exploration expenditures.

- Unrecovered development expenditures.

- Capitalized interest (if allowed).

- Capital uplift (if allowed).

- Future abandonment cost fund.

Production rates. Agreements include provisions that require the parties, or the management committee, to establish a production, or lifting, schedule that sets forth the estimated total quantity of oil and gas to be produced, saved, transported and lifted annually. Generally, the production level is consistent with the maximum efficient rate (MER), which is both technical and economic.

Royalty holidays and tax holidays. These government incentives encourage E&P companies to maximize their investment early in the life of production. During a specified period (e.g., the first two years of production), royalty provisions may be waived. This leaves E&P companies with more money to invest in drilling and development activities. Similarly, the host government may grant a tax holiday specifying a period during which the E&P company is exempt from income taxes.

Accounting, audit and financial reporting. Accounting provisions in the main agreement, and sometimes in an exhibit or annex to the contract's accounting procedures, state who is responsible for keeping the books, as well as the currency and language in which they are kept. Audit requirements are also specified, such as frequency and whether or not affiliate companies that provide services may be audited.

The provisions define the basis of accounting (e.g., GAAP or IFRS) and specify whether or not documentation may be maintained out of country, especially before major operations such as drilling begin. Depreciation methods, capital versus expense requirements and expenses that are eligible for cost recovery by the operator are also typically defined.

Governing law and dispute resolution. The governing law typically is the law of the host country's jurisdiction, although some jurisdictions adopt an international standard. If a dispute arises, contracts generally stipulate that the parties attempt an amicable resolution; if their attempts fail, arbitration or expert determination is usually provided for. Contracts typically stipulate using an international arbitration forum, such as the International Court of Arbitration, the London Court of International Arbitration or the Singapore International Arbitration Centre.

Relinquishment and surrender. Agreements generally contain a relinquishment obligation which requires the operator to surrender certain parts of the contract area to the host government after a given period of time. These areas typically have not been, and are not expected to be, exploited.

Termination and withdrawal. An agreement generally ends upon either the term's natural expiration or when a party exercises its termination rights. Termination rights usually favor the host government and may include: (1) the operator's failure to discover hydrocarbons before the exploration phase expires and/or (2) the operator's insolvency.

Ring-fencing and cross-fencing. Ring-fencing means that neither costs nor production can be transferred for recovery outside the contract area, such that only the costs for work in a particular license area can be recovered from production in that area. However, at their discretion, governments can remove ring-fencing and allow cross-fencing cost transfers. This incentive is most effective when the government seeks to increase exploration in a particular area by allowing a company to immediately recover certain exploration expenditures in a frontier area with production proceeds from a currently producing area.

Accounting considerations

Although a host government may legally own the reserves in a PSC, the E&P company has the right to explore, develop and produce the oil and gas. These activities are substantially equivalent to owning mineral interests or shares of reserves; therefore, Reg. S-X Rule 4-10 applies. PSC rights are viewed as the equivalent of concession rights, and the basic accounting rules are the same, in which the E&P company: (1) records revenues from the sale of oil and gas production and not from the provision of contractor services, (2) recognizes reserves to the extent of its share in future production under the PSC and (3) amortizes capitalized costs over its share of proved reserves.

According to the 2019 *PricewaterhouseCoopers Survey of U.S. Petroleum Accounting Practices* (Question B12), when recording cost recovery proceeds as revenue, nine of 11 respondents to the question amortize capitalized costs recoverable from the host government or company over their entitled share of future production, including recovery oil (i.e., the same as amortization of capitalized costs that are not recoverable). The other two respondents reported amortizing capitalized costs by the cost recovery proceeds based on the ratio of capitalized costs recoverable compared to total recoverable costs.

Assume that Smith Oil Co. (Smith) operates under a PSC in which it has a 45 percent working interest and the NOC has a 55 percent working interest. Its operating agreement calls for annual gross production to be shared in this order:

1. Royalty of 10 percent of annual gross production.

2. Cost oil is limited to 60 percent of annual gross production, with costs to be recovered in the following order: (a) operating costs (based on WI), (b) exploration costs (Smith, 100 percent) and (c) development costs (based on WI).

3. Annual gross production remaining after cost recovery becomes profit oil in which: (a) the government receives 15 percent and (b) the remaining 85 percent is shared by Smith and the NOC based on their respective WI ownership percentages.

During 2019:

- Recoverable operating costs: $6 million.

- Unrecovered exploration costs: $60 million.

- Unrecovered development costs: $120 million.

- Gross production for the year: two million barrels of oil.

- Agreed-upon posted price: $60 per barrel.

The parties' allocated production is shown in Figure 24-2. The host government's proceeds are increased, and Smith's share is decreased, by income taxes or other taxes levied by the government.

Figure 24-2

Production sharing calculations – PSC arrangement

December 31, 2019	To be allocated	Host government	NOC 55%	Smith 45%
		(bbls)		
Royalty (10% of 2,000,000)	200,000	200,000		
Cost oil (60% of 2,000,000)	1,200,000			
Profit oil [2,000,000 x (100% – 10% – 60%)]	600,000			
Cost allocation				
Operating costs ($6,000,000 ÷ $60 = 100,000 bbls)			55,000	45,000
Exploration costs ($60,000,000 ÷ $60 = 1,000,000 bbls)[1]				1,000,000
Development costs ($120,000,000 ÷ $60 = 2,000,000 bbls)[2]			55,000	45,000
Profit allocation				
Government = 15% (remainder split = 55% ÷ 45%)		90,000	280,500	229,500
Total	**2,000,000**	**290,000**	**390,500**	**1,319,5000**

[1] Limited to the cost oil bbls to be allocated of 1.2 million bbls, less 100,000 bbls of operating costs allocated.

[2] Given that total cost oil to be allocated is 1.2 million bbls, the development costs allocation cannot exceed 100,000 bbls.

Disclosures

ASC 932-235-50-4 requires public companies to disclose the net quantities of their interests in proved reserves. Common practice is to classify PSC reserves as part of an E&P company's reserves at a country/territory level. It also is acceptable to separately disclose PSC reserves from other recognized reserves; however, this is not a common practice.

Service contracts

Service contracts are not as common as PSCs; nonetheless, they present a number of accounting challenges. Service contracts generally are classified as either risked or non-risked. In practice, risked service contracts are more common than non-risked. The E&P company incurs all costs and risks related to exploration, development and production. In return, if it achieves production, the company receives a fee representing recovery of its costs, plus a return for the risk assumed instead of a share of the future production. The fee typically is based on a sliding scale linked to the level of production at prevailing commodity prices.

In non-risked service contracts, the E&P company provides services: exploration, development and production. The host government pays the E&P company a fee to cover its incurred costs, plus a return (profit). The host country bears all exploration and development risks. For accounting purposes, the service provider is not deemed to be engaged in oil- and gas-producing activities. Non-risked service contracts are used in areas such as the Middle East, where substantial capital is available, but industry expertise and technology may be lacking. Fees earned vary widely over various ranges depending on project success.

Additional considerations

In addition to the operational risks and complex contractual arrangements, a number of other factors contribute to the challenges faced in international petroleum operations.

Local accounting requirements

Accounting for foreign operations may require keeping two sets of accounting records. Financial systems must be designed to accommodate the accounting requirements of both the home country and the country in which operations are conducted.

For example, IDCs are an important part of U.S. petroleum accounting, but they are not recognized in some foreign accounting and tax frameworks. Some countries allow interest capitalization; others do not. The concepts of depreciation and amortization may not exist in areas where tax laws allow operators to expense all costs as incurred. Finally, governments may require that reports be prepared in more than two currencies or that they demonstrate the effects of inflation. These differences can create further complexity for accounting, reporting and information systems.

Dismantling obligations

The dismantling, removal and abandonment (DR&A) of offshore and onshore installations or structures after facility shutdowns can become complicated, especially because regulations, technology and costs can change over time. Furthermore, there is growing scrutiny from governmental authorities and/or NGOs as to the extent and sufficiency of the dismantling activities. Under most PSCs, title to fixed assets (e.g., wells, storage facilities and pipelines) vests in the host country, either at inception or upon payout. In addition to holding title to the fixed assets, the host country typically is obligated to perform DR&A activities.

Some governments require E&P companies to deposit funds in an escrow account to pay for future DR&A obligations at the time of asset retirement. Chapter 19 further describes these obligations.

Lifting imbalances

Accounting for lifting imbalances may be especially challenging in international operations. Lifting imbalances occur when the volumes actually lifted from a site by an interest owner differ from the volumes to which the owner is entitled. The operator is responsible for notifying all participants of the following amounts, which are used to calculate entitlements:

- Total production.

- Actual royalty production.

- Actual cost recovery production.

- Actual investment credit production.

- Actual profit production.

The operator provides details of each party's over-lift or under-lift position and each party's final over-lift or under-lift in relation to the others. When a party is over-lifted at year-end, or another period specified in the agreement, it should notify the operator and other parties of its intended method of settlement (generally in cash or in-kind).

Transfer pricing

If a U.S. company's foreign subsidiary sells crude oil to its U.S. parent at a transfer price of $60 per barrel when the market price is $57 per barrel, the $3 per barrel profit shifts from the U.S. parent to the foreign subsidiary. To prevent these income shifts, the IRS imposes significant nondeductible penalties for transfer prices that are not transacted at arm's length. To avoid these penalties, the company must:

- Determine a method to support transfer pricing at arm's length.

- Maintain documentation supporting arm's length transfer pricing.

- Provide this documentation in a timely manner to the IRS, if requested.

Accounting for ownership interests

The structure of a company's participation will determine how each party reflects its ownership interest. If participation is an undivided interest, each party typically would reflect its pro rata share of the assets, liabilities, revenues and expenses (pro rata consolidation). ASC 810-10-45-14 applies pro rata consolidation to ownership in unincorporated entities, such as partnerships and LLCs (which are similar to partnerships). If the ownership is structured through a corporation or a similar entity, even in cases when the agreement assigns benefits and risks to the owners as if they hold undivided interests, the participation should be evaluated according to proportionate consolidation or the equity method of accounting. Chapter 23 fully describes each of these accounting methods.

Reserves

A question sometimes arises about when and what volume of proved reserves should be recognized from foreign operations. For example, when a PSC or concession expects an extension, judgment should be used as to the likelihood of an extension which could impact the amount of reserves to be recognized.

Host government audits

Host government auditors periodically review the transactions and records of E&P ventures. Such reviews may, among other matters, address the following:

- **Overhead**

    - What types of home office costs are reimbursed to the venture?

    - Are they reasonable, supportable and directly related to venture operations?

    - What is the basis of the venture's overhead allocation?

    - Are allocations consistent from year to year and consistently applied to the company's other ventures?

- **Technical staff**

    - What is the nature of work invoiced for home office technical staff?

    - How are billing rates determined?

    - How do technical staff account for their time spent on the venture?

- **Costs in excess of AFEs**

    - What is the nature of any costs incurred that exceed the approved AFE amount?

    - Should excess costs qualify for cost recovery?

Reports of audit findings and their subsequent resolutions generally are time-consuming and they often involve multiple levels of management.

• • •

Offshore Operations and Enhanced Recovery

Key concepts

- **Offshore operations**

- **Accounting complexities**

- **Enhanced recovery**

The physical activities required for offshore exploration and production can differ dramatically from onshore projects. This chapter focuses on the distinctive aspects of offshore operations, as well as enhanced recovery methods, and analyzes the special accounting issues that result from these activities.

Offshore operations

Within U.S. territorial waters, oil and gas operators can acquire mineral leases from either state or federal governments. On the Atlantic and Pacific coasts, state governments own mineral rights to a distance of three miles from shore; however, in the Gulf of Mexico state ownership extends for nine miles. Beyond these perimeters, the federal government controls the leasing rights.

Leases are obtained from state or federal authorities through a process of competitive bidding. Typically, announcements of available offshore tracts specify a minimum royalty rate per acre and a fixed royalty rate on oil and gas production. Companies make competitive bonus bids for the tracts that interest them. In some cases, authorities ask for competitive royalty bids with a fixed bonus or, less frequently, net profit sharing leases.

Offshore leasing

Procedures for leasing outer continent shelf (OCS) areas from the U.S. government were established in the OCS Lands Act enacted in 1953. The Bureau of Ocean Energy Management (BOEM) of the U.S. Department of the Interior administers federal OCS oil and gas leases. Jurisdiction and ownership of mineral rights in most of the OCS worldwide were agreed upon in the 1958 Geneva Conventions on the Law of the Sea, specifically the Convention on the High Seas.

Offshore leasing guidelines seek to balance the needs of the federal government for environmental protection, resource development and a fair return, while also creating a reasonable and practical system.

Federal leasing procedures can be summarized in five steps:

1. To allow time for seismic surveys or other prospecting, BOEM publishes lists of available tracts several years in advance.

2. BOEM gives 30 days' notice in the Federal Register of a lease sale in a particular area. Companies can submit bids on any unleased blocks in the area, unless BOEM excludes a section for a specific reason. BOEM prepares an environmental impact statement and sets a hearing before the sale.

3. On the bid date, BOEM opens sealed bids on a block-by-block basis, revealing the bidder's name (or names, since companies often make joint bids) and the bid amount.

4. After opening the bids, BOEM determines a confidential minimum acceptable bid for each unleased block.

5. Two months after opening the bids, BOEM awards the lease to the highest bidder provided its bid exceeds the minimum acceptable amount.

Offshore leases generally cover 5,760 square acres (approximately nine square miles); contain a royalty rate ranging from 16.67 percent (one-sixth) to 18.75 percent (three-sixteenths) based on the fair market value of production; have a primary term of five years (eight to 10 years for water depths greater than 400 meters), and charge an annual rent due unless drilling or production operations commence as dictated in the lease terms.

Exploration and evaluation

Offshore operations employ the same types of exploration methods as onshore. Seismic, magnetic and gravimetric equipment are commonly used. Because many of the first offshore oil and gas prospects in the Gulf of Mexico contained salt domes, gravitational exploration methods became especially important.

Offshore exploration. 2D and 3D marine seismic exploration map a field's subsurface to improve the understanding of its geology. High-pressure air guns are used as an energy source to generate seismic waves that reflect off subsurface formations. Hydrophones, which record the reflected sound waves, are towed in long plastic tubes (streamers) behind a marine vessel at a specified depth. A single marine vessel will tow an array of streamers multiple miles long, enabling it to survey a large area in parallel. Offshore seismic surveys are typically more expensive than those conducted onshore as they experience significantly higher costs in equipment, personnel and logistics.

Evaluation wells. Platforms and related development wells designed for deepwater offshore reservoirs can cost hundreds of millions of dollars. Many fields must have proved reserves of 200 million equivalent barrels of oil or more before the cost of development is justifiable. Because a single well cannot produce this quantity of reserves, operators typically drill several evaluation wells to assess the probability of adequate reserves to justify development. These wells also help determine the precise location for constructing a permanent production platform. Evaluation wells use the same type of drilling equipment as exploratory wells and, especially if drilled in deepwater depths, rarely are completed, even though they verify the existence of proved reserves.

Drilling rigs

Early offshore drilling was simply an extension of onshore drilling. Some of the first offshore drilling occurred on piers stretching out hundreds of feet from the beaches at Santa Barbara, California. In the Louisiana marshes in the 1920s and 1930s, drilling platforms were floated by barge into dredge channels, which were sunk in water four to eight feet deep and then fastened in place by wooden pilings. In bays along the Gulf Coast, wooden drilling platforms were constructed on top of wooden pilings. If the wells were successful, production equipment was installed and oil was transported by flow lines to an onshore tank battery.

As offshore operations moved to deeper waters, drilling methods changed. Massive platforms rising hundreds of feet from the ocean floor to the water's surface were required along with special production facilities. A single producing well rarely could extract enough oil or gas to justify the facility costs. Instead, operators implemented carefully planned multi-well drilling programs for exploration, evaluation, appraisal and development activities.

Today, mobile rigs perform the exploratory and evaluation drilling, although these wells usually are abandoned even if they reveal the presence of oil or gas. Development wells are drilled from huge platforms with room to drill numerous wells, generally eight to 30 drill slots, or as many as 60 for deepwater platforms when a second platform for a large field is cost-prohibitive. Production facilities on the platform handle the oil and gas produced from all wells.

Physical conditions in the environment such as water depth, weather and distance from port or shore largely determine the choice of exploratory rig type. Related factors are the rig's positioning capabilities, support requirements including living accommodations and ease of transport to the location.

As described in Chapter 8, drillers use several types of mobile drilling rigs:

- **Drilling barges**. Drilling barges are not self-propelled and must be moved by tugboats, thus increasing travel time. Like submersibles, barges are moved to a drilling location and ballasted so that they rest on the seafloor. Once evaluation wells confirm the existence of adequate reserves, a fixed or floating platform is deployed to support ongoing developmental drilling and production. Barges typically work in shallow water and are best suited for areas such as the South Louisiana marshlands or parts of Nigeria.

- **Submersible rigs**. Similar to sunken barges, submersible rigs were among the earliest offshore exploratory rigs, although they are less commonly used today. A submersible rig has both lower and upper hulls. The lower hull provides buoyancy when floating the unit from one location to another, while the upper hull contains working space and crew quarters. When a rig arrives at the site, the lower hull is flooded and the rig sinks until the lower hull rests on the seabed.

  After drilling operations cease, ballast water is forced out of the lower hull and the unit is re-floated and moved to a new location. The difficulty of moving a submersible rig is a major disadvantage. Most submersible rigs operate in shallow water (less than 50 feet), although some can operate in 100-foot depths.

- **Jack-up rigs**. Used in much deeper water than submersible rigs, with a depth limit generally of 350 feet, jack-up rigs are relatively inexpensive. Gorilla class jack-ups can work in water as deep as 550 feet in the Gulf of Mexico and 400 feet in the North Sea. A jack-up rig has a watertight hull; while it is in transit, the legs are retracted above the hull.

  When the rig arrives at the drill site, its legs are jacked down to the seabed and its hull is lifted above the water's surface so that tides and waves will not interfere with drilling operations. Jack-up rigs are quite stable but are difficult to tow. The legs must be shortened or removed for long trips and the process of jacking platforms up and down increases operational risk.

- **Semi-submersible rigs**. Submersible rigs and jack-up rigs cannot be used in deeper waters. Semi-submersible rigs ("semis") operate in water depths to about 2,000 feet. A semi's hull is floated and submerged just below the water's surface. With a working deck similar to a jack-up rig, the semi is stabilized by ballasting pontoons and columns to a predetermined depth.

Older model semis generally are kept over the drill site with anchors. Newer rigs are self-propelled and kept in place without anchoring through the use of dynamic positioning technology, which uses electrically powered propellers and directed thrusts to position the rig. Semi-submersibles are especially useful in deep, rough waters such as the North Sea. A major disadvantage is their limited cargo and storage capacity, such that there is a significant dependence on supply ships and tugboats.

- **Drilling ships**. Also known as drillships, these seagoing vessels serve as platforms for exploratory drilling. They can work at greater depths than semis in deepwater of 5,000 to 7,000 feet or in ultra-deepwater up to 12,000 feet, with drilling depths that exceed 30,000 feet. Drillships resemble traditional oceangoing vessels and are self-propelled. Because they require a sailing crew, their operating costs are high. Drillships can move rapidly between work sites and store large quantities of material, thus requiring fewer support ships, which is an advantage compared to other rig types. Ballasting systems and thrusters provide dynamic positioning which ensures stability of the ship over the drill site, as drillships typically endure rougher seas and must overcome more technical challenges than other types of rigs.

Operations and production

The drilling operations of an offshore rig are fundamentally similar to those of an onshore rig, with additional special equipment and techniques for environmental factors. Despite anchoring or dynamic positioning, operators must manage a significant amount of movement, particularly the up and down wave action (heave). Motion compensators isolate the drillstring from the heave. Marine riser systems guide the drillstem from the drilling vessel to the subsea wellhead and provide a return path for the drilling fluid between the well and the vessel. Emergency disconnect equipment is used if the vessel is forced off location by an approaching hurricane, loss of power, broken anchor chains or a collision with a ship, such that the well can be re-entered safely.

Production platform. Whereas exploratory rigs focus on mobility, production platforms are designed for long-term, stable operations. Many factors determine the type of production platform chosen and its structural details. Fabricated onshore, the platform is either floated or transported on barges to the permanent location where it is erected. To facilitate drilling multiple wells, the platform contains drilling slots arranged in rows forming a rectangle. The drilling derrick is portable and is skidded from one drilling slot to another as drilling occurs. The wells are directional and extend away from the platform as depicted in Chapter 8.

Bottom-supported platforms can be used in shallow water less than 500 feet. They are made of concrete or steel and are designed to withstand severe environmental conditions such as hurricanes, icy seas, earthquakes and strong winds. Steel-jacket platforms sit on steel-jacketed legs that reach the seafloor; a gravity-base platform relies on a massive foundation to maintain its position and stability in rough seas.

Production in deeper water calls for various types of floating production platforms. A tension-leg platform is connected to fixtures on the seafloor by a tendon. A mooring system holds platforms in place. Semi-submersibles are common in deepwater depths because of their stability, which relies on a combination of ballast, anchoring systems and/or dynamic positioning.

Blowout preventer. On a non-floating rig, the blowout preventer is almost identical to the type used onshore, which is installed beneath the rig floor. Floating rig blowout preventers are installed at the wellhead on the seafloor to maintain well control during an emergency disconnect. Subsea blowout preventers are similar to onshore blowout preventers but are equipped for remote operation via electrical or hydraulic power.

Infrastructure. Production techniques for offshore activities are similar to those used onshore. Oil, gas and water separators resemble those used in onshore production. Oil is either accumulated in storage tanks for subsequent transport by tanker or transferred directly from separators and treaters into a tanker. If an oil pipeline has been constructed, the oil may be pumped from treating equipment directly into the pipeline. Gas is also gathered and transported to shore via pipelines. Many jurisdictions require water from the well site to have impurities removed before it can be discharged into the sea or reinjected into the reservoir. Additional equipment is installed on the platform or in tender ships to properly handle the water.

Offshore pipelines are laid by pipelay barges. Lengths of pipe are welded together in a continuous line, then lowered and laid along the seabed, although the pipeline may also be buried in softer and shallower seabed bottoms. Some pipelay barges are semi-submersible to minimize the effects of wind and waves in rough water. Flexible pipelines laid by reel barges have also been introduced in recent years.

Subsea. Underwater well work is subsea work and is performed by specially trained divers or an unmanned remotely operated vehicle (ROV). Divers wearing hard-shelled atmospheric diving suits (ADSs) operate in shallow water (less than 2,000 feet), whereas ROVs are used in deeper water.

Some offshore oil fields are too small to require a production platform. The equipment to support these subsea wells is positioned on the seafloor. Production from multiple subsea fields often is combined and sent to a common production facility. A floating production, storage and offloading (FPSO) vessel sometimes is used to process and store subsea production until a shuttle tanker can transfer the oil onshore. FPSO vessels are kept in position with mooring systems and dynamic positioning.

Well servicing. The purpose of offshore well servicing is similar to onshore servicing; however, the work is more complex and expensive. Since many offshore wells produce high volumes of oil, special care is taken to minimize production interruptions. Wireline units may be attached to a hoist on small platforms, while larger platforms or unmanned wells might require a barge, jack-up or semi-submersible vessel with workover equipment. Deepwater platforms are self-sufficient and maintain a wide range of well servicing infrastructure.

Plugging and abandonment

As described in Chapter 19, a major cost of offshore operations is incurred after oil and gas production ceases, with significant expenditures required for removal of the equipment and platform and clean-up of the seabed. Reclamation requirements vary across the globe, but they often cost much more than the original platform and facilities, particularly when oil storage facilities are a part of the structure.

The mechanics of offshore wells that are plugged and abandoned are similar to those of onshore wells. However, in addition to subsurface work, the subsea equipment must be removed. Since offshore platforms often serve as an oasis for marine life, despite creating a navigation hazard for vessels, government authorities sometimes allow these structures to be removed from the seabed, towed to designated areas outside of shipping lanes and sunk below the water's surface to form artificial reefs.

In some instances, operators are allowed to cut off the tops of platforms to a certain water depth, leaving the substructure in place. Small fish find protection in the shallower, sunlit water depths of these structures. As a result, offshore platforms, particularly in the Gulf of Mexico, are a popular destination for sport fishing.

Accounting complexities

Many of the challenges in accounting for onshore operations are compounded by offshore activities. These complications are recognized in ASC 932 and Reg. S-X Rule 4-10 and have been presented in previous chapters of this book. In this section, several topics are highlighted for special consideration.

Unproved properties

Acquisition costs of offshore properties are handled in the same way as for onshore leases. The bonus paid to the state or federal government is capitalized as are incidental acquisition costs. Offshore properties are large and the bonus costs are more significant than onshore lease bonus amounts. Accordingly, the costs of unproved offshore leases typically are assessed on a property-by-property basis for successful efforts impairment, as each lease is determined to be individually significant (see Chapter 7). For full cost accounting, it is not uncommon for the costs of acquiring unproved offshore properties to initially be excluded from the full cost amortization base (see Chapter 18).

Because offshore leases are generally large, both in area and cost, ASC 932-360-35-15 allows a portion of the leasehold cost for a single property to be transferred to proved property accounts if proved reserves are found on only a portion of the property. The guidance indicates that the allocable portion to be reclassified from unproved to proved is to be "determined on the basis of geological structural features or stratigraphic conditions." This language suggests that a lease is "large" only if it is believed to have more than one structural feature to be explored.

While ASC 932-360-35-15 is silent about whether or not the allocation can be based on relative surface acreage, this approach would seem to be reasonable. For instance, if a successful exploratory well finds proved reserves in a structural feature under an estimated 5,000 acres on a largely unexplored 50,000 acre lease, then perhaps 10 percent of the lease acquisition cost could be reclassified to proved property.

However, if G&G studies indicate the 50,000-acre lease contains only five geological structural features with possible oil and gas reserves under an estimated 20,000 surface acres, a more reasonable approach would be to allocate 25 percent of the lease acquisition costs to proved properties.

Geological and geophysical costs

The accounting rules for G&G costs incurred offshore are identical to those for onshore activities, although offshore costs likely will be greater. As described in previous chapters, the accounting for G&G costs depends on whether such costs are exploratory or developmental.

For successful efforts companies, all exploratory G&G costs are expensed as incurred, whereas development G&G costs are capitalized. If the G&G costs relate to both a proved area and an unproved area, then such costs should be allocated on a reasonable basis. A full cost company capitalizes all such costs as part of the full cost pool in a given cost center.

Exploration costs

Offshore exploratory drilling is generally much more expensive than onshore drilling to similar depths. As previously described, operators must use offshore platforms, barges and ships. Offshore rigs are costly to construct and move. Significant financial resources are required for transportation of materials, supplies and workforce; provision of lodging and food for the crews; and construction and maintenance of onshore support facilities.

Many offshore exploratory wells are drilled with no intention of being completed even if proved reserves are discovered. Such wells are stratigraphic test wells as defined in Reg. S-X 4-10(a)(30):

> [A] drilling effort, geologically directed, to obtain information pertaining to a specific geologic condition. Such wells customarily are drilled without the intent of being completed for hydrocarbon production. This classification also includes tests identified as core tests and all types of expendable holes related to hydrocarbon exploration. Stratigraphic test wells are classified as "exploratory type" if not drilled in a known area or "development type" if drilled in a known area.

The costs of offshore exploratory wells are accounted for in the same way as onshore exploratory wells. Under successful efforts, wells that find proved reserves are capitalized and unsuccessful wells are charged to expense. A full cost company capitalizes all exploratory well costs.

A troublesome point for successful efforts companies relates to accounting for evaluation wells. Prior to production, a permanent platform must be built for the drilling of development wells and installation of production equipment and storage. Before the high costs of construction can be justified, however, the operator drills evaluation wells (usually stratigraphic) to determine whether or not the formation contains adequate reserves.

As described in Chapter 9 and under ASC 932-360-35-20, companies using the successful efforts method may continue to defer costs of stratigraphic test wells that find oil and gas reserves in an area requiring a major capital expenditure before production can begin, provided that: (1) the well has found a sufficient quantity of reserves to justify its completion as a producing well and (2) the enterprise is making sufficient progress assessing the reserves and the economic and operating feasibility of the project. Otherwise, the stratigraphic test well is assumed to be impaired, and the related costs (including additional test wells and a production platform) should be expensed.

Development costs

The same rules of capitalization apply to offshore and onshore development costs. Again, a major difference is the magnitude of costs incurred and the substantial level of service facility costs to be allocated to various offshore activities. Another distinction is the timeline of offshore operations: from lease acquisition to first production can often take years rather than months, as is typically the case onshore.

Offshore development costs include stratigraphic test wells drilled into proved areas, whether or not successful. Stratigraphic test wells frequently are drilled to assist in determining the most favorable location for a permanent platform.

Production costs

Offshore production costs are charged to expense as incurred. A major element of such expenses can be the cost of operating support facilities, both onshore and offshore. An offshore production cost not found in onshore activities is that of transporting the oil or gas to shore by pipeline, barge or ship. Instruction 1 to Reg. S-X Rule 4-10(a)(16)(i) points out:

> The oil and gas production function shall be regarded as ending at a "terminal point", which is the outlet valve on the lease or field storage tank. If unusual physical or operational circumstances exist, it may be appropriate to regard the terminal point for the production function as:
>
> a.   The first point at which oil, gas, or gas liquids, natural or synthetic, are delivered to a main pipeline, a common carrier, a refinery, or a marine terminal; and
>
> b.   In the case of natural resources that are intended to be upgraded into synthetic oil or gas, if those natural resources are delivered to a purchaser prior to upgrading, the first point at which the natural resources are delivered to a main pipeline, a common carrier, a refinery, a marine terminal, or a facility which upgrades such natural resources into synthetic oil or gas.

Based on the above guidance, the cost of transporting the product from the platform or well to shore, and perhaps the costs of terminal facilities onshore, should be treated as production expenses.

Depreciation, depletion and amortization

To estimate the total quantity of proved reserves from an offshore project, the operator may drill wells for several years from the permanent platform. Production from the earliest wells can commence long before the entire drilling program is complete. Under both the successful efforts and full cost methods, this extended development period raises a question about the point at which capitalized exploration, acquisition and development costs should enter into the DD&A calculation.

ASC 932-360-35-7 and Reg. S-X Rule 4-10(c)(3)(ii) provide guidance for transferring such costs to the amortization base for successful efforts companies and full cost companies, respectively, as previously discussed in Chapters 16 and 18.

Support facilities

When a company engages in offshore operations, the costs of acquiring and operating support facilities are likely to be much higher than onshore sites. Port facilities, docks, transportation vessels, helicopters, midget submarines and supply centers are very expensive. In addition, these support facilities and equipment often service a project throughout its life cycle. Accordingly, a major accounting consideration involves developing procedures to charge costs to the appropriate activity (i.e., exploration, acquisition, development, drilling or production). This is especially important because most operator-owned facilities are used in joint operations.

Recognizing this problem, the Council of Petroleum Accountants Societies (COPAS) has issued several publications related to accounting procedures for offshore operations, including Model Form Interpretations 5 (MFI-5), MFI-45 and MFI-46. Although the COPAS documents are intended primarily for use in joint operations, they also provide guidance to accountants in classifying and recording costs and in allocating costs to specific activities. Under Reg. S-X Rule 4-10(a)(20)(ii) and ASC 932-360-25-16, the depreciation and amortization of support facilities, as well as their applicable operating costs, become exploration, development or production costs and should be accounted for as such.

Shared facilities

It is common for the operator of a platform to sublet platform space or services to operators of smaller platforms in the area. For example, the operator of a marginal field may enter into an agreement for a nearby platform to handle or process fluids, or for a nearby operator to provide daily oversight.

Removal and restoration

One of the most interesting and important accounting issues related to offshore activities is the accrual of costs related to platform removal and reclamation (see Chapter 19). Many factors result in different accounting policies among companies related to removal and restoration. Requirements vary in different parts of the world and international requirements have not been firmly established. In addition, because of the long and often uncertain period between the time a facility is installed and its ultimate removal, it is difficult to estimate the total cost of removal and reclamation.

Enhanced recovery

In oil reservoirs, only a small percentage of the initial hydrocarbons in place are produced (the "primary recovery factor"). Natural gas reservoirs typically exceed oil reservoir recovery factors, without any enhanced recovery techniques. Enhanced recovery efforts on gas reservoirs typically target additional gas liquids or condensate contained in the gas rather than the gas itself.

Primary recovery includes all production when the reservoir's natural drive mechanism such as gasdrive (gas cap or solution gasdrive), waterdrive (bottomwater or edgewater), combination drive or gravity drainage is the only source of energy pushing the reservoir contents to flow into the wellbore. Once in the wellbore, primary production may: (1) flow freely up the wellbore, (2) be pumped up or (3) be lifted using natural gas.

The primary recovery stage reaches its limit either when the reservoir pressure is too low to support economic production rates or when the proportion of gas or water production is too high in the production stream.

Secondary recovery represents the second stage of production during which an external fluid such as gas or water is injected into the reservoir through injection wells, with the purpose of maintaining reservoir pressure and displacing hydrocarbons toward the wellbore. Gas injection and waterflooding are the most common secondary recovery techniques applied. The secondary recovery stage reaches its limit similar to the primary recovery stage whereby production is no longer economic, and the gas or water production as part of the production stream becomes significant.

Enhanced recovery (historically synonymous with tertiary recovery as a third stage of oil recovery) refers to the stage during which formation pressure is not only restored but fluid flow through the reservoir is also improved. More recently, techniques used during enhanced recovery may be initiated throughout the productive life of a reservoir.[1]

The efficiency of a reservoir's primary drive mechanism depends on many factors, including:

- Physical and chemical composition of the reservoir formation and fluids.

- Depth, temperature and pressure of the reservoir.

- Physical characteristics of the wells penetrating the reservoir.

- Historical manner in which the reservoir has been produced.

Enhanced recovery methods are capital-intensive and usually require an extended period from the first investment until additional production occurs. These techniques are also not without risks. Projects may perform below expectations despite supportive engineering studies prior to their implementation.

Enhanced recovery methods

Artificial stimulation of oil reservoirs has been used since the early 20th century. Initial methods used injections of water or natural gas into the reservoir. Later methods have included injection of chemicals, steam and carbon dioxide (CO_2), as well as in-situ combustion (thermal recovery). A brief review of commonly employed enhanced recovery techniques provides insight into the related accounting issues.

Water injection. Water injection (waterflooding) is a simple method of improving recovery from a reservoir. It may be implemented as soon as production begins from the reservoir under pressure maintenance programs. If the waterflooding begins before natural reservoir pressure declines significantly, it is more synonymous with the primary recovery stage.

Water injection serves two functions: (1) it provides a means for disposing of water produced from the reservoir along with the oil and gas and (2) it increases total productivity by flushing oil out of the formation. Water is forced through injection wells into the reservoir and through the reservoir formation into the productive wells, carrying oil along with it. Waterflood projects commonly use a five-spot pattern as depicted in Figure 25-1.

Water injected or reinjected into the reservoir must be similar or identical to the water found in the reservoir, and it must also be clear, noncorrosive and free of materials that might plug the oil-bearing formation. If the water is produced from the reservoir or other subsurface sources, it will contain little oxygen and minimal treatment is required. However, if surface water is used, it may contain large amounts of oxygen as well as incompatible chemicals. As a result, the facilities needed for a water injection program may include not only injection wells and pumps, but also systems for de-aeration, filtration, chemical treatment and testing.

Figure 25-1
Five-spot waterflood pattern

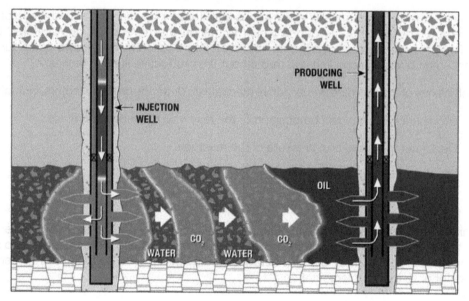

Chemical injection. Water flows through a reservoir more easily than oil due to its lower viscosity. In waterfloods, injected water sometimes can channel past the oil, greatly reducing the effectiveness of the waterflood. In this case, long-chain polymers (viscosifiers) can be added to thicken the water. The thickened water does not push past the oil as easily and results in better sweep efficiency of the oil in the reservoir. Due to the cost and quantity of chemical additives required and the narrow range of conditions in which such projects are feasible, polymer floods such as these are relatively rare.

Gas injection. Gas produced from a reservoir can be reinjected into the reservoir if there is no market for the gas or if its reinjection will increase the ultimate recovery of oil or condensate. If there is no nearby pipeline and regulators will not allow gas flaring, operators often reinject the gas (see Chapter 11).

Reinjection enhances the current production of oil or condensate. Reinjection also means that the gas can be produced in the future when a nearby pipeline may exist. In some situations, the reinjection of gas maintains an oil reservoir's pressure above a critical threshold called the "bubble point." The bubble point depends on the pressure, temperature and chemical composition of the oil and gas in a particular reservoir.

When pressure is above the bubble point, all gas in the reservoir is absorbed in the crude oil and is said to be "in solution." When pressure falls below the bubble point, gas bubbles out of the solution, much like the bubbles that form when you open a carbonated beverage. If the operator can maintain reservoir pressure above the bubble point, ultimate oil recovery generally will be much higher.

In gas reservoirs that contain condensate, the corollary to the bubble point is called the "dew point." Above the dew point, all condensate in the reservoir exists as gas. When the reservoir pressure falls below the dew point, the condensate can liquefy in the reservoir, thereby reducing the ultimate recovery of both condensate and gas.

In a gas cycling operation, the resulting gas stream after it has passed through the separators removing the condensate (lean gas) is reinjected into the reservoir where it maintains pressure and absorbs additional condensate, increasing the ultimate recovery.

In the previous examples, the reinjected gas can be part or all of the production, or the operator may obtain additional gas to provide the necessary volume. At some point, the incremental recovery of oil or condensate does not justify the additional expense of the reinjection compressors and related facilities. The operator may shut down the process and sell any excess gas in what is often called the blowdown phase.

Enriched gas and miscible injection. Propane or butane mixed with natural gas (enriched gas) or carbon dioxide (CO_2) can be injected into an oil reservoir. Enriched gas or CO_2 acts as a miscible solvent when it contacts oil. The oil absorbs the rich gas or CO_2, which reduces its viscosity and enhances its ability to flow. Reduced viscosity and increased pressure from injection increase the ultimate recovery factor. The solvent usually is removed during separation and reinjected.

The cost of propane or butane limits the number of enriched gas projects. Miscible CO_2 projects are expensive but are relatively common in areas where they have been shown to work well, particularly in West Texas and New Mexico. A common technique known as WAG ("water and gas" or "water alternating gas") injects a volume of CO_2 followed by a volume of water to displace it. This procedure achieves the desired effect at a lower cost.

Thermal stimulation. In reservoirs containing oil with high viscosity (generally heavy oil with high density indicated by an API gravity below 20 degrees), operators may stimulate production by heating the contents of the reservoir, injecting hot water or steam as depicted in the previous Figure 34-1. The water or steam lowers the viscosity and flushes the oil to the producing wellbore. The steam may be continuously injected, or the operator may use a cyclic steam-injection process called "huff-and-puff."

In huff-and-puff, the steam is injected periodically into the reservoir. As the steam condenses, the resulting hot water thins the oil and drives it to the wellbore. Another injection of steam follows, and the huff-and-puff cycle continues until the reservoir is heated.

Continuous steamflooding and huff-and-puff steam injection are quite common in the fields containing heavy oil near Bakersfield, California. Steamflooding provides significant markets for natural gas. The gas is burned in cogeneration facilities that generate: (1) heat to convert water to steam and (2) electricity used onsite or sold to a local electric utility.

Another thermal process is "fireflooding" or in-situ combustion. Air is injected into the reservoir and a fire is ignited that burns some of the oil residing in it. As the reservoir heats up, the heavy oil ideally flows into the producing well. Fireflooding is used only when other stimulation methods are not feasible, as results have been less successful than other enhanced recovery techniques.

Other methods. The enhanced recovery methods described in this chapter are used on many projects around the world. Other types include: (1) heating the reservoir via electrical currents, (2) introducing anaerobic bacteria to convert a portion of the hydrocarbons to gases to repressurize the reservoir and (3) repressurization using nitrogen or combustion flue gases.

Enhanced recovery accounting issues

Two major accounting questions relate to enhanced recovery: (1) determining when the related reserves should be included in the reserves disclosures and DD&A calculation and (2) accounting for material injected into the reservoir. See Chapter 12 for a more detailed discussion of these two accounting issues.

● ● ●

1 Zitha, P. and R. Felder, D. Zornes, K. Brown, and K. Mohanty. Increasing Hydrocarbon Recovery Factors.
   www.spe.org/en/industry/increasing-hydrocarbon-recovery-factors.

Basic E&P Income Tax Rules

This chapter presents an overview of the U.S. federal income tax laws and regulations unique to petroleum exploration and production. Countervailing tax policy, combined with the unique nature of the oil and gas industry, make taxation of income from oil and gas operations a complex and highly specialized area.

E&P companies should not rely solely on the information found in this chapter. Outside professional advice and direct reference to current tax laws and regulations are strongly advised.

Oil and gas taxes in the U.S.

The U.S. does not levy a special federal tax on income from oil and gas production. Instead, income from oil and gas activity is currently taxed within the parameters of the regular U.S. federal income tax system. This contrasts with many other countries that impose additional taxes on oil and gas production by way of either higher tax rates or special taxes.

Domestic tax laws provide many special rules for determining income and deductions from oil and gas exploration and production activities. To properly apply them, tax professionals must understand basic industry concepts.

On December 22, 2017, the Tax Cuts and Jobs Act (TCJA) was enacted and introduced significant tax reform to the U.S. The TCJA repealed the alternative minimum tax (AMT) for corporations, previously a significant consideration for upstream oil and gas companies. The TCJA also introduced significant changes related to the deductibility of interest expense, U.S. taxation of international operations and many other changes, including a Base Erosion and Anti-abuse Tax (BEAT) on foreign related-party payments.

Numerous states and some cities levy their own income taxes. In most cases, state and local taxes are based on federal taxable income, with certain adjustments allowed. Local jurisdictions may also impose other taxes, including real and personal property taxes and sales taxes. Virtually every state with oil and gas producing activities imposes a tax on the value or quantity of oil and gas produced within its jurisdiction, referred to as a production tax or severance tax.

Definition of an oil and gas property

It is important to clearly understand the concept of property as it forms the cornerstone of U.S. oil and gas income taxation. Almost all tax accounting for oil and gas activity is analyzed on a property-by-property basis, whether computing depletion deductions, calculating intangible drilling cost deductions or determining gain or loss on property disposition. Despite its emphasis on property, U.S. income tax law is almost silent on how to define the term. Internal Revenue Code (IRC) Sec. 614(a) states, "The term property means each separate interest owned by the taxpayer in each mineral deposit in each separate tract or parcel of land."

For purposes of this definition, "interest" means an economic interest. Therefore, an oil and gas property constitutes:

- Each separate economic interest owned by the taxpayer,
- In each separate mineral deposit,
- In each separate tract or parcel of land.

Generally, tax authorities interpret this brief definition literally, meaning that each mineral interest, such as a royalty interest, working interest, overriding royalty interest (ORRI), production payment or net profits interest (NPI) is a separate property, unless the same types of interests were acquired at the same time, from the same assignor and in geographically contiguous tracts.

If a taxpayer holds more than one operating interest in the same tract, the interests must be combined and treated as a single property unless an election is made to treat them separately. Two or more separate nonoperating interests in the same tract may be combined, with the permission of the IRS, upon demonstration by a taxpayer that the principal purpose of the combination is not tax avoidance. However, nonoperating interests cannot be combined with operating interests.

In some cases, contiguous tracts may require unitization, which dictates that contiguous tracts must be developed as a single property. IRC Sec. 614(b)(3) provides that the taxpayer's properties in a compulsory unitization are treated as one property. This rule applies to certain voluntary unitizations as well.

Generally, unitization is viewed as an exchange of the taxpayer's old properties for new properties. The transaction can result in a taxable gain to the extent of cash received to adjust the participants' share of unit costs. It also may give rise to an exchange of depreciable equipment costs for depletable leasehold costs by delaying or eliminating the deduction of such costs.

Economic interests

Determining whether a property interest is considered an economic interest is an important distinction. Only the owner of an economic interest may deduct depletion from oil and gas income generated by a producing property. U.S. tax regulations provide the following description of an economic interest:

> An economic interest is possessed in every case in which the taxpayer has acquired by investment any interest in minerals in place... and secures, by any form of legal relationship, income derived from the extraction of the mineral... to which he must look for a return of his capital. [Treas. Reg. Sec. 1.611-1(b)]

A large body of case law has developed around this description to clarify this concept. For tax purposes, an economic interest generally must meet all four of the following requirements:

1. It must represent a capital interest in the minerals in place.

2. It must provide the right to share in minerals produced or the right to proceeds from their sale.

3. The interest holder must look solely to proceeds from extraction for a return on investment.

4. It must be held as a matter of legal right.

Royalty interests, working interests, ORRIs and NPIs are common property interests in the industry that are considered economic interests, such that their holders are eligible to claim depletion on income derived from them.

If structured properly, production payments are treated as borrowings or loans for federal income tax purposes. Carved-out production payments are treated as borrowings by both the operator (grantor) and the investor (lender), while retained production payments are recorded as notes receivable at fair value by the assignor (retainer) and as a purchase money mortgage payable by the assignee.

However, there are two exceptions to this general rule.

- One of the exceptions arises when a production payment is retained in a leasing transaction by the mineral rights owner. In this case, the production payment retained is treated as an economic interest in the property. The lessor (transferor) treats income received from the production payment as income subject to deductions for depletion. The lessee records the amounts paid to reduce the principal of the production payment as a capitalized installment bonus. This can result in the capitalized amount of depletable basis increasing during the period of the production payment, even though reserves are decreasing. Knowledgeable lessees typically avoid this type of arrangement.

- Although infrequent, a second exception arises when a production payment is carved-out and sold with the proceeds pledged for use in exploring or developing properties from which the payment is carved. In this case, the production payment is considered an economic interest held by the investor. The investor treats income received from the production payment as income from its interest in the properties subject to deductions for depletion. The assignor of the production payment does not recognize income from the proceeds received on the assignment but must reduce deductible exploration and development costs by the amount received.

Leasehold basis

The acquisition costs for an oil and gas property are commonly referred to as leasehold basis, depletable basis or leasehold. For tax purposes, the term leasehold reflects all costs of acquisition that must be capitalized, such as:

- Purchase price allocable to the mineral interest in the case of an acquisition of a fee interest (mineral rights of a property).

- Lease bonus paid in the case of a leasing transaction.

- Finders' fees, commissions, legal fees, title disputes and other professional fees incurred in an acquisition.

- Delay rentals that have been capitalized (discussed further in Chapter 7).

If an oil and gas property is productive, capitalized leasehold costs are recovered through depletion deductions over the property's productive life. If the property is determined to be worthless as a result of events such as abandonment, lease termination, cessation of production or drilling of a non-producing well or dry hole, then any remaining capitalized leasehold costs must be deducted in the year the property is deemed worthless. Timing of the deduction for worthlessness is often an issue; it is important for the property holder or lease holder to identify a specific event to establish the time of worthlessness. Actions of the property holder or lease holder are important in determining whether the property should be deemed worthless for tax purposes.

For example, even if a dry hole was drilled on a lease, the lease would not be deemed worthless if a delay rental is later paid or additional exploration and development work is undertaken.

Geological and geophysical costs

Any geological and geophysical (G&G) costs paid or incurred in connection with the exploration for or development of oil and gas in the U.S. are to be amortized over 24 months utilizing a half-year convention. Costs paid or incurred by "major integrated oil companies," as defined in IRC Sec. 167(h)(5), are amortized over seven years.

The IRC definition of major integrated oil companies is slightly narrower than the traditional concept of companies that are not eligible for percentage depletion (described later in this chapter). Generally, these companies have more than 500,000 barrels per day of average daily worldwide crude oil production and more than $1 billion in gross receipts for a given taxable year.

In 2016, a tax court case, *CGG Americas v. Commissioner,* 147 T.C. 78, extended the amortization deduction for G&G costs to third-party service providers, even if they are not considered an E&P company or a taxpayer with a mineral interest. For example, a taxpayer hired as an independent contractor to conduct seismic surveys for an E&P company in connection with the exploration or development of oil or gas may deduct costs to conduct the surveys under IRC Sec. 167(h)(5).

G&G costs incurred in connection with oil and gas properties outside the U.S. are generally capitalized to the cost of the related property or leasehold and recovered through future depletion deductions. If G&G costs do not lead to a property acquisition, the costs are generally deducted in the year paid or incurred.

Development costs

For tax purposes, the costs incurred to develop an oil and gas property generally are divided into two categories: (1) intangible drilling and development costs (IDCs) and (2) tangible equipment costs (TDCs). Proper classification is important because the tax treatments differ significantly. In addition, tax professionals should understand the rules applicable to dry holes.

Intangible drilling and development costs. IDCs have no salvage value; they are incidental to and necessary for drilling wells or preparing wells for oil and gas production. IDCs are usually the single largest category of expenditures associated with drilling a well. IDCs are governed by the provisions of IRC Sec. 263(c) and Treas. Reg. Sec. 1.612-4.

IDCs include all amounts paid for labor, fuel, repairs, hauling, rents and supplies that are used for:

- Drilling a well.

- Clearing and draining ground, building roads and surveying before drilling a well.

- Assembling derricks, tanks, pipelines and other physical structures necessary to drill and prepare a well for production.

For federal income tax purposes, IDCs only include those intangible costs incurred in drilling a well and installing equipment in the well through the point that valves are placed at the wellhead to control production. An exception to this rule are other intangible costs incurred after the wellhead is installed that do not relate to installing equipment (e.g., removal of the rig from the drilling site and restoring the location). These costs are also treated as IDC for federal income tax purposes.

Labor costs and other intangible costs to install flow lines, treating equipment and storage tanks, however, are not subject to the IDC election for tax purposes. Therefore, these costs are classified as tangible equipment costs for federal income tax purposes.

A taxpayer holding an operating right to a U.S. oil and gas property must elect under IRC Sec. 263(c) whether to capitalize IDC or deduct it currently. The election must be made in the first year the taxpayer pays or incurs IDC, and it is generally binding for all future years. In almost all cases, an election is made to deduct IDC.

An election to deduct IDC currently is simply a matter of deducting it on the tax return in the first year such costs are paid or incurred. Given the importance of this initial election, most taxpayers also attach a statement to the income tax return for the year in which such costs are first incurred to further substantiate the election.

Those who fail to deduct IDC in the first year are deemed to have elected to capitalize these costs, which must then be allocated to leasehold costs and recovered through depletion. When expenditures are connected to the installation of tangible equipment, these amounts are allocated to tangible equipment costs and recovered through depreciation.

Taxpayers who make the initial election to deduct IDC can make a subsequent election under IRC Section 59(e), on an annual basis, to capitalize all or any portion of the IDC incurred in a given tax year. This is a year-by-year and dollar-by-dollar election. The capitalized portion is amortized ratably over a 60-month period beginning in the month costs are paid or incurred. Once made, the election cannot be changed retroactively.

Integrated oil and gas companies having elected to deduct IDC may deduct only 70 percent at the time those costs are incurred. The remaining 30 percent must be capitalized and amortized ratably over a 60-month period beginning in the month the costs are paid or incurred.

IDC for wells located outside the U.S. may not be deducted currently. At the election of the taxpayer, such costs are included in the adjusted basis of the oil and gas property for purposes of computing depletion. Alternatively, the costs can be amortized over 120-month period.

Common IDC items include costs in the pre-drilling, drilling, completion and post-completion phases of a well, as discussed below:

- Pre-drilling costs

  - Work performed by geologists to determine the exact location of the drill site (not G&G work to select leases).

  - Clearing the well site, digging slush pits, building roads and bridges and surveying to stake the well location; building the drilling rig pad site.

  - Laying flow lines for water to be used in drilling.

  - Installing tanks for water and fuel for drilling purposes.

  - Moving and erecting the drilling rig (if company-owned).

  - Constructing racks for drill pipe and other tubular goods to be used in the drilling process.

- Drilling costs

  - If contracting for drilling, the contractor's rates constitute the majority of IDC costs in this phase; drilling mud and other items may also be charged to the operator.

  - If using the operator's own drilling rig, the wages paid to the crew, drilling rig maintenance and supplies, depreciation on the rig, drilling mud, water, fuel, power, chemicals, bits, reamers and overhead related to the operation of the rig represent the IDC costs.

- Completion costs

  - Drill stem testing, well logging and other testing such as cores and side wall sampling.

  - Perforating, cementing, fracturing and acidizing.

  - Transporting and installing subsurface equipment.

- Post-completion charges and facilities expenses

  - Removing drilling equipment from the location (if operator-owned).

  - Restoring the land by filling slush pits and grading the area.

  - Repairing surface damages incurred during drilling.

  - Plugging and abandonment costs (if the well is a dry hole).

Well costs. Proper classification of well costs as IDC or tangible equipment costs is important for an oil and gas company. It is critical for joint venture operators to classify the venture's well costs properly when billing joint venture partners for their share of costs. This is commonly accomplished via joint interest billing (JIB), which allows all members of the venture to treat costs properly in accordance with their own elections.

Treas. Reg. Sec. 1.612-4(c) describes some items not included in IDCs:

> (c) *Nonoptional items distinguished.*
>
> (1) Capital items: The option with respect to intangible drilling and development costs does not apply to expenditures by which the taxpayer acquires tangible property ordinarily considered as having a salvage value. Examples of such items are the costs of the actual materials in those structures which are constructed in the wells and on the property, and the cost of drilling tools, pipe, casing, tubing, tanks, engines, boilers, machines, etc. The option does not apply to any expenditures for wages, fuel, repairs, hauling, supplies, etc., in connection with equipment, facilities, or structures not incident to or necessary for the drilling of wells, such as structures for storing or treating oil or gas. These are capital items and are returnable through depreciation.
>
> (2) Expense items: Expenditures which must be charged off as expense, regardless of the option provided by this section, are those for labor, fuel, repairs, hauling, supplies, etc., in connection with the operation of the wells and of other facilities on the property for the production of oil and gas.

Revenue Ruling 70-414 provides further explanation of costs excluded from IDC classification:

> [IDC] excludes expenditures incurred in installing production facilities. The items thus excluded consist of expenditures relating to the installation of equipment such as pumping equipment, flow lines, separators, storage tanks, treating equipment, and salt water disposal equipment. Equipment of a character that is ordinarily considered as having a salvage value, whether it consists of production facilities or equipment necessary for the completion of a well, including cost of casing in a well (even though cemented in the well to such an extent that it has no net salvage value), is a depreciable item, the cost of which may be recovered only through the depreciation allowance. *Harper Oil Company v. U.S.*, 425 F. 2d 1335 (10th Cir. 1979), 70-1 USTC 9330. A producing well is completed when the casing, including the so-called "Christmas tree", has been installed.

Costs of installing the following items are also not subject to the IDC expense option provided for in Treas. Reg. Sec. 1.612-4(c):

- Oil well pumps (upon initial completion of the well) including the necessary housing structures

- Oil well pumps (after the well has flowed for a time) including the necessary housing structures

- Oil well separators including the necessary housing structures

- Pipelines from the wellhead to oil storage tanks on the producing lease

- Oil storage tanks on the producing lease

- Salt water disposal equipment including any necessary pipelines

- Pipelines from the mouth of a gas well to the first point of control such as a common carrier pipeline, natural gas plant or carbon black plant

- Recycling equipment including any necessary pipelines

- Pipelines from oil storage tanks on the producing leasehold to a common carrier pipeline

Dry hole costs. If a well is drilled and found to be a dry hole, development costs associated with it should be deducted as dry hole costs. Leasehold costs may or may not be currently deductible depending on whether the entire lease is deemed worthless.

Offshore considerations. The classification of IDC when drilling and developing wells offshore has been the subject of controversy between the IRS and taxpayers, particularly when it comes to costs incurred to design, construct and install drilling platforms. However, several high profile court cases suggest that such costs are largely IDC in nature.

For example, in a 1976 case, the court concluded that template design platforms to be utilized in drilling offshore wells were largely IDC, even though portions might be technically capable of being dismantled, stored and re-used elsewhere.

In a 1981 case, the taxpayer deducted as IDC certain onshore fabrication costs for jackets, decks and pilings, and the court determined that neither the platforms themselves nor such components could ordinarily be considered as having salvage value.

In a 1986 case, the court concluded that tension leg platforms were not ordinarily considered as having salvage value; it rejected hypothetical methods of salvage and re-use that were neither borne out by experience nor taken into account in design and construction.

The IRS issued further guidance in Revenue Ruling 89-56 with respect to the above court cases, stating that the facts and circumstances of an offshore platform should be carefully analyzed to determine which expenditures, if any, are eligible to be deducted as IDC.

Tangible drilling costs

Purchased equipment that has salvage value should be recorded in the TDC account. This category can include surface and production casing, wellhead equipment, tanks, pumps, separators and other machinery.

In general, tax laws govern the definition of tangible costs, which include all costs of the physical assets along with installation costs. Accounting theory provides that costs of installing equipment, including subsurface equipment such as casing, should be included in the cost of tangible assets.

Because most companies elect to expense IDC for income tax purposes, and because the tax laws include installation costs of equipment (through the point that control valves are installed) in the election, these amounts are generally treated as IDCs. For financial accounting purposes, the distinction is not important because intangible drilling costs are recovered in the same way as tangible drilling costs.

Tangible equipment costs are capitalized and recovered over the life of the equipment by means of depreciation. IRS guidelines define the useful life of all types of tangible equipment for depreciation purposes. Under current law, most tangible production equipment has a tax depreciable life of seven years. Lease and well equipment may also be depreciated using a UOP method.

Certain equipment located on current or former Native American reservations may be depreciated using a life significantly shorter than regular depreciation allows. Most of this eligible equipment is located in the state of Oklahoma.

From time to time, depreciation rules are modified to provide an incentive for investment in tangible equipment. For example, the TCJA provides for 100 percent bonus depreciation (full expensing) of qualified assets acquired and placed into service after September 27, 2017 and extending through December 31, 2022, followed by a five-year phase-out.

New restrictions on taxpayers eligible for bonus depreciation were introduced under the TCJA. Taxpayers that are in certain regulated trades or businesses (e.g., natural gas pipeline transportation) are not eligible to claim bonus depreciation, but they also are not subject to the interest limitation rules discussed later in this chapter.

Other considerations

As noted in other chapters, GAAP provides different methods for determining the unit of property and aggregating costs. However, IRC Sec. 614 provides specific guidance for determining the unit of property for tax purposes.

Additionally, cost recovery for leasehold costs and development costs is generally the same for GAAP; therefore, financial accountants may not place a high level of importance on distinguishing between these types of costs, even though the distinction is critical to comply with tax rules.

Reconciling accounting data under GAAP to data required for U.S. tax purposes can be cumbersome. Errors in understanding and interpreting the data can often lead to amended returns or adjustments as the result of an IRS audit. Advances in technology have improved the availability of data and the burden of income tax reporting, but this area remains a challenge for many in the industry.

Tax depletion methods

By their nature, producing oil and gas properties are depleting assets. U.S. income tax law recognizes this by providing, in limited cases, a depletion deduction to owners of the economic interest. The depletion deduction is calculated separately for each unit of depletable property. Two methods exist for computing a depletion allowance: (1) cost depletion and (2) percentage (or statutory) depletion. Taxpayers eligible to claim percentage depletion must compute depletion using both methods and claim the higher of the two on a property-by-property basis.

Cost depletion

Under cost depletion, units-of-production from each property during the year are divided by proved, probable and prospective reserves attributable to the property at the beginning of the year to calculate a cost factor. This factor is multiplied by net leasehold costs of the property (capitalized minerals costs less depletion previously taken) to arrive at a cost depletion amount.

Reserves estimation challenges. Determining proved, probable and prospective reserves for cost depletion purposes has been a source of continuing controversy between taxpayers and the IRS. This is partly due to the requirement in the regulations to revise the original year's reserve estimate for each well only for subsequent operations or development. Accordingly, the effects of commodity price changes included in the SEC reserves disclosures according to ASC 932 are excluded from reserve volume changes for income tax depletion purposes.

Safe harbor election. In 2004, the IRS released Revenue Procedure 2004-19 that provides a safe harbor election which allows taxpayers to estimate probable or prospective reserves for purposes of computing cost depletion. By making the election, taxpayers may simplify the determination of the appropriate quantity of probable and prospective reserves for cost depletion calculations. Once elected, the company's estimate of its total recoverable units is equal to 105 percent of its proved reserves. The company must attach a statement electing the safe harbor to its federal income tax return for the first taxable year of the election. The election is effective until revoked and is non-revocable in the first year elected.

Despite the changes made to the reserves disclosure rules in ASC 932 (discussed in Chapter 30), the IRS has not revisited this topic, and the 105 percent rate election remains common practice. However, this safe harbor election still prohibits changes to proved reserves due to economic factors that are commonly reflected in SEC reserves. Therefore, E&P companies must identify and understand any downward adjustments to proved reserves that occur in order to determine if the downward adjustment is allowed for tax purposes.

Percentage depletion

The percentage depletion method (also referred to as statutory depletion) provides a deduction for a specified percentage of gross revenue from each domestic property. Currently, the depletion rate is 15 percent for non-marginal well production. Such depletion is limited to the property's taxable income (before the depletion deduction).

Percentage depletion is not generally available to integrated oil and gas companies. For this purpose, an integrated oil company is generally one that carries on directly (or through a related party) significant retail activities or refining in excess of 75,000 barrels a day on average for a given tax year. Independent producers and royalty owners also face limitations as their percentage depletion deduction is limited to U.S. production of 1,000 barrels of oil equivalent per day (BOED).

Ordering rules and elections are available to the taxpayer which can help maximize the percentage depletion deduction. Percentage depletion cannot exceed 65 percent of total taxable income (before the deduction) for a given tax year. However, amounts disallowed due to the 65 percent limit may be carried forward indefinitely, subject to the 65 percent limit each year.

Concessions. Special concessions exist for marginally profitable properties defined as:

- Oil and gas produced from a domestic stripper well property (generally 15 BOE or less of production per day, per well)

- Oil from a domestic property which is substantially all heavy oil (gravity of 20 degrees API or less)

Independent producers or royalty owners holding marginal properties receive an increase of one percent for each whole dollar that the reference price for crude oil in the immediately preceding calendar year is less than $20 per barrel.

Reference price is a defined amount based on the average wellhead price in the U.S. as published by the IRS each calendar year. For many years, the maximum depletion rate under this concession has been 15 percent, since the reference price has been greater than $20 per barrel.

Allowable depletion. Allowable depletion is the higher of either cost depletion or percentage depletion. It reduces a taxpayer's basis in each mineral property. Once the basis is reduced to zero, cost depletion can no longer be claimed. However, percentage depletion can be claimed as long as the property continues to produce oil and gas, subject to the limitation discussed earlier.

Tax depletion calculations

As an example, assume Operator JSB acquired a mineral lease and began drilling in January 2019. The well was successful and production began in April 2019.

During the year, 10,000 barrels of oil were produced and sold for total gross revenue after royalties of $577,500. Drilling, production and allocable overhead expenses on the property amounted to $492,500, leaving $85,000 of taxable income from the property before deducting depletion.

At December 31, 2019, the property had a leasehold basis of $548,525, before consideration of depletion for the current year. Reserves at December 31, 2019, totaled 360,000 barrels. Taxable income from all sources for 2019, before depletion, was $120,000. The mineral interest is a U.S. property and Operator JSB is an independent producer.

Figure 26-1 and Figure 26-2 illustrate tax depletion calculations using cost depletion and percentage depletion, respectively.

Figure 26-1

Cost depletion example

$$\frac{2019 \text{ production}}{\text{Beginning of year reserves}} \times \begin{array}{c} \text{Leasehold basis at} \\ \text{end of year} \end{array}$$

$$\frac{10,000 \text{ bbls}}{360,000 \text{ bbls} + 10,000 \text{ bbls}} \times \$548,525 = \mathbf{\$14,825}$$

Figure 26-2

Percentage depletion example

Gross revenues	$577,500
Statutory rate	x 15%
Percentage depletion before limitation	$ 86,625
Limit: Pre-depletion taxable income from the property	$ 85,000
Taxable income (all sources) before depletion	$120,000
Limitation based on taxable income	x 65%
Taxable income limitation	$ 78,000
Percentage depletion after limitations	**$ 78,000**

Based on the calculations in Figure 26-1 and Figure 26-2, the allowable depletion for 2019 would be $78,000, determined as the greater of $14,825 cost depletion or $78,000 percentage depletion. Operator JSB's leasehold basis beginning on January 1, 2020 would be $470,525 (calculated as $548,525 less $78,000). Additionally, $7,000 of percentage depletion (calculated as $85,000 less $78,000) would carryover to succeeding years.

Sharing arrangements

To reduce the costs and risks of developing oil and gas properties, two or more parties often join together in a sharing arrangement for exploration, in which one party contributes cash, property, services or other consideration in exchange for an interest in the mineral property owned by the other party.

Farmouts are a prevalent type of sharing arrangement where the owner (assignor) of an operating interest assigns all or a portion of the operating interest to another party (assignee) in return for the assignee's assumption of all or a portion of the costs of developing the property.

Sharing arrangements take many forms including:

- Drilling a well in exchange for the entire operating interest (the assignor may or may not retain a nonoperating interest).

- Drilling a well in exchange for a portion of the operating interest.

- Drilling a well in exchange for a nonoperating interest.

- Pledging cash to the development of a property in exchange for an operating or nonoperating interest.

- Participating in a mixed sharing arrangement in which cash or other consideration, as well as development work, is contributed in exchange for a property interest.

Single tax property. A simple sharing arrangement involving a single tax property is considered a nontaxable transaction. If no consideration passes between the parties, other than a contribution to or assumption of an obligation to develop a property, then neither party realizes a taxable gain or loss from the transaction.

This concept is frequently referred to as the pooling of capital doctrine. Other U.S. tax principles generally applicable to sharing arrangements include:

1. Only the party that incurs and pays a cost can deduct it for tax purposes.

2. Only operating interest owners can deduct IDC and depreciation, and only to the extent of their fractional share of the operating interest held through complete payout. The fractional share of IDC or equipment costs incurred in excess of the fractional share owned in the operating interest must be capitalized and added to depletable leasehold costs.

For example, assume that Company X agrees with Company Y to drill and equip a well on Company Y's undeveloped property at no cost to Company Y, in exchange for a 75 percent operating interest. Company X incurs $1,000,000 of IDC and $400,000 in equipment costs.

- Company X can deduct $750,000 of its IDC ($1,000,000 x 75%).

- Company X can depreciate $300,000 of its equipment costs ($400,000 x 75%).

- The remaining $250,000 of IDC and $100,000 of equipment costs are added to Company X's depletable leasehold costs.

- Company Y has no right to deduct any costs to drill or equip the well since such costs were borne entirely by Company X.

Multiple tax properties. The tax consequences of entering into a mixed sharing arrangement are more complex. In general, the transaction must be divided into two parts: (1) the pooling of capital doctrine is applied to development work contributions and (2) potential tax gain or loss flows from the contribution of cash or other consideration. The pooling of capital doctrine works well in situations where a single tax property is involved; when multiple properties are involved, there is a risk of inadvertently triggering the recognition of taxable gains.

This situation can occur in earned acreage situations whereby a contribution is made to the development of one tax property and an interest is earned not only in that property, but in other properties as well. The IRS made it clear in Revenue Ruling 77-176 that the pooling of capital doctrine does not extend to such cases; the carrying party (i.e., the party paying its own costs and those costs of another party) is considered to be paid for rendering services, and the carried party (i.e., the party whose costs are paid by another party) is treated as having sold a portion of the interest in the properties.

Accordingly, both parties to the sharing arrangement would be required to recognize taxable income or gain based on the fair market value of the property (the earned acreage). Most joint ventures tend to utilize tax partnerships for an area of mutual interest (AMI) or JOA in order to reduce the risk of such a result when earned acreage is present in the terms of a joint venture agreement. See the "Partnerships" section later in this chapter for further discussion.

Tax implications of organizational structures

Because of economic uncertainties in exploring for and producing oil and gas, two or more parties often join together to locate and develop prospects. Joint efforts to explore for oil and gas take a variety of legal forms: joint ventures, partnerships, corporations and certain hybrid entities (such as S corporations and limited liability companies, which combine the legal and tax characteristics of both partnerships and corporations).

Joint ventures

In the U.S. it is common for working interest owners to jointly develop a property. Their rights and obligations are outlined in two documents: (1) a joint venture agreement and (2) a joint operating agreement. Under a typical joint operating agreement, one working interest owner is designated as the operator of the joint venture, while others assume the role of nonoperators.

Joint venture participants have an important decision to make about their tax status: whether to be treated as a partnership for tax purposes (often referred to as a "tax partnership," since no legal partnership entity exists) or elect out of the partnership tax provisions under IRC Section 761.

In practice, most choose to elect out if there is no significant carried interest or possibility of earned acreage. If participants meet the criteria and elect to be excluded from partnership provisions, then entity-level tax accounting is not required. Instead, participants can independently report their shares of revenue and expenses for tax purposes. In addition, each participant can make an election to expense or capitalize IDC.

Joint venture participants may elect exclusion from IRS partnership provisions if they meet three conditions:

1. Each participant owns an interest in the oil and gas property as a co-owner, either in fee or under a lease that grants exclusive operating rights.

2. Participants reserve the right to take in-kind or dispose of their individual shares of production.

3. Participants do not jointly sell the oil and gas produced, although each may delegate the right to sell their share to one of the participants for a period not to exceed one year. This right may be renewed annually.

If a joint venture does not qualify for exclusion from IRS partnership provisions, the joint venture is required to file an annual partnership federal income tax return and report income and deductions to the joint venture parties in accordance with IRS partnership tax rules.

Partnerships

Partnerships are separate entities for tax and legal purposes. In contrast to joint ventures, partnerships account for revenues and expenses at the entity level. Partnerships file tax returns but pay no entity-level U.S. federal income tax (even though some states and foreign jurisdictions tax partnerships as entities). Instead, the partnership is treated as a conduit, and each partner accounts for and pays taxes based on their allocable shares of net income or loss and for their shares of credits. Two types of partnerships are used: general and limited.

In a general partnership, all partners have unlimited personal liability for legal obligations of the partnership. By contrast, a limited partnership has one or more general partners with unlimited personal liability and one or more classes of limited partners. Typically, the personal liability of a limited partner does not exceed the partner's contributed capital. Because of relatively high risks in oil and gas exploration and production, limited partnerships are a common form of organization, particularly when operations are funded by outside investors. However, investors are often subject to passive loss rules if the form of entity limits an investor's legal liability.

Limited liability companies (LLC) with multiple shareholders are treated as a partnership for federal income tax purposes, unless the LLC makes an election to be taxed as a corporation. Many important tax elections are made by the partnership, rather than by the partners, and these actions are binding on all partners. For example, the partnership makes the initial year election to capitalize or expense IDC, and it determines whether oil and gas properties will be combined or remain separate for tax purposes. Each partner can then make the year-by-year, dollar-by-dollar election to capitalize otherwise deductible IDCs (as previously discussed) and amortize them over a 60-month period.

Frequently, a joint venture may take the form of a partnership solely for federal income tax purposes, even if it is not organized as a legal partnership. Tax partnerships may be elected in order to:

- Make special allocations of deductible items where one party contributes a disproportionate amount of the costs.

- Mitigate the risk of recognition of phantom income (taxable income, but no cash) where earned acreage is present.

Utilization of a tax partnership enables joint venture participants to specially allocate income and deductions from the partnership based on relative contributions to the joint venture as outlined in the JOA. In order to receive this benefit, tax returns must be filed, thereby increasing administrative costs to the operator, which is usually designated as the tax matters partner. In addition, complex capital account maintenance rules must be followed in order to make sure that allocations in the JOA have substantial economic effect in order to be respected for federal income tax purposes.

Although most income and deduction items are accounted for at the entity level, oil and gas depletion is calculated only at the partner level. The partnership is obligated to provide partners with sufficient information to calculate depletion deductions. Refer to Chapter 29 for a discussion of tax considerations related to master limited partnerships (MLPs).

Corporations

A corporation is a separate legal entity organized under state law. It offers shareholders legal liability limited to their investment in the corporation. Corporations file their own income tax returns and pay federal and state taxes on net income.

Profits are distributed to shareholders in the form of dividends, which are subject to taxation at the shareholder level. Accordingly, the price paid for the limited liability provided by a corporation is two levels of tax on its distributed profit.

S Corporations

An S corporation is a hybrid entity that combines the legal characteristics of a corporation with many of the tax advantages of a partnership. Other than for federal income tax purposes, an S corporation acts like any other corporation. It is incorporated under state law and offers its shareholders limited legal liability.

For income tax purposes, S corporations are conduit entities that pay no income tax at the corporate level. Line items of income, loss and credit flow directly to shareholders' individual returns. Similar to oil and gas partnerships, critical tax elections, such as the treatment of IDC and whether to aggregate or separate oil and gas properties, are made at the S corporation level.

Eligibility for S corporation status is strictly limited. A corporation must file an election statement subject to IRS approval, and meet five requirements:

- The corporation must be a domestic corporation that is not a member of an affiliated group.

- The corporation may have no more than 100 shareholders for tax years beginning after December 31, 2004.

- Shareholders may only be individuals, estates or certain qualifying trusts.

- No shareholder may be a non-resident alien.

- The corporation may have only one class of stock.

The treatment of S corporations for state income tax purposes varies. Some states require a separate S corporation election for state tax purposes; others accept the federal election. Some states fail to recognize S corporations as pass-through entities and treat them like regular corporations for state income tax purposes.

Limited liability companies

A limited liability company (LLC) is an entity formed under state statutes that allow it to combine the corporate characteristic of limited liability with the tax conduit benefits of a partnership. Because of widespread LLC use, most states now have limited liability company statutes in place. Oil and gas entities that seek the advantages of a hybrid form of organization, but that do not meet S corporation requirements, often consider LLC status.

Loss limitations

Investors in the oil and gas industry encounter the complex provisions of U.S. tax law which limit the use of losses to offset income from other unrelated activities. These loss limitation rules fall into two broad categories: (1) at-risk rules and (2) passive loss rules.

At-risk rules

Under current at-risk rules, individuals engaged in oil and gas exploration and production can deduct a loss for tax purposes only to the extent they are at risk for such activity at year-end. An individual is considered at-risk to the extent of the cash and adjusted basis of any property contributed to the activity, plus amounts borrowed to fund the activity for which the individual is personally liable, or for which the individual has pledged property (other than property used in the oil and gas activity) as security for the loan.

For purposes of deducting partnership losses, partners in an oil and gas partnership are at risk to the extent of their contributions to the partnership (assuming the amounts contributed are at-risk at the individual level), and generally to the extent of loans to the partnership for which the partners could be held personally liable.

Loss deductions disallowed due to at-risk limitations are not necessarily lost. Disallowed losses can be carried forward indefinitely and deducted in succeeding tax years when at-risk amounts with respect to the activity are increased.

At-risk rules also contain anti-abuse provisions which address abrupt year-end increases in the at-risk amount. If a partner's at-risk amount decreases immediately after year-end, the partner (taxpayer) must demonstrate the transactions were undertaken for valid business purposes and not merely to avoid the at-risk rules.

Passive loss rules

Passive loss rules provide that investors cannot use losses or tax credits generated by passive activities to offset wage and salary income, business profits from activities in which the investor materially participates, or investment income such as dividends, interest or royalties. Instead, passive losses and credits can only be used to offset income from other passive activities.

Disallowed passive losses and credits are not irretrievably lost, but rather they are suspended and carried forward to offset passive income in future years. In addition, suspended losses and credits may be used in full in the year the passive investment is disposed of in a taxable transaction.

Passive loss rules apply to individuals, estates, trusts and certain closely held Subchapter C corporations. They do not apply directly to a partnership or a Subchapter S corporation, but rather to a partner's or a Subchapter S corporation shareholder's distributive share of passive losses and credits.

In general, a passive activity is any trade or business activity (including oil and gas) in which the taxpayer does not materially participate. To meet the material participation standard, a taxpayer must maintain regular, continuous and substantial participation in the activity.

Due to the nature of the oil and gas industry, passive loss rules do not apply to any investor who holds a working interest in an oil and gas property, either directly or through an entity that does not limit the investor's legal liability. The working interest exception applies regardless of the investor's level of participation in the activity. For this purpose, a working interest is solely the interest burdened with the cost of developing the property. Interests created out of the working interest such as overriding royalties, net profits interests or production payments do not qualify for the working interest exception.

Income tax credits and deductions

Oil and gas companies, like other taxpayers, are eligible to claim certain income tax credits and deductions as further described herein.

Enhanced oil recovery credit

IRC Sec. 43 allows an income tax credit for qualifying costs paid or incurred as part of an enhanced oil recovery (EOR) project. The credit is equal to 15 percent of qualified costs attributable to a domestic EOR project. Domestic projects that involve application of a qualified tertiary recovery method are eligible. They must be located in the U.S. and meet other criteria specified in tax regulations. In addition, a petroleum engineer must certify that the EOR project meets the specified requirements in Section 43.

Qualifying EOR costs include qualified tertiary injectant expenses, intangible drilling and development costs, and tangible property costs paid or incurred with respect to an asset that is used for the primary purpose of implementing an EOR project.

Approved qualified tertiary recovery methods include:

- Cyclic steam injection
- Steam drive injection
- Caustic flooding
- Carbon dioxide augmented waterflooding
- Immiscible nonhydrocarbon gas displacement

- Gas flood recovery methods
- In situ combustion
- Immiscible carbon dioxide displacement
- Chemical flood recovery methods
- Mobility control recovery method

The EOR credit is phased out ratably to the extent the average price of crude oil in the preceding calendar year is greater than $28 per barrel (inflation adjusted). A complete phase-out occurs when the excess is $6 or greater. The EOR credit has not been available in recent years due to average crude oil prices far exceeding the reference price.

Marginal well credit

The Marginal Well Credit (MWC) under IRC 45I originated from the American Jobs Creation Act in 2004. The credit is a production-based tax credit that incentivizes taxpayers to conduct exploration and production activities when oil and gas prices are low. It is especially beneficial to producers who have limited daily production.

A marginal well is one with average daily production of not more than 15 barrels of oil equivalents per day, or average daily production of not more than 25 barrels of oil equivalents per day with water production of 95 percent or more of waste output. If a well produces both oil and gas, the production of both commodities must be taken into account when determining if it qualifies as a marginal well.

The maximum credit allowed for qualified marginal wells is $3 per barrel for oil production and $0.50 per one Mcf of natural gas production. The credit is only available if commodity prices are below certain levels. Since enactment, the MWC has been largely unavailable due to commodity prices exceeding the threshold limit.

Research activities credit

Oil and gas companies, like other taxpayers, are eligible to claim a research and development (R&D) tax credit for increasing research activities. Historically, this was not a significant item for oil and gas companies; however, due to the recent levels of investment in non-conventional reserves in the U.S., a greater number of oil and gas companies have begun claiming an R&D tax credit.

Interest expense limitation

Under the new TCJA, taxpayers are subject to an amended IRC Sec. 163(j) that limits the deductibility of interest. Under the new limitation, interest expense is limited to the sum of: (a) the taxpayer's business interest income for the year, (b) 30 percent of the taxpayer's adjusted taxable income (ATI) for the year and (c) the taxpayer's floor plan financing interest expense for the year. Certain taxpayers in the business of pipeline gas transportation are not subject to this limitation. However, these taxpayers are also not eligible to claim bonus depreciation.

Passthrough deduction

The TCJA introduced a new passthrough deduction for individuals with IRC Sec. 199A qualified business income. The new law allows a 20 percent deduction on qualified income from passthrough entities (i.e., partnerships, S corporations and sole proprietorships); however, the deduction is generally limited by W-2 wages of the passthrough entity. Partnerships are common in the oil and gas industry, but often W-2 wages of the partnership are low. As a result, investors in such passthrough entities may find limited benefit from the new passthrough deduction provision. Investments in MLPs are not subject to the W-2 wage requirement.

International taxes

This section is intended to provide a summary of the principles of international taxation of oil and gas taxpayers. The TCJA amended the international tax regime from a worldwide system to a modified territorial system. Post tax reform, dividends from the earnings of foreign corporations receive a 100 percent dividends-received deduction. A foreign tax credit is available to offset U.S. income tax owed on foreign source income earned by branches. Taxpayers can also elect to deduct foreign taxes rather than claiming a credit; however, the deduction is typically less beneficial than the credit.

The foreign tax credit is subject to many limitations and oil and gas companies are subject to special limitations when claiming it. Accordingly, oil and gas companies must carefully track and compute foreign source income from oil and gas activities and taxes paid on such income. Many oil and gas companies pay taxes outside the United States at rates higher than the U.S. marginal rate of 21 percent, and therefore they generate excess foreign tax credits that are not able to be utilized to offset U.S. tax on non-oil and gas foreign source income.

Several exceptions to the 100 percent dividends-received deduction on foreign source dividends exist, mainly related to passive income (e.g., interest). Additionally, the TCJA also introduced a new foreign source income inclusion, Global Intangible Low Taxed Income (GILTI). GILTI is intended to tax the earnings of foreign corporations that exceed an applicable return on tangible assets. Coinciding with GILTI is the Foreign Derived Intangible Income (FDII) deduction, which is a special deduction intended to provide an incentive for U.S. taxpayers to hold intellectual property within the U.S.

As noted previously, the TCJA also introduced the Base Erosion Anti-abuse Tax (BEAT), which is a new minimum tax calculated on an adjusted taxable income without regard to certain payments made to foreign related parties.

State income taxes

Generally, the starting point for state taxable income (STI) is federal taxable income (FTI). The states then require modifications to FTI to arrive at STI. Discussed below are common modifications which may be significant to an E&P company, depending on a number of factors specific to each entity's facts and circumstances.

Intangible drilling costs

States generally conform to the federal treatment of IDC. However, in Alaska, all IDC must be capitalized. In Pennsylvania, only one-third of current year IDC may be expensed; the remaining costs must be capitalized and amortized over a period of 10 years.

Percentage depletion modifications

Depletion is one of the key areas of non-conformity between FTI and STI for oil and gas companies. The non-conforming states generally require a modification to percentage depletion, with some states, such as Alaska, only allowing cost depletion and other states requiring a state-specific percentage depletion calculation.

Several modifications by state follow:

- Alaska does not permit percentage depletion for oil and gas taxpayers.

- California does not conform to certain elements of the percentage depletion rules.

- Colorado allows for an enhanced depletion deduction for oil shale.

- Louisiana has its own percentage depletion calculation; percentage depletion is 15.8 percent of gross income of the property, although gross income excludes 72 percent of rents and royalties paid or incurred with respect to the property. Percentage depletion is not to exceed 36 percent of income of the property computed without depletion but with a deduction for federal income taxes. It currently requires a 28 percent reduction in the deduction.

- Oklahoma allows a taxpayer the election to calculate percentage depletion as 22 percent of gross income of the properties. For major oil companies (defined by local statute), the deduction may not exceed 50 percent of the net income of the taxpayer computed without depletion.

Bonus depreciation

States may decouple from the federal bonus provisions in a number of ways. For example, some states adopt the IRC as of a certain date, while others provide for their own recovery method. With the recent enactment of the TCJA and allowable 100 percent allowable bonus depreciation through 2022, it is unclear how states will react, and more states may decouple from the IRC.

Texas, for instance, conformed to the IRC as of January 1, 2007. As a result, Texas does not allow any deductions not provided for in the IRC as of that date. Alaska generally conforms to the IRC, but Oil and Gas Taxpayers (as defined by local statute) must use IRC Section 167 to compute depreciation as it existed on June 30, 1981.

Arkansas and California both have static IRC conformity, similar to Texas, but they both specifically decouple from bonus depreciation. Pennsylvania generally conforms to the IRC but it specifically decouples bonus depreciation, requiring the add-back of those amounts to STI. The taxpayer would then deduct an additional three-sevenths of allowable depreciation excluding the bonus assets, until the point at which the full amount of disallowed bonus is recovered.

State apportionment

In addition to the required modifications to FTI to arrive at STI, most states require that income is apportioned or allocated to the state on the basis of a specified business formula in order to calculate the amount of tax due the state. There are several ways in which states apportion income: three factor (average of property, payroll and sales), three factor with double-weighted sales and, increasingly more common, by way of a single sales factor.

Under the single sales factor approach, states require income to be sourced to the state by calculating a percentage of sales delivered within or into the state in comparison to the taxpayer's total sales delivered. Many states have represented that single sales factor apportionment is the most fair and accurate methodology for economically distributing tax liabilities among the states.

Additional state income tax considerations

States are not consistent on the deductibility of state and local income taxes. Only Arkansas and New Mexico allow a deduction for all state and local income taxes. Colorado and Louisiana require an add-back of their own state income taxes, but not the income taxes of other jurisdictions.

Utah requires an add-back of any state or local taxable income, franchise, privilege, corporate stock or business and occupations tax. Oklahoma requires an add-back of state and local income taxes but provides for a deduction of accrued Oklahoma income tax. The rest of the significant oil and gas jurisdictions with state and local income taxes do not allow for their deduction.

Although the Texas franchise tax is considered an income tax for ASC 740 purposes, the states are split on whether it is an income tax, and therefore they are also split on whether it must be added back.

Sourcing oil and natural gas sales

Historically, many oil and gas companies have sourced their sales of oil and natural gas based on the production site (at the wellhead). This methodology has been used frequently since the ultimate destination of natural gas is typically unknown once it is injected into an interstate pipeline. Additionally, a large percentage of oil sales are export sales that leave the country. Many oil and gas companies have historically sourced these sales to the location of origin, causing overstated sales factors in origin states. This industry practice often results in overstated sales sourced to states in which resources are produced or refined.

Many states in which oil and gas companies operate provide for ultimate destination sourcing for sales of Tangible Personal Property (TPP). Ultimate destination sourcing allows sales of products to be sourced to the final delivery point (ultimate destination). With recent technological advancements, access to reliable electronic interstate pipeline flow data has become more readily available. These developments have provided oil and gas companies, and their service providers, with data that can be used to better determine more representative sales factors by state for those states that follow the ultimate destination principle.

However, prior to looking to the ultimate destination principle, one of the first considerations for sourcing sales in the oil and gas industry is to determine whether or not a state codifies a specialized industry apportionment formula for sales of oil and natural gas products. If the state has no such provisions, then oil and gas companies must perform an analysis to understand whether each state in which they operate, or create a market, considers oil or natural gas products being sold as TPP.

To the extent the products are considered TPP, companies can use the sourcing rules for tangibles. Many states that have adopted the Uniform Division of Income for Tax Purposes Act ("UDITPA") source TPP sales to the ultimate destination of the property. Most of the oil-producing states have a destination test in place for sourcing sales.

It is essential that oil and gas companies regularly evaluate their approach to sourcing sales in order to identify potential areas for overstated sales factors.

● ● ●

Midstream Operations

- Natural gas measurement

- Natural gas processing

- NGL processing

- Pricing

- Transportation

- Pipeline operations

- Crude oil marketing

- Natural gas marketing

- NGL marketing

- Storage facilities

Photograph by istock.com/stanley45

Both raw crude oil and natural gas are gathered initially from the wellhead. Crude oil can generally be transferred directly from the gathering pipeline to a major transmission pipeline. However, significant processing is required for raw natural gas, including the removal of liquids to produce residue gas and natural gas liquids (NGLs).

The starting point for midstream operations is the wellhead, which connects to a gathering system consisting of a group of small diameter pipelines (less than 20 inches) that transport crude oil or natural gas from the producing wells and fields. Crude oil gathering systems may transport crude oil to a tank farm and then to a major crude oil transmission pipeline or an oil refinery. Natural gas gathering systems typically transport gas to a gas processing plant or to a major natural gas transmission pipeline, depending on whether the natural gas is considered "wet gas" or "dry gas."

Gas processing plants, major transmission pipelines for both crude oil and natural gas and terminal facilities are described later in this chapter. As described in Chapter 2, oil refineries are considered part of downstream operations and are not discussed herein.

Natural gas measurement

Crude oil and natural gas are measured in a gathering system through the use of meters positioned at intervals along the pipeline. Meter types used and volume determinations differ for crude oil versus natural gas. See Chapter 11 for an in-depth description of crude oil measurement.

Natural gas is measured when gas flows through a meter that records temperature, pressure and other information needed to calculate gas volumes. Several types of meters are used to measure natural gas volumes:

- **Ultrasonic**. These meters measure the speed at which sound travels in the gaseous medium within the pipe. Such meters work best with no liquids present in the measured gas, so they are used primarily in high-flow, high-pressure applications (e.g., at pipeline meter stations). At such stations, the gas is always dry and lean and small proportional inaccuracies are tolerable due to the large volumes of gas being moved.

- **Turbine**. A small, internal turbine measures gas speed, transmitting the measurement to a mechanical or electronic counter. Because the volume of gas is inferred from its flow, good flow conditions are important. These meters do not impede gas flow but they are limited in terms of measuring lower flow rates.

- **Rotary**. Volumes are measured with two figure-eight-shaped lobes (i.e., rotors) that spin in alignment. With each turn, they move a specific quantity of gas through the meter. Rotary meters often are used in high volume or high pressure applications.

- **Orifice**. Volumes are measured by determining the pressure difference across a deliberately designed and installed flow disturbance. Orifice, or differential flow, meters often cannot sustain a wide range of flow rates; however, they are widely used since they are easy to maintain in the field and have no moving parts.

As mentioned in Chapter 1, the standard volume unit of measure in the U.S. is Mcf, which is the amount of gas expressed in thousand cubic feet at standard atmospheric pressure and temperature. The Btu content of gas is measured by analyzing a sample's hydrocarbon composition using a gas chromatograph.

Natural gas processing

Once crude oil is gathered from the producer's wellhead, it is transported to a tank farm, major oil-transmission pipeline or oil refinery. However, natural gas typically goes to a processing facility. Therefore, processing is only relevant to natural gas.

As illustrated in Figure 27-1, natural gas from the wellhead may contain significant NGL content (i.e., wet gas) and impurities (sulfur, water and carbon dioxide) that must be removed at a processing plant before the residue gas (i.e., dry gas) can enter major natural gas transmission pipelines. Residue gas consists mostly of methane and is sold at the tailgates of gas processing plants. Although gas processing is expensive and reduces the energy content and value of the processed gas, recovered NGLs have many uses in manufacturing and petrochemicals.

Figure 27-1

Gas processing schematic

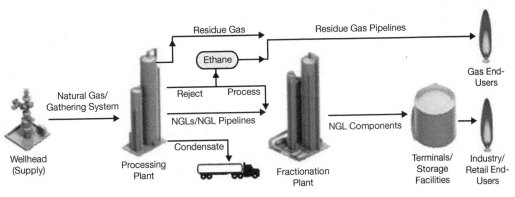

Processing plants

Gas processing plants combine separation, purification, compression, extraction, liquids handling and measurement equipment that range from low capacities to more than 1.0 Bcf per day. Since the mid-1970s, processing technologies have lent themselves to modular plant units that fit onto trucks for ready mobility. The ability to transition to new sources of gas extends a processor's lines of business.

Gas processing uses two general technologies: lean oil absorption and cryogenics. Both produce liquids and can be used for most gas streams. However, they differ in terms of capital and operating costs.

- **Lean oil absorption**. Older technology uses chemical processes to extract NGLs from a gas stream as it passes through a series of oil-bearing contactor towers. Lean oil plants usually are block-mounted and cannot be moved easily. Furthermore, they are inefficient at extracting the lighter ends of NGL components, such as ethane. However, inefficiencies are partially offset by the advantages related to minimal fuel usage for compression and flexibility in the volume of residue gas that can be processed efficiently.

- **Cryogenics.** Despite high fuel expenses driven by large amounts of gas and refrigerant compression, cryogenics (refrigeration) has become the preferred technology for gas processing over the last few decades, whereby a plant cools the gas to a range of 15 degrees Fahrenheit (°F) to (40)°F and, at the lower temperature, recovers about 70 percent of ethane, 90 percent of propane and virtually all of the heavier NGL components, including butane and natural gasoline. In addition to high fuel expense, an additional drawback is reduced plant efficiency. A cryogenic plant's efficiency falls rapidly at throughput levels below 50 percent of its rated capacity.

   A typical cryogenic plant cools gas to a range of (150)°F to (225)°F, recovering 95 percent of the ethane. Cryogenic processes condense NGLs from the gas stream by chilling through one or a combination of two basic methods (cycles): refrigeration and expansion. Refrigeration uses various working fluids to chill the wet gas stream. Expansion uses a large pressure drop through valves and/or turbines to achieve very cold temperatures, sometimes adding refrigeration to chill the feed gas.

In addition to the two technologies previously described, several other types of plants operate today. A bobtail plant refers to a gas plant that removes the NGLs as a single stream, sending it to a fractionation plant to separate the NGLs into components. A cycling plant handles residue gas for reinjection into a reservoir. A straddle plant is situated on a transmission pipeline system, as opposed to a single plant situated between the field gathering system and the pipeline. A gasoline plant removes natural gasoline from the gas stream.

Residue gas

Residue gas has a heat content of approximately one million British thermal units (MMBtu) per Mcf at atmospheric pressure. Residue gas volume and heat content are much lower than the volume and heat content of corresponding "wet" gas entering the natural gas processing plant. Processing shrinkage, or plant volume reduction (PVR) and plant thermal reduction (PTR), results primarily from: (1) using gas as fuel to operate the plant, (2) extracting the NGLs and impurities and (3) measuring volumes inaccurately, creating plant losses and meter differences. Extraction loss is greater for a natural gas stream with a high liquid content than for a stream containing less liquid. This shrinkage factor is considered when determining the plant's production volumes of NGLs and residue gas.

Once determined, the volumes of residue gas delivered from the plant are multiplied by the Btu content of the residue gas. This amount is allocated among the leases or wells, based on their respective volumes of theoretical residue gas delivered to the plant (measured at the plant inlet meter), less theoretical shrinkage (i.e., extraction loss, gas used as fuel by the processing plant, or volumes returned to producers for use in operations).

Gas plant settlement and allocation

The record-keeping and accounting for natural gas processing are complex. Detailed calculations determine the volumes and proceeds of products sold, as well as products taken in-kind. Midstream companies typically prepare gas settlement statements that verify volumes and prices of products sold as used by producers to record product sales.

Such settlement statements include the property name, actual and theoretical residue gas and NGLs, volume of extraction and processing loss, volumes sold, gallons per Mcf (GPM) of each product, Btu equivalent, price paid per product, deductions taken by the plant owner and the total settlement amount for the producing property.

To settle residue gas collectively sold by the plant owner/operator (i.e., the midstream company), a reasonable allocation is made to each lease or field that supplied the gas. First, the total amount sold by the plant is determined. That amount is then allocated among the leases or wells, based on theoretical residue gas supplied to the plant, as calculated for each lease. Proceeds from gas sales usually are the amounts received from gas purchasers. Some gas contracts allow the plant owner to reduce the gross sales revenue by specified charges per Mcf in order to cover dehydration or other services performed to make the gas saleable.

To attribute the volume of residue gas sold to a specific lease or well, companies should consider the volume of gas received at the plant from the lease or well, less an allocated portion of gas consumed in the plant, less extraction loss and the volume of any residue gas returned to the producer for lease or well operations. Assume that the gas streams from Leases A, B and C enter a gas processing plant. Sales allocations are based on the volumes measured at the plant inlet meter (24,502 Mcf, 20,960 Mcf and 26,113 Mcf, respectively). Assume that the actual residue gas collectively sold by the plant operator is 54,000 Mcf, of which 4,000 Mcf was taken in-kind by Lease C owners. Figure 27-2 illustrates a typical allocation approach:

Figure 27-2
Residue gas sold allocation

Lease	Inlet volume	Theoretical shrinkage	Theoretical residue	Taken in-kind	Residue gas sold allocation[1]
			(in Mcf)		
A	24,502	(5,289)	19,213	–	18,753
B	20,960	(4,345)	16,615	–	16,217
C	26,113	(6,616)	19,497	4,000	15,030
Total	71,575	(16,250)	55,325	4,000	50,000

[1] Computed as actual residue gas collectively sold (54,000 Mcf) divided by total theoretical residue gas volumes (55,325 Mcf), multiplied by the theoretical residue gas volumes per lease, the product of which is reduced by any gas taken-in kind for each lease.

Note that this example assumes production is from individual leases that are covered by individual contracts between the producer and the gas plant owner. However, sometimes multiple leases are covered by one contract, which includes a residue pooling provision that combines all of the leases into a single lease.

When allocating the residue gas, the gas plant owner would allocate the volumes of gas sold to the producer as if they were from a single lease. The producer would then further allocate these volumes to the multiple leases (i.e., the residue pool) that are party to the contract containing the residue pooling provision. The allocation method used by the producer is specified by the terms of the residue pooling provision and generally is based on each lease's pro rata portion of the total acreage included in the residue pool.

NGL processing

Natural gas is more than 90 percent methane, which is the simplest and smallest hydrocarbon molecule, consisting of one carbon atom bonded with four hydrogen molecules (CH_4). NGLs initially come out of gas processing plants as y-grade or raw feed. Once they go through a fractionation plant (discussed below), they turn into NGL purity products made up of slightly larger natural hydrocarbon molecules of ethane (C_2H_6), propane (C_4H_8), butane (C_4H_{10}) and natural gasoline (five to 10 carbon atoms per molecule). Liquefied petroleum gas (LPG) is a popular term for propane or a propane/butane mixture that has been compressed into a liquid for use in backyard gas barbecue grills, rural home heating, and cooking and other applications.

Like crude oil and natural gas from the wellhead, NGLs produced from a plant must meet minimum quality requirements for acceptance by a carrier or purchaser. The plant operator draws NGL samples to identify gross impurities that might require a shutdown or diversion of plant production until cured.

NGLs delivered into a pipeline are spot sampled by the plant operator or automatically sampled continually, depending on contract terms with the purchaser or carrier. For truck or rail deliveries, the operator samples each load, using a chromatograph similar to those that measure natural gas. Constituents, including any impurities, are reported by volume percent. Chromatograph analyses often report chemically distinct constituents at a far greater level than is recognized by field marketing arrangements. In these cases, the constituents are grouped simply, by market designation, and totalled for settlement purposes.

For example, the analysis may report hexanes plus (C_6+) in addition to pentanes (C_5) but the processing agreement may only address settlement to pentanes plus. The accountant would simply add the reported percentages attributable to hexanes and pentanes, arriving at the settlement quantity of pentanes plus (C_5+). Upon carrier acceptance, the liquids are transported to a user or a market center, which has facilities for NGL receipt, storage and fractionation, and which offers standard exchange and delivery procedures to facilitate the trading of liquids.

Fractionation plants

A fractionation plant receives an NGL stream from one or more natural gas processing plants and fractionates the stream into separate products. Fractionation heats and cools the NGL mix in tall towers, drawing off components from the height at which they settle. A single plant may fractionate the yield of several natural gas processing plants, reducing the need for site-specific fractionation facilities. This approach also offers a more economical way to transport NGLs from the gas plant to a shipping point, because only one pipeline is needed to move the mixed liquids. Fractionation facilities operate continuously, with consumers and/or nearby storage awaiting the finished products.

Allocations to producers

Two methods are used to determine NGL allocations to producers. The first, and most commonly used, allocates the actual product extracted and delivered at the plant tailgate. The second method allocates a specified percentage of theoretical NGL volumes (similar to the previous description for residue gas).

Allocation of actual product extracted. To illustrate the first method, assume that gas streams from two properties, Lease A and Lease B, enter a gas processing plant. The producer retains title to the gas throughout processing, and therefore the plant does not take title to the product.

Wellhead tests indicate the theoretical amount of each liquid in GPM that may be produced from the gas stream at a particular wellhead. The ratio of a plant's actual volumes to theoretical volumes is called the recovery factor. Recovery factors are calculated for each individual product extracted in the plant. The recovery factor is multiplied by the theoretical gallons of the product, for each lease, to determine their allocated volumes. Generally, contracts provide for separate settlement calculations for each of the individual components extracted.

At the plant inlet, the gas is measured again and tested, yielding a total Mcf and GPM from the two combined gas streams. Volumes measured at the plant inlet should be allocated back to the two leases. In addition, plant operators measure volume and quality at the plant's tailgate. The basis for the settlement payment is, typically, the quantities extracted and delivered for sale during the month.

The example shown in Figure 27-3 below shows the calculations for allocating ethane revenues based on the following assumptions:

- A total of 44,000 Mcf of wet gas is processed from Lease A (24,000 Mcf) and Lease B (20,000 Mcf).

- The ethane theoretical GPM at Lease A is 0.120 and at Lease B is 0.100.

- Total actual ethane sold is 4,600 gallons at a price of $0.420 per gallon.

Ethane allocation – Actual product extracted

	Lease A		Lease B		Total
Wet gas (Mcf)	24,000		20,000		44,000
Ethane theoretical GPM	x 0.120		x 0.100		
Ethane theoretical gallons (b)	2,880	+	2,000	=	4,880
Total actual ethane gallons sold (a)					4,600
Plant's ethane recovery factor (a) ÷ (b)					0.9426
Applied to each lease	x 0.9426		x 0.9426		
Actual ethane allocated by lease	2,715	+	1,885	=	4,600
Ethane price per gallon	x $0.420		x $0.420		
Allocated ethane revenues	**$1,140**		**$ 792**		

The processing plant extracted almost 95 percent of the ethane that was, theoretically, in the gas stream. The quantity of saleable liquids actually recovered in the plant differs from the theoretical liquid content of the gas. This is due to variations among the test conditions, plant operating conditions, the plant's designed operating efficiency and processing losses.

Allocation of specified percentage. Settlement based on theoretical gallons may result in a lower producer's negotiated share than when it is based on actual gallons extracted.

In this second example, the facts are the same, except that the producer and the gas processing plant have entered into a percentage of proceeds arrangement whereby the plant remits 80 percent of NGL sales proceeds to the producer for Lease A and Lease B, retaining 20 percent as compensation for its services, which the producer would recognize as expense.

The calculations for allocating ethane revenues using this method are shown in Figure 27-4 below.

Figure 27-4

Ethane allocation – Specified percentage

	Lease A	Lease B
Wet gas (Mcf) processed	24,000	20,000
Ethane theoretical GPM	x 0.120	x 0.100
Ethane theoretical gallons	2,880 +	2,000
Ethane price per gallon	x $0.420 x	x $0.420
Ethane sales proceeds	$1,210	$ 840
Remitted to producer (%)	80%	80%
Allocated ethane revenues	**$ 968**	**$ 672**

Variations

In certain processing arrangements, the producer may be paid a sliding-scale percentage of the price per gallon, with the percentage varying according to either, or both, the price and GPM of the gas. The lower the price and/or GPM, the smaller the producer's percentage; conversely, the higher the price or GPM, the larger the producer's percentage. Contracts may base the producer's payment on the processor's gross NGL sales proceeds, or on proceeds after deducting cash discounts, transportation costs or marketing costs.

Although a sliding scale approach is more complicated, it reduces the range of processing fees so that they more closely approximate a plant operator's processing costs, providing a steady source of profits. In this scenario, the producer assumes more risk of variations in NGL prices and gas quality.

Pricing

Because the sales prices for processed commodities depend on index prices (described further in this chapter's marketing section), commodity price changes affect a midstream company's earnings and gross margin. Midstream companies benefit from some element of revenue predictability because a portion of their service fees (e.g., gathering, processing, etc.) are fixed and explicitly stated in contractual arrangements.

Crude oil pricing

As mentioned, prices may be based on a fixed, stated price at the beginning of the contract term. However, most crude oil contracts are negotiated at least a month before any transactions take place. Oil prices may derive from fluctuating reference prices (such as published posted prices or index prices) to approximate current market prices as the oil is delivered. Certain contracts specify a minimum floor or maximum ceiling price, in conjunction with a fluctuating reference price, to provide added protection for the producer in negotiating the transaction price.

Index prices for crude oil are determined at market centers (spot markets). The spot market applies to purchase or sale transactions of a commodity, such as crude oil or refined products, for near-term delivery. The spot market often is called the physical market, since it entails buying and selling physical volumes. Spot markets at different U.S. trading locations consist of many buyers and sellers entering into transactions from the wellhead to the refinery. The price of West Texas Intermediate (WTI) crude oil, often referenced as the prevailing price of crude oil in the U.S., is established at Cushing, Oklahoma.

Crude oil prices also are determined via posted price bulletins, which may also be referred to interchangeably as "crude oil price bulletins," "price bulletins" or "posted prices." These publications list the prices that a purchaser might pay for various types of oil, as well as prices for crude oil that range above or below an API gravity of 40 degrees.

Lower gravity oil, which is below 40 degrees, and extremely high gravity oil, which is more than 45 degrees, generally receive a discount adjustment subtracted from the posted price. In some instances, oil with gravity greater than 40 degrees API, up to a stated maximum acceptable gravity, receives a premium adjustment that is added to the posted price. Ultimately, these amounts depend on the difference between the bulletin's stated benchmark API gravity and the actual API gravity of the oil delivered.

Posted price bulletins serve primarily to indicate prices, rather than as solicitations to buy. Prices are tied to many factors, including: the physical quality of the oil, other prices in the same geographical area, proximity of products to buyers, costs and risks of transport, supply versus demand, pricing history and the New York Mercantile Exchange (NYMEX) oil futures market.

Although price bulletins vary in format, most contain the following information:

- A list of crude types by geographical area, state, county or even a particular field. The list includes distinguishing chemical or physical characteristics (sour, intermediate and sweet refer to the sulfur content; light and heavy refer to API gravity).

- Posted prices for each type of crude at a stated benchmark API gravity (generally 40 degrees).

- The bulletin number and effective date of change to the posted price.

- A gravity adjustment scale of price decrements or increments for crude oil with an API gravity below or above 40 degrees.

Other prices referenced in the sales contract may incorporate the daily closing NYMEX crude oil futures price, plus a premium or discount. To determine the oil sales price, contracting parties may agree to average each closing futures price for every day in the month that the NYMEX is open and trading.

Clear disclosure of reference pricing in contract terms is important, including the averaging formula or dates to be used and the source when quoting NYMEX prices (e.g., The Wall Street Journal, Bloomberg Businessweek or Reuters America). Certain sources, in arriving at their closing prices, may include or exclude the final one or two prices of the day. Various publications will survey oil traders or other sources for the prices of recent oil transactions. These publications call out the highest and lowest prices quoted, compile the data and publish an index of crude oil prices.

Natural gas pricing

Natural gas is a commodity, meaning that it is essentially the same product no matter where it is produced and sold. Commodity markets are inherently volatile, with frequent and drastic price changes. Natural gas prices are driven by activity at market centers, or hubs, where pipeline systems intersect and certain services facilitate trading. Market centers help promote competition (especially for smaller customers), improve service reliability and increase access to multiple pipelines. More than 30 major market centers are active in the U.S., most notably the Henry Hub in Louisiana.

The trading price of natural gas differs across the major hubs, depending on supply and demand at each location. The difference between the Henry Hub price and that of another hub is called the location differential. Contract terms for natural gas may express index prices and fees (e.g., gathering, processing, transportation, etc.) in Mcf, MMBtu or decatherms (equivalent to one MMBtu). MMBtu is the most recently and commonly used measurement.

From a production standpoint, most companies record gas production in Mcf, which makes it easier when analyzing reserves. Most state and federal regulatory agencies require reporting in Mcf. The U.S. is the only market that does not use the metric system to measure volume. Prices are independent of gas temperature or pressure. Therefore, the total Btu determined at one pressure base equals the total Btu determined or reported at another pressure base.

When gas quantities are expressed in volume (Mcf), but the price initially is expressed in heat content (MMBtu), the price per MMBtu must be converted to the price per Mcf by multiplying the price per MMBtu by the heating value (Btu) of a unit of gas volume (Mcf). For example, if the price is $2 per MMBtu, and the Btu content is 1.10 MMBtu per Mcf at 14.73 psia, then the price per Mcf is $2.20 ($2 x 1.10).

For proper comparison, both the Btu content and the Mcf must be measured using the same pressure base. If one Bcf is measured at 14.65 psia, the equivalent volume at a higher pressure of 14.73 psia would be smaller. To ensure proper accounting, volume readings are taken at the wellhead and at a delivery point agreed to by the producer and the midstream company, typically where the natural gas enters and leaves the midstream company's gathering system.

This agreed-upon delivery point is the "custody transfer point," and the measurements are taken by custody transfer meters. Producers typically install check meters on the gathering lines downstream of the midstream company's meters to independently validate the accuracy of the measured volumes. Note that the midstream company's measured volumes and the producer's rarely agree; therefore, contracts typically specify a maximum percentage that the meters can differ.

Effect of commodity prices

Midstream companies that purchase wet gas from producers benefit when the sales prices of NGLs and residue gas exceed those of the wet gas. Furthermore, midstream companies must consider the processing costs of natural gas and the impact to earnings and gross margin. In other words, the sales price for NGLs and/or residue gas must cover both the cost of purchasing the wet gas from the producer and the costs to process it. During those periods when NGL and residue gas prices are low, as compared to wet gas prices, the impact to a midstream company's earnings and gross margin will be unfavorable.

Transportation

The key function of midstream companies is to construct, maintain and operate crude oil and natural gas pipelines. In the U.S., over 215,000 miles of pipeline carry crude/refined oil and hazardous liquid products, while natural gas is transported via approximately 320,000 miles of transmission and gathering pipelines and over 2.2 million miles of distribution main and service pipelines. This vast network of gathering systems that connect wells in production basins to major crude and natural gas pipelines (transmission lines) forms the roadway of the oil and gas economy, transporting products from production basins to key market hubs, downstream refiners and petrochemical manufacturers.

Federal Energy Regulatory Commission

Transmission lines are the most efficient and economical means of transporting crude oil and natural gas across long distances; in fact, they are the primary transportation mode. Transmission lines are classified as either interstate or intrastate. The development and operation of interstate natural gas pipelines is regulated by the Federal Energy Regulatory Commission (FERC) under the Natural Gas Act of 1938 (NGA). Unlike crude oil pipelines, which are regulated under the Interstate Commerce Act of 1887 (ICA), the NGA allows FERC to regulate both the construction and abandonment of natural gas pipelines.

An interstate pipeline, as defined by the U.S. Energy Information Administration, is "engaged in...transportation subject to the jurisdiction of Federal Energy Regulatory Commission (FERC) under the Natural Gas Act." Interstate pipelines transport natural gas and crude oil across state lines and, therefore, participate in interstate commerce. Conversely, intrastate pipelines generally are not subject to FERC jurisdiction and are instead regulated by local or state agencies. For example, the Texas Railroad Commission regulates common carrier intrastate crude oil pipelines in Texas.

Crude oil pipelines

The ICA authorizes the FERC to regulate interstate crude oil pipeline rates, as well as terms and conditions of service, but not to regulate a pipeline's entry into or exit from a market. This means the FERC is not required, or even authorized, to approve pipeline construction. This lack of federal regulation creates even greater hurdles for pipeline operators because each state the new pipeline crosses imposes different construction rules and regulations. However, while not required, the pipeline developer may petition the FERC to issue an advance ruling about its proposed rates, terms and conditions, which can reduce some of the uncertainty that can deter investment in a pipeline project.

Unlike the traditional cost-based rates that generally apply to interstate natural gas pipelines, oil pipeline rates are based on several approaches, predominantly: (1) the oil pipeline rate index, (2) negotiations and settlements and (3) competition (market-based rates). Cost-of-service ratemaking is employed only in limited circumstances. Another key difference between the regulation of crude oil and natural gas pipelines is that the ICA requires all crude oil pipelines to operate as common carriers, meaning the operator must transport any party's crude that "reasonably requests service." This means that if an oil pipeline is constrained, and a new customer requests transportation, the pipeline must allocate its capacity among all of its customers, including the new one, such that existing customers may lose some of their capacity. The FERC allows crude oil pipelines to discount their rates to any shippers who commit to long-term contracts, but even those shippers remain subject to allocation.

By contrast, interstate natural gas pipelines serve customers on a contract-carriage basis, which entitles customers to firm capacity on the pipeline. If a new customer requests service on a constrained interstate natural gas pipeline, the pipeline is not required to provide capacity.

In addition, a crude oil pipeline may set aside capacity, free from any prorationing, for shippers that are willing to pay a premium. In other words, the shipper backstopping the project must pay a higher rate than the party requesting a short-term commitment. Conversely, natural gas pipeline shippers with long-term commitments typically pay lower rates.

Natural gas pipelines

Under the NGA, a company may not construct, commence service on, or abandon an interstate natural gas pipeline without prior FERC authorization. An entity that intends to construct or expand such a pipeline must obtain a FERC "certificate of public convenience and necessity." The FERC then decides if the proposed pipeline project, as well as its proposed terms, conditions of service and rates, serve the public interest.

The FERC's authorization comes with federal eminent domain authority, as well as federal preemption of related state and local laws for the approved project. This provides assurance to the pipeline developer that a state or local authority cannot block the project.

Pipeline operations

Although crude oil and natural gas pipelines look similar, perform essentially the same service and are constructed in the same manner, they operate differently due to differences in the commodities they transport. The general physical principles governing crude oil and natural gas pipelines are the same, but natural gas is many times more compressible than oil, which is a critical factor in understanding their differences. Additionally, refined products pipelines have many of the same behaviors, operations and issues as crude oil and natural gas pipelines, although they are typically more challenging to operate given they have discrete delivery windows and must keep multiple products flowing in a pipeline at all times with minimal contact in order to avoid product downgrades at the end of delivery.

Crude oil pipeline operations

Similar to natural gas pipelines, crude oil pipelines are separated into gathering lines and transmission lines. The crude oil collected by the gathering lines is aggregated into transmission lines that transport the crude oil to either a market hub or a refinery. Unlike natural gas, which is more or less fungible and therefore can be transported by any natural gas pipeline, crude oil pipelines operate as either multiproduct (batched) or single product (unbatched) lines. Multiproduct lines concurrently transport various grades within the same pipeline, resulting inevitably in interface loss as the batched grades move through the pipeline. Operators monitor the batches, using gravitometers and valves to direct the flow to their intended customers.

Linefill. A minimum amount of crude oil is required to fill a new line before deliveries can be made at take-off points or at the end of the line. Linefill has long-term characteristics (similar to PP&E) rather than characteristics typically associated with operating inventory. See additional discussion of the accounting considerations related to linefill in Chapter 28.

Linepack. Compressor stations along a pipeline require a certain volume of gas to maintain pressure and facilitate movement, such that injecting gas volumes increases the pipeline pressure. Pipeline companies often use linepack to manage the pressure within a pipeline segment. When demand slows, they can store gas in an inactive segment. Using linepack to manage pressure also enables them to efficiently address hourly demand fluctuations.

Customer nominations and imbalances. When customers want to ship via a crude pipeline, they notify the operator through a nomination. Regulated pipelines post tariffs that outline the general shipping terms and conditions. The tariff also specifies the price to transport a barrel of crude from one point to another. Through nomination, customers notify shippers that they agree with the pipeline's general terms and conditions, including the allowable grade and quantity. The pipeline operator provides an injection date based on its batching plan for the pipeline. Once the crude reaches the delivery point, each party receives its nominated share.

Any difference between the shipper's nominated amount and the actual amount delivered is considered an imbalance. Unlike natural gas pipelines, where imbalances are settled between each shipper and the pipeline, crude oil pipelines expect the largest shipper to serve as the balancing shipper. The balancing shipper absorbs the imbalance, then works to determine the root cause of the imbalance and remediate with all counterparties.

For example, assume that in December 2019, Company A nominates 1,000 barrels on MidCo's transmission line, which moves crude on FERC Tariff 123 from Midland, Texas (point A) to Cushing, Oklahoma (point B) for $2 per barrel, plus a two percent pipeline allowance. Company A subsequently injects into the pipeline 1,000 barrels. Company B nominates 1,000 barrels on Tariff 123, but only injects 800 barrels, and Company C nominates 1,000 barrels on FERC Tariff 123 and injects 1,000 barrels.

Assume that Company C acts as both the balancing shipper and the pipeline operator and that the WTI NYMEX price for a barrel at Cushing, Oklahoma on December 31, 2019, is $50 per barrel. At the delivery point, Company A receives 1,000 barrels; Company B receives 1,000 barrels; and Company C is left with 800 barrels. Company C, as the operator, then contacts Company B to schedule the additional receipt of 200 barrels.

As the operator, Company C must account for these imbalances as either a receivable or liability at estimated net realizable value at the time the variance occurred, depending on whether the operator is owed barrels from another shipper or owes barrels to another shipper. If Company C is unable to account for the barrels prior to month-end close, it should record a $10,000 receivable (200 barrels x $50 per barrel) from Company B.

Crude oil transportation contracts. Crude oil transportation contracts and tariffs generally are fee-based arrangements, whereby a specified fixed fee per barrel transported (subject to escalation, if applicable) is multiplied by the volume delivered. Typically, the revenue associated with these arrangements is recognized over time as the volumes are transported. However, certain crude oil pipeline transportation agreements include minimum volume commitment terms in which customers are required to ship a minimum volume over an agreed-upon period, with make-up rights. The revenue recognized pursuant to these agreements is recognized when it is probable that the shipper will meet all or a portion of its minimum volume commitment within the make-up period (i.e., the shipper will exercise its make-up rights).

Natural gas pipeline operations

As described earlier, gathering lines collect natural gas from the production basin and transport it to the gas processing plant, where it is treated and the residue gas is extracted. The gas then is injected into the transmission line. Transmission lines deliver natural gas to local distribution companies (LDCs), which use smaller distribution lines to deliver natural gas to homes and businesses, including power plants.

Compressor stations located approximately every 50 to 60 miles along the pipeline boost the pressure lost, through friction, when natural gas moves through the steel pipe. Natural gas moves through transmission lines as fast as 30 miles per hour, so it may take several days for gas from Texas to arrive at a utility receipt point in the Northeast. Along the way, the transmission line will interconnect with many other natural gas pipelines, which offers pipeline system operators a great deal of flexibility in moving the gas.

Pipeline gas imbalances. Pipeline gas imbalances occur when a pipeline delivers to a customer a volume of gas that differs from the volume of gas injected into the pipeline, as discussed further in Chapter 13.

Gas transportation contracts. There are two major types of gas transportation agreements:

- **Firm agreement**. The pipeline guarantees a specific volume of available capacity for the shipper's use each month, regardless of its actual usage. Firm contracts are like leases for renting a home: the pipeline does not refund money to a shipper that does not use all of the pipeline volume, just as a landlord does not refund rent for nights spent away from home.

  Firm agreements require each shipper to pay a specified monthly fee (reservation charge) to reserve a set capacity. The pipeline calculates the charge by multiplying the maximum daily quantity (MDQ) specified in the transportation agreement by the reservation charge per MMBtu for that service. The shipper pays the reservation charge regardless of whether or not it moves its maximum daily quantity.

  Historically, firm service has been purchased from pipelines. However, FERC Order 636 allows a shipper to release its allotted capacity to another party in a secondary market. The shipper posts the released firm capacity on an electronic bulletin board. To ensure open access to all market services, FERC regulations stipulate how the released capacity is posted, bid upon and awarded. Capacity released to the secondary market may be relinquished for less than the amount paid by the original transporter. The original transporter retains its binding contract with the pipeline, which it pays regardless of any loss on released capacity. This secondary market has become an important price driver in gas transportation services.

  Another option allows a shipper to exceed the maximum delivery volume of gas for a specified time, such as 24 hours, without incurring additional penalties. If a pipeline offers this firm transportation with overrun capability service, and it is stipulated in the contract, the shipper normally pays a fee for it.

  In addition to the reservation charges described above, firm agreements include a commodity charge – a variable cost based on the actual volume of gas shipped. Pipelines also collect additional volumetric charges, such as FERC surcharges. These are specified in each pipeline's tariff. Generally, these charges increase with transportation distance.

- **Interruptible agreement.** Allows a transporter to interrupt or reduce its service to a shipper. In addition to the applicable FERC surcharges, the shipper pays only the actual volumetric transportation charges (commodity charges) incurred to transport gas when pipeline capacity is available, after accommodating shippers with firm agreements.

Tariffs

As mentioned previously, interstate and some intrastate pipelines fall under the FERC's regulatory authority. Their terms, conditions and rates are regulated by FERC approved pipeline tariffs. Tariff and rate-case negotiations among pipelines, their customers and the FERC are complex and lengthy.

Pipeline tariffs filed with the FERC appear in a common format showing a map of the pipeline system, followed by a list of rates for various pipeline services, including ancillary services such as storage. Also provided is a detailed description of the operator's services (collectively with the pipeline services, the "rate schedules"). The rate schedules are followed by a list of general terms and conditions (GTC) common to all of the pipeline's rate schedules: definitions, payment provisions, ways in which services may be interrupted or emergency conditions declared, as well as information about a pipeline electronic bulletin board. The final item is a standard agreement form for each rate schedule.

Pipelines subject to FERC regulation also display in their tariffs the maximum and minimum rates they will charge for service under each rate schedule. Shippers and pipelines negotiate these rates for a specified range of services. The length (term) of a transportation or storage contract also is negotiated. Although the term is provided by a prospective shipper in its nomination, the pipeline will advise whether or not the service requested is available for that term.

Crude oil marketing

Oil is one of the world's most important sources of energy. Its value is driven by demand for refined petroleum products, particularly in the transportation sector. Petroleum products power virtually all motor vehicles, aircraft, marine vessels and trains worldwide. Products derived from oil, such as motor gasoline, jet fuel, diesel fuel and heating oil, supply the energy consumed by households, businesses and manufacturers around the globe. The principal activities required to transport crude oil from producing wells to end users encompass not only gathering and transportation but also marketing.

After oil and gas are discovered, many processes must occur to bring them to market. Oil, natural gas and NGLs are fungible commodities; therefore, their sales values are not enhanced by product differentiation strategies such as packaging or advertising. Instead, marketing and pricing are influenced by: (1) the commodity's physical quality, (2) the location of both commodity and customer, (3) potential customers and (4) supply and demand for the commodity. In the U.S., federal price controls regulated the industry until the 1980s. Since then, oil and gas prices have been based on open market supply and demand.

Crude oil market factors

Several general factors are important to the marketing of crude oil in the U.S.:

Physical quality. Crude oil varies in density (measured in degrees of API gravity) and in sulfur content. As a general rule, the greater the density or sulfur content, the lower the value of the crude and its eventual market price.

Location. Each delivery (run of oil) from a lease storage tank is accompanied by a run ticket, or a report from the LACT unit, stating the volume and date of withdrawal. Crude oil is priced separately, based on the date it is removed from the tank. Sales contracts specify the price for the indicated time period. The values of all the runs during the month are accumulated, with settlement made monthly by the purchaser. Additionally, transportation costs and local supply versus local demand create price differences based on production locations.

For example, the wellhead value of crude oil produced on the North Slope of Alaska and transported to market via the Trans-Alaska Pipeline System and ocean tanker is far less than the wellhead value of similar quality crude oil produced near the large and more accessible refineries along the Gulf Coast in Texas and Louisiana.

Potential customers. Ultimately, crude oil is sold to refiners who separate and process it into refined products, such as gasoline and diesel fuel. The U.S. refinery business is competitive: about 45 companies own 90 percent of the country's refining capacity.

Some refiners process only certain types of crude oil or are more profitable refining a selected type. Generally, refineries are most profitable if the quality and type of crude oil are relatively constant for several months or years. Because of variations in crude oil gravity and sulfur content and the needs of individual refineries, crude oil is not as fungible as dry natural gas. Crude oil is transported from a well to a refinery via truck, barge, rail car, tanker or pipeline. Consequently, crude oil is sold at the lease site to either: (1) refiners that arrange for transportation to refineries or (2) other companies that purchase crude oil at well sites and transport it for resale to refiners.

Crude oil marketing contracts

Several contractual arrangements are used to market crude oil:

- Royalty owners allow the working interest owners to: (1) market the lease's entire production and (2) arrange for royalty owners to receive their share of sales proceeds (rather than take their royalty interest share of oil in-kind and market it themselves).

- Nonoperators in joint operating agreements also have the right to take their share of oil in-kind and market it; however, the nonoperators typically allow the operator to market the gross production from the lease per the terms of the JOA.

- E&P companies, particularly large operators, may employ crude oil marketers (or crude oil traders) to sell the oil they produce. The marketer's goal is to negotiate the best possible contract price. Some companies have separate divisions or subsidiaries to market their own oil production along with oil from other producers.

  At times, the best price for crude oil is not reached by selling the product; exchanging it for other crude oil may be the better option. For example, assume that Company A produces California crude and owns a Texas refinery. Company B produces Texas crude and owns a California refinery. A and B may agree that A's oil production will be given to B for its California refinery. In exchange, a similar volume of B's Texas oil production will be given to A for its Texas refinery. Any exchange differential due to variances in crude oil quality, local market price or transportation costs is paid by the liable party (i.e., either Company A or Company B).

- In addition to selling to refineries, E&P companies may market crude oil to nonrefiners known as crude oil trading companies. These trading companies can be a producer's subsidiary but often are marketing agents independent of producers and refiners. Key employees who negotiate the purchases, sales and exchanges of crude oil are called crude oil traders.

Sales arrangements are expressed in written, negotiated agreements containing the names of the parties to the contract, date of the agreement, property name and location, transporter, sales volume or production time period, delivery point, price, and geographic, physical or chemical characteristics of the oil. The oil producer or operator is referred to as the seller and the refiner or oil trader is the purchaser. A set of GTC in the agreement specifies remedies if the contract is not followed. Parties often adhere to the GTC written by one of the major oil companies; modifications are noted in the contract.

Four basic types of crude oil sales arrangements exist:

- **Evergreen**. Evergreen sales contracts, or month-to-month sales contracts, are negotiated for an initial 30-day period and renewed monthly thereafter until either party cancels. During times of oil price volatility, evergreen contracts reflect a negotiated price per barrel based on either a fluctuating market price, an indexed price, or a fixed price plus adjustments or escalations.

- **Spot**. Spot sales contracts involve the short-term sale of a stated volume of production for a brief period, such as a few days or months. Spot sales contracts provide for the sale of crude oil based on a negotiated price between the buyer and seller. For example, parties may agree to buy/sell 100 barrels per day of South Texas light crude oil for each day of March 2020 at $30 per barrel. Once the time period ends or the sale occurs, the contract is fulfilled. While evergreen and spot sale contracts allow producers to change oil purchasers on short notice, this is not a common trend within the industry.

- **Exchange**. In an exchange contract (buy/sell arrangement), producers exchange crude oil production for another stream of oil production. An exchange contract was demonstrated in the previous example of the two companies exchanging Texas crude oil for California crude oil.

- **Futures contract**. During contract negotiations in a volatile market, oil marketers may recommend that their companies purchase or sell financial instruments, such as futures contracts, to protect against future pricing volatility. A futures contract, in contrast to a spot transaction, sets up a future purchase or sale of crude oil. Specifically, it agrees to future delivery of a given quantity of crude. The contract specifies the volume, type or grade of crude oil, price, the date upon which the crude will be bought or sold and the delivery location.

  The crude oil underlying futures contracts often are called marker, or benchmark, crudes. The buying and selling of futures contracts occurs on organized exchanges. For example, West Texas Intermediate (WTI) is the benchmark crude traded on the NYMEX, while Brent crude is the marker crude for futures traded on the Intercontinental Exchange (ICE).

Natural gas marketing

While natural gas has been used as an energy source since the 1800s, natural gas marketing is a relatively new concept to the natural gas industry, starting in the mid-1980's. Prior to the deregulation of the natural gas commodity market and the introduction of open access to natural gas pipelines, there was no role for natural gas marketers.

Producers sold to pipelines, who then sold to local distribution companies and other large volume natural gas users. Local distribution companies (LDCs) sold the natural gas purchased from the pipelines to retail end users, including commercial and residential customers. Price regulation at all levels of the supply chain left no place for others to buy and sell natural gas.

However, with accessible competitive markets, the enactment of various environmental regulations (e.g., the Clean Air Act of 1990) and an increasing focus on clean energy sources, natural gas marketing has become an integral component of the natural gas industry. Understanding the history of natural gas deregulation of pricing provides insight into the natural gas marketing function.

As noted previously, prior to the mid-1980s, the natural gas industry was a regulated market where pipelines purchased natural gas from the producer, transported it to the customer and sold it at a regulated price. Through a variety of FERC orders starting in 1983 (including FERC Orders 436 and 500), pipelines became less involved in the business of purchasing gas from suppliers and reselling to customers (i.e., performing the merchant function).

Furthermore, prior to the issuance of FERC Order 636 in 1992, functions performed and charged to customers by interstate pipelines at a single rate included transportation, marketing and storing natural gas. These functions were unbundled per FERC Order 636; interstate pipeline customers now only contract for the service(s) needed. As a result of the FERC orders, pipelines became more engaged in transporting (and storing) gas for a fee, while producers and other entities (e.g., natural gas marketers) began to sell gas directly to customers.

Natural gas market factors

When making purchase and sale decisions, natural gas marketers consider several factors:

Physical quality. Produced natural gas can be processed to extract NGL and remove impurities. This results in a dry residue natural gas that is over 90 percent methane. Dry natural gas is more fungible than crude oil; such gas is more readily combined and transported through a pipeline system that delivers dry gas from the well or processing plant to millions of end users such as individual residences.

Location. Since gas is transported almost exclusively by pipeline in the U.S., location plays a greater role in gas marketing than in crude oil marketing.

Supply versus demand. In the U.S., the natural gas annual productive capacity approximates annual demand, which is substantially less in the summer than in the winter due to its use for home heating. Supply and demand factors drive many U.S. gas wells to produce below their capacities; for this reason, wells may be shut-in at times during the year. However, wells may produce at capacity in the summer and transport gas to underground gas storage facilities.

Producers. In order to realize revenue, a producer takes one of two paths: (1) it can sell some or all of its natural gas production to a third-party gas marketer or (2) it may contract with a gatherer, processing plant or pipeline to transport the gas to downstream customers. Some of the natural gas may be used in producer facilities, such as field equipment or company-owned refineries. A producer may even purchase additional gas from other sources to add to its own supplies.

For producers, the marketing process involves selling the upcoming month's gas, negotiating prices and determining sales and delivery points. This cycle is completed prior to the close of the NYMEX futures contracts sales, generally five working days before the end of the month. The majority of sales are arranged the week before a closing date, or more commonly, in the two days before a closing date. This timing is known as the bid cycle (bid week).

If a producer has not sold the gas at the wellhead, any pipeline transportation needed to sell the gas downstream must be scheduled (as part of the "nomination process") with a pipeline company. The producer (shipper) notifies the pipeline company of the quantity of gas to be shipped (i.e., generally the MMBtu of gas per day), the dates when the gas will be shipped, the receipt point (i.e., meter) into the pipeline, the delivery point where gas will be taken by a customer and the volumes to be delivered.

The pipeline company (transporter) confirms the respective nominated quantities and terms with producers and customers. While nominations are estimates of gas flow for a given day and month, actual gas flow is likely to differ, due to pipeline pressures, fuel usage, pipeline loss or other conditions. Each party should maintain accurate volumetric records of transactions. Any volume variances are recorded and resolved at a delivery point where the title transfers from the producer to the transporter/purchaser, as determined by the contract.

Marketers and marketing companies. Marketers and marketing companies are middlemen in the disposition of natural gas. A true gas marketing company is neither a physical producer nor a user of natural gas; it purchases gas for resale. Value is added by aggregating supplies and markets and by creatively using available transportation services and storage. Local distribution companies oftentimes purchase gas from marketers and marketing companies and resell it to residential, commercial and industrial users, including electric power generators.

Potential customers. The FERC has allowed pipelines to act as transporters – not as gas purchasers or resellers. This has enabled producers to sell gas to local gas utilities and even directly to the utilities' former customers. Thousands, if not millions, of potential customers are now available to producers. In response, several large gas marketing companies have emerged to perform the merchant function of buying and selling gas.

End users. End users of gas include residential, commercial and industrial customers. Residential use consists primarily of home heating, which is largely weather dependent. Households also use small amounts of gas in stoves, clothes dryers, water heaters and other appliances. Residential users typically purchase gas from LDCs. Commercial users include shopping centers, office buildings, restaurants and small stores.

Traditionally, commercial users purchase gas from LDCs; however, some are actively moving to purchase gas from third-party marketing companies. Industrial users, including electric power generators, comprise the largest segment of the natural gas market. Gas can serve as feedstock or can be used directly to fuel on-site boilers and other machinery. Industrial customers have created the most competitive price structures due to increased sophistication in the gas market. In addition, they are the segment of users most likely to have alternate fuel capability.

Natural gas marketing contracts

The various contractual arrangements discussed previously for crude oil are the same as those arranged by gas marketers, as discussed herein in more detail. Natural gas buyers and sellers can hedge prices using futures, options or other derivative products, as described in Chapter 34. Natural gas purchase and sales agreements can be categorized as "spot" or "term."

- Spot contracts are used for both gas and crude oil. They are brief documents that typically address sales for as long as one month, although longer periods also may be covered. Most contracts have an evergreen clause that permits automatic renewal beyond the primary term. Spot contracts historically contain no penalty for nonperformance by either party, as they provide for "best efforts performance" (of an "up to" quantity). However, some contracts do specify liquidated damages for nonperformance.

- Term contracts generally are for one month or longer. They contain negotiated, detailed contract provisions specifying price, volume, delivery point, contract term and additional elements.

Spot and term contracts typically differ in how their performance obligations are met. A term contract may establish a maximum daily quantity which the seller must be prepared to make available each day during the contract term. The buyer's requirement to take gas (if not 100 percent) may be specified prior to each month through notice to the seller. Although the quantity normally is a set daily amount throughout the month, it can vary. In extreme cases, the seller may be required to make the maximum daily quantity available on any day the buyer wishes to purchase it; however, the buyer may only be obligated to take minimal amounts throughout any month during the contract term. While these provisions are the subject of major negotiations, they often reflect the buyer's desire to serve specific target markets and uses.

The following are important contractual terms and provisions:

- **Delivery point**. This is the location where the gas is considered to be delivered to the buyer. Title, ownership responsibilities and risks transfer at this point (typically at a specified gas meter, either at the lease, on a gathering system, on a pipeline or at a hub).

- **Pricing**. Pricing provisions usually are very simple. A specific price is set for the sale of a certain gas quantity during a specified time period, usually no longer than one month. Some long-term contracts specify fixed prices. Fixed pricing often is used to lock in gas supply economics on projects, such as cogeneration plants or power generation projects. Pricing provisions allow for price redetermination (i.e., the parties can renegotiate the price at specified times). Frequently, parties negotiate a fixed price that changes according to either an escalation factor (a scheduled percentage change), a government inflation indicator (such as the Consumer Price Index) or the price of alternate fuels. Absent a fixed price, a spot contract should clearly provide a fluctuating reference price, or index price, along with any premium or discount to the index chosen. Index prices are listed in periodicals, such as *Inside FERC's Gas Market Report, Natural Gas Weekly Update* and Natural Gas Intelligence's *Daily Gas Price Index*.

NGL marketing

Compared to the market for crude oil and natural gas, the market for NGLs is limited. However, NGLs are attracting attention as a growing source of revenue for producers. In a low gas price environment, the value of NGLs may support continued drilling (after considering other factors, such as processing and transport costs).

On an energy equivalent basis, most NGLs generally offer greater economic value as feedstock for petrochemical and motor gasoline production than they do as components of a natural gas stream. NGL marketing activities include term and spot sales, as well as open market and contract purchases.

NGL market factors

Several factors affect the marketing of NGLs at U.S. natural gas plants, including:

Physical quality. NGLs consist of distinct types of hydrocarbons with different markets and competitive products.

The marketing of the hydrocarbon constituents of NGLs is contingent upon its usage:

- Ethane is used primarily in the petrochemical industry as a feedstock for producing ethylene, a basic building block for a wide range of plastics and other chemical products.

- Propane is used for heating, as an engine and industrial fuel, and as a petrochemical feedstock for producing ethylene and propylene.

- Normal butane is used as a petrochemical feedstock in the production of ethylene and butadiene (a key ingredient of synthetic rubber), as a blendstock for motor gasoline and to produce isobutane through isomerization.

- Isobutane is fractionated from mixed butane (a mixed stream of normal butane and isobutane) or produced from normal butane through the process of isomerization. Isobutane is used in refinery alkylation to enhance the octane content of motor gasoline, to produce isooctane and other octane additives and to produce propylene oxide.

- Natural gasoline, a mixture of pentanes and heavier hydrocarbons, is used primarily as a blendstock for motor gasoline, a crude oil diluent that aids in transportation and as a petrochemical feedstock.

Location. The extraction of NGLs in gas processing plants serving several producers leads many producers to market to or through gas plant owners. In a broad geographical sense, the location of NGL production, compared with primary markets, can also affect the pricing and marketing of NGL components.

Supply versus demand. The U.S. typically produces more NGLs than it uses on an annual basis. However, sometimes imports of NGLs are necessary to supply high, seasonal demand and to supply some regions of the country that are not supplied sufficiently by domestic sources. Certain NGLs are also imported because U.S. production is insufficient to satisfy total petrochemical demand. The strong demand for NGLs is aided by a system of NGL pipelines that move the products to major markets.

However, just as crude oil can be sold at the lease and delivered into trucks, NGLs can be temporarily stored at processing plants to be sold and delivered into special trucks to meet regional demands, rather than passing through an NGL pipeline to a major petrochemical plant.

Potential customers. A major NGL end-user market in the U.S. is the petrochemical industry concentrated on the Gulf Coast. Olefin plants use ethane and propane as key feedstocks for making basic petrochemicals such as ethylene and propylene. Alternative major feedstocks for many plants are naphtha and gas oil, which are products from crude oil refining. Variations in the price of crude oil can affect the cost of naphtha and gas oil and, indirectly, the price of ethane and propane, as petrochemical plants seek the most economical feedstocks available.

Other major markets include rural home heating and cooking, agricultural use of liquefied petroleum gas (LPG or bottled gas) consisting of primarily propane, and crude oil refining that can use butanes and natural gasolines as blendstocks for making refined products such as gasoline. Major oil and gas companies with gas production facilities, refineries and petrochemical plants market NGL to downstream intercompany facilities. However, a typical independent producer's potential customer is generally either: (1) a gas plant owner who simply buys the wet gas or (2) a gas plant NGL customer in transactions arranged by the gas plant owner.

NGL marketing contracts

Pricing is determined by industry postings provided at the main market centers of Conway, Kansas and Mont Belvieu, Texas. The Oil Price Information Service (OPIS), a division of the United Communications Group, publishes PetroScan, an online, real-time petroleum price database of NGL, gas and petroleum product prices. PetroScan and/or the weekly Oil Price Information Service newsletter often serve as a pricing reference in contracts for settlement purposes. OPIS definitions and specifications are available from the publisher on request and should be documented in any payment calculation or audit procedure.

Marketing fees are deducted as: (1) a percentage of the posted prices or actual resale prices or (2) a fixed number of cents or even fractions of a cent per gallon sold. Transportation and fractionation charges ("T&F charges") are established with the facilities or equipment owners in the form of fixed amounts per gallon. A market price may be severely discounted in the case of products that fail to meet the purchaser's specifications. In some cases, a seller may incur a cost for proper disposal of contaminated products.

Entities involved in the marketing of NGLs include primary and secondary market centers for the transportation, purification, storage and marketing of NGLs. NGL marketers may be plant owners or operators who previously purchased natural gas streams from producers through gas purchase contracts. The operators would then hold title to the NGLs and the gas. Producers of the natural gas stream receive a price for the wet gas based on the value of all the products in the stream: residue gas, any byproducts (such as sulfur) and the NGLs.

Similar to the crude agreements discussed previously, entities will enter into agreements to sell NGL hydrocarbons. The agreements vary in term (evergreen, spot, term) and will detail the specifics of the agreement such as product, quantity, price, duration and transportation method. If a producer has a gas processing agreement, the producer retains title to the NGLs and can sell them to a marketer, market center or industrial end user, using the same type of specifications.

Typical contracts in the field provide a producer with an allocation of liquid revenues or in-kind products attributable to a well's production. Preprinted industry forms allow delivery dates, quantities, location, delivery method, special product specifications and price to be inserted when negotiated. Industry standards and specifications for measurement are usually referenced in the measurement sections of the contract. Penalties are stated for any quantities of product delivered from the plant that fail to meet purchaser specifications. It is also common to find provisions for small losses of the product.

Exchanges of one product for another with a specified price differential, other price adjustments or monthly fees for storage services should be clearly stated in the contract. In addition, most agreements provide for an audit of the settlement price.

Storage facilities

Demand for oil and gas fluctuates seasonally, while production and pipeline transportation are relatively constant in the short term. Storage of these commodities during periods of low demand helps to ensure that sufficient supplies are available during periods of high demand. Below is an overview of the different types of storage facilities for crude oil, natural gas and NGLs, followed by a description of several of the accounting topics specific to midstream companies that provide storage services.

Crude oil storage

Surface storage is usually associated with liquid products, including crude oil and gasoline. Surface storage services are often referred to as "terminalling services." In connection with surface storage, products are typically held in tanks that can be directly transferred to a ship or other means of transportation. Tank capacities vary according to a field's early production rates and remoteness from pipelines. Terminalling facilities do not require as much storage capacity as underground storage, and less time is required to inject and withdraw the products.

In the U.S., the only substantial underground crude oil storage is the Strategic Petroleum Reserve (SPR). As mentioned in Chapter 1, the U.S. government began storing crude oil in underground leached salt caverns in the Gulf Coast area, Michigan and New York in 1977 to prevent a major supply disruption, such as an abrupt decrease in foreign oil imports. Approximately 642 million barrels of crude oil were in SPR storage as of October 18, 2019.[1]

Natural gas storage

Natural gas storage has been defined, traditionally, as a series of operations whereby a quantity of production is injected into an underground depository to meet later demand. Natural gas can also be stored in smaller volumes in tanks above or below ground. Accordingly, natural gas on its own may be stored in a number of different ways; however, it is most commonly held underground, under pressure, in three types of facilities. As described herein, natural gas may also be stored in liquid or gaseous form in above-ground tanks.

Each storage type has distinct physical characteristics (porosity, permeability and retention capability) and economics (site preparation and maintenance costs, deliverability rates and cycling capability), which determine how suitable it is for specific applications.

Depleted reservoirs. Located in oil and natural gas fields, depleted reservoirs are the most commonly used underground storage facilities, primarily due to their wide availability. They usually are located along major pipelines and gathering systems or near gas processing facilities that are close to consumption centers. Using these depleted reservoirs for storage is efficient because it takes advantage of already constructed wells, gathering systems and pipeline connections. Compared to aquifers, depleted reservoirs are more efficient because they require less base gas (pad or cushion gas), which refers to volumes of company-owned gas used to maintain appropriate pressure in the storage facility so that it can safely inject and withdraw gas.

Aquifers. Natural aquifers also can be converted to gas storage facilities. Aquifers are underground, porous rock formations that are natural water reservoirs. Although the geology of aquifers is similar to depleted reservoirs, they usually require more base gas and closer monitoring of injections and withdrawals. Their deliverability rates may be enhanced by certain techniques, such as a water drive, which maintains the reservoir pressure. In addition to requiring more base gas, natural aquifers are more costly to convert to underground storage than are depleted reservoirs.

Salt caverns. Salt caverns are optimal for underground storage because they not only require less base cushion than depleted reservoirs or aquifers, but they also permit very little gas to escape unless it is specifically withdrawn. The result is very high withdrawal and injection rates and minimal base gas requirements. Furthermore, a salt cavern's walls are as structurally strong as steel, making them resistant to reservoir degradation. However, salt caverns are usually smaller than the other two storage options previously discussed. Salt caverns are located primarily in the U.S. Gulf Coast, although they have recently been created (through leaching) in salt formations elsewhere in the U.S.

Figure 27-5 summarizes each type of underground storage facility:

Figure 27-5
Underground natural gas storage types

Type	Cushion gas	Injection period	Withdrawal period
		(days)	
Depleted reservoir	50%	200 – 250	100 – 150
Aquifer reservoir	50% – 80%	200 – 250	100 – 150
Salt formation	20% – 30%	20 – 40	10 – 20

NGL storage

The most common type of NGL storage is a one-to-three-day supply of NGLs stored in above-ground bullet tanks (an industry term which is descriptive of the tank shape). Liquids are transported from storage facilities by a connection to an NGL pipeline or by trucks or rail cars loaded at plant terminals. Underground storage is also used for NGLs, either as a mix of products or a "purity product" (the pure product or the liquids that meet the specifications of the purchaser). Many underground storage facilities are located near gas processing plants and wholesale market delivery or consumption points.

Owners and operators of storage facilities

The principal owners and operators of storage facilities are interstate pipeline companies, intrastate pipeline companies, local distribution companies (LDCs), gas processing plant owners and independent storage service providers. If a storage facility serves interstate commerce, it is subject to the jurisdiction of the FERC; otherwise, it is state-regulated.

Owners and operators of storage facilities are not necessarily the owners of the product held in storage. Product maintained in storage facilities can belong to the shippers, LDCs, or end users who retain title to the product. However, the type of entity that owns or operates the facility has some control over how that facility's storage capacity is utilized.

The deregulation of underground storage for natural gas has placed a premium on high-deliverability storage facilities. Many salt formation and other high-deliverability sites, both existing and under development, belong to independent storage service providers – often smaller, specialized companies started by entrepreneurs who recognized the potential profitability of these specialized facilities. These facilities are used almost exclusively by third-party customers, such as marketers and electricity generators, who can most benefit from their characteristics.

Prior to 1994, interstate pipeline companies, subject to the jurisdiction of the FERC, owned all of the natural gas transported on their pipeline systems, as well as natural gas held in storage. These companies had exclusive control over the capacity and utilization of their storage facilities. With the implementation of FERC Order 636, interstate pipeline companies are now required to operate their storage facilities on an open-access basis; that is, the major portion of working gas capacity at each site beyond that reserved to maintain system integrity (i.e., base gas) and for load balancing is required to be made available for use by third parties on a nondiscriminatory basis.

Seasonality

Natural gas storage volumes are highly seasonal and higher natural gas prices are typically associated with low storage periods. In northern states, higher demand occurs in the winter for space heating, while in the higher more demand exists in the summer to generate electricity for air conditioning. Overall, natural gas demand is higher in the winter than in the summer. Usually when prices are high during the early months of the refill season (April through October), many users of storage adopt a wait-and-see attitude. They limit their gas intake, anticipating that the prices will decrease before the heating season begins (November to March).

However, in instances when that decrease does not occur, they are forced to buy natural gas at higher prices. This is particularly true for LDCs and other operators who rely on storage to meet seasonal demand for their customers. Conversely, entities that use storage as a marketing tool (hedging or speculating) will refrain from storing large volumes of natural gas when the prices are high.

Expectations for future commodity prices also impact storage levels. In a backwardation market, in which commodity prices are expected to decrease in the future, there is no incentive for companies to store crude oil or natural gas. Therefore, companies are more likely to sell product in hopes of capitalizing on the current higher commodity prices.

Conversely, in a contango market, in which commodity prices are expected to increase, companies will store their crude oil or natural gas with the expectation that they will be able to sell the product at a higher price in the future.

As discussed above, transactions at market centers are the primary means by which oil and gas prices are set. As a result, several storage facilities are located at or near these market centers. For example, futures contracts are often used by marketers to mitigate risk associated with fluctuating oil prices by specifying the quantity of oil to be delivered on a set date at a designated delivery point.

In the U.S., this location is typically Cushing, Oklahoma, a major market center for oil, where the crude oil tanks had approximately 76 million barrels of working storage capacity and stocks in transit as of September 30, 2019.[2] Natural gas storage facilities in the U.S. usually are located along major transmission lines to enable pipeline companies to balance the pipeline system for operational purposes and to manage supply and demand.

Pipeline companies will have gas storage facilities located strategically at or near major transmission-line interconnects and/or areas with high demand for natural gas. Specifically, the southern U.S. producing region has gas storage locations located near market hubs, while the Northeast consumption region has storage facilities to meet demand in colder winter months.

• • •

1 https://www.eia.gov/petroleum/supply/weekly/.

2 https://www.eia.gov/petroleum/storagecapacity/ Source: Energy Information Administration, Form EIA-813 "Monthly Crude Oil Report".

28 Accounting for Midstream Operations

Historically, natural gas was stored primarily by pipeline companies. They charged one inclusive fee that covered the cost of transportation and other pipeline-company functions, such as compression, withdrawal, matching buyers and sellers, intrahub transfer, temporary storage ("banking" or "parking") and long-term storage.

As the natural gas market has grown in national importance, the market structure and rules have changed, especially as a result of Federal Energy Regulatory Commission (FERC) Order 636 and its subsequent amendments. This order requires pipelines to unbundle transportation services from their other functions and charge fees for the specific services they perform. Under current market rules, pipeline companies primarily transport natural gas, while producers and others sell natural gas, predominantly to end users or local distribution companies (LDCs). In turn, this has encouraged producers, major end users and LDCs to seek storage rights, as they are needed to meet their sales commitments.

This chapter provides an overview of accounting considerations for midstream operations. See Chapter 27 for additional discussion of the midstream sector.

Contractual arrangements

Producers often do not own the gathering systems that transport the crude oil or natural gas from the wellhead, nor do they own the gas processing plants that extract the NGLs and/or residue gas from the natural gas produced at the wellhead. Therefore, producers enter into contracts with companies that own or operate these assets, which in most cases are midstream companies. Described below are several different types of contracts.

Fee-based contract

Fee-based arrangements are contracts in which the midstream company charges a stated price for each volume of crude oil or natural gas transported or each volume of natural gas processed. The fee is stated explicitly in the contract terms.

For example, a gas gathering contract may include terms as follows:

> ... Customer agrees to pay Gatherer each Month during the Term of this Agreement a gathering fee of fifteen cents ($0.15) per MMBtu ("Gathering Fee") of gas delivered by Gatherer for Customer's account at the Redelivery point.

An example gas processing contract may include terms similar to the following:

> ... Seller shall pay a processing fee of one dollar per Mcf ($1 per Mcf) on all volumes of gas delivered by the Seller hereunder at the Point(s) of Receipt and measured at the Point(s) of Measurement.

In fee-based arrangements, the midstream company generally does not take title to the producer's crude oil or natural gas and is, therefore, considered a service provider to the producer. The midstream company recognizes service revenue for the fees related to the gathering and/or processing services provided.

Acreage dedication contract

To help ensure there is sufficient capacity within a midstream company's gathering system, producers enter into agreements whereby 100 percent of the crude oil or natural gas produced is "dedicated" to the midstream company for the life of the oil and gas producing field. These arrangements are called acreage dedications.

Producers customarily dedicate the volumes of crude oil and natural gas to be produced from their underlying minerals in return for a firm commitment by the midstream company to gather, process, purchase or transport such volumes. By agreeing to acreage dedications, the midstream company guarantees the use of its assets and that the maximum amount of crude oil and natural gas will be transported on its gathering system. Therefore, acreage dedication arrangements require that the midstream company will make the necessary enhancements to its gathering system to ensure that all current and future volumes produced can be gathered from the field.

An example of acreage dedication in a crude gathering contract is included below:

> "... during the Term, Producer: (a) exclusively dedicates and commits to deliver to Midstream Co. under this Agreement, as and when produced, all of the Crude Oil owned by Producer and produced from the Dedicated Properties; (b) commits to deliver to Midstream Co. under this Agreement, as and when produced, all Crude Oil under the Control of Producer that it has produced from the Dedicated Properties; (c) agrees not to deliver any Dedicated Production to any other gatherer, purchaser, marketer or other Person prior to delivery to Midstream Co. at the Receipt Points, unless otherwise agreed in writing between the Parties; and (d) dedicates and commits the Dedicated Properties to Midstream Co. for performance of the Services pursuant to this Agreement."

Minimum volume commitment

Acreage dedication contracts involve producers committing all of the crude oil and natural gas they produce to the midstream company for gathering, processing, etc. Contracts that include minimum volume commitments (MVCs) involve customers (producers and others) committing to transport a certain amount of crude oil or natural gas (minimum volumes) via the midstream company's gathering system or major transmission pipelines.

Contracts typically allow the customers to fulfil their MVC during a specified timeframe or "makeup period," subject to available capacity on the pipeline. This is considered a customer's makeup right. To the extent that the minimum volumes are not transported during the makeup period, the customer is obligated to pay the midstream company based on the MVC, irrespective of the volumes actually transported.

At inception and at subsequent reporting periods, the midstream company must estimate whether or not it expects the customer will meet its MVC within the makeup period. If it is determined that the customer will meet its MVC within the makeup period, any payment the midstream company receives for temporary differences related to deficiency quantities (the shortfall between MVC and the actual volumes transported) must be deferred.

The midstream company is allowed to recognize these deferred amounts as revenue when either: (1) the customer delivers sufficient volumes to meet the MVC or (2) the likelihood that the customer will exercise its makeup right becomes remote, which may occur when either the makeup period expires or the pipeline lacks sufficient capacity. If the midstream company determines that the customer will not exercise all of its makeup rights in a contract, it should estimate the value of these unexercised rights, referred to as "breakage," for revenue recognition purposes. When determining an estimated breakage amount, the midstream company should consider the probability that the customer will not meet all or some of its MVC during the makeup period and recognize estimated breakage as revenue in proportion to the pattern of exercised rights.

Wellhead purchase

Unlike the fee-based arrangements described above, which entail services provided, wellhead purchase arrangements (gas purchase arrangements) involve the producer selling the unprocessed natural gas ("wet gas") to the processor at the wellhead or some other defined point (e.g., at a certain point on the gathering system). The purchase price for the wet gas is specified in the contract. The processor provides no service to the producer because the processor purchases all of the wet gas prior to processing it. Gas purchase arrangements may include fees or deductions that reduce the amounts paid by the processor to the producer, including processing fees, low-volume fees, dehydration fees, transportation and fractionation (T&F) and marketing.

The processor records these fees/deductions as a reduction of the purchase price for the commodities. When entering into these contracts, the ultimate goal for the midstream company is to earn a profit based on the difference between the amounts remitted back to producers for the purchase of the wet gas (less any costs incurred) and proceeds from sale of the residue gas or NGLs to a third party.

Percentage of index

Percentage of index (POI) arrangements also entail the processor remitting proceeds to the producer for the purchase of natural gas at the wellhead. However, under POI contracts, the processor generally purchases natural gas from the producer at: (1) a percentage discount to a specified index price, (2) a specified index price less a fixed amount or (3) a percentage discount to a specified index price, less an additional fixed amount.

For example, the POI arrangement may specify that the processor will purchase wet gas from the producer at 80 percent of NYMEX Henry Hub, less 15 cents per MMBtu.

Accounting for POI arrangements

Facts. The producer sells wet gas at the wellhead to a processor. The processor takes control of the commodity at the wellhead and may process, store or sell the wet gas at its discretion. The processor contracts with third parties to sell the processed gas (residue gas) and natural gas liquids (NGLs), delivers the commodities directly to the third-party customers and negotiates any pricing discounts or premiums relative to the market index. The price paid by the processor to the producer is 80 percent of the index price of the processed commodities at the time the processor receives the gas, less a fixed gathering and processing fee per unit of gas received at the wellhead. (continued on next page)

(continued from previous page)

Question. How should the processor account for this arrangement?

Analysis. The processor is the principal for the sale of the residue gas/NGLs to third-party customers and should recognize product revenue for the gross proceeds received. The processor records, as product costs, the 80 percent of the index price remitted to the producer. The gathering and processing fees reduce the purchase price of the commodity.

Percentage of proceeds

In percentage of proceeds (POP) arrangements, the processor agrees with the producer to process the natural gas and remit back to the producer a certain percentage (usually stated in the contract) of the sales proceeds. The sales prices for the natural gas/NGLs usually are tied to an index price.

For example, a processor and producer may agree that the processor will remit 80 percent of the proceeds generated from the sale. In other words, the midstream company keeps 20 percent of the sales proceeds as the fee for its processing services.

In POP arrangements, the processor is considered the service provider to the producer because the processing and marketing services are undertaken on the producer's behalf, yet the processor does not take control of the residue gas or NGLs. The processor would recognize service revenue for the net fees it retains for the services it provides.

Accounting for POP arrangements

Facts. The producer signs a gas processing service contract with the processor. The producer retains title to the wet gas throughout processing. The processor remits the residue gas back to the producer and sells the NGLs to third-party customers.

The processor obtains legal title to the NGLs, momentarily, before legal title transfers to a third-party customer, because the NGLs are processed and sold on the same day. The processor is contractually required to sell the NGLs in a specified location upon completion of processing. The processor cannot store the NGLs or direct them to another location for sale. The processor retains 20 percent of the actual sales proceeds, as compensation for its services, and remits 80 percent of the proceeds to the producer. The processor also is entitled to a fixed gathering fee per unit of gas it receives from the producer.

Question. How should the processor account for this arrangement?

Analysis. The processor concludes that it does not take control of the NGLs before they are transferred to a third-party customer; therefore, the processor is selling the commodities on the producer's behalf (i.e., as an agent). In addition, the processor is delivering the residue gas back to the producer. As such, the processor is providing processing and marketing services to the producer and should recognize service revenue for the net amount retained from the commodity sale (i.e., 20 percent of proceeds) and the fixed gathering fees.

Percentage of liquids

Alternatively, instead of taking a percentage of the sales proceeds, the producer may agree to take back a portion of the processed NGLs (with the remainder going to the processor). These contractual terms are included in "percentage of liquids" (POL) arrangements. Similar to POP arrangements, the processor is considered the service provider to the producer in POL arrangements.

For example, the producer may agree to let the midstream company retain 10 percent of the NGLs processed (i.e., 90 percent of the NGLs are remitted back to the producer). The midstream company can then sell its 10 percent to a third-party purchaser.

Accounting for POL arrangements

Facts. The processor performs services for the producer (a customer) in exchange for 30 percent of the "y-grade" yield (the mixed NGL stream extracted from the wet gas). Assume the y-grade is readily convertible to cash and the contract duration is 20 years. The volume and mix of commodities that will result from processing are not specified.

Question. How should the noncash consideration (y-grade) be valued?

Analysis. The transaction price can be measured once the volume, mix and market price of the y-grade becomes known (that is, once the processing services are complete). Therefore, the service revenue will be measured based on the y-grade price on the date the processing is complete. Since the quantity, mix and value of noncash consideration is unknown at the time of contract inception, and such variability is related to the services performed, the processor may value the noncash consideration on the date the uncertainties are resolved.

If there is variability due to both the form of the consideration and for other reasons (e.g., variability based on the company's performance under the contract), companies should apply the variable consideration guidance only to the variability resulting from reasons other than the form of the consideration.

ASC 606 specifies that noncash consideration should be measured at fair value at contract inception. One complexity of POL arrangements is determining the transaction price for the processed residue gas/NGLs, since the processor is retaining the processed commodity as compensation for its services (versus receiving a fee). The processed residue gas/NGLs are noncash consideration. Depending on the contractual terms, the processor may measure fair value when the volume, mix and market price become known. This means the processor will recognize revenue based on the market price upon completion of its services.

This is appropriate when the transaction price depends on the volume, mix and market price at the completion of service and the variables are not specified in the contract. In these situations, the variability associated with the "form of consideration" (market price) and reasons "other than form of consideration" (volume and mix) are interrelated to the midstream company's processing services. This conclusion relates to a specific type of arrangement; it may not be acceptable to value noncash consideration at a date other than contract inception in other fact patterns.

Keep-whole

In keep-whole arrangements, the midstream company takes natural gas from the producer and, upon processing, retains the NGLs extracted and returns the equivalent volumes of processed residue gas to the producer. Depending on the contract terms, the producer may take the processed residue gas volumes or proceeds from the midstream company's sale of the equivalent residue gas volumes. Because extraction of NGLs from the natural gas during processing reduces the Btu content of the natural gas, the midstream company must either purchase natural gas at market (index) prices for return to the producers or make supplemental cash payments to the producers equal to the value of this natural gas.

Product loss allowance

Certain crude oil transportation contracts include a product loss allowance (PLA) intended to offset losses due to evaporation, measurement interface losses and other losses in transit. As long as the PLA is intended to cover actual usage or losses (historical usage or losses consistent with the contractual allowance), the product received in-kind does not represent part of the transaction price. In this case, the reason for the PLA is to facilitate the service provided to the shipper or to allow for natural losses (shrinkage) that occur during transportation. The intent of the allowance is to enable fulfilment of the contract rather than to compensate for transportation services. Therefore, the PLA should not be recognized as revenue.

Product loss allowance received in-kind

Facts. Midstream company enters into a transportation contract with a customer to provide natural gas transportation services. The contract provides a 5% product loss allowance to account for the natural shrink that occurs when transporting the gas through a pipeline, which is intended to cover actual losses that occur. On average, Midstream loses 4% to 6% of the product during the transportation process.

Question. How should Midstream account for the product loss allowance?

Analysis. Midstream would determine the intent of the product loss allowance is to allow for the natural shrink that occurs when transporting gas through a pipeline, and it does not represent compensation for the transportation services. Therefore, the allowance does not impact the transaction price for the transportation services, and actual losses that occur (within the 5% allowance) would not be reflected as an operating cost of the company.

If Midstream retains some excess natural gas (e.g., because it only loses 4% during transportation in a particular period) and subsequently sells the commodity to a third party, the sales revenue would be recorded at that time. Midstream would present the proceeds from the sale as product revenue as it typically sells natural gas as part of its ongoing major or central operations.

Although the description above focuses on crude oil pipelines, the concepts and examples are also relevant to natural gas pipelines. For example, contracts related to the transportation of natural gas may include a PLA related to fuel usage or gas used to operate compressors.

Inventory

Crude oil and natural gas marketing companies can use storage and transportation assets to hold and store large quantities of inventory, enabling them to take advantage of market arbitrage opportunities.

Accounting methods

Commodity market conditions can be considered either in "backwardation" or "contango." In a backwardation market, expected future prices are below the spot price. Conversely, in a contango market, the future price of a commodity is expected to be higher than its spot price. Backwardation encourages marketers and producers to sell commodities as soon as they are acquired, whereas a contango market creates an incentive to purchase commodities and store them for future sale at a higher price. Oftentimes, marketers transacting at market hubs can purchase crude oil or natural gas at current prices for storage and simultaneously enter into "futures" or "forward positions" for future delivery at higher prices.

Crude oil, natural gas and NGL marketers typically account for their inventories using a weighted average cost of goods (WACOG) methodology. Under this methodology, all purchased commodities enter a pool of similar products, separated by an appropriate combination of commodity type, grade or quality and physical location. With each new acquisition, the weighted average cost of the pool is updated, based on the acquisition price and acquisition quantity. After a sale, the sold quantity exits the pool at the weighted average cost of the pool.

For example, assume that MarketCo has 100 barrels of crude oil inventory at the beginning of January. MarketCo acquired this inventory in a prior period for $50 per barrel. In January, MarketCo purchases another 100 barrels for $56 per barrel, which it sells in February for $53 per barrel. The company would record revenues in February of $5,300 as a result of the sale. The company's inventory, as a result of these transactions, would be as follows:

Figure 28-1
Illustrative inventory reconciliation

	Volume (bbls)	Price per bbl	Value
January 1	100	$50	$5,000
January purchase	100	$56	5,600
January 31	200		10,600
January WACOG		$53	
February sale	(100)	$53	(5,300)
February 28	100		$5,300
February WACOG		$53	

GAAP requires companies to record inventories at the lower of cost or net realizable value (NRV). Midstream companies typically have controls in place to perform this analysis periodically; public companies do so at least quarterly. GAAP allows accountants to base inventory costs on the first-in first-out (FIFO), the last-in first-out (LIFO) or the WACOG method.

If the NRV price is less than the carrying value (cost) of the inventory, a company should reduce the inventory value to the market price. If the NRV price is more than the carrying value of inventory, no adjustment is permitted. To determine the NRV price, companies usually consider the product location and quality. For crude oil, NRV price usually considers product location and quality.

For example, crude oil NRV price can be based on West Texas Intermediate (WTI) or North Texas Sweet prices. For crude oil, transportation costs also must be considered (pipeline, truck, rail, etc.). For natural gas, the NRV price can be based on index prices published in various periodicals (e.g., Platts Gas Daily).

Continuing the previous example, assume that MarketCo does not enter any additional purchases or sales during the year and, at the end of December, has 100 barrels of crude oil inventory at a weighted average price of $53 per barrel. Also assume that the NYMEX spot price for crude oil at December 31 is $50 per barrel.

MarketCo should record a lower of cost or NRV adjustment of $3 per barrel for the 100 barrels of crude oil inventory as illustrated in the journal entry below:[1]

LOE – change in inventory	300	
Inventory – crude oil		300
To record the lower of cost or NRV adjustment.		

Balance sheet and cash flow classification

The nature and intended use of c rude oi l and natural gas held by companies will affect the balance sheet and statement of cash flows classification, as summarized in Figure 28-2 below.

Figure 28-2

Intended use and classification of inventory

Type	Intended use	Classification
Working gas	Portion of natural gas that is expected to be sold or used in operations.	Classified as inventory (current or noncurrent, depending on the expected timing of sale or use).
Base gas (cushion gas)	Portion of natural gas necessary to force the saleable gas from a storage field into the transmission system and for system balancing. Not intended for sale and will not be fully recoverable until a storage project or related pipeline is abandoned.	Generally classified as part of property, plant and equipment; represents a permanent investment necessary to use a storage facility and maintain its reliability. Cash flows from base gas acquisitions and dispositions are classified as investing activities.
Linefill	Amount of crude oil required to fill a new pipeline before deliveries can be made at take-off points or at the end of the line.	Classified as part of property, plant and equipment given its long-term characteristics; carried at historical cost and assessed for impairment under ASC 360. Given it is essential to pipeline function, its cash flows are classified as investing activities.

Imbalance settlement clauses

Imbalance settlement clauses, which are included in gas transportation agreements with pipeline companies, should be analyzed to determine whether they meet the definition of a derivative under ASC 815, *Derivatives and Hedging*.

In particular, the imbalance settlement option in the contract may not meet the criteria to be considered a derivative in ASC 815-10-15-83 (as further clarified by guidance found in ASC 815-10-55-5 through 55-7) with respect to a notional amount, even though it may meet the criteria in ASC 815-10-15-99, in part because the gas can be readily converted to cash. Even if the contract meets the definition of a derivative, the cash price used in settlement may result in a derivative fair value of zero. Nevertheless, the disclosures specified in ASC 815-10-50 are still required.

If the imbalance settlement option in the contract meets the definition of a derivative, it may not qualify for the normal purchases and normal sales (NPNS) exception provided in ASC 815-10-15-13. It is improbable at inception, and throughout the term of the contract, that settlement of imbalances always will result in physical delivery (i.e., it will not net settle). Further information on derivatives and ASC 815 can be found in Chapter 34.

Pipeline gas imbalances generally are recorded as gas imbalance receivables or payables at values that reflect the contractual arrangements with the pipeline. For example, contracts may specify the valuation of volumes related to gas imbalances at: (1) current mainline index prices, (2) the pipeline's weighted average cost of goods sold, (3) a weighted average sales price or (4) another accepted method. Additionally, imbalance receivables should be evaluated to determine if the carrying value is collectible. If a portion is not collectible, it should be adjusted to reflect the amount expected to be received.

Exchanges

Contracts in which counterparties exchange commodities between two different locations are exchange contracts. In exchange contracts, prices are adjusted for a difference in location or when a less valuable crude oil is exchanged for a higher value product. Occasionally, a company will exchange its crude oil for another company's crude oil rather than selling it. These exchanges arise to meet location, quality or timing needs and are intended to reduce transportation costs or to meet an integrated company's need for a different quality of crude for its local refinery, among other needs.

The exchange may be structured whereby one party receives a differential from the other for an agreed-upon difference in value of the crude barrels that they exchange. Alternatively, it may be structured as a sale of the company's crude oil in exchange for the company's purchase of other crude oil. Each company pays the other for the full purchase price of oil received in the exchange. Normally, the acquired oil is sold during the same month the exchange occurs.

Exchange contracts often are structured as purchases and sales of inventory with the same counterparty, resulting in a single exchange. Therefore, from an accounting perspective, such contracts are generally subject to the net versus gross guidance in ASC 845, *Nonmonetary Transactions*. However, it is important that the substance of each transaction be analyzed carefully to ensure it does not meet the definition of a derivative under ASC 815, and thus qualify for derivative treatment.

Additionally, consideration should be given to gross versus net presentation of resulting revenues and expenses based on guidance in ASC 606. In evaluating exchange contracts, it is important to consider the facts and circumstances in the context of the entity's various activities, rather than solely focusing on the terms of the individual contracts. Further guidance is provided in ASC 815.

NPNS exception

When evaluating the accounting treatment for oil and gas contracts, entities must choose either:

- The NPNS scope exception in ASC 815 for contracts meeting the definition of a derivative, in which sales are recorded in accordance with ASC 606 and costs are expensed as incurred. Under the NPNS exception in ASC 815, the derivative is not accounted for at fair value; therefore, fluctuations in commodity prices do not affect the buyer's and/or the seller's financial statements.

- Fair value accounting, in which the market value of the gas contracts and associated obligations are estimated each quarter. Under fair value accounting, fluctuations in expected commodity prices affect the financial statements of companies that are a party to natural gas contracts.

To qualify for the NPNS exception, the contract must provide for the purchase or sale of something other than a financial instrument or derivative instrument that will be delivered in quantities expected to be used or sold by the company over a reasonable period in the normal course of business. Therefore, natural gas contracts that do not involve an option to change contracted volumes, and which are not expected to net settle (offset against another contract), typically qualify for the exception, and the costs are therefore expensed as incurred.

The following criteria are required for transactions to qualify for the NPNS scope exception: (1) normal terms (including normal quantity with no optionality); (2) clearly and closely related underlying; (3) probable physical settlement; and (4) documentation.

To qualify for this scope exception, a contract's terms must be consistent with the terms of an entity's normal purchases or sales (i.e., the quantity purchased or sold must be reasonable in terms of the entity's business needs). Determining whether or not the terms are consistent requires judgment.

To make this judgment, an entity should consider all relevant factors, including:

- The quantities provided under the contract and the entity's need for the related assets.

- The locations to which the items will be delivered.

- The period of time between entering into the contract and delivery.

- The entity's prior practices with regard to such contracts.

Furthermore, to identify contracts that qualify as normal purchases or normal sales, an entity should consider the following types of evidence:

- Past trends.

- Expected future demand.

- Other contracts for delivery of similar items.

- Customs for acquiring and storing the related commodities (from the entity's perspective as well as the industry in which it operates).

- Operating location(s).

For example, MarketCo needs to supply its customers 10,000 MMbtu of natural gas exactly six months from now. It enters into a forward contract to purchase 10,000 MMbtu of natural gas at $2 per MMbtu. Six months from now, the gas will be delivered to MarketCo's customers and the cost of $20,000 will be paid to the contract counterparty.

Because this contract is not expected to net settle, and the amount and location are consistent with what MarketCo would do in its normal course of business, the NPNS exception applies. MarketCo does not record any amounts for the transaction at the inception date or during the six months prior to gas delivery as it does not take possession of the gas (i.e., no asset or liability should be recognized on the balance sheet). MarketCo records the purchase cost of $20,000 as an expense on the income statement at the time of delivery.

Storage contracts

Typically, storage contracts are fee-based arrangements in which customers pay a rate per volume to store their product. In some cases, however, storage of liquids is offered to customers in return for fixed-fee payments that are not linked to actual storage volumes. The terms of service and fixed monthly payments may instead be determined by transportation service arrangements negotiated with shippers.

Storage contract terms

The rates charged to customers for storage services are typically based on market demand and specified in the contract. In addition to volume-based charges, the storage owner earns a service fee for the shipper's injection and withdrawal of the natural gas. The storage agreement specifies the storage location, duration, limits on injections and withdrawals, maximum storage capacity and other terms.

Revenues recognized for storage services generally are not exposed to commodity price risk because rates per volume, or other fixed-fee structures, are not tied to a pricing index. However, companies that provide storage services can be affected by commodity prices indirectly; when producers are not producing as much natural gas or crude oil as usual, they will be injecting lower volumes into storage facilities.

To determine the proper accounting for a physical storage contract, an entity must first evaluate the arrangement to determine whether or not it contains a lease. If not, the entity should assess whether or not it is a derivative in its entirety. If not, the last question is whether the contract contains any embedded derivatives that require separation from the host contract. If neither lease nor derivative accounting applies, the entity must account for the physical storage agreement as an executory contract on an accrual basis.

In accounting for a storage contract following an executory contract model, the customer should expense the cost of storage as a period cost when incurred. The storage owner should recognize revenue from storage fees in accordance with ASC 606.

Storage contract gains and losses

The cause of storage gains and/or losses depends on the product. For natural gas, storage gains and/or losses can result from problems with cavern integrity or improperly calibrated meters. For crude oil, storage gains and/or losses typically result from leaks, evaporation, water content and unproved meters.

Storage gains and losses are determined based on the difference between the calculated ending storage-volume balance and the physical measurement for a given period. The ending storage volume is calculated by adding injection activity and subtracting withdrawal activity from the beginning storage volume. The beginning storage volume is based on the calculated ending storage volume from the prior period. Injection and withdrawal activity is measured in meters.

Typically, both the company providing the storage and the customer install their own respective meters at the facility. The storage company typically performs a "variance analysis," comparing the two sets of meter readings. Storage contracts may specify a "maximum tolerable variance" (e.g., one percent). Any differences greater than the specified maximum tolerable variance may require further analysis and/or recalibration of the meters. Company policy typically requires periodic meter recalibration or "proving."

Liquefied natural gas

Liquefied natural gas (LNG) is natural gas that for shipping and storage has been cooled to a liquid state at a cryogenic temperature of (265)°F. The volume of natural gas in its liquid state is about 0.167 percent (one six hundredth) of its volume in its gaseous state. Liquefying natural gas makes it more convenient to move the gas long distances when pipeline transport is not feasible. Markets that are too distant from producing regions to connect directly to pipelines can access natural gas because of LNG.

LNG is shipped in special tankers to terminals. At these terminals, the LNG is returned to its gaseous state and transported by pipeline to distribution companies, industrial consumers and power plants. The U.S. has the ability to both import and export LNG. However, the shale revolution has virtually eliminated the need for LNG imports and the U.S. has begun to export its natural gas. The first shipment of LNG from the lower 48 states departed in February 2016 and the U.S. became a net exporter of LNG the same year. In 2016, the U.S. imported approximately 88 billion cubic feet (Bcf) of LNG from three countries, compared to the 187 Bcf it exported to 18 countries.[2]

The demand for natural gas continues to grow worldwide. Natural gas delivered by pipelines to Mexico and to U.S. LNG export facilities reached 10.9 Bcf per day in July 2019 and averaged 10.0 Bcf per day in the first seven months of the year, 30 percent more than in the same period of 2018. The EIA expects that U.S. natural gas exports will continue to increase as new LNG facilities come online.

Midstream companies offer many services related to LNG, including sales and marketing, storage, regasification and transportation. LNG contracts generally are fee-based and can be structured so that title transfers at multiple points in the product transfer process. A close reading of the contract will help determine the accounting implications.

When evaluating LNG contracts, accounting standards related to leases, derivatives, inventory and revenues should all be considered. For example, contracts to provide LNG services may include MVCs and makeup rights. When accounting for revenue for these contracts, companies must also assess breakage, as discussed earlier in this chapter.

Another important aspect of revenue accounting for LNG contracts involves determining when the performance obligation has been satisfied. Specifically:

1. When does control of a commodity transfer to the customer – over time or at a point in time?

2. If control transfers over time, how will progress toward complete satisfaction be measured?

3. When is it appropriate to use the practical expedient to measure progress (i.e., recognize the amount of revenue that the entity has a right to invoice)?

LNG contracts should be reviewed to determine if they qualify as a lease under ASC 842, *Leases*. Contracts for LNG storage and transportation contain a lease if: (1) substantially all of the capacity is obtained by the customer throughout the period of use and (2) the customer makes decisions that most significantly affect the economics derived from use of the asset. In this regard, it is important to identify the presence of a physically distinct asset. In some instances, one customer may not use the entire capacity of the LNG storage facility or transportation means (e.g., a marine vessel or truck).

For example, a contract providing the use of a portion of the storage capacity of a facility is not physically distinct because it cannot be distinguished from other concurrent users of the storage facility. However, if a customer has sole access to a storage tank at an LNG facility, or even substantially all of the tank capacity, then it may be considered a physically distinct asset.

Regulatory accounting

Industry-specific accounting guidance for regulated operations is predominantly codified as ASC 980, *Regulated Operations*. Regulated entities that meet certain criteria under ASC 980 are required to apply its guidance. The purpose of ASC 980 is for financial reporting to reflect the economic effects of certain rate-regulated activities and regulatory actions that arise in the normal course of regulated operations. Its basic premise is that the actions of a regulator will affect the statements prepared for financial reporting only if the action has an economic effect on the regulated entity and meets the requirements for recognition or deferral under the standard. A regulated entity should comply with GAAP applicable to entities in general. If the entity also is subject to ASC 980, the applicable provisions of the standard are applied as an adjustment to or in lieu of other GAAP (when specifically required by ASC 980).

ASC 980 offers guidance for: (1) determining whether or not a reporting entity has regulated operations subject to rate-regulated accounting and (2) accounting for certain assets, liabilities and transactions that arise from regulated operations.

As outlined in ASC 980-10-15-2, a reporting entity is required to apply ASC 980 if it meets three criteria:

- Rates are established by an independent third-party regulator or the entity's own governing board,

- Rates are designed to recover costs of service, and

- Rates designed to recover costs can be charged to and collected from customers.

The reporting entity should assess and document whether or not it continues to meet each of these criteria, setting forth the significant factors considered, at least annually or any time rate structures change or regulatory developments occur. The unit of account for the application of ASC 980 can be a transaction, a group of transactions, a separable operation of the reporting entity or the reporting entity in its entirety. The unit of account is based on the level at which it meets the criteria in ASC 980-10-15-2. Documentation should address the rationale for determining the unit of account if specific or different factors affect various parts of the business (e.g., service territories, customer classes or functional activity such as generation).

Certain changes to the regulatory or competitive environment in which a regulated entity operates may mean that the regulated entity is no longer qualified to apply ASC 980 to all or certain portions of its operations. Whether and when a regulated entity no longer meets the criteria for application of rate-regulated accounting for all or a portion of its operations is highly judgmental. ASC 980-20 includes examples of factors that may lead a regulated entity to conclude it fails to meet the criteria in ASC 980-10-15-2.

Regulatory assets. One of the primary categories in which regulated entities differ from unregulated ones is their ability to defer certain expenditures as regulatory assets that would otherwise be expensed under GAAP. Specific criteria exist for the recognition and measurement of regulatory assets, as summarized in Figure 28-3 below.

Figure 28-3

Regulatory assets – Key areas of accounting consideration

Area	Accounting considerations
Initial recognition and measurement	Incurred costs may be capitalized as a regulatory asset if the amounts are probable of recovery through rates.
	Regulatory assets initially are measured as the amount of the incurred cost.
	If a cost does not meet the criteria for deferral as a regulatory asset at the date incurred, it should be expensed; a regulatory asset subsequently may be recorded if and when the criteria for recognition are met.
Subsequent measurement	Regulatory assets typically are amortized over future periods consistent with the period of recovery through rates.
	If all or part of an incurred cost recorded as a regulatory asset is no longer probable of being recovered, the amount that will not be recovered should be written off to earnings.
	If a regulator subsequently allows recovery of costs that were previously disallowed, a new asset is recorded; classification of the new asset depends on how the asset would have been classified had it been previously allowed.

Per ASC 980-340-25-1(a), in evaluating whether or not an incurred cost is eligible for deferral as a regulatory asset, a regulated entity should determine if the cost is probable of recovery through future revenue from rates that the regulator allows to be charged to customers.

Determining the probability of rate recovery of an incurred cost is a matter of judgment; relevant parties should evaluate the preponderance and quality of all available evidence. Different forms of evidence will provide varying degrees of support for management's assertion that a regulatory asset is probable of recovery.

A specific rate order specifying the nature of the cost, and the timing and manner of recovery, is generally the best evidence that recovery is probable. However, the regulatory process does not always permit an entity to obtain a rate order prior to issuing its financial statements.

Regulatory liabilities. ASC 980-405-25-1 names specific criteria to recognize three types of regulatory liabilities that may result from regulatory actions:

- Refunds of amounts previously collected from customers.

- Current collections for future expected costs.

- Refunds of gains.

These liabilities represent a regulated entity's obligations to its customers. A regulated entity may be eligible for rate recovery of amounts recorded as liabilities under GAAP (incurred but not reported personal-injury claims or environmental liabilities). Regulated entities may question whether or not such liabilities should be recorded in their financial statements. Liabilities that are recorded pursuant to GAAP generally are not within the scope of ASC 980-405-25-1 because they are not created or imposed by regulatory actions. Therefore, the requirement to recognize such liabilities does not depend on whether or not the regulator has allowed recovery of the related costs.

ASC 980-405-40-1 specifically states that a regulator can eliminate only those liabilities that it previously imposed. Therefore, in addition to potential regulatory liabilities, regulated entities should record all liabilities that would be recorded by entities in general. If the liability will be recovered through rates, the regulated entity may be able to record a regulatory asset, assuming it meets the criteria in ASC 980-340-25.

A regulator may require that a regulated entity reduce customers' rates in future periods that do not meet existing conditions. For example, the entity may be required to provide future rate concessions as part of a general rate case or may reduce future rates in the form of credits agreed upon in connection with a business combination ("merger credits") or a FERC license renewal. The regulated entity should not accrue the effects of regulator-ordered future rate reductions in advance but should recognize them as reduced revenue in future periods.

Group and composite depreciation

In practice, midstream companies, use two depreciation methods to depreciate multiple asset groups: the "group method" or the "composite method."

- **Group method.** The group method typically is used for groups of assets that are largely homogeneous and have approximately the same useful lives. When applied to a largely homogeneous population, the group method more closely approximates a single-unit depreciation profile because the variance from the average useful life is not meaningful.

- **Composite method.** The composite method is useful when the assets are heterogeneous and have different lives. Under composite depreciation, companies apply a single depreciation to functional groups of property with similar economic characteristics. For FERC-regulated entities, the FERC-accepted composite depreciation rate is often applied to the total cost of the composite group until the net book value equals the salvage value.

Some companies use group depreciation for pipeline systems and related components that are too numerous and low in value to track individually. Some entities apply the composite method for component parts of larger assets, which also contain numerous subcomponents and parts that are impractical to track separately. Under both methods, a reporting entity depreciates the balance over the average life of the assets in the group.

For nonregulated entities, depreciation estimates often are based on a variety of factors, including age (for acquired assets), manufacturing specifications, technological advances, the contract term for assets on leased or customer property and historical data concerning useful lives of similar assets. To apply either the group or composite method of depreciation, a reporting entity should have quantitative data to support the chosen method, such as: the expected useful life of the assets, the dispersion of useful lives from the average for group depreciation and the calculations supporting the weighted average depreciation rate for the composite method.

Periodic studies also should be performed to support ongoing use of either method. The necessary frequency of such studies often is a function of the extent of changes in relevant inputs since the last study. In practice, for assets regulated by the FERC or other governing bodies, these depreciation studies typically are completed as a part of rate proceedings or tariff filings; the changes in economic lives, if applicable, are implemented prospectively, when the new rates are billed. For nonregulated assets, if the estimated economic life changes, the changes are made prospectively upon determination of the revised life.

In general, neither the group nor composite depreciation method results in recognizing a gain or loss when an asset is retired. If an asset is retired before or after the average service life of the group, the resulting gain or loss is included in the accumulated depreciation account, reflecting the difference between the original cost and cash received. The result is that the gain or loss on disposal remains in accumulated depreciation.

Both methods simplify the bookkeeping process and tend to smooth any potential differences caused by over or under depreciation. As a result, periodic income is not distorted by significant gains or losses related to asset disposal. Only in very limited circumstances should a gain or loss on disposal be recognized in earnings. This would occur only after unforeseen or unexpected retirements. For example, the early retirement of an entire processing facility due to storm damage likely would be considered abnormal and result in the recognition of a loss.

Both methods of depreciation are acceptable under GAAP, and either may be applied by any reporting entity as long as it is selected when the asset is placed in service. Certain entities may use more than one method of depreciation, such as applying unit depreciation to fixed assets with large unit costs while applying the group method to assets with lower unit costs.

Contributions in aid of construction

Contributions in aid of construction (CIAC) received by midstream companies are unique to the industry and generally are used to defray the costs of building or extending existing facilities. In contrast to customer advances, which are received with the expectation of eventual return, CIACs are permanent collections from the customer for a particular purpose.

The FERC Uniform System of Accounts requires companies under its guidance to subtract the amount of the contributions from the related plant account balances. This concept is consistent with the FERC ratemaking treatment because the rate base generally is determined "net of CIAC received." However, some companies record a CIAC liability when they receive the contribution. Given that the CIAC is related to the construction of the plant, the amount is amortized over the depreciable life of the underlying asset.

Midstream companies also may receive construction advances from developers. These amounts may be refunded to the developers once the development meets certain service milestones (e.g., number of customers added or volume of commodity delivered). The amounts are retained by the company if the developer does not meet the milestones on schedule. Advances generally are recorded as liabilities until refunded or until the milestone period lapses. Once the milestone period lapses, any retained advances usually are reclassified to reduce the related plant balance.

• • •

---

1 The example herein assumes that MarketCo's oil cost equals the NYMEX market price for crude oil traded at Cushing, Oklahoma. A company would also need to consider differentials for grade and location to account for the true NRV for that pool of barrels.

2 Natural gas deliveries to U.S. LNG export facilities set a record in July, August 19, 2019 https://www.eia.gov/todayinenergy/detail.php?id=40953.

CHAPTER

29

Master Limited Partnerships

Photograph by istock.com/sarkophoto

A publicly traded partnership (PTP) is an entity treated as a partnership for U.S. federal income tax purposes that is publicly traded on an established securities market, a secondary market or the substantial equivalent of such markets. Entities operating as PTPs include limited partnerships (LPs), limited liability companies (LLCs) and Bermuda holding companies. Businesses operating as PTPs include those involved in natural resources-related operations, financial asset management, real estate investments, amusement parks and death care. Natural resources related PTPs are commonly referred to as master limited partnerships (MLPs).

History of MLPs

The first publicly traded MLP in the U.S. was launched in 1981 when Apache consolidated its drilling partnerships into Apache Petroleum Company. At that time, there was no limit on the type of business that could be organized as an MLP. Consequently, more than 100 MLPs appeared in a myriad of industries, including restaurants, hotels, financial services and even professional sports teams. The enactment of Section 7704 of the Internal Revenue Code (IRC) in 1987 reduced the scope of qualified businesses and the universe of MLPs contracted. Today, the bulk of MLPs exist across the oil and gas value chain, including companies engaged in upstream, midstream and downstream activities.

During the last decade, the number of MLPs filing for initial public offerings (IPOs) accounted for the majority of total energy IPOs. For example, in 2013 the 21 energy MLP IPOs comprised more than 80 percent of total energy IPOs. In late 2014, the dramatic fall in crude oil prices drastically reduced the number of MLP IPOs, to just six from the beginning of 2015 through the end of 2016. The secondary capital market activity related to MLPs dropped during this timeframe as well. Nonetheless, MLPs continue to represent a unique and significant aspect of the energy industry.

Common MLP terms

Before analyzing the benefits of MLPs and certain legal structures, an overview of common MLP terms is important to understanding concepts described herein. A partnership agreement is the principal governing document of the MLP. It establishes the legal structure and defines the partners' roles, responsibilities, rights and authority.

Many of the provisions in an MLP partnership agreement resemble those of non-MLP partnerships, including:

- **Capital accounts**. These accounts are established and tied to the economics of each unitholder, based on the requirement that the partnership liquidate positive capital-account balances (liquidation provision). The capital account balance is increased by profits, gains and contributions and decreased by deductions, losses and distributions. MLPs vary in their allocation of net income and loss to the capital account, but the allocation is defined in the partnership agreement, including any special allocations required for a specific class of unitholders.

- **Capital account revaluation**. This provision addresses the treatment of unrealized appreciation in the event of a change in the equity structure ("book-up" or "book-down"). The principles of Internal Revenue Code (IRC) §704(c) should be applied to adjust the capital accounts and allocate unrealized economic gain or loss.

- **Debt allocations**. When forming an MLP and making the subsequent public offering, the presence of nonrecourse debt, and more importantly, the allocation of that debt, is crucial. Recognizing this, many MLPs specifically address nonrecourse debt allocations in the partnership agreement based on Treasury Department regulations.

- **Partnership conventions**. MLPs adopt various conventions to aid with required calculations, especially with respect to the large volume of trading that may occur. For example, to compute adjustments under IRC § 743(b), MLPs generally adopt a convention that deems the price paid for a limited partner interest as the lowest quoted closing price of the limited partner interest during the calendar month in which the transfer is deemed to occur.

  MLPs also generally use a monthly convention to allocate income and loss between the buyer and seller of these interests. This grouping of buy/sell transactions into monthly tranches follows provisions of Treasury Department regulations, issued under IRC §706.

- **Partnership representative.** The partnership agreement addresses the designation of a partnership representative, which is given sole authority to act on behalf of the partnership with respect to all U.S. federal income tax matters as well as certain state tax matters. In most cases, this is the general partner (or its designee). Unless otherwise limited by provisions of the partnership agreement, the partnership representative may, in its sole discretion, exercise any of the powers granted to it by the Bipartisan Budget Act of 2015 (see H.R. 1314, P.L. No. 114-74, including amendments) and Treasury Department regulations thereunder, including, but not limited to: (1) binding the partnership and the partners with respect to decisions made in all tax matters and (2) determining whether to pay proposed tax assessments through the partnership or push out such assessments to the affected partners.

- **Tax elections and conventions**. The general partner (GP) has broad authority to make tax elections and establish conventions that promote economic uniformity in the interests. When units are exchanged (bought or sold) in the public market, an MLP usually will elect under IRC §754 to permit the revaluation of property and make a step-up (or step-down) in basis to the partnership's property, under IRC §743(b). This step-up or step-down will add deductions or income, respectively, to the unit's purchaser.

- **Liquidation**. The MLP's potential liquidation often influences many of the allocations and hypothetical calculations that impact other provisions of the partnership agreement. Most agreements require liquidation, in accordance with positive capital account balances, after all items of income, gain, deductions and losses have been allocated to the unitholders. MLPs generally look to the net termination gains/losses provision for direction about the final allocation, which usually follows cash distribution provisions.

- **General partner**. The GP is the entity that controls the MLP, manages its operations on behalf of the limited partners and typically is controlled by a sponsor, the entity that created the MLP.

- **Investors**. Refers to the public investors; limited partners or unitholders refer to either the sponsor, the investors or both.

- **Common units**. Common units represent limited partner interests; they are the equity interests traded on securities exchanges (e.g., NYSE and NASDAQ). Holders of common units are entitled to distributions payable from the MLP and certain rights and privileges defined by the partnership agreement.

- **Subordinated units**. Subordinated units have marginal rights to receive partnership distributions, relative to common units, during a specified subordination period. When the period expires, subordinated units are converted to common units. The subordination period typically lasts three years from the date of the IPO, but may expire earlier after meeting specified cash-distribution thresholds. The partnership agreement may require the subordination period to end gradually (i.e., a stated percentage of subordinated units each year) or all at once at a specific time if the partnership meets specified targets ("cliff vesting," as applied to all subordinated units). Many MLPs initially include both common and subordinated units; the subordinated units typically are held by the sponsor.

- **Qualifying income.** Defined by the IRC as:

  - Interest.

  - Dividends.

  - Rents from or gains from the sale of real property.

  - Gains from the sale of an asset held for the production of qualifying income.

  - Gains from commodities, futures, forwards and options (for commodities).

- **Incentive distribution rights**. The GP may be assigned incentive distribution rights (IDRs) to further align its interests with the limited partners, who seek consistent and/ or growing cash distributions. IDRs give the GP the right to receive an increasing share of total partnership distributions after meeting target distribution levels. IDR terms, as outlined in the partnership agreement, often stipulate that the GP may receive as much as 50 percent of cash distributions when the distributions occur in the highest tier of target distributions (high splits). See Figure 29-7 for an example.

IDRs may be issued as a class of nonvoting interests, separate from the units held by the general partner and transferrable without unitholder approval. Alternatively, IDRs may be embedded within the general partner's interest, in which case they typically cannot be detached and subsequently transferred.

Benefits of an MLP

MLPs often are viewed as mutually beneficial for both unitholders and sponsors. As discussed herein, unitholders have the benefit of limited liability and liquidity, no double taxation and tax-deferred distributions, as well as competitive returns, while sponsors benefit from retaining operational and financial control, having upside potential through IDRs, valuation premiums and a lower cost of capital.

Unitholder benefits

Limited liability and added liquidity. The personal liability of unitholders is limited, yet they benefit from the liquidity of a publicly traded security.

No double taxation. Earnings are taxed only at the investor level, based on the investor's share of the partnership's income.

Tax-deferred distributions. In most cases, investors earn a tax-deferred return of capital, since cash distributions generally exceed the investor's share of taxable income.

Competitive returns. Long-term investment returns historically have been much higher than those of other asset classes. When a sponsor creates an MLP, it often perceives that prospective public investors seek steady cash distributions at a relatively high yield, considering the investment's risk profile and market rates of interest. Although this is true, investors also typically expect competitive total return on their investments, including long-term appreciation on the value of their partnership units. Therefore, MLPs must focus on increasing both their cash distributions and their unit price.

Not surprisingly, most MLPs operate in the midstream sector, where established tariff regimes, predictable volumes of product transported or processed, and long-term customer contracts historically have brought relatively steady and reliable cash flows. When an MLP increases its cash distributions, the value of its units also generally increases, delivering the total return that investors seek.

Sponsor benefits

Operational and financial control. MLPs offer the ability to retain control while raising substantial capital through the sale of limited partner interests. Unlike corporations, which are generally controlled by a majority vote, partnership agreements typically assign operational authority to the GP, who manages the operations on behalf of the limited partners and typically is controlled by the sponsor. Limited partners usually have very little influence over MLP operations.

Significant upside through IDRs. IDRs may come in the form of a separate class of equity or as rights embedded in the general partner's interest. Either way, IDRs entitle the GP to an increasing proportion of distributable cash flow as the partnership achieves its benchmarks.

Valuation premium. Units usually trade based on a multiple of cash flow or yield, as opposed to a multiple of earnings. Therefore, units historically have traded, on average, at a higher multiple than those of comparable businesses organized as corporations. These higher multiples reflect both greater transparency of the valuation basis (actual and forecast distributions, which tend to be relatively predictable) and the tax-advantaged status of an MLP. A sponsor may realize enhanced valuation of its equity when the market recognizes (1) the valuation premiums on assets that already have been, or are expected to be, contributed to the MLP over time; and (2) the valuation premiums associated with the sponsor's GP interest and, if applicable, related IDRs.

Access to and cost of capital. Because MLPs are not subject to entity-level income taxes, their cost of capital often is lower than that of corporate entities. This may aid in their growth as they compete against corporations for opportunities and resources.

Additional benefits

In addition to a favorable pass-through tax structure, several other factors prompt business leaders to consider creating an MLP.

Growth opportunities. The rapid expansion of unconventional resource development in the U.S. has increased the demand for midstream infrastructure and prompted increased investment in processing, transportation and storage assets. Funding the development costs to access unconventional resources and meeting the projected requirements for new pipelines and storage capacity are expected to require billions in additional capital investment during the coming decades.

Low interest rate environment. MLPs often rely on the capital markets to finance their growth and development. Historically low interest rates in the U.S. during the last several years made MLPs particularly attractive to yield-seeking investors, helping to propel their growth. However, sponsors should be aware that a sharp rise in interest rates could turn investors' attention to alternate forms of income investing (e.g., certificates of deposit and treasury bonds) and potentially slow MLP formation and growth. For example, lower commodity prices, when combined with expectations of rising interest rates, would negatively impact the issuance of high-yielding asset classes, including MLPs.

Tax considerations

Income tax considerations are critical to maximizing value. Tax consequences and reporting requirements for MLPs differ considerably from those of a corporation. Figure 29-1 highlights some of the key tax-related differences between an MLP and a corporation. In addition to allocating taxable income or loss to unitholders and the general treatment of distributions as a nontaxable return of capital, other tax considerations arise from both the publicly traded nature of an MLP and the partnership tax rules outlined in the IRC.

Fungibility. Because units are traded on the open market, each unit must be interchangeable with any other unit of the same MLP. In other words, for units to be traded on a national exchange, the characteristics of each unit must be the same, regardless of where it was purchased (i.e., units must be fungible). Although fungibility is not a tax concept, the evaluation of unit fungibility must consider the tax consequences for unitholders.

Unit fungibility requires adherence to two distinct sections of the IRC:

- **IRC §704(c) compliance – remedial method**. At its simplest level, IRC §704(c) requires that a partnership's asset and capital account values be increased or decreased to fair market value (i.e., "booked-up" or "booked-down") if the partnership's equity structure changes. This ensures that unrealized appreciation or depreciation is forever tagged to existing partners' capital accounts and that new partners entering the partnership do not share in any of the historic gains or losses.

A change in the partnership's equity structure can result from an equity offering, an asset acquisition in exchange for units or the vesting of compensation units issued to management. When a change occurs, the value of the MLP must be adjusted to account for the price at the time of the event. Said differently, when the fair value of the contributed property does not equal its tax basis, the MLP is revalued, allocating appreciation among the unitholders, in accordance with their sharing ratios. Treasury Department regulations stipulate three methods by which this book-up or book-down can be accomplished: (1) traditional, (2) traditional with a cure and (3) remedial. However, only the remedial method ensures that each partner receives tax deductions equivalent to the value of the units acquired.

The remedial method requires that new partners entering the partnership receive deductions based on their respective economic interests in the partnership. If insufficient deductions remain in the partnership to accomplish this through proration, existing partners may be required to pick up income to fund deductions to the incoming partners. As a result, the partnership would have no new deductions; instead, the existing deductions would be reallocated so that new partners receive the tax deductions equal to the economic deductions to which they are entitled.

The remedial method reallocates tax deductions to unitholders who contributed high-basis property (e.g., cash) away from contributors of low-basis property (e.g., appreciated assets). It also ensures fungibility among the units. Therefore, MLPs use the remedial method to comply with §704(c) provisions and fungibility requirements. Given that the sponsor generally is the original contributor of low-basis property, it typically receives remedial income as the MLP grows.

- **IRC §743(b) basis adjustments**. MLPs that make an election provided by IRC §754 are allowed to make IRC §743(b) basis adjustments. An IRC §743(b) basis adjustment arises when a partner purchases an existing interest in a partnership and the existing basis of that interest differs from what the partner paid for it. These basis adjustments either increase or decrease a buying partner's tax basis (i.e., future deductions) in the partnership's assets.

  For example, if an interest has $20 of tax basis in the MLP's assets, and a unitholder buys a unit on the open market for $22, the unitholder is entitled to $22 of value in the MLP and should receive the corresponding tax deduction. A basis adjustment of an additional $2 is created to ensure that the unitholder's basis equals its investment.

Tax shield. The tax shield is a measure of the tax deferral benefit the MLP can generate for its public unitholders. More specifically, it is the ratio of an investor's allocated taxable income to the cash distributions received (which typically are not subject to current tax as a return of capital). Investors have come to expect various levels of tax shield, based on the assets held by the MLP. For an MLP in the midstream sector, a tax shield of 80 percent is typical. For an MLP focused on E&P, tax shields often are lower, sometimes less than 50 percent, because these MLPs do not generate large tax deductions, as compared with those in midstream. Tax shield and yield can be related inversely: Investors often receive a lower tax shield if they purchase an MLP with a higher yield.

Figure 29-1
Comparison of MLPs to corporations

Attribute	MLPs	Corporations
Entity-level taxation	**Nontaxable** Treated as partnerships and do not pay any federal income tax. Though some exceptions apply, generally not subject to state income tax.	**Taxable** Pay federal income tax on earnings. Pay state income tax on earnings.
Investor taxation	**Unitholder taxation** All taxable income and loss is allocated to unitholders, each paying tax according to their individual tax circumstances.[1] Taxable income is not a function of distributions. Distributions are viewed as a nontaxable return of capital to the extent of the unitholder's basis. Distributions that exceed basis generally are treated as capital gains.	**Shareholder taxation** Shareholders are taxed only on dividends and may be taxed on dividends at preferential rates. The Tax Cuts and Jobs Act (TCJA) reduced the maximum corporate tax rate down to 21%, changing the blended rate to 36.8%, given the 20% (highest) qualifying dividends tax rate (21% + [(1 − 21%) x 20%]).
Net Investment Income Tax (NIIT)	**Passive activities** Certain unitholders may be subject to the NIIT imposed on passive activities, due to their allocation of taxable income.	**Gross income from dividends** Shareholders may be subject to the NIIT on their gross income from dividends.
Qualifying-income test	**Qualifying-income test applies** Of the income generated, 90 percent must come from passive sources, such as interest, dividends, real property rents and income derived from mineral or natural resources. If the MLP fails this test, it will be treated as a corporation and pay federal income tax on its earnings.	**No qualifying-income test** Pay federal income tax on earnings.
Distributions	**Distributions are not required/guaranteed** Generally, a partnership agreement includes a definition/calculation of "available cash" which is used to determine quarterly distributions. However, during economic stress, distributions may be curtailed.	**Dividends are not required/ guaranteed** Generally, dividends are at the discretion of the board and are not required to be declared.
Financial reporting for income taxes	**Typically does not apply** MLPs do not recognize federal income tax expense and generally are not subject to state income taxes. Certain states, notably Texas, are exceptions; they may levy an entity-level income tax.	**Account for all income tax obligations** Must recognize current and deferred taxes for their federal, state and foreign income-tax obligations.
Federal income tax reporting	**Form 1065, Schedule K-1** Report income to the IRS on Form 1065, *U.S. Return of Partnership Income*. Unitholders are issued a Schedule K-1, which details their allocation of the profit or loss.	**Form 1120, Form 1099** Report income to the IRS on Form 1120, *U.S. Corporation Income Tax Return*. Shareholders are issued a Form 1099, which details the amount of dividends they received.
State tax reporting	**Unitholder reporting obligations** Unitholders generally are required to file a tax return in each state in which the MLP operates or derives income.	**No shareholder reporting obligation** Shareholders generally are not required to file tax returns in each state in which the corporation operates or derives income.

Figure 29-1
Comparison of MLPs to corporations (cont.)

Attribute	MLPs	Corporations
Interest expense limitation	**Applies at the partnership level** Certain taxpayers are subject to a limitation on the deductibility of interest. Deductible and excess business interest expense of the partnership retain their character at the partner level. A partnership's adjusted taxable income (ATI) takes into account Section 734(b) basis adjustments to partnership property, but partner-specific basis adjustments and remedial items of income or loss are taken into account at the partner level in determining a partner's ATI. The partnership's ATI and partners' share of excess items is allocated to the partners using a set of steps prescribed by Treasury Department regulations. Excess business interest expense of a partnership is carried forward by the partner, not the partnership.	**Applies at the corporate entity** Taxpayers are subject to a limitation on the deductibility of interest. Under the new limitation, interest expense is limited to the sum of: (a) the taxpayer's business interest income for the tax year, (b) 30 percent of the taxpayer's ATI for the tax year and (c) the taxpayer's floor plan financing interest expense for the tax year. The excess business interest expense is carried forward by the corporation and utilized in years in which sufficient ATI is generated.
Passthrough entity deduction	**20 percent deduction on qualified business income (QBI)** The deduction is generally limited by W-2 wages of the passthrough entity. However, investments in MLPs are not subject to the W-2 wage limitation. Additionally, QBI from a PTP is treated separately from QBI from other partnership investments by the partner.	**No corresponding deduction.**

The unitholder's tax shield has an inverse effect on the sponsor's tax position. The sponsor generally is the original contributor of low-basis property. Therefore, the sponsor generally recognizes remedial income so that the public unitholders can receive tax deductions equal to their economic deductions. As a reminder, no new deductions can be created under the remedial method; it only allows the reallocation of existing deductions. An increase in the tax shield to public unitholders therefore produces a corresponding increase in the remedial income (i.e., cash tax due) recognized by the sponsor (and vice versa). The sponsor should be aware of this relationship and work with tax advisers to find a fair balance between the public unitholders' tax shield and the sponsor's remedial income allocations.

Unit buy-backs. An MLP may purchase outstanding limited partner units from public unitholders. One factor that may lead to the purchase is a decline in unit price. Although this option may be attractive from a future cash flow perspective, unit purchases may produce adverse consequences from an income tax perspective. The tax consequences of any potential unit repurchases should be carefully considered.

Structuring an MLP

This section, and Figure 29-2, summarizes the critical steps that sponsors should consider prior to forming an MLP. Although not all-inclusive, the critical components of forming a typical MLP are captured herein.

Figure 29-2
MLP formation

Pre-IPO	<ul><li>Sponsors form general partner</li><li>Sponsors (or affiliates) and the GP form a limited partnership – the MLP</li><li>The MLP is capitalized (GP receives 2% interest and sponsors receive remaining 98% of limited partners interest)</li><li>Sponsors contribute qualifying assets to the MLP and the MLP assumes related liabilities</li><li>The MLP moves assets and liabilities down to its operating subsidiaries at the IPO date</li></ul>
IPO and Post-IPO	<ul><li>IPO of common units open to the public</li><li>GP maintains GP interest</li><li>The MLP must have 90% of gross income representing "qualifying income"</li><li>MLP distributes 100% of available cash (generally cash on hand during a quarter less cash reserves established by GP for future business needs and distributions)</li><li>Sponsors or an affiliate (the GP) receives cash, common units, subordinated units and rights to receive a greater portion of the MLP's incremental cash flow in the future (also known as incentive distribution rights or IDRs)</li></ul>

Several legal entities typically are used to form MLPs, including LPs, LLCs and operating companies. Each structure has the same general tax effect – treatment as a pass-through entity.

Limited partnerships

Most currently trading MLPs are limited partnerships. In this structure, there is one GP and numerous limited partners (investors). The GP makes all management decisions and may have personal liability for certain partnership obligations. Limited partners are not liable for partnership obligations beyond their capital contributions; this protects them from personal liability for partnership debt.

At the IPO date, the sponsor typically owns 100 percent of the MLP's general partner interest. Historically, it was common for a GP to own a two percent economic interest in the MLP. However, it is becoming more common for the GP to hold a smaller economic interest. After an IPO, the GP may elect not to exercise its right to participate in the MLP's subsequent equity offerings, which dilutes its initial economic interest.

MLPs organized as LPs may offer only one class of limited partner interests (common units) or several classes, including subordinated units and IDRs. The availability of various equity classes gives the MLP greater flexibility for financing.

Figure 29-3

Illustrative limited partnership with IDRs

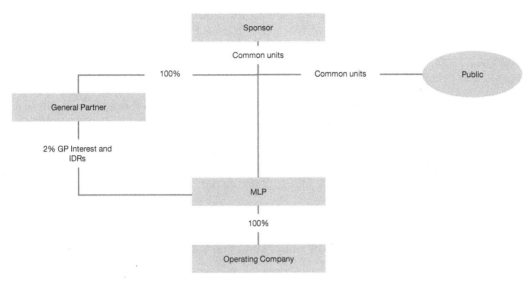

Limited liability companies

In an LLC structure, all investors are deemed "members." Unlike an LP, in which a GP retains all control, MLPs structured as LLCs generally have a managing member elected by the LLC unitholders. All LLC members have limited liability, similar to corporate stockholders, but they also enjoy the benefits of a partnership for tax purposes, including the flow-through of income (and losses) to the unitholders. The LLC structure may use both common units and subordinated units. MLPs formed using an LLC typically do not include IDRs in their capital structure.

Figure 29-4

Illustrative limited liability company without IDRs

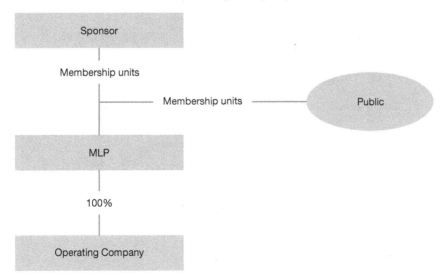

Operating companies

Sponsors may contribute a varying percentage of the ownership (as much as 100 percent) in one operating company (OpCo) or more to form an MLP. Upon contribution, each OpCo becomes a lower-tier partnership within the MLP legal structure. These lower-tier partnerships often are established or continued for purposes of accounting control, managing legal liability, maintaining existing contractual obligations and separating regulated assets from nonregulated assets.

The sponsor also may contribute to the MLP each legal entity that holds a GP interest in any OpCo to the MLP. Owning each OpCo's GP enables the MLP to control and consolidate the entire OpCo group. The economic interests in each OpCo retained by the sponsor (i.e., 90 percent for OpCo 1 and 50 percent for OpCo 2 in Figure 29-5) are reflected in the MLP financial statements as noncontrolling interests. Unlike voting rights that entitle unitholders to control the MLP, economic rights allow unitholders to receive a proportional share of MLP earnings.

Figure 29-5
Illustrative operating company

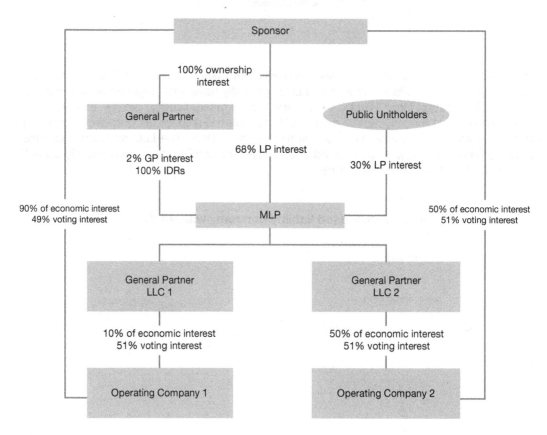

Contribution of assets

Asset selection is an iterative and complicated process. The specific assets that a sponsor contributes to an MLP are determined by multiple factors, including qualifying income requirements, cash distribution goals and the ability to produce the SEC required financial statements. Sponsors should consider the following critical factors when selecting assets to contribute to an MLP.

Qualifying income. As mentioned, an MLP is treated as a partnership for tax purposes only if its activities generating qualifying income represent 90 percent or more of its gross income. Failure to achieve this 90 percent threshold will cause the MLP to be taxed as a corporation. No grace period or cure exists if the 90 percent threshold is not achieved throughout every annual period. Therefore, ensuring the appropriate level of qualifying income is one of the first steps in selecting the assets to contribute to an MLP.

Stable cash flows. A vast majority of MLPs provide steady and predictable distributions to investors, who differentiate "traditional" from "variable" MLPs. Therefore, sponsors must consider the type of cash flows generated by the contributed assets and determine whether the MLP will be marketed as a traditional or variable MLP.

- **Traditional MLPs**. A large majority of the MLPs that exist today are traditional, in that they generate steady revenue streams and exhibit manageable and consistent operating costs and capital expenditures, producing stable net cash inflows. Traditional MLPs are traded based on these stable cash flows and the yield they provide, rather than the net income they produce.

  Traditional MLPs are easily identified by their stated minimum quarterly distributions (MQDs) to unitholders. Long-term revenue contracts (take-or-pay contracts) are common among midstream companies because they historically have created a relatively high level of confidence in predictable cash flows. Upstream companies with mature fields, proven reserves and a robust hedging program also may offer a high degree of predictable cash flows.

- **Variable MLPs**. While variable MLPs have existed for a long time, only a few remain. Variable MLPs distribute all of their available cash, without regard to achieving either an MQD or a regular distribution. The MQDs that are common among traditional MLPs do not exist in a variable MLP, as distributions will fluctuate with changing commodity prices and/or market conditions.

Availability of financial statements. Asset selection should take into account financial reporting requirements specific to the selected assets. Sponsors should consider the existence, availability and quality of historical financial information, the supporting financial and operational records needed to prepare the required financial statements and the ability of the MLP's independent accountants to audit or review these financial statements.

If the SEC considers the contributed assets to represent a business (which is usually the case), it likely will require the registration statement to include multiple years of audited annual financial statements and, depending on the filing date, perhaps unaudited interim financial statements.

Depending on the time it takes to go public, the SEC may require updating of the registration statement to include more current annual and interim financial statements, all of which will be subject to audit or review by the independent auditors. Sponsors should consider the guidance included in the SEC's Financial Reporting Manual (FRM), *Chapter 1220*, for additional financial statement requirements.

Nonqualifying income

It is common for businesses being considered for contribution to an MLP to generate nonqualifying income related to legacy businesses or other vertically integrated activities. When certain assets do not appear to meet the requirements for qualifying income, the sponsor has several options:

- Select other assets to contribute to the MLP.

- Request a private letter ruling (PLR) from the IRS to opine that the income generated, in fact, meets the requirements.

- Contribute the assets to a corporate subsidiary owned by the MLP.

Rather than separating valuable assets or changing the business model, sponsors might establish a corporation below the MLP to hold the nonqualifying assets. This corporation (blocker corporation) typically is owned 100 percent by the MLP but taxed as a separate and distinct entity. The corporation files its own tax returns and pays income taxes. Any after-tax cash it earns and distributes to the MLP generally is considered qualifying income to the MLP. Therefore, nonqualifying income earned by the corporation does not negatively affect the MLP in terms of qualifying income.

Qualifying income

As mentioned previously, qualifying income is defined by the IRC as: interest; dividends; rents from or gains from the sale of real property; gains from the sale of an asset held for the production of qualifying income; and gains from commodities, futures, forwards and options (for commodities).

Highly relevant to the energy industry, qualifying income also includes gross income generated from exploration, development, mining or production, processing, refining, transportation (including pipelines transporting gas, oil or products thereof), or marketing of any mineral or natural resources, including fertilizer, geothermal energy and timber. Since the introduction of the qualifying income test, most new MLPs operate in the natural resource industries. Although U.S. legislative history and statutory guidance established a broad framework defining and limiting the types of activities that generate qualifying income, MLP sponsors saw considerable room for interpretation. Therefore, they sought further guidance from the IRS through a process known as "private letter rulings."

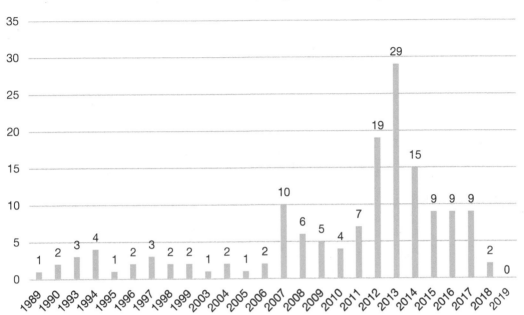

Figure 29-6

Growth of Private Letter Rulings – 1989 through 2019

Private letter rulings

A PLR is a written ruling from the IRS that is made in response to a taxpayer's request for the interpretation of relevant tax laws in light of a given set of facts and circumstances. Once the ruling is issued, the taxpayer may rely on it for its tax position, with some conditions and limitations. A PLR is specific to the requesting taxpayer and may not be held as authority by any other taxpayer, even a taxpayer with a similar set of facts and circumstances. Requesting a PLR requires the payment of fees to the IRS and receiving a response can be a lengthy process. See Figure 29-6 for PLR activity from 1989 through 2019.

In early 2014, the IRS paused its PLRs related to certain qualifying income to better ensure consistency in its rulings across the energy industry. The IRS internal review and the associated pause in activity created uncertainty in the MLP sector. Many planned IPOs were put on hold, awaiting the outcome of the review. In March 2015, the IRS announced that it would resume its rulings on qualifying income.

In January 2017, final regulations under Section 7704(d)(1)(E) addressing qualifying income derived from minerals or natural resources by PTPs were released. Because the final regulations do not include an exhaustive list of qualifying activities, the IRS has put taxpayers on notice that it is reasonable to anticipate that a PLR would be necessary to confirm the application of qualifying income rules to any activity that is not listed in the final regulations.

Other MLP considerations

Establish nexus. When an MLP is considered to be doing business in a particular jurisdiction, it is said to have "nexus" in that jurisdiction. Nexus can be created several ways, such as by conducting business in a state, establishing operations and employees in a state, or selling goods in a state. A physical presence (e.g., an office) can also establish nexus. Depending on state income tax rules, an MLP may be subject to income, gross receipts and franchise taxes.

Tax consequences. A sponsor's contribution of assets to an MLP often results in its receipt of both cash and partnership units, which may be taxed as a sale of assets to the MLP. This likely will lead to the sponsor's recognition of a gain and may result in cash taxes. If a contribution (or a portion thereof) is treated as a sale, the consequences to the sponsor are the same as if the assets were sold to a third party. By contrast, the formation of an MLP without sale treatment generally is a tax-deferred event.

Equity method investments. If the contributed business or businesses hold significant equity method investments, the registration statement, as well as post-IPO annual filings. must include audited financial statements for those significant equity method investments (as defined by Rule 3-09 of Regulation S-X). In addition, certain unaudited financial information is required for interim periods. Therefore, sponsors should evaluate the availability and timeliness of these financial statements both before going public and upon becoming a public company.

Significant acquisitions. If the contributed business or businesses constitute a significant acquisition(s) (as defined by Rule 3-05 of Regulation S-X) during any of the periods for which audited financial statements are required, the registration statement must include audited annual and unaudited interim financial statements for the acquired business(es). The number of periods that this requirement encompasses will depend on the level of significance.

Consolidations. Merger transactions among MLPs likely will result in considerations that are not present in transactions with a C-corp or other non-MLP structures. Synergies and economies of scale are likely to drive value. In addition, the merged structure is likely to be complex, from both a financial and income tax perspective. Therefore, MLPs should identify issues early so that they can be considered in the valuation of the potential merged entity.

Minimum quarterly distributions

An MQD is an essential feature of a traditional MLP making it possible to offer stable and predictable cash flows and relatively high distribution yields. Under a partnership agreement, an MLP typically is required to distribute all available cash to unitholders. Generally, available cash is defined as all cash and cash equivalents on hand at the end of a quarter, less a set amount of cash reserves established by the GP to allow for the proper conduct of the MLP's business and other specified adjustments.

Assuming that the MLP generates sufficient quarterly cash flow from its operations or from other sources, the MLP will issue an MQD to unitholders. The partnership agreement specifies the MQD formula to calculate the distribution. Although MLPs are not required by securities or tax laws to make quarterly distributions, this unique feature makes MLPs an attractive investment.

Common units typically are entitled to arrearages when MQD thresholds are not met, whereas subordinated units are not. Instead, subordinated unitholders receive their entitled MQDs only after the common unitholders receive theirs (including any arrearages). Any remaining excess is distributed among the common and subordinated unitholders on a pro rata basis.

As illustrated in Figure 29-7, if the MLP achieves its MQD, the GP initially is entitled to two percent of cash distributions, which is commensurate with its two percent GP interest.

Figure 29-7
Illustrative quarterly cash distribution

Quarterly cash distribution	Limited partner share (common/subordinated)	GP share (IDR + 2% GP interest)
MQD per Level 1 Target (10% yield)	98%	2%
Level 2 Target (upon achieving 11% yield)	85%	15%
Level 3 Target (upon achieving 12.5% yield)	75%	25%
Thereafter (upon achieving 15% yield)	50%	50%

However, if the MLP's distributions exceed its MQD and the partnership agreement includes IDRs, the GP's share of cash distributions above the MQD will increase.

As shown in Figure 29-7 above, the GP's share of the MQD increases to 15 percent in Tier 2 and 25 percent in Tier 3, ultimately reaching as high as 50 percent of the total partnership distributions for each $1 increment distributed beyond Tier 3, while the GP's interest remains at two percent. Limited partners, in turn, experience a corresponding reduction in their share of incremental cash distributions above specified levels but they still receive distributions that exceed the MQD. Through the use of an "IDR reset," the GP has the right, but not the obligation, to adjust the MQD and the target distribution thresholds to higher amounts, entitling the GP to incentive distributions.

The partnership agreement typically does not require unitholder approval for the IDR reset, but it does set certain conditions, such as prohibiting outstanding subordinated units and/ or IDRs paid at higher share-target levels. In addition, in the event of an IDR reset it is not uncommon for the partnership agreement to allow the GP to receive additional common units, based upon a preset formula.

Throughout 2018 and 2019, a number of MLPs extinguished their IDRs by issuing the IDR holder (generally the sponsor) a number of common units based on the value of the IDR interest and a predefined formula pursuant to specific provisions of the partnership agreement.

Growing the MLP

The valuation of an MLP is greatly influenced by its growth prospects and strategic plans. An MLP can expand its operations in three fundamental ways:

Subsequent sponsor contributions (dropdowns). When establishing the MLP, the sponsor often identifies assets that will be contributed (dropped down) to the MLP after the IPO, as disclosed in the registration statement. The sponsor often grants the MLP a right of first offer (ROFO) for specific assets. The ROFO gives the MLP the option, but usually not the obligation, to purchase those assets from the sponsor before they are offered to other potential buyers. The sponsor typically designs its dropdown schedule with the specific goal of achieving steady growth in MLP cash distributions.

New asset creation. MLPs may develop new assets through capital projects, funding them through equity or debt issuances or by retaining cash from operations (rather than distributing substantially all available cash to unitholders).

These options do not differ, fundamentally, from those available to a corporation. However, it may be challenging to retain cash from operations to fund growth in an entity that is designed to distribute substantially all available cash to unitholders. A smaller distribution also could shift potential investors' perception of the yield they could expect from investing in the MLP. As a result, it is more common for the sponsor to develop or acquire new assets and later contribute them to the MLP.

Third party asset acquisition. The MLP can use equity, debt or retained cash from operations to acquire assets from third parties. However, retaining cash for asset acquisitions presents challenges, as described above.

Governance

As mentioned, the partnership agreement is the MLP's principal governing document. In addition to establishing its legal structure, the agreement includes, but is not limited to, provisions that:

- Define the duties and authority of the GP, including removal provisions.

- Specify the rights and restrictions of limited partners.

- Detail how profit/loss and distributions are allocated to the unitholders.

- Clarify termination and dissolution provisions.

An MLP typically is managed by the board of directors and officers of its GP. MLPs commonly have no employees and the GP frequently maintains all management authority, a provision that assists the MLP sponsor in retaining operational and financial control.

If the MLP has no employees, the GP is responsible for supplying employees and other personnel needed to conduct operations. To address this responsibility, the GP and MLP typically create various agreements (omnibus agreement, services agreement, etc.) under which the sponsor provides employees and services to meet the MLP's operational and financial reporting needs, including components of the MLP structure.

Board of directors

The composition and function of an MLP's board of directors differs from that of a corporation. Rather than having an entirely separate board, MLPs commonly ask the GP's board of directors to fulfill part of that function. An MLP's board of directors typically qualifies for certain exemptions from governance rules, such as requiring a majority of board members to be independent or establishing compensation or nominating and governance committees.

In addition, the MLP has independent directors. Consistent with certain transition provisions available to other new registrants, only one independent director is required at the time of the IPO. A second director must be appointed within 90 days and the board must be fully independent within one year.

General partner

Although the partnership agreement requires the GP to act in good faith, it also may limit and make exceptions to the GP's fiduciary responsibilities to both the limited partners and the MLP. These contractual provisions enable the MLP to conduct transactions that otherwise would be prohibited by laws governing the fiduciary responsibilities of the GP (e.g., related-party transactions with the sponsor and the GP).

These laws require the GP to act in either its "individual capacity" or its capacity as the MLP's GP. When making decisions in its "individual capacity," the GP is allowed to consider any factors it chooses. Therefore, it has no duty or obligation to consider the interests of the MLP or those of its limited partners. This means that the traditional shareholder protections expected from a corporation may not exist in an MLP.

Limited partners

With very few rights in the MLP's governance process and no oversight of day-to-day operations, limited partners typically can vote only on substantial changes to the partnership agreement (e.g., replacing the GP), approving strategic acquisitions and liquidating the MLP.

Audit committee

MLPs must have an audit committee, with a minimum of three independent directors, each of whom must meet the qualification and experience requirements of the securities exchange on which the MLP units are traded. The above-noted transitional independence relief also applies to the audit committee.

Conflicts committee

The partnership agreement typically establishes a conflicts committee, composed entirely of independent directors, to review selected transactions for potential conflicts of interest between the sponsor and the partnership. Because the GP has limited fiduciary responsibility to the limited partners, committee approval may be necessary for significant related-party transactions. However, the GP is not required to seek approval of the conflicts committee on all matters.

Omnibus agreement

It is common for an MLP to make an omnibus agreement with the sponsor that describes the nature and specific features of the relationship between the two parties. In particular, an omnibus agreement specifies how to deal with potential conflicts, using the provisions discussed herein:

- **Noncompete provision**. Requires the sponsor to give the MLP the first opportunity to pursue the acquisition of assets or a business that is in the same line of business as the MLP or in a specific geographic area.

- **Right of first offer**. Allows the MLP to purchase, at a favorable price, certain assets that were not contributed by the sponsor during the IPO. The price the MLP pays is accretive to its distributable cash flow, thus giving the MLP the ability to boost cash distributions in the short-term.

Accounting and reporting considerations

The complexity of MLP structures provides for a number of challenges from an accounting and financial reporting perspective, including the accounting for asset drop downs, financial statement presentation of partnership equity and earnings per unit (EPU), and allocation of shared costs between the GP and MLP.

Common control transactions

For accounting purposes, dropdowns from a sponsor into an MLP are considered common control transactions and not business combinations under the guidance in ASC 805, *Business Combinations*. Unlike accounting for business combinations, common control transactions are not accounted for at fair value. Rather, they generally are recognized initially by the MLP at the sponsor's historical carrying amount of the transferred net assets or equity interests. If the MLP transfers cash in the exchange, any difference between the cash and the carrying amount of the net assets is treated as an equity transaction (e.g., capital distribution or contribution).

Common control transactions do not result in a change in control at the sponsor level, and therefore they do not affect the sponsor's consolidated financial statements beyond reclassifications between the controlling and noncontrolling interests within equity (i.e., MLP units held by the public).

Because MLP dropdowns combine two or more commonly controlled entities that historically have not been presented together in the MLP's financial statements, the financial statements to be issued for periods including and following the dropdown are generally considered to be those of a different reporting entity. The resulting change in reporting entity requires retrospective combination of the entities for all periods during which the MLP and the newly contributed business were under common control of the sponsor. However, for purposes of calculating EPU under the two-class method for the pre-dropdown periods, the earnings or losses of the transferred net assets must be allocated entirely to the GP in accordance with ASC 260-10-55-111. This does not change the historical earnings per limited partner unit.

In making this decision, the Emerging Issues Task Force (EITF) observed that the limited partners did not have any contractual rights to these earnings prior to the dropdown transaction, and the rationale for a strict contractual approach to allocating undistributed earnings was preferable to methods that were pro forma in nature and therefore would not reflect the actual economic rights to undistributed earnings.

The timing of this recasting of prior period financial statements can be critical when the MLP plans to access the capital markets shortly after the dropdown transaction but before issuing the next annual financial statements. In this case, the MLP must consider whether or not the recasting of its previously issued financial statements to reflect the dropdown transaction would be material from a legal perspective (i.e., they would represent a fundamental change).

If material, the SEC requires the filing of recasted prior period financial statements before raising capital from an existing shelf registration statement. If the company is filing a new registration statement and not merely raising capital from an existing shelf registration statement, the company must consider whether the acquisition is material to the financial statements. If deemed material, the company would be required to issue recasted financial statements prior to filing the new registration statement. Companies should also consider the need to issue pro forma financial statements in accordance with Reg. S-X Rule 3-05 to reflect the acquisition.

Partnership equity accounts

The equity section of the balance sheet normally is labeled "partners' equity" or "members' equity," in contrast to a corporation's "shareholders' equity" or "stockholders' equity." Similar to reporting entities with multiple classes of common or preferred stock, MLPs must report each equity class separately, either on the face of the balance sheet within the equity section or within the footnotes. Each partner or member class's rights, preferences and privileges should be included in the disclosure.

Furthermore, a statement of changes in partners' or members' equity should be included for each ownership class and for each period for which an income statement is presented. If the MLP maintains separate accounts for various components within individual partners' equity accounts (e.g., undistributed earnings, earnings available for withdrawal and unallocated capital), it should present the balance within each component on the face of the balance sheet or in the footnotes.

In addition, if the results of MLP operations create a deficit balance for some members, this fact should be disclosed. Furthermore, the MLP should disclose any legal limitations on liabilities for each partner or member.

Allocation of earnings

Earnings per unit calculation. Publicly traded MLPs often issue multiple classes of securities that may participate in partnership distributions, according to a formula specified in the partnership agreement. A typical MLP consists of publicly traded common units held by a GP interest, limited partners and IDRs.

Depending on the MLP's structure, IDRs may be classified as a separate form of nonvoting limited partner interest, one that the GP initially holds but generally may transfer or sell apart from its overall interest. Alternatively, IDRs may be embedded in the GP interest so that they cannot be detached and transferred apart from the GP's overall interest.

Certain MLP elements present unique and sometimes challenging accounting considerations in calculating EPU and presenting multiple classes of equity. MLPs must present earnings per common unit on the face of the income statement. All securities that meet the definition of a participating security in ASC 260, *Earnings per Share*, should be considered in computing basic EPU, using the two-class method.

Guidance in ASC 260-10-50 provides specific EPU disclosure requirements for each period for which an income statement is presented. Additionally, with respect to MLPs, ASC 260-10-50-3 notes the following:

> In the period in which a dropdown transaction occurs that is accounted for under the Transactions Between Entities Under Common Control Subsections of Subtopic 805-50, a reporting entity shall disclose in narrative format how the rights to the earnings (losses) of the transferred net assets differ before and after the dropdown transaction occurs for purposes of computing earnings per unit under the two-class method.

Under the two-class method, EPU is calculated as though all of the MLP's earnings for the period were distributed according to the terms of the securities (i.e., as stipulated in the partnership agreement), regardless of whether or not:

- The GP has discretion over the distribution amounts in any particular period.

- Earnings actually are distributed during a particular period from an economic or practical perspective.

- The MLP has other legal or contractual limitations that would prevent it from distributing all of its earnings for the period.

The guidance in ASC 260-10-45-59A through 45-70 clarifies which securities are considered participating, how to apply the two-class method of computing EPU and, for a participating security, how to allocate undistributed earnings to that security.

IDRs that are separate securities. As outlined in ASC 260-10-55-103 through 55-106, IDRs that are a separate class of LP interest are participating securities because they have a right to participate in earnings with common equity holders. Therefore, in calculating EPU, current period earnings are allocated to the GP, limited partners, and IDR holders using the two-class method in ASC 260. When calculating EPU under the two-class method, the MLP would reduce (or increase) net income (or loss) for the current reporting period by the amount of available cash that has been or will be distributed to the GP, limited partners, and IDR holders for that reporting period.

The partnership agreement may contractually limit the amount of distributions to holders of the IDRs. Therefore, the MLP should allocate the undistributed earnings, if any, to the GP, limited partners, and IDR holders, utilizing the distribution waterfall (i.e., a schedule included in the partnership agreement that prescribes distributions to the various interest holders at each threshold). The undistributed earnings should be allocated to the IDRs based on the contractual participation rights of the IDRs to share in current period earnings. Therefore, if the partnership agreement includes a "specified threshold" as described in ASC 260-10-55-30 at which the IDRs stop participating in earnings, an MLP should not allocate undistributed earnings to the IDRs once the specified threshold has been met.

The MLP should allocate any excess of distributions over earnings to the GP and limited partners based on their respective sharing of losses per the provisions for allocation of losses to the partners' capital accounts, as specified in the partnership agreement, for the period presented. If the IDR holders do not share in losses, the MLP would not allocate the excess of distributions over earnings to the IDR holders. However, if the IDR holders have a contractual obligation to share in the losses of the MLP on a basis that is objectively determinable (as described in ASC 260-10-45-67), the MLP should allocate the excess of distributions over earnings to the GP, limited partners, and IDR holders based on their respective sharing of losses, as specified in the partnership agreement, for the period presented.

IDRs that are embedded within the GP interest. IDRs that are embedded within the GP interest are not separate participating securities. However, because the GP and LP interests are separate classes of equity, the MLP would still apply the two-class method in computing EPU for the GP and LP interests, as provided in ASC 260-10-55-107 through 110.

For purposes of the EPU calculation, in certain circumstances the MLP would reduce (or increase) net income (or loss) for the current reporting period by the amount of available cash that will be, but has not yet been, distributed to the GP (including the distribution rights of the embedded IDRs) and limited partners for that reporting period.

In addition, MLPs may have multiple classes of equity securities. In these situations, the presentation of EPU is only required for the classes of common units, although the MLP is not precluded from presenting EPU for all classes of participating securities. This is similar to reporting entities that have issued both common and participating preferred stock, whereby entities are only required to present EPU for common stock but are not precluded from presenting EPU for participating preferred stock.

Allocation of shared costs

The GP often provides employees and centralized services to the MLP and, in some cases, the services of other entities it operates, such as other subsidiaries or equity investees. The GP must have policies and procedures to allocate these costs, systematically and rationally, to the entities and to regulated assets, where applicable, using an accepted methodology. When costs are shared or not clearly attributable to the MLP's operations, the GP may use an allocation model based on headcount, labor expense, plant and equipment balances, operating income or another appropriate metric.

MLPs should disclose the methodology used to allocate expenses between the sponsor and the MLP; they also should use an appropriate control structure to ensure consistent application. Because this is a subjective area, the SEC focuses on ensuring that MLPs have clear and detailed disclosures of how allocated costs are determined, including the underlying calculations and judgmental areas, to ensure compliance with Item 402 (b)(1)(v) of Regulation S-K. The cost allocation for tax purposes can vary based on transfer pricing requirements under IRC Section 482.

Spin-offs and carve-outs

As an MLP business grows and evolves, the GP continuously evaluates the mix of assets and returns on those assets within the MLP. The GP may make business decisions to remove certain assets to keep the MLP within its distribution growth model. Although outright sales to third-party buyers are common, some MLPs may elect to "spin off" the subject assets to existing equity holders. As is the case with dropdowns, spin-offs are considered transactions with entities under common control. Historical financial statements presented for periods before the spin-off are considered "carve-out" financial statements from the MLP.

Carve-out financial statements refer to the separate historical financial statements of a subsidiary, division or other subset of a business. The term carve-out indicates that the business unit's financial statements were not prepared separately in the past; rather, they were "carved out" of the larger consolidated accounts. Generally, carve-out financial statements appear in an IPO of securities or to comply with Reg. S-X Rule 3-05 for audited financial statements of an acquired business.

Preparing carve-out financial statements is complex and subjective. Each situation is unique, requiring separate consideration. Specific accounting guidance governing the composition of the carved-out entity is limited. However, as a general rule, the carve-out financial statements should portray the business being carved out as if that business had historically prepared separate stand-alone financial statements.

The GP should evaluate the carve-out disposition to determine whether discontinued operations presentation is appropriate under ASC 205, *Presentation of Financial Statements*. However, the GP should not adjust its historical financial statements to remove the business being spun off.

● ● ●

---

1 The partnership share of taxable profit and loss allocated to each limited partner typically produces a much smaller taxable income than the amount of cash distributed during the same period (20 percent is the representative historical relationship). The largely deferred character of distributions to limited partners (provided they do not exceed the tax basis of the limited partner's investment), when combined with the much smaller allocated taxable income, creates a "tax shield." Essentially, taxes are deferred on the majority of the unitholder's income stream from the investment until it is sold.

Financial Statement Disclosures

- **Disclosure requirements**

- **Full cost considerations**

- **SEC disclosure requirements**

- **Common SEC comment letter focus areas**

This chapter focuses on the disclosures required by ASC 932. Related SEC disclosure rules, including full cost disclosures, also are addressed. Chapter 31 specifically addresses disclosure of the standardized measure of oil and gas reserves.

Disclosure requirements

Oil and gas reserves are paramount to E&P companies and important to the users of their financial statements. During the past several decades, as the disclosure requirements for companies with significant oil and gas producing activities have evolved, so have the disclosures required for oil and gas reserves.

Statement of Financial Accounting Standards No. 69 (FAS 69) was the first disclosure requirement regarding oil and gas reserves. Released by the FASB in November 1982, it was followed a month later by the SEC's Reg. S-K §229.302, which adopted the requirements of FAS 69 to replace existing disclosure requirements for oil and gas producing activities.

In December 2008, the SEC issued its final rule on the Modernization of Oil and Gas Reporting. Referred to as the "Final Rule," this pronouncement made significant changes to the disclosure requirements for SEC registrants. It was "intended to provide investors with a more meaningful and comprehensive understanding of oil and gas reserves, which should help investors evaluate the relative value of oil and gas companies." The Final Rule stated that, "[i]n the three decades that have passed since adoption of these disclosure items, there have been significant changes in the oil and gas industry." It added that, "[t]he amendments are designed to modernize and update the oil and gas disclosure requirements [and related definitions] to align them with current practices and changes in technology."

In July 2009, the FASB released the ASC to simplify access to authoritative accounting standards. FAS 69 was integrated into the ASC in Section 932. In January 2010, the FASB issued ASU 2010-03 to align the oil and gas reserves estimation and disclosure requirements of ASC 932 with those in the Final Rule.

All of the ASC 932 disclosure requirements are applicable to public companies with significant oil and gas producing activities, with certain disclosure requirements of ASC 932 applicable to private companies as well. Other sections of the ASC also have disclosure requirements that are relevant to oil and gas companies.

In addition, SEC regulations require certain other disclosures to be made in the audited financial statements, the supplemental (unaudited) information or elsewhere in SEC filings.

Publicly traded companies

Certain ASC 932 disclosures are required only for companies that are publicly traded. Even though some enterprises are not considered to be publicly traded under the SEC rules, they may, however, meet the ASC 932 definition of publicly traded. For example, certain limited partnerships that file reports with the SEC or certain private entities that offered securities under Regulation D of the Securities Act of 1933[1] also may be required to include ASC 932 disclosures in their annual financial statements.[2]

ASC 932-235-20 defines a publicly traded company as a business entity that has any of the following characteristics:

a. Whose securities are traded in a public market on a domestic stock exchange or in the domestic over-the-counter market (including securities quoted only locally or regionally)

b. That is a conduit bond obligor for conduit debt securities that are traded in a public market (a domestic or foreign stock exchange or an over-the-counter market, including local or regional markets)

c. Whose financial statements are filed with a regulatory agency in preparation for the sale of any class of securities in a domestic market.

Other examples that require ASC 932 disclosures include the financial statements required for a significant acquisition of a working interest in oil and gas producing properties (Reg. S-X Rule 3-05)[3] and the associated Article 11 pro forma financial statements.

ASC 932-235-50-2 requires supplemental disclosures for publicly traded companies with significant oil and gas producing activities. A company is regarded as having significant oil and gas producing activities if such activities are at least 10 percent of the company's total activities, which a company should calculate based on any of the following three tests:

- Revenues from oil and gas producing activities (including both sales to unaffiliated customers and sales or transfers to the enterprise's other operations) are 10 percent or more of the combined revenues (including both sales to unaffiliated customers and sales or transfers to the enterprise's other operations) of all the enterprise's industry segments.

- Results of operations of oil and gas producing activities (including equity earnings or losses from oil and gas producing activities of equity method investees and excluding the effects of income taxes) are 10 percent or more of the greater of the:

    - Combined operating profit of all industry segments that did not incur an operating loss.

    - Combined operating loss of all industry segments that did incur an operating loss.

- The identifiable assets of oil and gas producing activities (tangible and intangible company assets that are used by oil and gas producing activities, including an allocated portion of assets used jointly with other operations and the investment balance in the oil and gas producing activities of equity method investees) are 10 percent or more of the assets of the company, excluding assets used exclusively for general corporate purposes.

The SEC expects that the general requirement for disclosure of material amounts will require that some ASC 932 disclosures be made if, "the discounted present value of a registrant's oil and gas reserves is significantly in excess of 10 percent of consolidated total assets," even if the three tests noted previously are not met.[4] However, SEC rules do not define what is "significantly in excess of 10 percent."

Overview of required disclosures

Below is a list of disclosures required by ASC 932 and ASC 235, *Notes to Financial Statements*, for companies with oil and gas producing activities:

- Whether publicly traded or not, an entity engaged in oil and gas activities must disclose its:

  - Method of accounting for costs incurred in such activities.

  - Manner of disposing of capitalized costs relating to those activities.

  - Information about continued capitalization of exploratory well costs.

  - Accounting policy for suspended well costs (for companies following the successful efforts method of accounting only).

- Publicly traded enterprises that have significant oil and gas producing activities also must disclose certain supplemental information, which is not required to be audited:

  - Proved oil and gas reserves, proved developed oil and gas reserves, and proved undeveloped (PUD) oil and gas reserves quantities as of the beginning and end of the year and changes in reserves quantities during the year.[5]

  - Capitalized costs and the related accumulated DD&A relating to oil and gas producing activities as of the end of the year.

  - Costs incurred in property acquisition, exploration and development activities for the year.

  - Results of operations for oil and gas producing activities for the year.

  - A standardized measure of discounted future net cash flows relating to proved oil and gas reserves quantities as of year-end and standardized measure changes for the year.[6]

- Interim financial statements must disclose information about any major discovery or other favorable or adverse event that causes a significant change from the most recent annual supplemental disclosures concerning oil and gas reserves. Interim financial statements also must include information about significant changes from the information on continued capitalization of exploratory well costs presented in the most recent annual financial statements. Any impairment of exploratory well costs that were capitalized for a period of greater than one year after the completion of drilling at the most recent annual balance sheet date is considered significant for determining whether or not the change should be disclosed in interim financial statements.

- For enterprises following the full cost method, additional disclosures are required as follows:

  - Total amortization expense per equivalent unit for each cost center for each year that an income statement is presented.

  - A separate statement on the face of the balance sheet of the total capitalized costs excluded from the amortization base as well as certain related disclosures for the excluded costs in the notes to the financial statements.

  - The amount of any ceiling test write-down.

Reg. S-K Subpart 1200 requires and allows additional disclosures of oil and gas operations outside of the financial statements.

Accounting for costs incurred and disposals

All companies engaged in oil and gas producing activities must disclose the method of accounting for costs incurred and the manner of disposing of capitalized costs related to those activities (successful efforts or full cost, referred to as the "accounting method disclosure"). The accounting method disclosure is deemed to be an integral part of the financial statements. It can be included either on the face of the financial statements or in the notes to the financial statements, or both – or by another approach indicating that the disclosure is an integral part of the financial statements. Companies may include the disclosure in a note that includes all of the company's significant accounting policies, which many public companies include as part of the discussion of the accounting for oil and gas properties, as noted in the following example disclosure.

> **Oil and gas properties.** The successful efforts method is used for crude oil and natural gas exploration and production activities. All costs for development wells, related plant and equipment, proved mineral interests in crude oil and natural gas properties, and related asset retirement costs are capitalized. Costs of exploratory wells are capitalized pending determination of whether the wells have found proved reserves. Costs of wells that are assigned proved reserves remain capitalized. Costs also are capitalized for exploratory wells that have found crude oil and natural gas reserves even if the reserves cannot be classified as proved when the drilling is completed, provided the exploratory well has found a sufficient quantity of reserves to justify its completion as a producing well and the company is making sufficient progress assessing the reserves and the economic and operating viability of the project.

Capitalized exploratory well costs evaluation

Continued capitalization of exploratory well costs beyond one year is permitted under certain criteria (see Chapter 9). If any exploratory well costs continue to be capitalized beyond one year, the following disclosures are required by ASC 932-235-50-1B (see a sample disclosure at Figure 30-1).

a. The amount of capitalized exploratory well costs that is pending the determination of proved reserves. An entity also shall separately disclose for each annual period that an income statement is presented changes in those capitalized exploratory well costs resulting from all of the following:

    1. Additions to capitalized exploratory well costs that are pending the determination of proved reserves

    2. Capitalized exploratory well costs that were reclassified to wells, equipment, and facilities based on the determination of proved reserves

    3. Capitalized exploratory well costs that were charged to expense.

This disclosure shall not include amounts that were capitalized and subsequently expensed in the same annual period.

b. The amount of exploratory well costs that have been capitalized for a period of greater than one year after the completion of drilling at the most recent balance sheet date and the number of projects for which those costs relate. Additionally, for exploratory well costs that have been capitalized for periods greater than one year at the most recent balance sheet date, an entity shall provide an aging of those amounts by year, or by using a range of years, and the number of projects to which those costs relate.

c. For exploratory well costs that continue to be capitalized for more than one year after the completion of drilling at the most recent balance sheet date, a description of the projects and the activities that the entity has undertaken to date in order to evaluate the reserves and the projects, and the remaining activities required to classify the associated reserves as proved.

Reserves quantity information

Publicly traded enterprises must disclose annually certain data related to their proved oil and gas reserves. The disclosure is included as supplemental information under ASC 932-235-50-4 through 50-11B as follows:

50-4   Net quantities of an entity's interests in proved oil and gas reserves, proved developed oil and gas reserves, and proved undeveloped oil and gas reserves of each of the following shall be disclosed as of the beginning and the end of the year:

    a. Crude oil, including condensate and natural gas liquids (If significant, the reserve quantity information shall be disclosed separately for natural gas liquids.)

    b. Natural gas

    c. Synthetic oil

    d. Synthetic gas

    e. Other nonrenewable natural resources that are intended to be upgraded into synthetic oil and gas.

Net quantities of reserves include those relating to the entity's operating and nonoperating interests in properties. Quantities of reserves relating to royalty interests owned shall be included in net quantities if the necessary information is available to the entity; if reserves relating to royalty interests owned are not included because the information is unavailable, that fact and the entity's share of oil and gas produced for those royalty interests shall be disclosed for the year. Net quantities shall not include reserves relating to interests of others in properties owned by the entity.

50-5   Changes in the net quantities of an entity's proved reserves of oil and gas during the year shall be disclosed. Changes resulting from all of the following shall be shown separately with appropriate explanation of significant changes:

   a.   Revisions of previous estimates. Revisions represent changes in previous estimates of proved reserves, either upward or downward, resulting from new information (except for an increase in proved acreage) normally obtained from development drilling and production history or resulting from a change in economic factors.

   b.   Improved recovery. Changes in reserve estimates resulting from application of improved recovery techniques shall be shown separately if significant. If not significant, such changes shall be included in revisions of previous estimates.

   c.   Purchases of minerals in place.

   d.   Extensions and discoveries. Additions to proved reserves that result from either of the following:

      1.   Extension of the proved acreage of previously discovered (old) reservoirs through additional drilling in periods subsequent to discovery

      2.   Discovery of new fields with proved reserves or of new reservoirs of proved reserves in old fields.

   e.   Production.

   f.   Sales of minerals in place.

50-6   The disclosures of net quantities of proved reserves of oil and of gas and changes in them required by paragraphs 932-235-50-4 through 50-5 shall be presented in the aggregate and separately by geographic area (see the following paragraph) in which significant reserves (see paragraph 932-235-50-6B) are located. If an entity's proved reserves of oil and of gas are located entirely within its home country, the entity shall disclose that fact.

50-6A Any one of the following may constitute a geographic area, as appropriate for meaningful disclosure in the circumstances:

   a.   An individual country

   b.   A group of countries within a continent

   c.   A continent.

50-6B In determining whether reserves are significant:

      a. An entity shall consider all facts and circumstances and not solely the quantity of reserves.

      b. At a minimum, net quantities of reserves shall be presented in the aggregate and separately by geographic area and for each country containing 15 percent or more of an entity's proved reserves, expressed on an oil-equivalent-barrels basis.

Reserves shall include an entity's proportionate share of reserves of equity method investees.

50-7 Net quantities disclosed in conformity with paragraphs 932-235-50-4 through 50-6B shall not include oil or gas subject to purchase under long-term supply, purchase, or similar agreements and contracts, including such agreements with governments or authorities. However, quantities of oil or gas subject to such agreements with governments or authorities as of the end of the year, and the net quantity of oil or gas received under the agreements during the year, shall be separately disclosed if the entity participates in the operation of the properties in which the oil or gas is located or otherwise serves as the producer of those reserves, as opposed, for example, to being an independent purchaser, broker, dealer, or importer.

50-8 In determining the reserve quantities to be disclosed in conformity with paragraphs 932-235-50-4 through 50-7:

      a. If the entity issues consolidated financial statements, 100 percent of the net reserve quantities attributable to the parent and 100 percent of the net reserve quantities attributable to its consolidated subsidiaries (whether or not wholly owned) shall be included. If a significant portion of those reserve quantities at the end of the year is attributable to a consolidated subsidiary or subsidiaries in which there is a significant noncontrolling interest, that fact and the approximate portion shall be disclosed.

      b. If the entity's financial statements include investments that are proportionately consolidated, the entity's reserve quantities shall include its proportionate share of the investees' net oil and gas reserves.

      c. If the entity's financial statements include investments that are accounted for by the equity method, the entity shall separately disclose the net reserve quantities required by paragraphs 932-235-50-4 through 50-7 for both of the following:

            1. Consolidated entities

            2. The entity's share of equity method investees.

The entity may, in addition to separate disclosure, disclose a combined total for items (1) and (2) for each of the quantities required to be disclosed by this paragraph.

50-9 In reporting reserve quantities and changes in them, oil and synthetic oil reserves and natural gas liquids reserves shall be stated in barrels, and gas and synthetic gas reserves in cubic feet.

50-10 If important economic factors or significant uncertainties affect particular components of an entity's proved reserves, explanation shall be provided. Examples include unusually high expected development or lifting costs, the necessity to build a major pipeline or other major facilities before production of the reserves can begin, and contractual obligations to produce and sell a significant portion of reserves at prices that are substantially below those at which the oil or gas could otherwise be sold in the absence of the contractual obligation.

50-11 An entity need not disclose the proved reserves in either of the following circumstances:

    a.   The government of a country containing reserves prohibits disclosing reserves in that country.

    b.   The government of a country containing reserves prohibits disclosing a particular field, and disclosing reserves in that country would have the effect of disclosing reserves in particular fields.

50-11A If a country's government prohibits disclosing the reserves in that country but does not prohibit including those reserves as part of a more aggregated total quantity of reserves (for example, the quantity of reserves disclosed for a group of countries within a continent or a continent), the entity shall include the reserves located in that country in total reserves disclosed for the most disaggregated geographic area that does not violate specific government prohibitions.

50-11B 50-11B If a government restricts the disclosure of estimated reserves for properties under its authority, or of amounts under long-term supply, purchase, or similar agreements or contracts, or if the government requires the disclosure of reserves other than proved, the entity shall indicate that the disclosed reserve estimates or amounts do not include figures for the named country or that reserve estimates include reserves other than proved.

Capitalized costs

ASC 932-235-50-2b requires supplemental disclosure of the aggregate amount of capitalized costs related to an enterprise's oil and gas producing activities as of year-end. The aggregate related accumulated depreciation, depletion, amortization and valuation allowances also must be disclosed at year-end.

ASC 932-235-55-2 is the source for Figures 30-1 and 30-2, which illustrate a suggested format for disclosures of oil and gas reserves quantities. Figure 30-3 shows the format suggested in ASC 932-235-55-3 for disclosing capitalized costs. Note that ASC 932-235-55-3 does not require disclosure of capitalized costs by major geographic area but companies commonly provide such information.

Capitalized costs of support equipment and facilities may be disclosed separately or included, as appropriate, with capitalized costs of proved and unproved properties. ASC 932-235-50-14 requires the separate reporting of significant capitalized costs of unproved properties.

Figure 30-1

Illustrative disclosures of oil and gas reserves quantities

RESERVE QUANTITY INFORMATION (a)
FOR THE YEAR ENDED DECEMBER 31, 20X0

	Total	Total – by Product		Continent A		Continent B – Country A		Other Countries in Continent B		Other Continents/ Countries	
	All products	Oil	Synthetic Oil	Oil	Synthetic Oil	Oil	Synthetic Oil	Oil	Synthetic Oil	Oil	Synthetic Oil
Proved developed and undeveloped reserves (consolidated entities only):											
Beginning of year	X	X	X	X	X	X	X	X	X	X	X
Revisions of previous estimates	X	X	X	X	X	X	X	X	X	X	X
Improved recovery	X	X	X	X	X	X	X	X	X	X	X
Purchases of minerals in place	X	X	X	X	X	X	X	X	X	X	X
Extensions and discoveries	X	X	X	X	X	X	X	X	X	X	X
Production	(X)	(X)	(X)	(X)	(X)	(X)	(X)	(X)	(X)	(X)	(X)
Sales of minerals in place	(X)	(X)	(X)	(X)	(X)	(X)	(X)	(X)	(X)	(X)	(X)
End of year	X (b)	X	X	X	X	X	X	X	X	X	X
Entity's share of proved developed and undeveloped reserves of investees accounted for by the equity method:											
Beginning of year	X	X	X	X	X	X	X	X	X	X	X
Revisions of previous estimates	X	X	X	X	X	X	X	X	X	X	X
Improved recovery	X	X	X	X	X	X	X	X	X	X	X
Purchases of minerals in place	X	X	X	X	X	X	X	X	X	X	X
Extensions and discoveries	X	X	X	X	X	X	X	X	X	X	X
Production	(X)	(X)	(X)	(X)	(X)	(X)	(X)	(X)	(X)	(X)	(X)
Sales of minerals in place	(X)	(X)	(X)	(X)	(X)	(X)	(X)	(X)	(X)	(X)	(X)
Entity's share of investees accounted for by the equity method, end of year	X	X	X	X	X	X	X	X	X	X	X
Total consolidated and equity interests in reserves, end of year	X	X	X	X	X	X	X	X	X	X	X

Note: Total consolidated and equity interests in reserves as of the end of the year is permitted, but it is not required (see ASC 932-235-50-8(c)).

(continued on next page)

(continued from previous page)

Figure 30-2
Illustrative disclosures of oil and gas reserves quantities (cont'd)

RESERVE QUANTITY INFORMATION
FOR THE YEAR ENDED DECEMBER 31, 20X0

	Total	Total – by Product		Continent A		Continent B – Country A		Other Countries in Continent B		Other Continents/ Countries	
	All products	Oil	Synthetic Oil	Oil	Synthetic Oil	Oil	Synthetic Oil	Oil	Synthetic Oil	Oil	Synthetic Oil
Proved developed reserves (consolidated entities only):											
Beginning of year	X	X	X	X	X	X	X	X	X	X	X
End of year	X	X	X	X	X	X	X	X	X	X	X
Proved undeveloped reserves (consolidated entities only):											
Beginning of year	X	X	X	X	X	X	X	X	X	X	X
End of year	X	X	X	X	X	X	X	X	X	X	X
Oil and gas subject to long-term supply, purchase or similar agreements with governments or authorities in which the entity participates in the operation of the properties where the oil or gas is located or otherwise serves as a producer of those reserves (consolidated entities only):											
Total under contract (quantity subject to agreement) – end of year	X	X	X	X	X	X	X	X	X	X	X
Received during the year	X	X	X	X	X	X	X	X	X	X	X

(a) Oil and synthetic oil reserves started in barrels.

(b) Includes reserves of X barrels attributable to a consolidated subsidiary in which there is an X percent noncontrolling interest.

Note: If applicable, reserve quantity information is required for gas and synthetic gas reserves and other products by ASC 932-235-50-4.

The table above discloses quantities of proved and undeveloped reserves and oil and gas subject to long-term supply, purchase or similar agreements with governments or authorities in which the entity participates in the operation of the properties where the oil or gas is located or otherwise serves as the producer of those resources attributable to consolidated entities (see ASC 932-235-50-4 and 50-7). The entity shall disclose the same information for the entity's share of reserves of investees accounted for by the equity method, if applicable (see ASC 932-235-50-8).

The table above discloses information for the total quantity of reserves for all products, in addition to disclosing the information by product. This disclosure is permitted, but it is not required (see ASC 932-235-50-4).

ASC 932-235-50-13 through 50-14 suggest separate disclosures of capitalized costs for the following asset categories, or for a combination of these categories:

- Proved properties.

- Unproved properties.

- Wells and related equipment and facilities (all development costs, plus the costs of drilling any exploratory wells and exploratory-type stratigraphic test wells that find proved reserves).

- Support equipment and facilities used in oil and gas producing activities.

- Uncompleted wells, equipment and facilities.

In addition, ASC 932-235-50-15 requires that if a company's financial statements include equity method investments, the company's share of the investee's net capitalized costs related to oil and gas producing activities as of the end of the year should be disclosed separately from the company's capitalized costs related to consolidated entities, as shown in Figure 30-3 below; the combined total of capitalized costs should not be disclosed.

Figure 30-3
Illustrative disclosure of capitalized costs

Capitalized costs relating to oil and gas producing activities at December 31, 202X	Consolidated	Entity's share of equity method investees
Proved oil and gas properties	$ X	$ X
Unproved oil and gas properties	X	X
Accumulated depreciation, depletion and amortization	(X)	(X)
Net capitalized costs	$ X	$ X

Acquisition, exploration and development costs

ASC 932-235-50 requires the disclosure of costs incurred for oil and gas property acquisition, exploration and development activities, regardless of whether the costs were capitalized or charged to expense.

> **50-18** All of the following types of costs for the year shall be disclosed (whether those costs are capitalized or charged to expense at the time they are incurred under the provisions of paragraphs 932-360-25-7 through 25-14, 932-360-40-2, and 932-720-25-1):
>
>   a. Property acquisition costs
>
>   b. Exploration costs
>
>   c. Development costs

As defined in paragraphs 932-360-25-9 and 932-360-25-13, exploration and development costs include depreciation of support equipment and facilities used in those activities and do not include the expenditures to acquire support equipment and facilities.

50-19 The amounts in the preceding paragraph shall be disclosed separately for each of the geographic areas for which reserve quantities are disclosed in accordance with paragraphs 932-235-50-6 through 50-6B. If significant costs have been incurred to acquire mineral interests that have proved reserves, those costs shall be disclosed separately from the costs of acquiring unproved properties.

50-20 If the entity's financial statements include investments that are accounted for by the equity method, the entity shall separately disclose the amounts required by paragraphs 932-235-50-18 through 50-19 for both of the following:

   a.   Consolidated entities

   b.   The entity's share of equity method investees.

   The entity shall not disclose the combined total of items (a) and (b).

Figure 30-4 displays the format proposed in ASC 932-235-55-4 for disclosing costs incurred. Such disclosures should include the capitalized costs related to asset retirement obligations.[7]

Figure 30-4

Illustrative disclosure of acquisition, exploration and development costs

	Total	Continent A	Continent B – Country A	Continent B – Other Countries	Other Continents/ Countries
Consolidated entities:	$X	$X	$X	$X	$X
Acquisition of properties	X	X	X	X	X
Proved	X	X	X	X	X
Unproved	X	X	X	X	X
Exploration costs	X	X	X	X	X
Development costs	X	X	X	X	X
Entity's share of equity method investees:					
Acquisition of properties					
Proved	$X	$X	$X	$X	$X
Unproved	X	X	X	X	X
Exploration costs	X	X	X	X	X
Development costs	X	X	X	X	X

Results of operations

ASC 932-235-50 requires the disclosure of historical results of operations for oil and gas producing activities by major geographical area. If oil and gas producing activities represent substantially all of the business activities of the reporting entity, and those oil and gas producing activities are located substantially in a single geographic area, results of operations need not be disclosed if that information is provided elsewhere in the financial statements. If oil and gas producing activities constitute an operating segment (as defined in ASC 280-10-50-1 through 50-18), results of operations may be included with segment information disclosed elsewhere in the financial report. Figure 30-5 shows an illustrative results of operations disclosure as prescribed by ASC 932-235-55-5.

The required disclosures include:

50-23 The results of operations for oil- and gas-producing activities shall be disclosed for the year. That information shall be disclosed in the aggregate and for each geographic area for which reserve quantities are disclosed in accordance with paragraphs 932-235-50-6 through 50-6B. All of the following information relating to those activities shall be presented:

   a. Revenues

   b. Production (lifting) costs

   c. Exploration expenses (Generally, only entities utilizing the successful efforts accounting method will have exploration expenses to disclose, since entities utilizing the full cost accounting method generally capitalize all exploration costs when incurred and subsequently reflect those costs in the determination of earnings through depreciation, depletion, and amortization, and valuation provisions.)

   d. Depreciation, depletion, and amortization, and valuation provisions

   e. Income tax expenses (see paragraph 932-235-50-25)

   f. Results of operations for oil- and gas-producing activities (excluding corporate overhead and interest costs) (see paragraphs 932-235-50-26 through 50-27)

50-24 Revenues shall include sales to unaffiliated entities and sales or transfers to the entity's other operations (for example, refineries or chemical plants). Sales to unaffiliated entities may be contracts with customers within the scope of Topic 606; see disclosure requirements in Section 606-10-50. Sales to unaffiliated entities and sales or transfers to the entity's other operations shall be disclosed separately. Revenues shall include sales to unaffiliated entities attributable to net working interests, royalty interests, oil payment interests, and net profits interests of the reporting entity. Sales or transfers to the entity's other operations shall be based on market prices determined at the point of delivery from the producing unit. Those market prices shall represent prices equivalent to those that could be obtained in an arm's-length transaction. [continued on next page]

[continued from previous page]

Production or severance taxes shall not be deducted in determining gross revenues, but rather shall be included as part of production costs. Royalty payments and net profits disbursements shall be excluded from gross revenues.

50-25　Income taxes shall be computed using the statutory tax rate for the period, applied to revenues less production (lifting) costs; exploration expenses; depreciation, depletion, and amortization; and valuation provisions. Calculation of income tax expenses shall reflect tax deductions and tax credits and allowances relating to the oil- and gas-producing activities that are reflected in the entity's consolidated income tax expense for the period.

50-26　Results of operations for oil- and gas-producing activities are defined as revenues less production (lifting) costs; exploration expenses; depreciation, depletion, and amortization; valuation provisions; and income tax expenses. General corporate overhead and interest costs shall not be deducted in computing the results of operations for an entity's oil- and gas-producing activities. The disposition of interest costs that have been capitalized as part of the cost of acquiring qualifying assets used in oil- and gas-producing activities shall be the same as that of other components of those assets' costs. However, some expenses incurred at an entity's central administrative office may not be general corporate expenses, but rather may be operating expenses of oil- and gas-producing activities, and therefore should be reported as such. The nature of an expense rather than the location of its incurrence shall determine whether it is an operating expense. Only those expenses identified by their nature as operating expenses shall be allocated as operating expenses in computing the results of operations for oil- and gas-producing activities.

50-27　The amounts disclosed in conformity with paragraphs 932-235-50-21 through 50-28 shall include an entity's interests in proved oil and gas reserves (see paragraphs 932-235-50-3 through 50-11B) and in oil and gas subject to purchase under long-term supply, purchase, or similar agreements and contracts in which the entity participates in the operation of the properties on which the oil or gas is located or otherwise serves as the producer of those reserves (see paragraph 932-235-50-7).

50-28　If the entity's financial statements include investments that are accounted for by the equity method, the entity shall separately disclose the amounts required by paragraphs 932-235-50-22 through 50-27 for both of the following:

　　a.　Consolidated entities

　　b.　The entity's share of equity method investees.

The entity shall not disclose the combined total of items (a) and (b), except that an entity may, in addition to separate disclosure, disclose the combined total of items (a) and (b) for the amounts required by paragraph 932-235-50-23(f).

Figure 30-5

Figure 30-5
Illustrative results of operations

	Total	Continent A	Continent B – Country A	Continent B – Other Countries	Other Continents/ Countries
Consolidated entities:					
Revenues					
Sales	$ X	$ X	$ X	$ X	$ X
Transfers	X	X	X	X	X
Total	X	X	X	X	X
Production expense	(X)	(X)	(X)	(X)	(X)
Exploration expense	(X)	(X)	(X)	(X)	(X)
Depreciation, depletion, amortization and valuation provisions	(X)	(X)	(X)	(X)	(X)
	X	X	X	X	X
Income tax expense	(X)	(X)	(X)	(X)	(X)
Results of operations from producing activities (excluding corporate overhead and interest costs)	$ X	$ X	$ X	$ X	$ X
Entity's share of equity method investees:					
Revenues					
Sales	$ X	$ X	$ X	$ X	$ X
Transfers	X	X	X	X	X
Total	X	X	X	X	X
Production expense	(X)	(X)	(X)	(X)	(X)
Exploration expense	(X)	(X)	(X)	(X)	(X)
Depreciation, depletion, amortization and valuation provisions	(X)	(X)	(X)	(X)	(X)
	X	X	X	X	X
Income tax expense	(X)	(X)	(X)	(X)	(X)
Results of operations for producing activities (excluding corporate overhead and interest costs)	$ X	$ X	$ X	$ X	$ X
Total consolidated and equity method investees results of operation for producing activities (excluding corporate overhead and interest costs)	$ X	$ X	$ X	$ X	$ X

Note: Disclosure of the total consolidated and equity method investees results of operations for producing activities (excluding corporate overhead and interest costs) is permitted, but it is not required (see ASC 935-235-50-28).

Full cost considerations

Whether publicly traded or not, companies using the full cost method are subject to additional disclosure requirements as described below.

Amortization

Subparagraph (c)(7)(i) of Reg. S-X Rule 4-10 requires additional disclosures related to the amortization per unit of production for each cost center:

> i.   For each cost center for each year that an income statement is required, disclose the total amount of amortization expense (per equivalent physical unit of production if amortization is computed on the basis of physical units or per dollar of gross revenue from production if amortization is computed on the basis of gross revenue).

Unproved property costs

As described in Chapter 18, special disclosures are required for unproved property costs that have been excluded from amortization. This requirement is found in paragraph (c) (7) (ii) of Reg. S-X Rule 4-10:

> ii.   State separately on the face of the balance sheet the aggregate of the capitalized costs of unproved properties and major development projects that are excluded, in accordance with paragraph (i)(3) of this section, from the capitalized costs being amortized. Provide a description in the notes to the financial statements of the current status of the significant properties or projects involved, including the anticipated timing of the inclusion of the costs in the amortization computation. Present a table that shows, by category of cost, (A) the total costs excluded as of the most recent fiscal year; and (B) the amounts of such excluded costs, incurred (1) in each of the three most recent fiscal years and (2) in the aggregate for any earlier fiscal years in which the costs were incurred. Categories of cost to be disclosed include acquisition costs, exploration costs, development costs in the case of significant development projects and capitalized interest.

Ceiling test

Per Reg. S-X Rule 4-10 (c)(4)(ii), full cost companies should disclose separately any expense resulting from the write-down of net capitalized costs in excess of the full cost ceiling. If the excess is not charged to expense because of certain subsequent events, as described in Chapter 18, the company should disclose that the excess existed and disclose why the excess was not charged to expense per SAB Topic 12.D, Item 3(c). Although the SAB Topic does not specifically require disclosure of the excess amount, many full cost companies choose to disclose it.

SEC disclosure requirements

In addition to the supplemental disclosures described previously, the SEC requires other disclosures unrelated to the financial statements. These disclosures are contained in the forepart of securities registration statements and of annual reports filed on Form 10-K with the SEC.

These requirements, found in Reg. S-K Subpart 1200, include:

- A summary of oil and gas reserves at year-end, including separate categories for proved developed, proved undeveloped and total proved reserves. The disclosure of probable and possible reserves is optional. Material reserves should be disclosed separately by product type.

- For new registrants, and existing registrants with material reserve additions, a summary of the technology or technologies used to estimate the reserves. It is not necessary to disclose proprietary technologies, or a proprietary mix of technologies, at a level that would cause competitive harm.

- A disclosure describing the internal controls the registrant uses in its reserves estimation process.

- A report listing the qualifications of the technical person primarily responsible for overseeing the preparation of the reserves estimates. In addition, if a third-party conducted a reserves audit, the qualifications of the technical person primarily responsible should also be included. Although the SEC does not require that an independent third-party prepare the reserves or conduct a reserves audit, the company must file the report of any third-party used to prepare or audit its reserves as an exhibit to the relevant registration statement or other filing.

- Information related to PUD reserves, including:

  - Total quantity of PUDs at year end.

  - Material changes in PUDs that occurred during the year (including PUDs converted into proved developed reserves).

  - Investments and progress made during the year to convert PUDs to proved developed reserves.

  - Reasons why material concentrations of PUDs have remained undeveloped for five years or longer after initial disclosure as PUDs.

Additionally, the following disclosures are required for each major geographic area for each of the previous three fiscal years:

- Production-related information including:

  - Volumetric production data by final product sold for each country and field that contains 15 percent or more of the registrant's total proved reserves expressed on an oil-equivalent-barrels basis (unless prohibited by the country in which the reserves are located).

- – Average sales price (including transfers) per unit of production.

- – Production cost per unit of production (excluding ad valorem and severance taxes).

- Total net productive and dry wells drilled, broken down by exploratory wells and development wells drilled, by appropriate geographic area.

- Any other exploratory or development activities, including implementation of mining methods for purposes of oil and gas producing activities.

In addition, for the current date or end of the latest fiscal year, the following should also be disclosed:

- Number of wells, both gross and net, being drilled as of the balance sheet date (including wells temporarily suspended, waterfloods being installed, pressure maintenance operations and any other related activities of material importance).

- Gross and net productive oil and gas wells.

- Gross and net developed acreage by geographic area.

- Gross and net undeveloped acreage by geographic area and, if material, minimum remaining terms of leases and concessions.

- Information about obligations to provide fixed quantities of oil and gas in the future under existing contracts including: principal sources of oil and gas that the registrant will rely upon; the amounts the registrant expects to receive from each principal source and from all sources combined; and the total quantities of oil and gas that are subject to delivery commitments. If the registrant has been unable to meet any significant delivery commitments in the past three years, the circumstances concerning such events and their impact should also be disclosed.

Reg. S-K allows optional disclosures that are not addressed in ASC 932. Disclosures of probable and possible reserves and a reserves sensitivity analysis table therefore should be included in the forepart of securities registration statements and of Form 10-K annual reports filed with the SEC.

Common SEC comment letter focus areas

The SEC Division of Corporation Finance has a long history of reviewing filings by public companies under the Securities Act of 1933 and the Securities Exchange Act of 1934. An important goal of these reviews is to monitor and improve compliance with applicable disclosure and accounting requirements, consistent with the SEC's mission of investor protection.

Registrants in the upstream subsector typically receive comments focused on the accounting and disclosure requirements associated with oil and gas properties, specifically the underlying reserves and impairment considerations, with particular attention given to PUD reserves and supplemental oil and gas disclosures.

A description of specific focus areas of the SEC and examples of comments issued follows in the sections herein.

Commodity price impacts

One focus area for recent comment letters relates to how registrants have disclosed the impacts of and responses to a depressed commodity price environment. SEC staff has requested that registrants explain how they have considered providing more extensive disclosures regarding the impact of current commodity prices on liquidity, capital resources and the results of the company's operations. The staff also has requested disclosure outlining the company's strategy to respond to low commodity prices.

Many SEC registrants have elected to describe the effect of the price environment in the company's MD&A, including discussion of potential impairments. The nature of the comments in this area differ for full cost companies due to the nature of the ceiling test calculation. The SEC staff expects full cost companies to reasonably estimate a potential impairment and to record it in the subsequent reporting period. Full cost companies have, therefore, been requested to quantify the potential impairment and disclose the key inputs to the ceiling test calculation.

Comment letters on this topic that have been issued to successful effort companies often focus on providing more qualitative and quantitative information regarding any potential impairments and any future effects of a continued low commodity price environment.

See the following examples of SEC comment letters related to commodity price impacts:

Example 1. Your disclosure on page xx states that if the current low commodity price environment or downward trend in oil prices continues, there is a "reasonable likelihood" that you could incur further impairment to your full cost pool in fiscal 20X0 and 20X1. Considering the manner in which the full cost ceiling test limitation is calculated, we expect that you have an adequate basis to quantify reasonably possible near-term impacts of ceiling test impairments. Revise your disclosure to quantify the extent to which the impact of current prices will be reflected in your accounting and reporting based on your reasonable expectation of future impairment, especially in the near term. In this regard, we believe that reasonably likely effects of the prevailing changes in market prices quantified pursuant to Item 303 of Regulation S-K can be distinguished from an outlook or forecast of future results which may entail a broader range of uncertainties. See Section III.B of SEC Release 33-6835.

Example 2. Please provide expanded disclosure regarding impairment charges you may incur in the future related to depressed commodity prices. Specifically, describe the assumptions used in testing your oil and natural gas properties for impairment, discuss the degree of uncertainty associated with these key assumptions, and explain how they can be reasonably expected to be affected by changes in circumstances.

Example 3. Items 303(a)(1), (2)(ii) and (3)(ii) of Regulation S-K require you to address the reasonably likely effects of trends and uncertainties on liquidity, capital resources, and results of operations. Given the current pricing environment and uncertainty regarding duration, explain to us how you have considered providing more extensive discussion, including, where reasonably practicable, quantification of the impact of current commodity prices on your liquidity, capital resources and results of operation.

Your response specifies that you have a basis to state there is a reasonable likelihood of further ceiling test impairments. However, you do not believe that you can reliably quantify the reasonably possible near-term financial impact. Based on the nature of the full cost ceiling limitation, it appears that you should have sufficient information to estimate the potential near-term financial impact of further impairment, especially with a view toward the next reporting period. Please revise your disclosure to provide quantification if you continue to believe further impairment charges are reasonably likely in the near-term.

PUD reserves conversion

The SEC has frequently commented on the level of detail a company discloses when describing material changes in PUD reserves. Comment letters often focus on planned timing of the conversion of PUDs, the effect of reduced capital spending and capital budgets and material PUDs that remain undeveloped for more than five years after initial booking.

To assess the likelihood that a registrant can develop PUDs within the five-year window, the SEC staff evaluates information provided by the registrant, including conversion rates (one would expect a conversion rate of approximately 20 percent per year in order to convert all PUDs within five years of initial booking), historical capital expenditures and disclosures regarding planned future capital spending.

In certain instances when a registrant disclosed that it planned to reduce capital spending, the staff has requested more information about how those plans will affect the registrant's ability to effectively fund the development of its PUDs within the five-year window from initial booking.

Expanding on the earlier section about lower commodity price environments, when registrants disclosed uncertainties in their ability to develop properties due to commodity prices and/or anticipated possible downward revisions to their reserves, the SEC staff has asked why this was not disclosed as a material trend or uncertainty under Reg. S-K 303 (this rule requires companies to disclose the reasonably likely effects of trends and uncertainties on liquidity, capital resources and results of operations).

In many cases, the staff requested quantification of this effect in accordance with SEC Release No. 33-8350, which requires quantitative disclosure of the reasonably likely effects of material trends and uncertainties be provided, if reasonably available. Comment letters also requested information about the degree of uncertainty associated with key assumptions and potential events reasonably expected by management.

See below for examples of SEC comment letters related to PUD reserves conversion:

Example 1. Tell us the extent to which any of your proved undeveloped reserves will not be converted from undeveloped to developed within five years since your initial disclosure of these reserves, explain how you were able to satisfy the criteria in Rule 4-10(a)(31)(ii) of Regulation S-X with your initial disclosure, and if such quantities are material submit the revisions that you proposed to comply with Item 1203(d) of Regulation S-K.

Example 2. It appears that you converted only X% of your beginning of year proved undeveloped reserves (PUDs) to developed during the year ended December 31, 20X0. In the prior year, you converted only X% of PUDs to developed. Given your history of PUD conversion, please tell us the specific facts and circumstances that explain why you believe you will be able to convert all your PUDs to developed within five years of booking. As part of your response, please also address whether the downward revision in your forecasted production and pace of development discussed in your first quarter 20X1 earnings call will have any impact on your PUD volumes.

We note your disclosures indicating that expenditures for development of proved undeveloped reserves (PUDs) during 20X0 are expected to be significantly less than previously reported, and for subsequent years, significantly more. Please expand your disclosure to clarify the extent to which development plans for years after 20X0 are based on assumptions that commodity prices will increase from the current levels, and quantify the reasonably likely material effects on your development plans, proved reserves, and property impairment testing if the assumed price increases do not occur. The guidance in Item 303(a)(1), (2)(ii) and (3)(ii) of Regulation S-K requires you to address the reasonably likely effects of trends and uncertainties on liquidity, capital resources, and results of operations. Guidance in SEC Release 33-8350 clarifies that quantified disclosure regarding the material effects of known material trends and uncertainties should be provided if quantitative information is reasonably available. Given the importance that commodity price assumptions have in any reserve estimate following the guidance in Rule 4-10(a) of Regulation S-X, we believe that the reasonably likely effects of changes in commodity prices would be quantified to comply with the aforementioned guidance. Therefore, if you have proved undeveloped reserves that are reasonably likely to remain undeveloped if commodity prices do not improve, you should quantify the implications for your development plans, disclosed reserves and accounting.

Disclosure in your filing states that a reduction in commodity prices from current levels may result in a decrease in your actual capital expenditures. Please address the impact to capital expenditures necessary to fund the development of your proved undeveloped reserves assuming commodity prices stay at current levels. Refer to Rule 4-10(a)(31) of Regulation S-X.

Standardized measure

ASC 932-235-50 guides registrants in their calculation and disclosure of the standardized measure for discounted future net cash flows and the changes in the standardized measure. SEC comments in this area focus primarily on disclosures that improperly exclude or aggregate certain required line items. The SEC staff also may ask questions to better understand outliers or significant changes or amounts included in the supplemental oil and gas disclosures. Frequently, SEC staff have requested the underlying data or support for assumptions used in the standardized measure calculation.

See below for an example of an SEC comment letter related to supplemental disclosures:

> We note the changes reflected in the line item relating to revisions in the net quantities of your proved reserves for the period ending December 31, 20X0 appears to be an aggregation of the changes attributable to two or more separate causes. In this regard, we note the XX Bcfe in downward revisions in your proved undeveloped reserves disclosed on page XX is significantly more than our calculation of the XX Bcfe in downward revisions in your total proved reserves disclosed on page XX. Please provide us with the net change in reserve quantities, on a disaggregated basis, for each of the underlying causes relating to the revisions in your total proved reserves for the period ending December 31, 20X0. To the extent that such changes are individually significant on a disaggregated basis, please expand your disclosure to identify the individual causes and include details within an accompanying narrative to comply with the disclosure requirements pursuant to FASB ASC paragraph 932-235-50-5. We note that your standardized measure reflects estimates of production costs, costs to develop and produce the proved reserves and abandonment costs, based on economic conditions and overhead incurred as of December 31, 20x0. Tell us the amount of future abandonment costs reflected in your standardized measure of discounted future net cash flows relating to proved oil and gas reserves, and the extent to which such costs are associated with future activities, such as drilling new development wells and constructing incremental offshore infrastructure that will eventually require future decommissioning.
>
> Please submit a reconciliation between the total proved undiscounted future net income shown in the report at Exhibit 99.1 of $XX million and your disclosure of future cash inflows less the future production and future development costs as of December 31, 20X0, which amounts to $XX million. Please explain and provide any details necessary to understand the reasons for the difference in these two estimates.
>
> Please expand your disclosure of the changes in net quantities of proved reserves to include for each period the reasons for significant changes in reserves for each line item where such change is evident to comply with FASB ASC 932-235-50-5.

• • •

1   Regulation D of the Securities Act of 1933 established certain exemptions from the registration requirements of the Act for private offerings of securities to qualified investors or at limited markets.

2   SEC's Codification of Financial Reporting Releases, 406.02.d.ii.

3   The SEC addresses financial statements for acquired oil- and gas-producing properties in the SEC Division of Corporate Finance Financial Reporting Manual, Sections 2065.11-12, found at: https://www.sec.gov/divisions/corpfin/cffinancialreportingmanual.pdf#topic2.

4   SEC's Codification of Financial Reporting Releases, 406.02.d.i.

5   ASC 932-235-50 requires the disclosure of reserves information as of the beginning and end of the year. From a practical standpoint, to present the changes in the standardized measure for three years, companies often disclose SMOG at the beginning and the end of each of the three years.

6   See Chapter 31 for details of standardized measure disclosures.

7   Refer to SEC sample letter sent to oil and gas producers, dated February 24, 2004, found at: http://www.sec.gov/divisions/corpfin/guidance/oilgasletter.htm.

CHAPTER

31

Standardized Measure of Oil and Gas Reserves

ASC 932 requires disclosure of "a standardized measure of discounted future net cash flows relating to proved oil and gas reserve quantities" for publicly traded companies that have significant oil and gas producing activities. The required disclosure is often called the standardized measure, or SMOG as a popular acronym, coined by a major oil company's treasurer about the time FAS 69, now ASC 932, was adopted.

As a standardized measure, SMOG is intended to be a comparative benchmark value rather than an estimate of fair value. Comparisons can be made of a company's results over time or measured against other oil and gas companies. SMOG is not a measure of fair value because of its:

- Use of a 10 percent discount rate.

- Exclusion of any resources other than proved reserves.

- Use of current prices and costs.

SMOG may be used by analysts in several ways. For example, an analyst might construct a model of future production and annual cash flows using proved reserves and SMOG disclosures. Adjustments would be made to the inputs in order to estimate the fair value of a publicly traded E&P company's underlying assets, primarily oil and gas producing properties.

The analyst may then compare the benchmark value per share to the share's market value. If a company's benchmark value to market value is high compared to its peers, this could indicate that its stock is a better buy than the stock of its peers. The quality of management, exploration prospects, unusual contingent liabilities not reflected in the benchmark value and other factors can also account for a company's high ratio of benchmark value to market value.

SMOG disclosure requirements

The SMOG requirements are specified in ASC 932-235-50-30 through 50-33 as provided herein. Supplemental disclosures are not required to be audited. As a rule, the proved reserves disclosures and SMOG disclosures are never audited, as they are not included within the audited financial statements or subject to a separate attest examination by a CPA. However, auditing standards do require the auditor to read "other information" in documents containing audited financial statements to determine whether such information is materially inconsistent with information appearing in the financial statements; that other information would include SMOG disclosures.

The limited procedures the auditor should perform on these disclosures are described in *Auditing Standard 2705.07* (AS 2705.07) and *Auditing Interpretations 19* (AI 19) and include procedures such as performing inquiries of management about the methods used in preparing the information, comparing the consistency of the information with other available data and assessing the qualifications of the individuals involved in preparing such information. Additionally, AS 1210 provides guidance to the auditor who uses the work of a specialist in performing an audit in accordance with the standards of the PCAOB. See Chapter 15 for additional discussion of the Auditing Standards guidance related to these disclosures.

50-30 A standardized measure of discounted future net cash flows relating to an entity's interests in both of the following shall be disclosed as of the end of the year:

    a.   proved oil and gas reserves (see paragraphs 932-235-50-3 through 50-11B)

    b.   oil and gas subject to purchase under long-term supply, purchase, or similar agreements and contracts in which the entity participates in the operation of the properties on which the oil or gas is located or otherwise serves as the producer of those reserves (see paragraph 932-235-50-7).

The standardized measure of discounted future net cash flows relating to those two types of interests in reserves may be combined for reporting purposes.

50-31 All of the following information shall be disclosed in the aggregate and for each geographic area for which reserve quantities are disclosed in accordance with paragraphs 932-235-50-3 through 50-11B

    a.   Future cash inflows. These shall be computed by applying prices used in estimating the entity's proved oil and gas reserves to the year-end quantities of those reserves. Future price changes shall be considered only to the extent provided by contractual arrangements in existence at year-end.

    b.   Future development and production costs. These costs shall be computed by estimating the expenditures to be incurred in developing and producing the proved oil and gas reserves at the end of the year, based on year-end costs and assuming continuation of existing economic conditions. If estimated development expenditures are significant, they shall be presented separately from estimated production costs.

    c.   Future income tax expenses. These expenses shall be computed by applying the appropriate year-end statutory tax rates, with consideration of future tax rates already legislated, to the future pre-tax net cash flows relating to the entity's proved oil and gas reserves, less the tax basis of the properties involved. The future income tax expenses shall give effect to tax deductions and tax credits and allowances relating to the entity's proved oil and gas reserves.

    d.   Future net cash flows. These amounts are the result of subtracting future development and production costs and future income tax expenses from future cash inflows.

    e.   Discount. This amount shall be derived from using a discount rate of 10 percent a year to reflect the timing of the future net cash flows relating to proved oil and gas reserves.

    f.   Standardized measure of discounted future net cash flows. This amount is the future net cash flows less the computed discount.

50-32 If a significant portion of the economic interest in the consolidated standardized measure of discounted future net cash flows reported is attributable to a consolidated subsidiary or subsidiaries in which there is a significant noncontrolling interest, that fact and the approximate portion shall be disclosed.

50-33 If the financial statements include investments that are accounted for by the equity method, the entity shall separately disclose the amounts required by paragraphs 932-235-50-30 through 50-32 for both of the following:

    a.   Consolidated entities

    b.   The entity's share of equity method investees.

The entity may, in addition to separate disclosure, disclose a combined total for items (a) and (b) for each of the amounts required to be disclosed by this paragraph.

Disclosures as of year-end

The format suggested in ASC 932 for the standardized measure disclosure is shown in Figure 31-1.

Figure 31-1
Illustrative example from ASC 932-235-55-6 – SMOG

Consolidated entities:	Total	Continent A	Continent B – Country A	Continent B – Other Countries	Other Continents/ Countries
Future cash inflows[a]	$X	$X	$X	$X	$X
Future production and development costs[a]	(X)	(X)	(X)	(X)	(X)
Future income taxes[a]	(X)	(X)	(X)	(X)	(X)
Future net cash flows	X	X	X	X	X
10% annual discount for estimated timing of cash flows	(X)	(X)	(X)	(X)	(X)
Standardized measure of discounted future net cash flows	**$X** [b]	**$X**	**$X**	**$X**	**$X**
Entity's share of equity method investees:					
Future cash inflows[a]	$X	$X	$X	$X	$X
Future production and development costs[a]	(X)	(X)	(X)	(X)	(X)
Future income taxes[a]	(X)	(X)	(X)	(X)	(X)
Future net cash flows	X	X	X	X	X
10% annual discount for estimated timing of cash flows	(X)	(X)	(X)	(X)	(X)
Standardized measure of discounted future net cash flows	**$X**	**$X**	**$X**	**$X**	**$X**
Total consolidated and equity method interests in the standardized measure of discounted future cash flows	**$X**	**$X**	**$X**	**$X**	**$X**

(a) Future net cash flows were computed using prices used in estimating the entity's (or the investee's) proved oil and gas reserves, and year-end costs, and statutory tax rates (adjusted for tax deductions) that relate to existing proved oil and gas reserves. This includes those mineral interests related to long-term supply agreements with governments for which the entity (or the investee) participates in the operation of the related properties or otherwise serves as the producer of the reserves but does not include other supply arrangements or contracts that represent the right to purchase (as opposed to extract) oil and gas (see paragraph 932-235-50-7).

(b) Includes $X attributable to a consolidated subsidiary in which there is an X percent of noncontrolling interest.

Note: Disclosure of total consolidated and equity interests in the standardized measure of discounted future cash flows is permitted, but it is not required (see ASC 935-235-50-33).

Special considerations

Future net cash flows relating to an entity's interest in proved oil and gas reserves should include the cash outflows associated with the settlement of an asset retirement obligation (ARO). Exclusion of the cash outflows associated with a retirement obligation would be a departure from the required disclosure. However, an entity is not prohibited from disclosing the fact that cash outflows associated with AROs are included in its standardized measure disclosure as a point of emphasis.

Future cash outflows related to AROs included in future development costs should generally be consistent with future cash outflows used to measure ARO liabilities. However, two exceptions should be considered:

1. Future cash outflows used to measure ARO liabilities include an inflation assumption, whereas those included in future development costs in the SMOG disclosure should be based on prices as of the balance sheet date.

2. Timing of the future cash outflows used to measure ARO liabilities are based on management's internal assessment of the end of the productive life of a field or well, whereas the timing of future development costs included in the SMOG disclosure should be based on the productive life resulting from applying prices used in estimating the entity's proved oil and gas reserves to the year-end quantities of those reserves.

Disclosures of changes in SMOG

In addition to a SMOG disclosure as of year-end, ASC 932 also calls for disclosure of: (1) the aggregate SMOG change for the year and (2) the significant reasons for the changes in SMOG during the year. ASC 932-235-50-35 through 50-36 lists major reasons that may exist for SMOG changes and calls for their disclosure if the amounts are individually significant.

50-35 The aggregate change in the standardized measure of discounted future net cash flows shall be disclosed for the year. If individually significant, all of the following sources of change shall be presented separately:

a. Net change in sales and transfer prices and in production (lifting) costs related to future production

b. Changes in estimated future development costs

c. Sales and transfers of oil and gas produced during the period

d. Net change due to extensions, discoveries, and improved recovery

e. Net change due to purchases and sales of minerals in place

f. Net change due to revisions in quantity estimates

g. Previously estimated development costs incurred during the period

h.   Accretion of discount

i.   Other – unspecified

j.   Net change in income taxes

In computing the amounts under each of the above categories, the effects of changes in prices and costs shall be computed before the effects of changes in quantities. As a result, changes in quantities shall be stated at prices used in estimating proved oil and gas reserves and year-end costs. The change in computed income taxes shall reflect the effect of income taxes incurred during the period as well as the change in future income tax expenses. Therefore, all changes except income taxes shall be reported pretax.

50-35A If the financial statements include investments that are accounted for by the equity method, the entity shall separately disclose the amounts required by the preceding paragraph for both of the following:

a.   Consolidated entities

b.   The entity's share of equity method investees.

The entity may, in addition to separate disclosure, disclose a combined total for items (a) and (b) for each of the amounts required to be disclosed by this paragraph.

50-36   Additional information necessary to prevent the disclosure of the standardized measure of discounted future net cash flows and changes therein from being misleading also shall be provided.

SMOG computation example

The remainder of this chapter illustrates how SMOG and SMOG changes can be computed and disclosed. For this example, assume a company has proved reserves as of December 31, 2018, in only one field, Field No. 1. During 2019, the company discovers proved reserves in a second field, Field No. 2, and acquires a third field, Field No. 3, on June 30, 2019.

The following is a summary of various SMOG computations. SMOG for Field No. 1 is computed as of December 31, 2018 and again as of December 31, 2019. Next, individual components of Field No. 1's SMOG changes for 2019 are calculated. The example then demonstrates Field No. 2's SMOG as of December 31, 2019.

Changes in SMOG for 2019 are calculated for Field Nos. 2 and 3, including changes related to discovery, acquisition, and subsequent changes from the date of acquisition for Field No. 3 to December 31, 2019. SMOG changes for Field No. 2 do not include changes other than those related to discovery and production during December 2019. Other changes are not considered significant because this discovery was made late in 2019.

Figure 31-2
Figure 31-2
Illustrative example from ASC 932-235-55-7 – Changes in SMOG

	Consolidated	Entity's share of equity method investees	Total consolidated and entity's share of equity method investees
Net change in sales and transfer prices and in production (lifting) costs related to future production	$X	$X	$X
Changes in estimated future development costs	X	X	X
Sales and transfers of oil and gas produced during the period	(X)	(X)	(X)
Net change due to extensions, discoveries, and improved recovery	X	X	X
Net change due to purchases and sales of minerals in place	X	X	X
Net change due to revisions in quantity estimates	X	X	X
Previously estimated development costs incurred during the period	X	X	X
Accretion of discount	X	X	X
Other – unspecified	X	X	X
Net change in income taxes	X	X	X
Aggregate change in the standardized measure of discounted future net cash flows for the year	$X	$X	$X

Note: Disclosure of total consolidated and entity's share of equity method investees' amounts is permitted but is not required (see ASC 935-235-50-35A).

The SMOG and SMOG change computations by field are ultimately combined to determine the company's consolidated SMOG and SMOG changes as of and for the year-ended December 31, 2019, respectively.

Many companies calculate the standardized measure and related changes in the aggregate or by major geographical area, rather than by field. Field-by-field computations are often impractical. Calculations in the aggregate are generally less precise than by field but can employ the same calculation concepts illustrated in the field-by-field example presented.

Assume the following information shown in Figure 31-3 relating to the company's ownership in reserves in Field No. 1 at December 31, 2018. Figure 31-3 presents the reserves amounts in barrels for oil and Mcf for natural gas. Accordingly, the natural gas reserves are recalculated to the units of oil equivalent using a ratio of six Mcf per one barrel of crude oil.

Although the ratio is imprecise and the actual conversion ratio would depend on the physical qualities of natural gas, the ratio of 6:1 is commonly used to convert natural gas reserves and production volumes to equivalent units.

Figure 31-3

Assumptions – Field No. 1

	Reserves			Future development costs	Future income taxes
	Bbls	**Mcf**	**BOE**		
2019	50,000	150,000	75,000	$250,000	$220,500
2020	40,000	120,000	60,000	150,000	186,900
2021	30,000	90,000	45,000	–	163,800
2022	20,000	70,000	31,667	–	106,400
2023	10,000	50,000	18,333	–	49,000
Total	**150,000**	**480,000**	**230,000**	**$400,000**	**$726,600**

Price per barrel	$50.00	
Price per Mcf		$2.00
Production costs per BOE		$20.00

Future income taxes

For this example, future income taxes are provided as given numbers. However, actual SMOG calculations require the projected revenues, projected operating expenses, depreciation, depletion and other factors in arriving at each year's tax outflow. ASC 932's illustration of the standardized measure of discounted future net cash flows (shown in Figure 31-1) suggests that the effects of income taxes on future net cash flows from production of proved reserves are to be computed for each future year. This year-by-year approach is also required by ASC 932-235-50-31, which states:

> *Future income tax expenses.* These expenses shall be computed by applying the appropriate year-end statutory rates, with consideration of future tax rates already legislated, to the future pretax net cash flows relating to the entity's proved oil and gas reserves, less the tax basis of the properties involved. The future income tax expense shall give effect to tax deductions and tax credits and allowances relating to the entity's proved oil and gas reserves.

The SEC has formally confirmed a staff position prohibiting use of the short-cut method for calculating income taxes for the purposes of SMOG calculations. On March 31, 2001, the SEC staff issued its Frequently Requested Accounting and Financial Reporting Interpretations and Guidance. Section F.3.(j) of this guidance notes the following:

> (j) The calculation of the standardized measure of discounted future net cash flows relating to oil and gas properties must comply with paragraph 30 of SFAS 69. The effects of income taxes, like all other elements of the measure, must be discounted at the standard rate of 10% pursuant to paragraph 30(e). The "short-cut" method for determining the tax effect on the ceiling test for companies using the full-cost method of accounting, as described in SAB Topic 12:D:1, Question 2, may not be used for purposes of the paragraph 30 calculation of the standardized measure.

Future net cash flows

Figure 31-1's illustration of the SMOG disclosure shows a line for future net cash flows. These are computed for Field No. 1 in Figure 31-4 below based on the formula shown herein.

Figure 31-4
Future net cash flows – Field No. 1

		2019	2020	2021	2022	2023	Total
Future cash inflows	(a)	$2,800,000	$2,240,000	$1,680,000	$1,140,000	$600,000	$8,460,000
Future costs:							
Production costs	(a)	(1,500,000)	(1,200,000)	(900,000)	(633,333)	(366,667)	(4,600,000)
Development costs	(b)	(250,000)	(150,000)	–	–	–	(400,000)
Future net revenues		1,050,000	890,000	780,000	506,667	233,333	3,460,000
Future income taxes	(b)	(220,500)	(186,900)	(163,800)	(106,400)	(49,000)	(726,600)
Future net cash flows		**$ 829,500**	**$ 703,100**	**$ 616,200**	**$ 400,267**	**$184,333**	**$2,733,400**

(a) Calculated from Figure 31-3.

(b) From Figure 31-3.

Present value

ASC 932 requires future net cash flows to be discounted at a standard rate of 10 percent per year. Figure 31-5 shows the present value of 1 factors (PV factors) based on the assumption that the cash inflows are received, on average, at the mid-point of each year. This is commonly known as the mid-year convention.

Figure 31-5
Present value of 1 factors

Year	PV factor	Mid-year convention	Formula
1	0.9535	0.5	$= 1 / (1.1) \wedge (0.5)$
2	0.8668	1.5	$= 1 / (1.1) \wedge (1.5)$
3	0.7880	2.5	$= 1 / (1.1) \wedge (2.5)$
4	0.7164	3.5	$= 1/ (1.1) \wedge (3.5)$
5	0.6512	4.5	$= 1 / (1.1) \wedge (4.5)$
6	0.5920	5.5	$= 1 / (1.1) \wedge (4.5)$
7	0.5382	6.5	$= 1 / (1.1) \wedge (6.5)$
8	0.4893	7.5	$= 1 / (1.1) \wedge (7.5)$

When the PV factors from Figure 31-5 are applied to future net cash flows from Figure 31-4, the total present value of proved reserves as of December 31, 2018, for Field No. 1 is calculated as $2,292,730, shown in Figure 31-6.

Figure 31-6

Computation of SMOG – Field No. 1 as of December 31, 2018

		2019	2020	2021	2022	2023	Total
Future cash inflows	(a)	$2,800,000	$2,240,000	$1,680,000	$1,140,000	$600,000	$8,460,000
Future costs:							
Production costs	(a)	(1,500,000)	(1,200,000)	(900,000)	(633,333)	(366,667)	(4,600,000)
Development costs	(a)	(250,000)	(150,000)	–	–	–	(400,000)
Future net revenues		1,050,000	890,000	780,000	506,667	233,333	3,460,000
Future income taxes [A]	(a)	(220,500)	(186,900)	(163,800)	(106,400)	(49,000)	(726,600)
Future net cash flows [B]	(a)	829,500	703,100	616,200	400,267	184,333	2,733,400
10% Discount = B x (1 – [C])		(38,572)	(93,653)	(130,634)	(113,516)	(64,295)	(440,670)
Standardized measure		$ 790,928	$ 609,447	$ 485,566	$ 286,751	$120,038	$2,292,730
Present value factors [C]	(b)	0.9535	0.8668	0.7880	0.7164	0.6512	
Supplementary calculations:							
Income tax present value = [A] x [C]		210,247	162,005	129,074	76,225	31,909	609,460
Pre-tax SMOG	(c)	$ 1,001,175	$ 771,452	$ 614,640	$ 362,976	$151,947	$2,902,190

(a) From Figure 31-4.

(b) From Figure 31-5.

(c) Often referred to as "PV-10," the pre-tax standardized measure is a non-GAAP measure and is not included in the ASC 932 disclosures.

Statement of standardized measure

Using the calculation in Figure 31-6, the standardized measure calculation for Field No. 1 is disclosed as depicted in Figure 31-7. This table shows, for the entire remaining life of total proved reserves, future cash inflows, production costs, development costs and income taxes discounted at 10 percent annually to arrive at the standardized measure of discounted future net cash flows.

Figure 31-7

Statement of standardized measure of discounted future net cash flows

Future cash inflows	$8,460,000
Future production costs	(4,600,000)
Future development costs	(400,000)
Future income taxes	(726,600)
Future net cash flows	2,733,400
10% annual discount for estimated timing of cash flows	(440,670)
Standardized measure of discounted future net cash flows relating to proved oil and gas reserves	**$2,292,730**

Computing SMOG changes

To calculate individual factors leading to changes in the standardized measure of Field No. 1 during 2019, the standardized measure is computed as of December 31, 2019, as shown in Figure 31-9 based on the assumptions provided in Figure 31-8 below.

Figure 31-8

2019 Assumptions – Field No. 1

Data for the year ended December 31, 2019		Bbls	Mcf	BOE
Production		42,000	162,000	69,000
Revenues		$3,000,000		
Production costs		(1,300,000)		
Revenues less production costs		$1,700,000		
Previously estimated development costs incurred		$ 230,000		

Reserves as of December 31, 2019:		Reserves			Future development costs	Future income taxes
		Bbls	Mcf	BOE		
	2020	45,000	140,000	68,333	$155,000	$237,650
	2021	35,000	100,000	51,667	50,000	202,300
	2022	20,000	70,000	31,667	–	117,775
	2023	10,000	50,000	18,333	–	54,425
	Total	110,000	360,000	170,000	$205,000	$612,150

		New reserves attributable to extensions, discoveries and improved recoveries			Future development costs
		Bbls	Mcf	BOE	
	2020	5,000	20,000	8,333	$5,000
	2021	5,000	10,000	6,667	–
	2022	–	–	–	–
	2023	–	–	–	–
	Total	10,000	30,000	15,000	$5,000

Price per barrel	$55.00	
Price per Mcf		$2.25
Production costs per BOE		$22.00

Based on the data provided above, the standardized measure for Field No. 1 at December 31, 2019, is $2,007,915, as computed in Figure 31-9. The aggregate change for 2019 in Field No. 1's standardized measure is a $284,815 decrease, calculated as the December 31, 2019, standardized measure of $2,007,915 less the December 31, 2018, standardized measure of $2,292,730.

The following is a list of the major reasons for changes in SMOG in the example below.

- Accretion of discount.
- Sale of oil and gas produced, net of production costs.
- Net change in prices and production costs.
- Revisions of quantity estimates, including extensions and discoveries.
- Changes in estimated future development costs.
- Change in estimated future income taxes.
- Changes due to timing and other factors.

Figure 31-9
Computation of SMOG – Field No. 1

		2020	2021	2022	2023	Total
Future cash inflows	(a)	$2,790,000	$2,150,000	$1,257,500	$662,500	$6,860,000
Future costs:						
Production costs	(a)	(1,503,333)	(1,136,667)	(696,667)	(403,333)	(3,740,000)
Development costs	(b)	(155,000)	(50,000)	–	–	(205,000)
Future net revenues		1,131,667	963,333	560,833	259,167	2,915,000
Future income taxes [A]	(b)	(237,650)	(202,300)	(117,775)	(54,425)	(612,150)
Future net cash flows [B]		894,017	761,033	443,058	204,742	2,302,850
10% Discount = [B] x (1 – [C])		(41,572)	(101,370)	(93,928)	(58,065)	(294,935)
Standardized measure		**$ 852,445**	**$ 659,663**	**$ 349,130**	**$146,677**	**$2,007,915**
Present value factors [C]	(c)	0.9535	0.8668	0.7880	0.7164	
Supplementary calculations:						
Income tax present value = [A] x [C]		226,599	175,354	92,807	38,990	533,750
Pre-tax standardized measure	(d)	**$1,079,044**	**$ 835,017**	**$ 441,937**	**$185,667**	**$2,541,665**

Effect of extensions and discoveries	2020	2021	2022	2023	Total
Future cash inflows	$320,000	$297,500	$ –	$ –	$617,500
Future production costs	(183,333)	(146,667)	–	–	(330,000)
Future development costs	(5,000)	–	–	–	(5,000)
Future net undiscounted revenues from extensions (pre-tax)	**$ 131,667**	**$150,833**	**$ –**	**$ –**	**$282,500**
Future net discounted revenues from extensions (pre-tax)	**$ 125,544**	**$130,742**	**$ –**	**$ –**	**$256,286**

(a) Calculated from Figure 31-8.

(b) From Figure 31-8.

(c) From Figure 31-5.

(d) Often referred to as "PV-10," the pre-tax standardized measure is a non-GAAP measure and is not included in the ASC 932 disclosures.

An analysis of each of the major reasons for changes in SMOG is presented in the following tables. Field extensions, new discoveries and improved recoveries are an especially important element of the disclosed SMOG changes. Additionally, as discussed later in this chapter, the acquisition or disposal of reserves can also impact the disclosure of changes in SMOG.

Accretion of discount

A basic feature of the FASB's standardized measure is the discounting of future cash flows at a standard rate of 10 percent per year. Thus, with all other factors remaining constant, the value of reserves in the ground increases with the passage of time by 10 percent per year. The actual amount of accretion resulting from an actual year-by-year calculation of accretion should be less than 10 percent per year, given that the first year cash flow accretion can only be as great as its discount at the beginning of the year, or approximately five percent, not 10 percent, resulting from the mid-year convention discussed previously. Because ASC 932-235-50-35 requires all changes except income taxes to be reported pre-tax, the accretion is based on the pre-tax SMOG value as of the beginning of the year.

Figure 31-10 reflects both the actual year-by-year calculation of accretion as well as an approach using a simple computation of 10 percent of the beginning pre-tax SMOG to calculate the SMOG change attributable to accretion for Field No. 1.

Figure 31-10
Change due to accretion of discount – Field No. 1

Year-by-year calculations		2019	2020	2021	2022	2023	Total	
Future net revenues	(a)	$1,050,000	$890,000	$780,000	$506,667	$233,333	$3,460,000	
x 12/31/2018 PV factors	(b)	0.9535	0.8668	0.7880	0.7164	0.6512	–	
= Pre-tax SMOG	[A]	1,001,175	771,452	614,640	362,976	151,947	2,902,190	[E]
Future net revenues (above)	(a)	$1,050,000	$890,000	$780,000	$506,667	$233,333	$3,460,000	
x 12/31/2019 PV factors		1.0000	0.9535	0.8668	0.7880	0.7164	–	
= Accreted pre-tax SMOG	[B]	1,050,000	846,615	676,104	399,253	167,160	3,141,132	
Accretion	[B] – [A]	$ 48,825	$ 77,163	$ 61,464	$ 36,277	$ 15,213	$ 238,942	[C]
Accretion as a % of [A]		4.9%	10.0%	10.0%	10.0%	10.0%	8.2%	

Alternative calculation		
Pre-tax SMOG at 12/31/2018	$2,902,190	[E]
x 10% discount rate	10%	
= Accretion (increase for 2019)	$ 290,219	[D]
Difference between year-by-year calculation and alternative calculation of accretion = [C] – [D]	$ (51,276)	

(a) From Figure 31-4.

(b) From Figure 31-6.

Sale of oil and gas produced, net of production costs

The production and sale of reserves obviously decreases the value of reserves in the ground and decreases SMOG. The resulting 2019 change in SMOG can be calculated from actual 2019 revenues of $3,000,000 less actual production expenses of $1,300,000 per Figure 31-8. Alternatively, the change can be calculated from projected 2019 revenues of $2,800,000 less projected production expenses of $1,500,000, as reflected in Figure 31-4.

Although the second measure is a more accurate method for calculating the change in SMOG, as it reflects the change in the expected future revenues and production expenses year-over-year, the first measure is typically what petroleum accountants are most familiar with, as it uses actual sales and production expenses disclosed elsewhere in the financial statements.

Net change in prices and production costs

ASC 932-235-50-35 requires that the "effects of changes in prices and cost rates shall be computed before the effects of changes in quantities" whereby quantity changes are stated based on current prices. SMOG changes due to net changes in prices and production costs can be described as follows:

1. The price change per equivalent unit (BOE) (see subsequent discussion herein).

2. The undiscounted effect of price change by multiplying the price change per BOE to the previous year's reserves quantity.

3. The discounted price change per BOE as follows:

    a. The difference in pre-tax net inflows before and after the 10% discount, the result of which is then divided by pre-tax net inflows before discount to arrive at the effective discount rate.

    b. The undiscounted price change calculated in number 2 above, discounted using the discount rate calculated in 3 (a) to arrive at the discounted price change per BOE.

The net change in pre-tax SMOG due to changes in prices and production costs could also be calculated similar to the price variance in traditional cost accounting variance analysis. At December 31, 2018, value (V-old) equals the product of the December 31, 2018, reserves quantity (Q-old) multiplied by a net price (P-old), where net price is the operating cash flow per BOE as of December 31, 2018. Similarly, the December 31, 2019, value (V-new) is calculated as (Q-new) multiplied by (P-new).

The (Q-old) equates to a December 31, 2018, reserves estimate because the SMOG change due to 2019 production is disclosed separately. When applicable, (Q-old) also excludes any reserves additions attributable to proved property acquisitions, extensions, discoveries or improved recoveries, as well as reserves sold during the year, because SMOG changes due to these factors are disclosed separately.

As required by ASC 932-235-50-35, the price variance is calculated as [(P-new less P-old) multiplied by Q-old], while the quantity variance is calculated as [(Q-new less Q-old) multiplied by P-new]. Accordingly, the basic formula providing the SMOG change attributable to price and cost rate changes is a price variance equal to the change in net price per BOE multiplied by the old quantity (estimated reserves at the beginning of the year).

The undiscounted changes in prices and production costs should then be multiplied by the beginning of year ratio of: (a) present value of future operating cash flow to (b) undiscounted future operating cash flow. Figure 31-11 shows the effect of changes in the price per BOE of $3.45 during 2019 on pre-tax SMOG (discounted) for Field No. 1.

Figure 31-11

Net change in prices and production costs – Field No. 1

As of December 31, 2019				**BOE**			
Future cash inflows	(a)	$6,860,000					
Future production costs	(a)	(3,740,000)					
Revenues less production costs		3,120,000	(c)	170,000			
Less portion attributable to:							
Extensions and discoveries	(b)	(287,500)	(c)	(15,000)			
Purchases of reserves in place	(d)	–		–			
		2,832,500		155,000		$18.27	
Plus: revenues less production costs	(c)	1,700,000	(c)	69,000			
Amounts attributable to prior years' discoveries and current year revenues, net		$4,532,500		224,000		$20.23	[A]
As of December 31, 2018							
Future cash inflows	(e)	$8,460,000					
Future production costs	(e)	(4,600,000)					
Revenues less production costs		3,860,000	(f)	230,000	[D]	$16.78	[B]
Less: amounts related to sales of reserves in place	(d)	–		–			
Beginning of year amounts before revisions		$3,860,000		230,000		$16.78	
Price change per equivalent unit (BOE)		[A] – [B]				$3.45	[C]
Undiscounted				$793,906	[E] = [D] * [C]		
Average pre-tax discount				(127,991)	[E] * [F]		
Effect of price change per BOE (discounted)				$665,915			
December 31, 2018							
Pre-tax future net revenues (undiscounted)			(g)	$3,460,000	[H]		
Pre-tax standardized measure (discounted)			(g)	(2,902,190)			
Effect of 10% discount				$ 557,810	[G]		
Average discount %				16.12%	[F] = [G] ÷ [H]		

(a) From Figure 31-9.
(b) Calculated as future cash inflows of $617,500 less future production costs of $330,000 from Figure 31-9.
(c) From Figure 31-8.
(d) In this example, there were no purchases or sales of reserves in place during 2018.
(e) From Figure 31-4.
(f) From Figure 31-3.
(g) From Figure 31-6.

Revisions of quantity estimates

ASC 932-235-50-35 requires that the SMOG change due to quantity revisions be based on current prices and year-end costs. SMOG changes due to quantity revisions can be described as follows:

- Compute the quantity revision.

- Compute its effect on undiscounted value based on current prices and costs.

- Compute the present value effect based on multiplying the undiscounted change by the ratio of: (a) the present value of future operating cash flows (future gross revenues less future production costs) to (b) the undiscounted future operating cash flows.

These steps are applied in Figure 31-12 below to the data for Field No. 1 for 2019.

Figure 31-12
Revisions of quantity estimates – Field No. 1

Reserves Roll-Forward		Bbls	Mcf	BOE
Reserves as of December 31, 2018	(a)	150,000	480,000	230,000
Less:				
Production	(b)	(42,000)	(162,000)	(69,000)
Sales of reserves in place		–	–	–
Plus:				
Purchases of reserves in place		–	–	–
Extensions and discoveries	(b)	10,000	30,000	15,000
		118,000	348,000	176,000
Reserves as of December 31, 2019	(b)	110,000	360,000	170,000
Revisions of previous estimates		**(8,000)**	**12,000**	**(6,000)**

SMOG changes due to revisions of previous estimates		
Revisions of previous quantity estimates (BOE)		(6,000)
Average price at the end of the year	(c)	$18.27
Change in SMOG due to revisions of estimates (undiscounted)		**$(109,645)**
Average discount %	(c)	x 16.12%
Less: average discount		(17,675)
Change in SMOG due to revisions of estimates (discounted)		**$(91,970)**

(a) From Figure 31-3.

(b) From Figure 31-8.

(c) From Figure 31-11.

Changes in estimated future development costs

ASC 932-235-50-35 calls for disclosure of any SMOG changes attributable to: (1) "previously estimated development costs incurred during the period," and (2) "changes in estimated future development costs."

The amount of development costs actually incurred during the year that reduced previously estimated development costs should be presented separately from the development costs related to new extensions and discoveries. This amount is determined from an analysis of the total development costs which were actually incurred during the year for each individual property.

Many companies may find it impracticable to perform a detailed analysis by property to determine which portion of the development costs incurred relate to the prior year discoveries. In this case, the practical solution would be to perform such analysis for development costs related to major properties and presume that development costs associated with other properties relate to prior years' discoveries.

Alternatively, since the company most likely would not engage in the significant development activities in the same year a major discovery is made, the development costs incurred in the subsequent year may be presumed to relate to prior years' discoveries.

The December 31, 2018, SMOG for Field No. 1 reflected $250,000 of future development and abandonment costs estimated to be incurred in 2019 (Figure 31-3). Actual costs were $230,000 (Figure 31-8). The related SMOG change in 2019 attributable to development cost changes can be presented in one of two ways:

1. Listed as actual costs incurred related to previously estimated development costs on one line and the change in estimated future development costs on another line.

2. Listed as previously estimated development costs that were to be incurred in 2019.

Both approaches have merit. However, as both approaches should exclude development costs not related to proved undeveloped locations at the beginning of the year which relate to current year extensions and discoveries, users of the first approach must be particularly careful to exclude such costs if the starting point for this amount is total development costs for the company in the current year.

Otherwise, the SMOG changes for both incurred costs and changes in estimated future development costs might be significantly overstated. To avoid this situation, future development costs attributable to reserves extensions and discoveries should be deducted from the changes in SMOG due to extensions and discoveries of the reserves as shown in Figure 31-13.

Changes in the estimated future development costs shown in Figure 31-13 resulted from a $20,000 difference between development costs actually incurred in 2019 ($230,000) compared to what had been expected ($250,000), plus a $50,000 increase related to revisions of the company's estimates of future development costs. The amount of $5,000 (discounted amount of $4,768) attributable to changes in estimated future development costs due to reserves extensions and discoveries will be netted against the changes in SMOG due to extensions and discoveries, less the related costs shown in Figure 31-16.

As the future cash outflows related to AROs are included in future development costs, the related changes in estimates for AROs are also reflected in the change in the future development costs line of the SMOG changes disclosures.

Figure 31-13
Changes in estimated future development costs – Field No. 1

	Estimated as of 12/31/2018	Attributable to new extensions and discoveries	Attributable to acquisition of properties	Actually expended during 2019	Other increases (decreases) in future costs	Estimated as of 12/31/2019
	(a)	(b)		(b)		(b)
2019	$250,000	$ –	$ –	$(230,000)	$(20,000)	$ –
2020	150,000	5,000	–	–	–	155,000
2021	–	–	–	–	50,000	50,000
2022	–	–	–	–	–	–
2023	–	–	–	–	–	–
Total	$400,000	$5,000	$ –	$(230,000)	$30,000	$205,000

Changes in SMOG due to:

Previously estimated future development costs to be incurred during 2019	(a)	$250,000
or		
Previously estimated development costs incurred during 2019	(b)	$230,000
Less: change in estimated future development costs	(c)	(23,340)
		$206,660

Amounts attributable to new extensions and discoveries

Undiscounted		$5,000
Discounted	(d)	$4,768

(a) From Figure 31-3.

(b) From Figure 31-8.

(c) Calculated as the change in estimated future development costs of $30,000 above less discount of $6,660 calculated using a discount factor of 0.8668 as it relates to the 2021 amount.

(d) Calculated as the change in estimated future development costs of $5,000 above less discount of $232 calculated using a discount factor of 0.9535 as it relates to the 2020 amount. The actual discount factor that would be applicable to development costs should be the appropriate factor considering the expected timing of the cash flows.

Note: Amounts attributable to new extensions and discoveries will be netted against the overall effect of new extensions and discoveries in SMOG changes.

Change in estimated future income taxes

ASC 932-235-50-35 states "all changes except income taxes shall be reported pre-tax." Consequently, the SMOG change attributable to changes in estimated future income taxes is simply the reverse of the net change in the present value of estimated future taxes as of the beginning and end of the year. If the present value of taxes decreases by $100,000, the related SMOG change is a $100,000 increase.

As presented in Figure 31-14, the SMOG change due to a change in income taxes is a decrease of $75,710.

Figure 31-14
Change in estimated future income taxes – Field No. 1

		Discounted	Undiscounted
Future income taxes estimated at December 31, 2018	(a)	$609,460	$ 726,600
Future income taxes estimated at December 31, 2019	(b)	533,750	612,150
Net change in future estimated income taxes		**$(75,710)**	**$(114,450)**

(a) From Figure 31-6.

(b) From Figure 31-9.

Changes due to timing and other factors

Aside from the standardized measure changes required to be delineated in ASC 932 disclosures, the SEC allows a catch-all category of "Other," which many companies call "Timing and other differences," or something similar. Presumably, these amounts refer to changes in production profile differences and the imprecision resulting from assumptions made in the required change line items.

The total amount of "Other" changes reflects the net change in present value that is not specifically identified in one of the individual computations. The "Other" amount reported depends in part on the approach taken to calculate accretion. As presented in Figure 31-10, if the company uses the short-cut approach to calculate accretion (10 percent of beginning of year SMOG), the "Other" category would potentially include a $51,276 difference between the two methods.

In the Figure 31-15 example, the "Other" category includes the effect of changes in timing of expected production between the 2018 and 2019 reserves estimates. The "Undiscounted" column is presented for illustration purposes to demonstrate that all other differences were accounted for in the overall analysis of SMOG changes.

While the "Other" category is a valid line item in the disclosure and is utilized by many publicly traded E&P companies, the amount included is arguably open to interpretation. Some companies prepare their standardized measure calculations in an organized manner with the idea that the "Timing and other differences" will be an insignificant number, under the presumption that it explains any production profile changes.

Other companies, specifically those with computer models and templates, can calculate the various prescribed changes in such a manner as to exclude production timing changes in "Other." The argument here is that timing changes are often indistinguishable from quantity revisions and sometimes from price revisions. Such companies question why the SMOG calculation would not be structured in such a way as to include the effects of timing changes with quantity variances or, perhaps, pricing changes.

Figure 31-15
Changes due to timing and other factors – Field No. 1

		Discounted	Undiscounted
Future Net Cash Flows as of December 31, 2018	(a)	**$2,292,730**	**$2,733,400**
Net change in prices and production costs	(b)	665,915	793,906
Changes in estimated future development costs	(c)	(23,340)	(30,000)
Sales and transfers of oil and gas produced	(d)	(1,700,000)	(1,700,000)
Net change due to extensions and discoveries	(e)	256,286	282,500
Net change due to purchases of minerals in place		–	–
Net change due to revisions in quantity estimates	(f)	(91,970)	(109,645)
Previously estimated development costs incurred	(c)	230,000	230,000
Accretion of discount	(g)	238,942	–
Other – unspecified		63,640	(11,761)
Net change in income taxes	(h)	75,710	114,450
Future Net Cash Flows as of December 31, 2019	(e)	**$2,007,915**	**$2,302,850**

(a) From Figure 31-6.

(b) From Figure 31-11.

(c) From Figure 31-13.

(d) From Figure 31-8.

(e) From Figure 31-9.

(f) From Figure 31-12.

(g) From Figure 31-10.

(h) From Figure 31-14.

This point is valid for producing properties more so than for development properties. Independent of price changes or reserves revisions, uncertainties about government regulation and financing may change the time when proved undeveloped reserves begin producing.

As stated earlier, the "Other" category should be a relatively immaterial amount; if not, the reason for it should be understood and an additional line item disclosure may be warranted. One approach to calculating the SMOG change due to timing changes compares:

- The present value ratio of future cash flows projected at the beginning of the year and accreted to year-end (and excluding the year's actual oil and gas sales and proved property sales).

- The present value ratio of equivalent future cash flows projected at the end of the year.

Hypothetically, if the December 31, 2018, SMOG reflected a present value ratio of 0.74 for discounted cash flows (accreted to December 31, 2019) to undiscounted cash flows after 2019, but the December 31, 2019, SMOG reflects a present value ratio of 0.68 for the equivalent cash flows, the decrease in present value ratio from 0.74 to 0.68 may indicate that the timing of production has been delayed, causing a decrease in SMOG.

The decrease of 0.06 is multiplied by the undiscounted future operating cash flow to measure the SMOG changes that may be due to timing differences. The ratio decrease may, however, be attributable to favorable price increases which extend the economic limit of the field's life, thus increasing reserves to be produced in later years and decreasing the overall present value ratio.

Extensions and discoveries

An important element of the disclosed SMOG changes is the increase caused by field extensions, new discoveries and improved recoveries. To illustrate this computation, the information for Field No. 2 for 2019 is used as an example.

Assume a discovery well and confirmation well were drilled in 2019 that established proved reserves in November. Relevant information for 2019 and data as of December 31, 2019, are presented in Figure 31-16 below.

Figure 31-16
Extensions and discoveries – Field No. 2

		2019				
Revenues		$1,000,000				
Production costs		(350,000)				
Revenues less production costs		$ 650,000				
Reserves as of December 31, 2019		**Bbls**	**Mcf**	**BOE**	**Future development costs**	**Future income taxes**
	2020	200,000	90,000	215,000	$500,000	$1,139,250
	2021	175,000	75,000	187,500	200,000	1,047,375
	2022	150,000	60,000	160,000	–	934,500
	2023	110,000	45,000	117,500	–	685,125
	2024	70,000	30,000	75,000	–	435,750
	2025	30,000	15,000	32,500	–	186,375
	2026	15,000	6,000	16,000	–	93,450
	Total	**750,000**	**321,000**	**803,500**	**$700,000**	**$4,521,825**
Price per barrel		$50.00				
Price per Mcf			$2.50			
Production costs per BOE				$20.00		

SMOG for proved reserves in Field No. 2 at December 31, 2019, is computed as $13,790,158, as shown in Figure 31-17 below. Because the discovery well was made near the end of the year, it is considered impractical to calculate changes other than actual sales and income taxes.

Since SMOG changes due to a new discovery must be computed based on pre-tax SMOG (discounted future net revenues), Figure 31-17 computes the present value of related income taxes and adds it to the SMOG value to calculate pre-tax SMOG.

Figure 31-17
Pre-tax SMOG and changes in SMOG – Field No. 2

		2020	2021	2022	2023	2024	2025	2026	Total
Production (BOE)	(a)	215,000	187,500	160,000	117,500	75,000	32,500	16,000	803,500
Future cash inflows	(b)	$10,225,000	$8,937,500	$7,650,000	$5,612,500	$3,575,000	$1,537,500	$765,000	$38,302,500
Future costs:									
Production costs	(b)	(4,300,000)	(3,750,000)	(3,200,000)	(2,350,000)	(1,500,000)	(650,000)	(320,000)	(16,070,000)
Development costs	(a)	(500,000)	(200,000)	–	–	–	–	–	(700,000)
Future net revenues		5,425,000	4,987,500	4,450,000	3,262,500	2,075,000	887,500	445,000	21,532,500
Future income taxes	(a)	(1,139,250)	(1,047,375)	(934,500)	(685,125)	(435,750)	(186,375)	(93,450)	(4,521,825)
Future net cash flows		4,285,750	3,940,125	3,515,500	2,577,375	1,639,250	701,125	351,550	17,010,675
10% Discount		(199,287)	(524,825)	(745,286)	(730,944)	(571,770)	(286,059)	(162,346)	(3,220,517)
Standardized measure		$ 4,086,463	$3,415,300	$2,770,214	$1,846,431	$1,067,480	$ 415,066	$189,204	$13,790,158 [A]
Income tax present value		1,086,275	907,865	736,386	490,824	283,760	110,334	50,295	3,665,739 [B]
Pre-tax SMOG		$ 5,172,738	$4,323,165	$3,506,600	$2,337,255	$1,351,240	$ 525,400	$239,499	$17,455,897
Present value factors	(c)	0.9535	0.8668	0.7880	0.7164	0.6512	0.5920	0.5382	

Changes in SMOG		
Sales and transfers of oil and gas produced, net of production costs	(a)	$ (650,000)
Extensions and discoveries	(d)	$18,105,897
Net change in income taxes		$ (3,665,739) [B]
Aggregate change in standardized measure		$13,790,158 [A]

(a) From Figure 31-16.

(b) Calculated from Figure 31-16.

(c) From Figure 31-5.

(d) As the field was discovered in 2019, all change in SMOG not associated with production or income taxes are attributed to discoveries.

For purposes of disclosing the change in the standardized measure of reserves for Field No. 2 (see Figure 31-23), the components would include sales and transfers of oil and gas produced, net of production costs, of $650,000; extensions and discoveries of $18,105,897; and the change in income taxes of $3,665,739.

Reserves acquired

In June 2019, the company acquired a new producing property, Field No. 3, which primarily has oil reserves. The quantity of the reserves, future production costs and future development costs presented in Figure 31-18 were estimated by the company and its reserves engineers at the June 30, 2019 acquisition date and at the year-end reporting date of December 31, 2019. The revenues, production costs and development costs incurred presented in Figure 31-18 for the six months ended December 31, 2019, represent actual amounts.

Figure 31-18
Properties acquired in 2019 – Field No. 3

Six months ended December 31, 2019

Production (BOE)	50,000
Revenues	$3,000,000
Production costs	(1,450,000)
Revenues less production costs	$1,550,000
Development costs incurred	$ 175,000

	Reserves as of 12/31/2018 and 12/31/2019		Future development costs		Future income taxes	
	June 30	December 31	June 30	December 31	June 30	December 31
	BOE	BOE				
2019	50,000	–	$200,000	$ –	$ 273,000	$ –
2020	150,000	145,000	550,000	650,000	829,500	716,100
2021	125,000	130,000	100,000	120,000	766,500	739,200
2022	90,000	90,000	–	–	567,000	529,200
2023	70,000	70,000	–	–	441,000	411,600
2024	40,000	40,000	–	–	252,000	235,200
2025	20,000	20,000	–	–	126,000	117,600
2026	8,000	10,000	–	–	50,400	58,800
Total	**553,000**	**505,000**	**$850,000**	**$770,000**	**$3,305,400**	**$2,807,700**
Price per BOE	$55.00	$50.00				
Production costs per BOE	$25.00	$22.00				

Reserves estimates prepared by the acquiring company may be substantially different from the reserves previously prepared by the seller due to changes in volume estimates, price changes from the previous period and other reasons.

Therefore, changes in SMOG related to acquisitions of reserves in place should be calculated at the date of acquisition and based on the company's estimates and assumptions at that date, including prices per unit-of-production and future production and development costs. Subsequent changes between the date of acquisition and the end of the year in which the property is acquired would be reflected within categories required by ASC 932-235-50-35. Figure 31-19 and Figure 31-20 illustrate for Field No. 3 the calculations of SMOG at the acquisition date of June 30, 2019 and as of December 31, 2019, respectively.

The discount rate used for 2019 in Figure 31-19 reflects the mid-year convention applied for the six-month period from the acquisition date to December 31, 2019. Although the properties were acquired on June 30, 2019, the standard mid-year discount rate applicable for the full year of 0.9535 was used for simplicity. The remaining discount rates are the same as those included in Figure 31-5.

Figure 31-19

Calculation of SMOG and pre-tax SMOG – Field No. 3

As of June 30, 2019		2019	2020	2021	2022	2023	2024	2025	2026	Total
Future cash inflows	(a)	$2,750,000	$8,250,000	$6,875,000	$4,950,000	$3,850,000	$2,200,000	$1,100,000	$440,000	$30,415,000
Future costs:										
Production costs	(a)	(1,250,000)	(3,750,000)	(3,125,000)	(2,250,000)	(1,750,000)	(1,000,000)	(500,000)	(200,000)	(13,825,000)
Development costs	(b)	(200,000)	(550,000)	(100,000)	–	–	–	–	–	(850,000)
Future net revenues		1,300,000	3,950,000	3,650,000	2,700,000	2,100,000	1,200,000	600,000	240,000	15,740,000
Future income taxes	(b)	(273,000)	(829,500)	(766,500)	(567,000)	(441,000)	(252,000)	(126,000)	(50,400)	(3,305,400)
Future net cash flows		1,027,000	3,120,500	2,883,500	2,133,000	1,659,000	948,000	474,000	189,600	12,434,600
10% discount*		(47,756)	(415,651)	(611,302)	(604,919)	(578,659)	(386,784)	(218,893)	(96,829)	(2,960,793)
Standardized measure		$ 979,244	$2,704,849	$2,272,198	$1,528,081	$1,080,341	$ 561,216	$ 255,107	$ 92,771	$ 9,473,807
Income tax present value*		260,306	719,011	604,002	406,199	287,179	149,184	67,813	24,661	2,518,354
Pre-tax SMOG		$1,239,550	$3,423,860	$2,876,200	$1,934,280	$1,367,520	$ 710,400	$ 322,920	$117,432	$11,992,161
Present value factors	(c)	0.9535	0.8668	0.7880	0.7164	0.6512	0.5920	0.5382	0.4893	

(a) Calculated from Figure 31-18.

(b) From Figure 31-18.

(c) From Figure 31-5. For simplicity, the PV factor for 2019 was not adjusted for a partial-year convention (i.e., although the properties were acquired on June 30, 2019, the standard mid-year discount rate applicable for the full year of 0.9535 was used).

The changes in SMOG from the date of acquisition to December 31, 2019, for Field No. 3 are presented in Figure 31-21. Figure 31-21 presents changes in SMOG from the date of acquisition to December 31, 2019 and does not include changes in the company's SMOG due to the acquisition of these reserves on June 30, 2019. From Figure 31-19, the pre-tax SMOG at the date of acquisition was estimated to be $11,992,161. The related tax effect at the date of acquisition was $2,518,354. The future income taxes at the date of acquisition are estimated based on the company's effective tax rate expected to be realized in the respective years (in this example, taxes related to future net revenues are given).

Because ASC 932-235-50-35 requires all changes to be presented pre-tax, the amount of future income taxes associated with the future revenues is also presented separately from pre-tax SMOG changes related to acquisition of the reserves. As presented in Figure 31-21, the company's future discounted tax amount as of December 31, 2019, is a total of $2,289,847, consisting of taxes related to acquired reserves of $2,518,354 less the related changes in income taxes after the date of acquisition of $228,507.

Figure 31-20

Calculation of SMOG and pre-tax SMOG – Field No. 3

As of December 31, 2019		2020	2021	2022	2023	2024	2025	2026	Total
Future cash inflows	(a)	$7,250,000	$6,500,000	$4,500,000	$3,500,000	$2,000,000	$1,000,000	$500,000	$25,250,000
Future costs:									
Production costs	(a)	(3,190,000)	(2,860,000)	(1,980,000)	(1,540,000)	(880,000)	(440,000)	(220,000)	(11,110,000)
Development costs	(b)	(650,000)	(120,000)	–	–	–	–	–	(770,000)
Future net revenues		3,410,000	3,520,000	2,520,000	1,960,000	1,120,000	560,000	280,000	13,370,000
Future income taxes	(b)	(716,100)	(739,200)	(529,200)	(411,600)	(235,200)	(117,600)	(58,800)	(2,807,700)
Future net cash flows		2,693,900	2,780,800	1,990,800	1,548,400	884,800	442,400	221,200	10,562,300
10% discount		(125,266)	(370,403)	(422,050)	(439,126)	(308,618)	(180,499)	(102,150)	(1,948,112)
Standardized measure		$2,568,634	$2,410,397	$1,568,750	$1,109,274	$ 576,182	$ 261,901	$119,050	$ 8,614,188
Income tax present value		682,801	640,739	417,010	294,870	153,162	69,619	31,646	2,289,847
Pre-tax SMOG		$3,251,435	$3,051,136	$1,985,760	$1,404,144	$ 729,344	$ 331,520	$150,696	$10,904,035
Present value factors	(c)	0.9535	0.8668	0.7880	0.7164	0.6512	0.5920	0.5382	

(a) Calculated from Figure 31-18.

(b) From Figure 31-18.

(c) From Figure 31-5.

Reserves sold

If a certain portion of reserves is sold during the year, the pre-tax effect of the cash flows eliminated from SMOG is reflected in the line item Purchases and sales of minerals in place. The related tax effect is included in the "Net change in income taxes" line item.

The SEC has expressed a view that reserves associated with discontinued operations should be reflected as sales in the period in which the sale occurred. Prior periods should not be retroactively restated to remove the reserves associated with the discontinued operations in the ASC 932 disclosures, despite the fact that the related revenues and costs associated with those reserves have been eliminated from prior period income statement totals in the primary financial statements.

Figure 31-21

Figure 31-21
Calculation of changes in SMOG – Field No. 3 – Post-acquisition date

1. Production

Actual revenues	(a)	$3,000,000
Less: actual production costs	(a)	(1,450,000)
Net decrease in SMOG		$1,550,000

2. Future development costs

Previously estimated development costs incurred in 2019	(a)	$ 175,000
Less: change in estimated future development costs (undiscounted)*	(a)	(95,000)
Less: change in estimated future development costs (discounted)*	(a)	$ (87,682)

3. Net changes in prices and production costs

		Amount		Quantity		Average price	
As of December 31, 2019				BOE		$ per BOE	
Future cash inflows	(c)	$25,250,000					
Future production costs		(11,110,000)					
		14,140,000	(a)	505,000			
Extensions and discoveries		–		–			
Purchases of reserves in place		–		–			
		14,140,000		505,000		$28.00	
Revenues less production costs	(a)	1,550,000	(a)	50,000			
		$15,690,000		555,000		$28.27	[A]
As of June 30, 2019							
Future cash inflows	(b)	$30,415,000					
Future production costs	(b)	(13,825,000)					
Beginning of year amounts before revisions		$16,590,000	(a)	553,000	[D]	$30.00	[B]
Price decrease per BOE	[A] – [B]					$(1.73)	[C]
Undiscounted	[C] x [D]					$(956,690)	[E]
Average pre-tax discount	[E] x [F]					227,788	
Discounted						$(728,902)	
Pre-tax future net revenues (undiscounted)					(b)	15,740,000	
Pre-tax standardized measure (discounted)					(b)	(11,992,162)	
Effect of 10% discount						**$3,747,838**	
Average discount %						23.81%	[F]

* Calculated as the change in estimated future development costs for the six months ended December 31, 2019, of $25,000 ($200,000 less $175,000) less the change in estimated future development costs for the years ended December 31, 2020 and 2021 of $100,000 undiscounted ($95,346 discounted) and $20,000 undiscounted ($17,336 discounted), respectively, based on data in Figure 31-18.

Figure 31-21

Figure 31-21
Calculation of changes in SMOG – Field No. 3 – Post-acquisition date (cont.)

4. Revisions of previous quantity estimates

(1) Compute the quantity revision (BOE):

		BOE	
Estimated proved reserves as of 12/31/2019	(a)	505,000	[G]
Acquisition date estimated proved reserves	(a)	553,000	
Less: actual quantities sold in 2019	(a)	(50,000)	
Acquired estimated reserves not sold in 2019		503,000	[H]
Reserves revision increase		2,000	= [G] – [H]

(2) Compute the effect on undiscounted value:

Reserves revision – increase (decrease) (BOE)	2,000
Price less production costs per BOE as of 12/31/2019	$28.00
Total increase (decrease) due to change in volumes	$56,000

(3) Compute the present value effect as of 12/31/2019:

Ratio of discounted to undiscounted future operating cash flow	76% = 1 – [F]
Change in SMOG due to quantity revisions	$42,666

5. Change in income taxes

	Dec. 31, 2019	June 30, 2019	
	(c)	(b)	Change
Undiscounted income taxes	$2,807,700	$3,305,400	$(497,700)
Discounted income taxes	$2,289,847	$2,518,354	$(228,507)

6. Changes in SMOG

		Discounted	Undiscounted
Future net cash flows as of June 30, 2019	(b)	$9,473,807	$12,434,600
Net change in prices and production costs	(d)	(728,902)	(956,690
Changes in estimated future development costs	(d)	(87,682)	(95,000)
Sales and transfers of oil and gas produced	(d)	(1,550,000)	(1,550,000)
Net change due to extensions and discoveries		–	–
Net change due to purchases of minerals in place		–	–
Net change due to revisions in quantity estimates	(d)	42,666	56,000
Previously estimated development costs incurred	(d)	175,000	175,000
Accretion of discount	(e)	1,135,831	
Other – unspecified		(75,039)	690
Net change in income taxes	(d)	228,507	497,700
Future net cash flows as of December 31, 2019		$8,614,188	$10,562,300

(a) From Figure 31-18.

(b) From Figure 31-19.

(c) From Figure 31-20.

(d) From Figure 31-21 (previous page).

(e) Calculated year-by-year accretion using information from Figure 31-19. See example in Figure 31-10.

Combined disclosure

The data from Field No. 1, Field No. 2 and Field No. 3 can be combined as shown in Figure 31-22 and Figure 31-23.

Figure 31-22
Combined SMOG as of December 31, 2019

	Field No. 1	Field No. 2	Field No. 3	Total
	(a)	(b)	(c)	
Future cash inflows	$ 6,860,000	$38,302,500	$25,250,000	$70,412,500
Future production costs	(3,740,000)	(16,070,000)	(11,110,000)	(30,920,000)
Future development costs	(205,000)	(700,000)	(770,000)	(1,675,000)
Future income tax expense	(612,150)	(4,521,825)	(2,807,700)	(7,941,675)
Future net cash flows	2,302,850	17,010,675	10,562,300	29,875,825
10% discount	(294,935)	(3,220,517)	(1,948,112)	(5,463,564)
Standardized measure	**$ 2,007,915**	**$13,790,158**	**$ 8,614,188**	**$24,412,261**

(a) From Figure 31-9.

(b) From Figure 31-17.

(c) From Figure 31-20.

Effects of the discovery of minerals in Field No. 2 are presented in the "Net change due to extensions and discoveries" and "Net change in income taxes" lines shown in Figure 31-23. Because the discovery was made near the end of the year, it was considered impractical to calculate all other changes, except for actual sales and income taxes.

The "Sales and transfers of oil and gas produced" line shown in Figure 31-23 represents sales after the date of discovery and before year-end; however, in most cases production will not be expected to start until subsequent years. At the same time, for Field No. 3 the SMOG changes are allocated between the "Purchases and sales of mineral interests" line and lines related to development costs, revisions in quantity estimates, accretion, and timing and other due to the fact that reserves were acquired on June 30, 2019.

Addition of reserves at June 30, 2019, are reflected in the line "Purchases and sales of mineral interests" shown in Figure 31-23, along with the related future income taxes at June 30, 2019, of $2,518,354, adjusted for the change in future income taxes for the six months ended December 31, 2019 of $(228,507), in order to arrive at the $2,289,847 reflected in the "Net change in income taxes" line shown in Figure 31-23.

Other changes represent the effect of changes in estimates and other changes for the period from June 30, 2019, to year-end. The "Net change in income taxes" line includes both the effects of the reserves acquisition on June 30, 2019, and the effects of other changes in SMOG, such as changes in prices, production costs and other.

When reserves are sold during the year, the SMOG changes associated with these reserves may include the lines that reflect the actual sales less production costs for the period prior to sale and the development costs incurred during the same period, with the difference going through the lines "Purchases and sales of mineral interests" and "Net changes in income taxes."

Figure 31-23
Combined changes in SMOG for the year ended December 31, 2019

	Field No. 1	Field No. 2	Field No. 3	Total
	(a)	(b)	(c)	
SMOG as of 12/31/2018	(d) $2,292,730	$ –	$ –	$ 2,292,730
Net change in prices and production costs	665,915	–	(728,902)	(62,987)
Changes in estimated development costs	(23,340)	–	(87,682)	(111,022)
Sales and transfers of oil and gas produced	(1,700,000)	(650,000)	$(1,550,000)	(3,900,000)
Net change due to extensions and discoveries	256,287	18,105,897	–	18,362,184
Purchases and sales of mineral interests	–	–	11,992,162	11,992,162
Revisions in quantity estimates	(91,969)	–	42,666	(49,303)
Previously estimated development costs incurred	230,000	–	175,000	405,000
Accretion of discount	238,943	–	1,135,831	1,374,774
Timing and other	63,640	–	(75,039)	(11,401)
Net change in income taxes	75,710	(3,665,739)	(2,289,847)	(5,879,876)
SMOG as of 12/31/2019	$ 2,007,915	$13,790,158	$ 8,614,188	$24,412,261
Aggregate change in SMOG	$ (284,814)	$13,790,158	$ 8,614,188	$22,119,532

(a) From Figure 31-15.

(b) From Figure 31-16 and Figure 31-17.

(c) From Figure 31-20 and Figure 31-21.

(d) From Figure 31-6.

• • •

Business Combinations

Photograph by istock.com/hartmanc10

In January 2017, the FASB issued ASU 2017-01, *Clarifying the Definition of a Business*, which changed the definition of a business. The guidance was issued in response to stakeholder feedback that the previous definition resulted in transactions being recorded as business combinations that seemed more like asset acquisitions.

As a result, the new ASU 2017-01 added an initial screen to determine if substantially all of the fair value of gross assets acquired is concentrated in a single asset or a group of similar assets. If the screen is met, the acquired assets and activities (collectively referred to as a "set") do not constitute a business. If the screen is not met, companies should evaluate the new framework that specifies the minimum required inputs and processes necessary for acquired properties to be considered a business.

This chapter is based on ASU 2017-01, which was effective for public companies for financial statements issued for fiscal years beginning after December 15, 2017 and interim periods within those fiscal years. For all other companies, the guidance was effective for financial statements issued for fiscal years beginning after December 15, 2018 and interim periods within fiscal years beginning after December 15, 2019. Early adoption was permitted, including adoption in an interim period. Companies should use the previous definition of a business provided by previous FASB guidance prior to adoption of ASU 2017-01.

While the update provided new guidance that companies are required to follow, the overall framework in accounting for business combinations is retained in ASC 805, which stipulates that all business combinations must be accounted for using the acquisition method.

Definition of a business

ASC 805 defines a business as: "An integrated set of activities and assets that is capable of being conducted and managed for the purpose of providing a return in the form of dividends, lower costs, or other economic benefits directly to investors or other owners, members, or participants."

The distinction between an asset acquisition and a business combination is important because the accounting is substantially different. A flowchart for making such determination is provided in Figure 32-1.

In a business combination, assets acquired and liabilities assumed are recorded at fair value, goodwill is recognized for any excess consideration and transaction costs are expensed. ASC 805 defines a business combination as: "A transaction or other event in which an acquirer obtains control of one or more businesses. Transactions sometimes referred to as true mergers or mergers of equals also are business combinations." The guidance applies to all business combinations regardless of whether the form of consideration transferred is cash, other assets, a business or subsidiary of the company, debt, common or preferred shares or other equity interests.

In an asset acquisition, contingencies assumed are only recorded if probable, goodwill is not recognized and transaction costs are generally capitalized. Furthermore, the measurement period (the period of time during which an acquirer may finalize its accounting for a business combination) is not available for an asset acquisition. Asset acquisitions are recorded at cost; however, companies may need to determine the fair values of individual assets when a group of assets is acquired, for instance, when the acquisition cost must be allocated to the individual assets based on their relative fair values.

The FASB definition of a business that is used for accounting purposes by both public and private companies is different than the definition used by public companies for SEC reporting purposes. The SEC definition evaluates a business by considering the facts and circumstances of the transaction and whether there is sufficient continuity of the acquired entity's operations prior to and after the transaction (see further discussion in Chapter 35).

Figure 32-1

Business combination versus asset acquisition flowchart

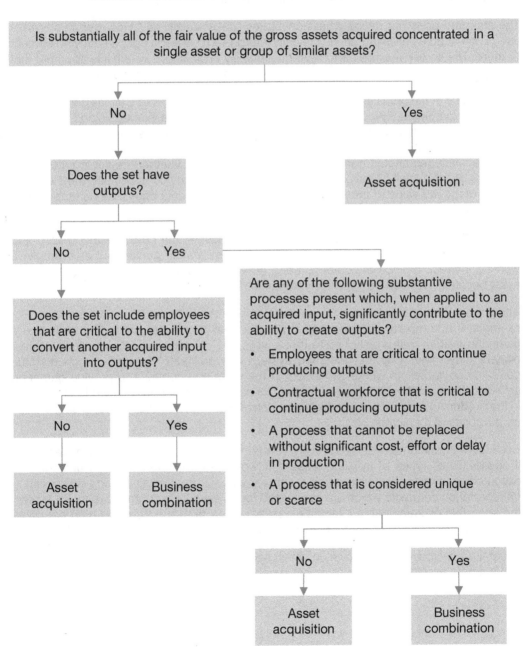

Application of the screen

The screen is intended to be a practical way for entities to identify transactions that should be asset acquisitions. It requires an entity to determine whether substantially all of the fair value of the gross assets acquired is concentrated in a single asset or group of similar assets. If so, the assets acquired are not considered a business. In determining whether a group of assets is similar, the use of the successful efforts or full cost method, as well as the unit of account used for depletion or impairment purposes, is irrelevant.

The standard does not define what constitutes "substantially all." However, this term is used in other areas of GAAP and is typically interpreted to mean approximately 90 percent or more. The screen may be performed qualitatively in situations where it is apparent that performing a quantitative test would indicate the transaction is an asset acquisition.

The fair value of the gross assets acquired is not necessarily the same as the consideration paid. For example, the denominator will exclude any liabilities assumed. In addition, gross assets should exclude cash, deferred tax assets and goodwill arising from the effects of deferred tax liabilities. The FASB noted that the tax form of the transaction and whether cash was included should not affect the determination of whether the set is a business. However, the fair value of the gross assets should include any consideration transferred in excess of the fair value of the net assets acquired (what would otherwise be recorded as goodwill in a business combination).

A single asset is an individual asset or a group of assets that could be recognized and measured as a single asset under the business combination guidance. For example, a working interest, a piece of equipment and an item of inventory would each be a single asset because they can be separately transferred.

Additionally, it may be possible to use certain physically attached assets separately. For example, if a company acquires working interests in a group of producing wells and a gathering system that is attached to those wells, the existence of other working interest owners may mean that the gathering system can be used separately, such that the company could sell its working interests in the wells and continue to provide gathering services to other working interest owners. Consequently, the individual working interests in the producing wells and the gathering system should not be grouped into a single asset for purposes of the screen.

Because this guidance was specifically written for in-place real estate leases (although it applies to all types of in-place leases), it would not be appropriate to analogize to executory contracts. For example, if a company acquires a pipeline along with existing transportation contracts which are accounted for as executory contracts, and not leases, the favorable or unfavorable intangible assets arising from the transportation contracts should not be combined with the pipeline as a single asset.

There are two scenarios, however, in which separately recorded assets must be grouped into a single asset. This grouping is only used for purposes of the screen and does not affect the unit of account at which the assets are measured or recorded.

- **Scenario 1.** A tangible asset that is attached to another tangible asset should be considered a single asset if the assets cannot be physically removed and used separately without incurring significant costs. Additionally, a tangible asset and an intangible asset representing the right to use the tangible asset represent a single asset. For example, a pipeline and the related rights-of-way would be considered a single asset because the pipeline is subject to the rights-of-way and they cannot be used separately.

- **Scenario 2.** In-place lease intangibles, including favorable and unfavorable intangible assets or liabilities, and the related leased assets, should also be considered a single asset because they cannot be used separately.

The screen can also be met if the fair value of the acquired set is concentrated in a group of similar assets. Entities should consider the nature of the assets and the risks associated with managing and creating outputs when determining if assets are similar. The FASB indicated that when the risks of managing and creating outputs are dissimilar, the substantive processes required to manage and create outputs might need to be more advanced. If the risks are not similar, the assets cannot be combined for the screen and the determination of whether the acquired set constitutes a business should be made using the framework rather than the screen.

Determining whether a group of assets is similar will require significant judgment and could be particularly challenging for oil and gas properties. Companies should consider factors such as:

- The type of commodity involved (oil or gas).

- The resource classification of each property (producing or non-producing reserves).

- The geographical location (onshore or offshore, state, county, basin).

- The type of geological formation and reservoir in which the reserves are located.

- The geopolitical environment in different locations.

- Other operational and business risks, including price risk.

Differences in any one of these factors could be an indication that the properties are not similar.

For example, two proved properties that both contain natural gas reserves trapped in the same geological formation may not be similar if one of the properties is producing and the other has not yet been developed. While there may be no difference in reserves risk between the two proved properties, a company should consider whether there are other operational or business risks that are dissimilar.

Figure 32-2 provides an illustration of how this analysis would apply to an acquisition of producing properties.

Figure 32-2
Screen – Acquisition of producing properties

Facts. Company A acquires multiple working interests in contiguous properties located in a single field in the Bakken formation for $4 million. All of the properties are producing crude oil. No employees are transferred to Company A. The fair value (FV) of each working interest and the reserve classifications are as follows:

	FV	Reserves classification
Property #1	$1,500,000	Proved developed producing
Property #2	1,300,000	Proved developed producing
Property #3	1,200,000	Proved developed producing
Total	**$4,000,000**	

Analysis. Company A determines that each of the properties is a single asset because, while they are contiguous, they may be used separately.

Company A then assesses whether any of the properties should be considered similar assets. The nature of the assets is similar in that they are each mineral interests in producing properties. Each property contains crude oil reserves, is located in the same geographic region and geological formation and involves known technology to lift the reserves. Additionally, there are no significant differences in operational or business risks. Consequently, Company A determines that the properties are similar.

Because all of the fair value of the gross assets acquired is concentrated in a group of similar assets, Company A concludes that the screen has been met. Thus, the transaction is accounted for as an asset acquisition.

Business combination framework

To be considered a business under the framework of the new definition, a set needs to have inputs and a substantive process that together significantly contribute to the ability to create outputs. The framework differentiates between sets for which outputs are not present and sets for which outputs are present when evaluating whether an input and a substantive process are present.

Generally, when a set does not have outputs it is more difficult to demonstrate that acquired processes can significantly contribute to the ability to create outputs. The presence of more than an insignificant amount of goodwill may indicate that an acquired process is substantive. However, a set is not precluded from qualifying as a business if there is no goodwill.

Importantly, ASU 2017-01 eliminated the requirement to evaluate whether a market participant could replace any missing inputs or processes in determining whether or not a set qualifies as a business. However, the new guidance retains the requirement to evaluate whether the set is capable of being managed as a business by a market participant. Therefore, it is not relevant whether the seller previously operated the set as a business or whether the acquirer intends to operate the set as a business. Figure 33-3 provides an illustration of how this guidance would apply to an acquisition of both producing and nonproducing properties.

Figure 32-3

Screen – Acquisition of producing and non-producing properties

Facts. Company B acquires multiple working interests in contiguous properties located in a single field in the Bakken formation for $10 million. The predominant resource is crude oil. No employees are transferred to Company B. The reserves associated with Property #4 have been classified as unproved by Company B because they will not be drilled within the next five years, in accordance with the SEC five-year rule. The expected costs to develop the proved undeveloped properties are significant. The FV of each working interest and the reserves classifications are as follows:

	FV	Reserves classification
Property #1	$ 800,000	Proved developed producing
Property #2	3,000,000	Proved undeveloped
Property #3	2,900,000	Proved undeveloped
Property #4	2,700,000	Unproved (based on SEC five-year rule)
Property #5	600,000	Unproved
Total	**$10,000,000**	

Analysis. Company B determines that each of the properties is a single asset because, while they are contiguous, they may be used separately.

Company B then assesses whether any of the properties should be considered similar assets. The nature of the assets is similar in that they are each mineral interests. Each property contains (or is expected to contain) crude oil reserves, is located in the same geographic region and geological formation and involves (or will involve) known technology to lift the reserves. However, the reserves classifications and the extent of development activities that have been performed are different.

Company B determines that properties #2, #3 and #4 are similar because, in addition to the factors discussed above, they each contain proved undeveloped reserves and there are no significant differences in operational or business risks. The classification of Property #4 as unproved because of the SEC five-year PUD rule is an entity-specific determination that should not affect the analysis.

Company B determines that there are no other properties that are similar to one another. That is, the risks associated with creating and managing outputs for unproved properties are significantly greater than for proved properties. Furthermore, the development activities necessary to convert the proved undeveloped properties to producing properties will result in significant costs that expose the undeveloped properties to greater pricing, capital investment and development risks than the producing property.

Company B determines the following units of account for purposes of the screen:

	FV	Gross assets	Ratio of FV to gross assets
Property #1	$ 800,000	$10,000,000	8%
Properties #2, #3 and #4	$8,600,000	$10,000,000	86%
Property #5	$ 600,000	$10,000,000	6%

Because substantially all of the fair value of the gross assets acquired is not concentrated in a single asset or group of similar assets, Company B concludes that the screen has not been met. Consequently, it will evaluate the framework to determine if the transaction is an asset acquisition or a business combination.

Outputs are not present

When a set does not have outputs, in order to demonstrate that an input and a substantive process can together significantly contribute to the ability to create outputs, the set will need to include: (1) employees that form an organized workforce and (2) an input that the workforce could develop or convert into outputs.

An organized workforce could be an input, a process or both. An organized workforce must have the necessary skills, knowledge or experience to perform an acquired process that, when applied to another input, is critical to the ability to develop or convert the acquired input into outputs.

Depending on the nature of the process, the acquired workforce necessary to satisfy these requirements may consist of a small number of people. Judgment will be required to determine whether the process performed by the employees is critical to the ability to convert an acquired input into outputs.

The standard cites a mineral interest as an example of an input that can be developed into outputs. Therefore, an acquisition of non-producing properties could be a business combination if employees that form an organized workforce are also acquired. This could be a change in practice because historically acquisitions of unproved properties were typically considered asset acquisitions. Figure 32-4 provides an analysis based on the new guidance.

Figure 32-4

Framework – Acquisition of unproved properties

Facts. Company C acquires working interests in multiple unproved properties, geological and geophysical (G&G) data (surveys, maps, seismic data), an at-market drilling services contract and employees including petroleum engineers, landmen and geologists. The fair value of the unproved properties and the G&G data are significant.

Analysis. Company C assesses the screen and concludes that each working interest and the G&G data are single identifiable assets. Because the fair value of the G&G data is significant and the nature of the G&G data is different than the nature of the working interests, the screen is not met.

Company C then assesses the framework for sets that do not have outputs. It determines that it has acquired inputs being the unproved properties, G&G data, a drilling services contract and employees.

It also determines that it has acquired an organized workforce because the acquired employees will be critical to the ability to convert the unproved properties into producing assets. It is not relevant that some of the unproved properties may be determined to contain no economically producible reserves. This is because the analysis focuses on the ability to develop the inputs rather than the probability of creating outputs.

Because Company C has acquired employees that form an organized workforce and an input that the workforce could develop or convert into outputs, it concludes that the transaction should be accounted for as a business combination.

Outputs are present

A set is determined to have outputs when there is a continuation of revenue before and after the transaction. When a set has outputs before and after the transaction, it is more likely that the set will be considered a business. However, the continuation of revenues does not, on its own, indicate that both an input and a substantive process have been acquired.

When determining whether a process has been acquired, the presence of contractual arrangements that provide for the continuation of revenues, such as customer contracts and leases, would not be indicative of an acquired process and should be excluded from the analysis.

The new guidance includes the following examples of substantive processes, which when applied to an acquired input significantly contribute to the ability to create outputs:

- Employees that form an organized workforce which has the necessary skills, knowledge or experience to perform an acquired process that is critical to continue producing outputs. A process is not critical if, for example, it is considered ancillary or minor in the context of all of the processes required to continue producing outputs.

- An acquired contract that provides access to an organized workforce that has the necessary skills, knowledge or experience to perform an acquired process that is critical to continue producing outputs.

- An acquired process that cannot be replaced without significant cost, effort or delay in the ability to continue producing outputs.

- An acquired process that is considered unique or scarce.

When a company buys mineral interests in producing properties that are not asset acquisitions under the screen, the transaction will likely be considered a business combination. This is because the production process in a producing well is facilitated through existing infrastructure at the well site (the constructed well, pipes, pumping equipment, etc.) which significantly contributes to the ability to continue producing outputs. Replacing those production processes or the infrastructure would likely result in significant costs and delays in production. Consequently, the existing production processes and infrastructure may constitute a substantive process, which when combined with the acquired mineral interests (inputs) results in the transaction being accounted for as a business combination under the framework.

Transactions involving both assets that have outputs (producing properties) and assets that do not have outputs (proved undeveloped properties or unproved properties) are common in the oil and gas industry. The FASB did not provide specific guidance for determining which set of criteria to evaluate when an entity acquires, as part of a single acquisition, assets that have outputs and assets that do not have outputs.

Under historical practice, most companies considered acquisitions of proved properties to be business combinations and acquisitions of unproved properties to be asset acquisitions. Transactions involving both proved and unproved properties required the application of judgment, and some companies established a threshold for distinguishing between asset acquisitions and business combinations based on the relative proportion of the fair value of the proved and unproved properties acquired.

Under ASU 2017-01, companies will need to exercise judgment in determining which set of criteria to evaluate the transaction against (that is, the criteria for sets without outputs or the criteria for sets with outputs). However, this judgment is now generally applied to the relative proportion of producing and non-producing properties, rather than proved and unproved properties. This determination could make the difference between an asset acquisition and a business combination. Figure 32-5 provides an illustration of how to apply this guidance to an acquisition of producing and non-producing properties.

Figure 32-5

Framework – Acquisition of producing and non-producing properties

---

Facts. The background of this example is the same as Figure 32-3, in which Company B concluded that it does not meet the screen because substantially all of the fair value of the gross assets acquired is not concentrated in a single asset or group of similar assets. Consequently, Company B must analyze the framework to determine whether the transaction should be accounted for as an acquisition of an asset or a business.

Analysis. Company B analyzes the framework for sets without outputs since 92% of the fair value is concentrated in non-producing properties (Properties #2, #3, #4 and #5). While Company B acquired inputs (the oil and gas properties), it did not acquire any employees. Since Company B did not acquire employees that form an organized workforce, it concludes the transaction is an asset acquisition.

Conforming accounting policies

Absent justification for different accounting policies, the acquired entity's policies should be conformed to those of the acquiring entity. Although not expected to exist in oil and gas companies, dissimilar operations or dissimilar assets or transactions of the acquired entity may be justification for different accounting policies.

The most common instance of differing accounting policies in acquisitions by oil and gas companies is typically the accounting method for oil and gas activities (successful efforts or full cost). This difference can create additional complexities under the acquisition method, especially in a situation where a successful efforts company acquires a full cost company, depending on location of the acquired assets in relation to the acquirer's existing asset base and the determination of asset groupings for amortization and impairment purposes.

In addition, application of other accounting policies should be conformed, such as in the assumptions used in determining fair value and those used for AROs.

Assets acquired, liabilities assumed and NCI

The acquirer should recognize the identifiable assets acquired and liabilities assumed on the acquisition date if they meet the definition of an asset or liability within FASB Concepts Statement No. 6, *Elements of Financial Statements* (CON 6). For example, costs that an acquirer expects to incur, but is not obligated to incur at the acquisition date (e.g., restructuring costs), are not liabilities assumed under ASC 805-20-25-2.

An acquirer may also recognize assets and liabilities that are not recognized by the acquiree in its financial statements prior to the acquisition date due to differences between the recognition principles in a business combination and other GAAP. This can result in the recognition of intangible assets by the acquirer in a business combination, such as a brand name or customer relationship, which the acquiree would not recognize in its financial statements because these intangible assets were internally generated.

Measurement of identifiable assets acquired and liabilities assumed is at fair value with limited exceptions as provided for in ASC 805. Under GAAP, fair value is based on the definition in ASC 820-10-20: "The price that would be received to sell an asset or paid to transfer a liability in an orderly transaction between market participants at the measurement date."

ASC 805 sets forth a broad principle with regard to the measurement of individual assets acquired and liabilities assumed. The acquirer should apply a disciplined, rigorous and well-documented process when determining the valuation inputs and assumptions used. Valuation inputs and assumptions used should be reasonable and supportable given the economic circumstances related to the asset or liability. In all instances, valuations should be performed by individuals (either internal or external valuation experts) who have the requisite expertise and experience to develop fair value measurements.

Measurement of identifiable assets acquired and liabilities assumed in an acquisition of oil and gas properties requires careful analysis. The following sections highlight some of the more important considerations.

Oil and gas properties

Careful consideration must be given to the underlying geological data; estimates of future prices, costs and discount rates based on rates commensurate with the risks involved in developing and producing the underlying properties; and any other significant assumptions specific to the transaction. Assumptions used in the valuation of oil and gas properties should be compared with recently completed company transactions, other company information such as budgets, or other comparable market transactions.

For additional discussion on valuation techniques commonly used in the oil and gas industry, refer to Chapter 33.

Financial derivative instruments

Oil and gas companies often hedge their oil and gas production associated with specific sales points where the underlying properties are located. As a result, upon the sale of related oil and gas properties, the underlying derivative contracts are usually included as part of the transaction and are recorded by the acquirer in addition to the oil and gas properties.

On the acquisition date, such derivative contracts are considered new contracts by the acquirer and must be recorded at fair value. As with any new derivative contract, the derivative must meet the criteria at the date of acquisition under ASC 815 in order to qualify for hedge accounting.

It is not uncommon for an acquiree to have a variety of financial instruments that meet the definition of a derivative instrument. The type and purpose of these instruments will typically depend on the nature of the acquiree's business activities and risk management practices.

From the acquiree's perspective, these financial instruments may have been:

- Scoped out of ASC 815.

- Used in hedging relationships.

- Used in an economic hedging relationship and marked-to-market previously by the acquiree.

- Used in trading operations.

Generally, the pre-acquisition accounting for the acquiree's financial instruments is not relevant to the post-combination accounting by the acquirer. Accordingly, several issues could arise with respect to an acquiree's financial instruments and hedging relationships and the subsequent accounting by the acquiring entity, as summarized below.

Re-evaluation of the acquiree's contracts. All contracts and arrangements of the acquiree should be re-evaluated at the acquisition date to determine if any contracts are derivatives or contain embedded derivatives that need to be separated and accounted for as financial instruments. This includes reviewing contracts that qualify for the normal purchase and normal sale exception and documenting the basis for making such an election. The determination is made based on the facts and circumstances at the acquisition date.

Designation and re-designation of the acquiree's pre-combination hedging relationships. To obtain hedge accounting for the acquiree's pre-combination hedging relationships, the acquirer should designate hedging relationships anew and prepare new contemporaneous documentation for each derivative instrument. The derivative instrument may not match the newly designated hedged item as closely as it does the acquiree's item.

In August 2017, the FASB issued ASU 2017-12, *Derivatives and Hedging (Topic 815): Targeted Improvements to Accounting for Hedging Activities,* which is intended to simplify the application of hedge accounting guidance in areas where practice had been problematic. See Chapter 34 for further discussion.

Potential inability to apply the short-cut method. Previous hedging relationships may not be eligible for the short-cut method because, upon re-designation of the hedging relationship, the derivative instrument may have a fair value other than zero (positive or negative) on the acquisition date which will prevent the hedge from qualifying for the short-cut method.

Asset retirement obligations

Acquisitions of oil and gas properties often entail the acquirer's assumption of the associated plugging and abandonment obligations. Consideration must be given to determining the fair value of assumed AROs. If a retirement obligation exists, it must be recognized at fair value using market participant assumptions, which may be different than the acquiree's carrying amount of the retirement obligation.

For example, assume oil and gas properties are acquired in a business combination. The acquirer determines that retirement obligations with a fair value of $100 million exist in relation to the acquired oil and gas properties. The appraiser has included the expected cash outflows in the cash flow model, establishing the value of the oil and gas properties at $500 million. That is, the appraised value of the oil and gas properties would be $100 million higher if the retirement obligations were disregarded.

Under ASC 805, the acquirer would record an asset for the oil and gas properties at a fair value of $600 million and a liability for the retirement obligations of $100 million.

Technically, the asset retirement cost (ARC) portion is included as part of the fair value of the oil and gas properties recorded. In an asset acquisition scenario, where the oil and gas properties are recorded at cost, the acquirer should separately record the ARC asset and ARO liability.

For additional discussion of AROs, refer to Chapter 19.

Intangible assets

ASC 805 provides specific criteria for determining whether an acquired intangible asset should be recognized separately from goodwill. Though not an all-inclusive list, the following are examples of intangible assets that may relate to oil and gas acquisitions:

* Customer contracts and relationships.

* Trademarks and trade names.

* Internet domain names.

* Pre-existing non-compete agreements.

* Favorable and unfavorable contract terms (off-market transportation contracts).

* Employment contracts.

* Patented and unpatented technology.

Noncontrolling interests

The noncontrolling interest is the portion of equity (net assets) in a subsidiary not attributable, directly or indirectly, to a parent (see ASC 810-10-45-15). The consolidated financial statements are presented as though the parent company investor and the other minority investors in partially owned subsidiaries have similar economic interests in a single entity. Minority shareholders are viewed as having an equity interest in the consolidated reporting entity.

The investments of these minority shareholders, previously presented between liabilities and equity as "mezzanine" or temporary equity, are now generally reported as equity in the parent company's consolidated financial statements. Transactions between the parent company and the minority shareholders are treated as transactions between shareholders, provided that the transactions do not create a change in control, as the interests of the minority shareholders are considered equity.

This means that no gains or losses are recognized in earnings for transactions between the parent company and the minority shareholders, unless control is achieved or lost as a result of the transaction.

In a partial or step acquisition where control is obtained, the acquiring company recognizes and measures at fair value 100 percent of the assets and liabilities of the acquiree, as if the entire target company had been acquired. Goodwill continues to be recognized as a residual. In addition, the noncontrolling interest is now recorded at fair value. The goodwill recognized includes goodwill for both the controlling and noncontrolling interests.

Note that GAAP allows the proportionate consolidation model used by oil and gas companies in accounting for interests in non-corporate entities (see Chapter 23).

Goodwill and bargain purchases

Goodwill is an asset representing the future economic benefits arising from other assets acquired in a business combination that are not individually identified and separately recognized. The amount of goodwill recognized is also impacted by measurement differences resulting from certain assets and liabilities not being recorded at fair value, such as income taxes or employee benefits.

ASC 805-30-30-1 provides for the measurement of goodwill as follows:

30-1 The acquirer shall recognize goodwill as of the acquisition date, measured as the excess of (a) over (b):

a.　The aggregate of the following:

    1.　The consideration transferred measured in accordance with this Section, which generally requires acquisition-date fair value (see paragraph 805-30-30-7)

    2.　The fair value of any noncontrolling interest in the acquiree

    3.　In a business combination achieved in stages, the acquisition-date fair value of the acquirer's previously held equity interest in the acquiree.

b.　The net of the acquisition-date amounts of the identifiable assets acquired and liabilities assumed measured in accordance with this topic.

A bargain purchase occurs if the acquisition date amounts of the identifiable net assets acquired, excluding goodwill, exceed the aggregate of the amounts specified in ASC 805-30-30-1(a) above.

Goodwill

In evaluating a company's justification for recording goodwill, consideration must be given to the expected economies of scale in connection with the acquirer's existing operations. Such considerations might include operational synergies, access to new customers, access to capital markets and favorable government relations. Whether or not goodwill should be recorded depends on the specific facts and circumstances of the transaction.

Goodwill is recorded only after a thorough identification and rigorous valuation of all acquired proved and unproved properties and any identifiable intangible assets. For example, a company may expect some operational synergies from a business combination. However, if the fair value of properties acquired (or other non-current assets) is sufficient to absorb the purchase price, then the entire purchase price is allocated to those assets and no goodwill is recorded.

It should also be noted that amounts might be properly allocated to goodwill as a result of the mechanics of applying the purchase accounting allocation method without raising any question about the validity of values assigned to identifiable assets. The most common example of this situation is the goodwill that could arise when, in accordance with ASC 740, deferred taxes are not recorded at present value amounts.

When goodwill is recognized, a company should assign it to a reporting unit. A reporting unit is defined as either an operating segment or one level below an operating segment. This can be a complicated assessment, and reporting units may vary significantly depending on the accounting method utilized by companies for their oil and gas properties and other factors.

In general, the reporting unit to which goodwill should be allocated for a full cost company is the associated full cost pool. This treatment is expected because operating results, cash flows, segment management reviews and other reports are not maintained or do not occur at a level lower than the full cost pool.

For a successful efforts company, the reporting unit to which goodwill may be allocated might exist at a much lower level than that of a full cost company since separate distinguishable operating results and cash flows are typically maintained at a lower level.

Once goodwill has been allocated to the appropriate reporting unit, companies should understand how the recoverability of goodwill will be evaluated using the impairment model included in ASC 350. Intangible assets that have finite useful lives are amortized over their estimated useful lives. ASC 350 provides specific guidance for testing impairment of goodwill and intangible assets not being amortized.

In 2014, the FASB issued ASU 2014-02, *Intangibles – Goodwill and Other (Topic 350): Accounting for Goodwill (a consensus of the Private Company Council)* (also referred to as the "goodwill alternative"). The goodwill alternative is only available to private companies to ease their financial reporting burdens by simplifying the goodwill impairment test and allowing the entity to amortize goodwill over a period of 10 years, or less in certain circumstances.

In January 2017, the FASB issued ASU 2017-04, *Intangibles – Goodwill and Other (Topic 350): Simplifying the Test for Goodwill Impairment.* The revised guidance eliminates step two of the goodwill impairment test, which requires a hypothetical purchase price allocation to measure goodwill impairment. A goodwill impairment loss will instead be measured at the amount by which a reporting unit's carrying amount exceeds its fair value, not to exceed the carrying amount of goodwill.

All other goodwill impairment guidance will remain largely unchanged. Entities will continue to have the option to perform a qualitative assessment (i.e., "step 0") to determine if a quantitative impairment test is necessary. The revised guidance is effective for public business entities that are SEC filers for annual and interim goodwill impairments in fiscal years beginning after December 15, 2019. Public business entities that are not SEC filers will be required to apply the guidance in fiscal years beginning after December 15, 2020. All other entities that have not elected the private company alternative in ASU 2014-02 will be required to apply the guidance in fiscal years beginning after December 15, 2021.

ASC 350 also requires disclosure of information about goodwill and other intangible assets in years subsequent to their acquisition. Required disclosures include:

- Information about changes in the gross carrying amount of goodwill from period to period (in the aggregate and by reportable segment).

- Impairment losses recognized during the period.

- The carrying amount of intangible assets by major intangible asset class for those assets subject to amortization and those not subject to amortization.

- Estimated intangible asset amortization expense for the next five years.

- Weighted-average amortization period in total and the amortization period by major business combination when the goodwill alternative is elected by a private company.

Bargain purchases

ASC 805 requires the recognition of a gain for a bargain purchase. A bargain purchase represents an economic gain which should be immediately recognized by the acquirer in earnings. If a bargain purchase is initially identified, the acquirer should re-assess whether all of the assets acquired and liabilities assumed have been identified and recognized, including any additional assets and liabilities not previously identified or recognized in the acquisition accounting.

Once completed, the acquirer should review the procedures used to measure the following items to ensure that the measurements used to determine a bargain purchase gain reflect all available information as of the acquisition date:

- Identifiable assets acquired and liabilities assumed.

- Noncontrolling interests in the acquiree, if any.

- Acquirer's previously held equity interests in the acquiree, if any.

- Consideration transferred.

After this review, if a bargain purchase is still indicated, it should be recognized immediately in earnings and attributed to the acquirer. A bargain purchase gain is no longer recognized as an extraordinary item. ASC 805 requires disclosure of: (1) the amount of the gain, (2) the line item where the gain is recognized and (3) a description of why the transaction resulted in a bargain purchase gain.

Income taxes

Under ASC 805, an acquirer should recognize and measure deferred taxes arising from the assets acquired and liabilities assumed in a business combination in accordance with ASC 740. The following points highlight the steps that would typically be completed in analyzing the income tax implications of a business combination.

Determine the tax considerations in the business combination. The legal structure and the tax status of the entities acquired (corporate entities, partnerships, limited liability corporations), as well as the tax structure of the transaction (taxable or nontaxable), should be considered. Generally, in a taxable transaction the tax bases of the assets acquired and liabilities assumed are adjusted to fair value based on the rules of the specific tax jurisdiction. Conversely, in a nontaxable transaction the historical tax bases of the assets and liabilities, net operating losses and other tax attributes of the target carry over to the acquirer.

Determine financial statement and tax bases of the net assets acquired. The financial statement reported amounts (book bases) of the identifiable assets acquired and liabilities assumed must also be determined. ASC 805 requires the acquired net assets to be recorded at fair value with certain exceptions. The tax bases of the identifiable assets acquired and liabilities assumed are determined based on each specific tax jurisdiction and related tax laws and regulations.

Identify and measure temporary differences. Temporary differences related to the book bases and tax bases of the acquired identifiable assets and assumed liabilities should be assessed. It should also be determined whether the temporary differences are deductible temporary differences or taxable temporary differences, with the appropriate deferred tax assets (DTAs) or deferred tax liabilities (DTLs) recorded in accordance with ASC 805-740-25-2.

Identify acquired tax benefits. The acquiring company should determine if there are any acquired net operating losses (NOLs), credit carryforwards or other relevant tax attributes that should be recorded as part of the business combination per ASC 805-740-25-2. Additionally, determine whether a valuation allowance is required to reduce DTAs if they are not considered to be realizable.

Consider the treatment of tax uncertainties. The accounting requirements for uncertain tax positions in ASC 805-740-25-2, is also a relevant fact to consider when assessing the income tax implications of a business combination.

Consider deferred taxes related to goodwill. Lastly, determine whether a DTA should be recognized for temporary differences associated with tax-deductible goodwill based on guidance in ASC 805-740-25-3.

• • •

Valuation of Energy Assets and Entities

Key concepts

- Common uses for valuation methods

- Income approach

- Market approach

- Cost approach

- Concepts specific to oil and gas properties

- Valuation variables by sector

- Midstream considerations

- Other valuation considerations

The valuation of oil and gas properties, one of the most significant factors in determining the valuation of an E&P company, refers to the ultimate value of petroleum resources that may be extracted in the future. Due to various geological and economic risks, oil and gas properties present unique complexities when applying traditional valuation techniques.

This chapter begins by describing several common valuation methods used in determining the fair value (FV) of an E&P company's oil and gas properties, predominantly determined based on a company's reserves. The application of these concepts specifically to the valuation of oil and gas properties is also discussed, as well as how the concepts are applied to other energy industry assets and entities.

The need for these estimates continues to increase due to several factors, including: changes in accounting standards for business combinations and fair value, significant commodity price volatility, and increased focus on streamlining operations and achieving economies of scale through acquisition and divestiture activities.

Common uses for valuation methods

ASC 820 defines an asset's fair value as, "the price that would be received to sell an asset or paid to transfer a liability in an orderly transaction between market participants at the measurement date."

This definition is based on a market participant's exit price, as opposed to an entry price. Exit prices differ from entry prices: entry prices may reflect a buyer's unique synergies, or other unique benefits, which may be included in the entry price and may not be available to all market participants.

An "arm's-length transaction" refers to a purchase or sale in which the buyer and seller are unrelated and the sales price is presumed to be fair value, unless available information indicates otherwise. There is a rebuttable presumption that the buyer and seller are both willing and competent parties to the transaction, are under no compulsion to enter into the transaction and have reasonable knowledge of the facts about the property's value and utility.

Quoted market prices for identical assets or liabilities in active markets are Level 1 inputs and are the best evidence of fair value. If they are available, they should be used as the basis for measurement. When they are not available, the estimate of fair value is based on quoted prices for similar assets (groups) in active markets, referred to as Level 2 inputs. Although ASC 820 states that assumptions should be those of "marketplace participants," if information is not available without undue cost and effort, a company may use its own assumptions (unobservable inputs), which represent Level 3 inputs.

Valuation techniques include three methods:

- Income approach.

- Market approach.

- Cost approach.

For proved oil and gas properties, the income approach is by far the most commonly used method. It is most appropriate when detailed reserves reports are available to project future cash flows based on the lives of the reserves.

E&P companies typically use the market approach as a corroborating method rather than the primary method for valuing proved oil and gas properties. However, it is frequently used to establish the fair value of acquired unevaluated acreage in business combinations given the relative simplicity of obtaining cost per acre information for the acquired properties as compared to calculating the fair value of probable and possible reserves using the income approach.

The cost approach is rarely used to value oil and gas properties but may be used to value other assets of an oil and gas company.

Valuation of oil and gas properties is common in the following circumstances:

- Allocating purchase price to individual assets in connection with a business combination or asset transaction accounted for under ASC 805, or in nonmonetary exchanges accounted for under ASC 845.

- Applying ASC 360 to determine potential asset impairment under the successful efforts method.

- Testing for goodwill impairment under ASC 350 requirements.

- Complying with ASC 820 for annual financial reporting requirements of private capital.

- Determining business enterprise value, if needed when issuing equity accounted for according to ASC 718.

- Evaluating whether to acquire or divest oil and gas properties.

- Allocating book values in proportion to relative fair values for certain property sales, as described in Chapter 20.

- Complying with tax rules.[1]

Depending on the purpose of the valuation, the underlying reasoning and valuation methodology may differ.

For example, determining fair value in a purchase price allocation considers what a market participant would expect to receive from the sale of the business or asset. Assumptions for capital structure, tax rates and synergies (such as cost savings) are based on circumstances for a typical market participant. Alternatively, when supporting a merger or sale, a valuation can assume a unique buyer with a specific capital structure, tax rate and synergies.

Performing a valuation for tax purposes requires the determination of fair market value (FMV), which is defined in Internal Revenue Service Ruling 59-60 as "the price at which the property would change hands between a willing buyer and a willing seller when the former is not under any compulsion to buy and the latter is not under any compulsion to sell, both parties having reasonable knowledge of relevant facts."

Conversely, valuations of oil and gas properties pursuant to the supplemental oil and gas disclosure requirements of ASC 932 represent standards for reporting and comparison purposes only and are not intended to reflect the fair value of oil and gas properties.

Income approach

The most common income approach is the discounted cash flow method (DCF) in which expected future net cash flows are discounted to present value, using an appropriate discount rate, to value a business or asset. The projected cash flows and discount rate are important factors, and each requires careful consideration of numerous facts, assumptions and judgment. The discount rate chosen should be consistent with the cash flows under consideration (i.e., pre-tax or post-tax, levered or unlevered, real or nominal) for appropriate results.

Forecasts

In an oil and gas property valuation, forecasts often are based on engineering and accounting data that is readily available for the business or asset being acquired. Production volumes are the foundation for the forecast. They are available from a company's internal reserves estimates, internal economic runs for particular fields and areas, or reserves reports prepared by independent petroleum engineers. Using production volume data, entities can develop an oil and gas cash flow forecast, using the following assumptions:

- Expected oil and gas prices.

- Capital expenditures necessary to produce the oil and gas reserves.

- Production and operating expenses.

- Production taxes.

- General and administrative expenses.

- Income taxes.

Although they typically are not included in the reserves report, corporate general and administrative expenses also should be considered.

Since an oil and gas property's life is finite, a cash flow forecast should run only for the life of the asset being valued. Traditional DCF techniques, outside of oil and gas property valuations, usually call for a finite forecast period, with a terminal value assumption in the final forecast year that captures all cash flows expected to extend beyond the forecast period.

A common valuation method to determine terminal value is the Gordon Growth Model, which assumes that cash flows in the last year of the forecast will continue, in perpetuity, at a specified growth rate. For oil and gas properties, it is not realistic to assume perpetuity, so the Gordon Growth Model is not appropriate. In addition, the last cash flow for an oil and gas property often includes a large cash outflow for the cost to plug and abandon the well, or other related AROs. The valuation also should include assumptions about material and equipment salvage values.

As a reference, in the Matter of Miller Energy Resources Inc. et al,[2] the SEC argued for the use of fair value assumptions in the valuation of oil and gas properties. The conclusion of a FV, as defined in ASC 820, or FMV, as defined in Internal Revenue Service Ruling 59-60, for oil and gas properties should not be confused with the standardized measure, PV-10 analyses, or reserves report outputs, as each of these are simply metrics to allow quick comparisons for investors.

Although these metrics are often used by investors and financial statement users, they often ignore significant inputs used to arrive at FV or FMV, including:

- New York Mercantile Exchange (NYMEX) pricing.

- Market-based discount rates.

- Federal income taxes.

- Reserve adjustment factors.

- Plugging and abandonment expenses.

- Corporate-level general and administrative expenses.

Discount rate

A dollar received or paid in the future is worth less than a dollar received or paid today due to the time value of money. To determine today's value of a dollar that will not be received until some point in the future, it should be discounted to the current period by selecting a discount rate that accounts for the inherent risks.

The discount rate, typically based on the weighted average cost of capital (WACC), is the rate of return that a business, project or asset must earn to induce a capital provider to invest debt or equity. Risk also is an important element in investment decision-making: a debt investor expects an interest rate that recognizes the risks of the business, project or asset, while an equity investor considers the expected dividend payments, as well as expected gains in share price.

Most cash flows are calculated using a leveraged basis, indicating that sources of capital typically include both debt and equity funding. Accordingly, they should use a WACC based on a blended cost of debt and cost of equity. If cash flows are prepared on an unleveraged basis, the cost of equity should be used. Consistency between the cash flows used and the WACC is critical. The WACC is, therefore, the weighted average of debt and equity returns, based on the debt-to-equity ratio for the business, project or asset. It also accounts for the interest tax shield that is available to users of debt in tax-paying entity structures.

If one assumes that a market participant is a tax-advantaged entity (paying no taxes at the corporate level and including owners of flow-through entities), a pre-tax WACC should be used. However, if the market participants are tax-paying entities, taxes should be considered in the cash flows and an after-tax WACC should be used. In addition, if the market participant is a tax-paying entity, a depletion benefit should be incorporated in the cash flows or overall value of the oil and gas properties.

Although cash flows and the discount rate can be calculated either pre-tax or post-tax, generally an after-tax DCF analysis is most appropriate as compared to a pre-tax analysis for purposes of determining fair value.[3] Accordingly, the remaining examples in this chapter assume that all amounts are post-tax.

The formula used to calculate a WACC is shown in Figure 33-1. Deriving the return on debt and equity can be complex and is beyond the scope of this textbook, although it is an important element of calculating a WACC.

Figure 33-1
Calculating a WACC on a post-tax basis

$$\text{WACC} \;=\; R_d\,(1 - T_c)\left[\frac{D}{D + E}\right] + R_e\left[\frac{E}{D + E}\right]$$

Where:

R_d = Pre-tax cost of debt

T_c = Corporate tax rate

R_e = Cost of equity

D = Market value of debt

E = Market value of equity

When planning for a transaction or other management analysis, a company may use its internal WACC or hurdle rate as the discount rate, subject to the size and risk of the interest or assets being valued. However, in valuations performed to comply with financial reporting or tax requirements, the company should assume the WACC of a typical market participant (i.e., the WACC assumes the risks are the same as a typical market participant and not a specific entity).

Figure 33-2 displays a range of recent industry WACCs for groups of similarly sized companies as of December 31, 2019. Note that discount rates may be determined outside the range displayed; thus, this information is for illustrative purposes only.

Figure 33-2
Illustrative WACCs by market capitalization

	Small Cap	Mid-Cap	Majors
Risk-free rate	2.3%	2.3%	2.3%
Equity risk premium	6.0%	6.0%	6.0%
Selected re-levered beta	1.6	1.9	1.4
Small stock premium	3.0%	1.0%	0.5%
Cost of equity	**14.8%**	**14.5%**	**11.0%**
Pre-tax cost of debt	10.3%	6.7%	6.7%
Tax rate	21.0%	21.0%	21.0%
Post-tax cost of debt	**8.1%**	**5.3%**	**5.3%**
Equity weight	75.0%	70.0%	85.0%
Debt weight	25.0%	30.0%	15.0%
WACC	**13.0%**	**11.5%**	**10.0%**

As shown in Figure 33-2, investors in small companies typically require larger returns than they expect from larger companies; therefore, some practitioners suggest that it is appropriate to upwardly revise the discount rate when estimating the value of a small company. This is particularly true in the oil and gas industry, when sudden downturns in commodity prices can disproportionately affect a small company, especially if it is leveraged heavily towards one or two properties. Small stock premiums typically are estimated by practitioners in various research studies in the range of zero percent to six percent. The small stock premium applied should consider the size of the subject company, consistent with the market-participant view described earlier.

Once a WACC is established, cash flows can be discounted back to their present values by converting the discount rate into a discount factor, which is the number to be multiplied by each year's cash flow to determine its present value. Assuming that the WACC calculation yields a 12 percent discount rate, the formula in Figure 33-3 calculates a discount factor for year one, where i equals the discount rate of 12 percent and t equals the time period of one year. A discount factor is calculated for each year in which a forecast of cash flows has been prepared.

Figure 33-3

Calculating the discount factor

$$\text{Discount factor} \quad = \quad \frac{1}{(1 + i)^t} \quad = \quad \frac{1}{(1 + 12\%)^1} \quad = \quad 0.89$$

The example in Figure 33-3 assumes that all cash flows occur at year-end. In reality, cash flows usually are spread throughout the entire year (sometimes evenly and sometimes not). To address this, a common valuation technique assumes a mid-year convention: cash flows are earned ratably during the year, which is the same as assuming that all cash flows are received at the year's midpoint. The discount factor formula is adjusted to reflect a mid-year convention, as shown in Figure 33-4.

Figure 33-4

Calculating the discount factor – Mid-year convention

$$\text{Discount factor} \quad = \quad \frac{1}{(1 + i)^{(t - 0.5)}} \quad = \quad \frac{1}{(1 + 12\%)^{(1 - 0.5)}} \quad = \quad \frac{1}{(1.12)^{(0.5)}} \quad = 0.94$$

In the first example, a $1 cash flow is assumed to be received at year-end and is worth 89 cents today. In the second example, the same $1 is assumed to be earned equally during the year. Since the cash is received sooner, the same dollar is worth more today: 94 cents.

Figure 33-5 shows a simple example of a DCF valuation. It assumes a five-year production profile, 4,100 barrels of oil reserves, an oil price based on an illustrative NYMEX WTI forward price curve (less assumed transportation and quality differentials), $15,000 in total abandonment costs over a two-year period and a 21 percent income tax rate. In an actual valuation, more detailed assumptions would be made regarding items such as inflation and capital spending.

Figure 33-5
Figure 33-5
Discounted cash flow valuation

	Year				
	1	2	3	4	5
Production volumes (bbls)	1,000	1,200	900	600	400
Forward price per barrel	$50	$51	$52	$53	$54
Revenues	**$50,000**	**$61,200**	**$46,800**	**$31,800**	**$21,600**
Production costs	(15,000)	(17,000)	(14,000)	(11,000)	(8,000)
Development costs	(20,000)	(15,000)	(10,000)	(5,000)	–
Abandonment costs	–	–	–	(5,000)	(10,000)
Pre-tax cash flow	**$15,000**	**$29,200**	**$22,800**	**$10,800**	**$ 3,600**
Income taxes at 21%	(3,150)	(6,132)	(4,788)	(2,68)	(756)
Net cash flow	**$11,850**	**$23,068**	**$18,012**	**$ 8,532**	**$ 2,844**
Discount factor at 12%*	0.9449	0.8437	0.7533	0.6726	0.6005
PV of cash flows	**$11,197**	**$19,462**	**$13,568**	**$ 5,739**	**$ 1,708**
Sum of PV					**$51,674**
Value per barrel					**$12.60**

* Based on using a half-year convention.

Tax depletion benefit

As defined previously, fair value is the value that a market participant with a reasonable knowledge of the relevant facts would pay for the asset or business. When using an income approach, such as DCF for a tax-paying entity, fair value often has two components:

- The present value of future cash flows generated by an asset or business.

- The present value (using the same after-tax discount rate) of the income tax benefits of deducting the purchase price through higher future depreciation, depletion and amortization (DD&A) charges.

The second factor is often called the "depletion bonus," "tax shield," or "tax depletion benefit" (TDB).

Although DD&A expenses are noncash items, they ultimately affect cash through lower future income taxes. This additional cash flow can be incorporated as a component of an income approach when using after-tax cash flows and an after-tax discount rate. Since the majority of large E&P companies use after-tax cash flows, this can be a source of value to a potential buyer/owner of oil and gas properties.

The TDB depends on the purchase price, which depends on the amount of the TDB, thus requiring an iterative calculation. Although most spreadsheet applications easily calculate a value that includes a TDB component, the formula in Figure 33-6 can also be used:[4]

Figure 33-6

Calculating a tax depletion benefit

$$\text{Value} \quad = \quad \frac{PV1}{[1 - ((E\% * EW) + (L\% - LW))]}$$

Where:

PV1 = Present value of a property's future cash flows, excluding the tax effects of depletion.

EW = Estimated fixed asset value as percent of total value.

E% = Percent that equates to the discounted present value of tax benefits from depreciating $1 of equipment costs. E% is a function of the allowable tax depreciation rates for the equipment asset class, the marginal income tax rate and the after-tax discount rate, as shown in Figure 33-7.

LW = Estimated leasehold value as a percent of total value.

L% = Percent that equates to the discounted present value of tax benefits from the depletion of $1 of leasehold costs. L% is a function of the percent of reserves to be produced each year (UOP method), the marginal income tax rate and the after-tax discount rate, as shown in Figure 33-8.

Figure 33-7

Computing E% for the tax depreciation benefit

Year	Well equipment depreciation rates	Tax rate	Discount factor for 12%*	E%
	[A]	[B]	[C]	[D] = [A] * [B] * [C]
1	14.29%	21.0%	0.9449	2.84%
2	24.49%	21.0%	0.8437	4.34%
3	17.49%	21.0%	0.7533	2.77%
4	12.49%	21.0%	0.6726	1.76%
5	8.93%	21.0%	0.6005	1.13%
6	8.92%	21.0%	0.5362	1.00%
7	8.93%	21.0%	0.4787	0.90%
8	4.46%	21.0%	0.4274	0.40%
	100.00%			**15.14%**

* Based on using a half-year convention.

Figure 33-8

Computing L% for the tax depletion benefit

Year	Future production of net reserves	% of Reserves produced	Tax rate	Discount factor for 12%	L%
	(bbls)	[A]	[B]	[C]	= [A] * [B] * [C]
1	1,000	24.4%	21.0%	0.9449	4.84%
2	1,200	29.3%	21.0%	0.8437	5.19%
3	900	21.9%	21.0%	0.7533	3.46%
4	600	14.6%	21.0%	0.6726	2.06%
5	400	9.8%	21.0%	0.6005	1.24%
	4,100	100.0%			16.79%

* Based on using a half-year convention.

Using the information in Figures 33-5, 33-7 and 33-8, and assuming that the equipment is allocated at 20 percent of the purchase price, the value of the asset or business would be calculated based on the formula in Figure 33-6 as follows:

$$\frac{\$51,674}{[1 - ((80\% * 16.79\%) + (20\% * 15.14\%))]} = \$61,855$$

The resulting TDB value is $10,181 ($61,855 less $51,674), which increases the implied value per barrel from $12.60 (Figure 33-5) to $15.09 ($61,855 ÷ 4,100 barrels).

Petroleum accountants vigorously debate the use of TDBs, particularly in purchase price allocations, which tie the value to a theoretical market participant. If the most likely market participant for an asset would benefit from the TDB, then the value is calculated including the TDB, even if the actual buyer may be a non-taxpaying entity. This is consistent with guidance in ASC 820 which requires determining the fair value of the assets acquired using the assumptions of market participants.

If it can be proved that a likely market participant for the asset would be a non-taxpaying entity, the TDB may not apply; however, additional documentation supporting this conclusion is highly recommended.

To continue the previous example, an analysis of comparable market transactions might show that buyers are not paying $15.09 per barrel for comparable reserves in the same locations. If the market appears to value such reserves at $12.60 per barrel for example, it should be considered which value is most appropriate: $15.09 per barrel from the DCF, $12.60 per barrel from the market, or a weighting of both value indicators.

Market approach

In many industries, fair value can be estimated as a multiple of historical or forward (projected) net income, cash flow, EBITDA (earnings before interest, taxes, depreciation and amortization) or similar measurements for a specified time. For oil and gas property valuations, however, these financial-based multiples are not as common because the timing of future production has a much larger effect on value than current or historical financial results. In addition, a multiple in one location may not indicate value for another property, where the life, decline curve and price differentials can contribute to very different future cash flows. However, when the market approach is appropriate, the following multiples are generally used:

- Daily production.

- 1P reserves (total volume of proved reserves).

- 3P reserves (total volume of all reserves).

- Undeveloped or unevaluated acreage.

Market-based approaches often are used as corroborating measures in oil and gas property valuations. In the previous example, the DCF analysis yielded a value of $15.09 per barrel; however, a question arises with regard to whether this value is realistic given the current market. Through the market approach, an understanding can be gained of the value per barrel for comparable property transactions.

The market approach requires the selection of comparable transactions. To be regarded as comparable, several factors should be analyzed, including but not limited to:

- Geographic location (country or region).

- Oil and gas weighting of reserves.

- Production profiles of reserves.

- Geologic profiles of reserves (oil sands, onshore, offshore, enhanced recovery areas).

- Reserves type (conventional or unconventional).

Recent transaction data is plentiful for some domestic geographies. However, data is less abundant for other domestic areas and international transactions. Also, data for international transactions can be skewed by government involvement on the side of either the buyer or the seller.

If the accountant cannot find sufficiently comparable transactions, certain adjustments can be made to convert the resulting transaction values to a more comparable basis. This is commonplace when oil and gas weighting or reserves production ratios differ; however, it is difficult to adjust for geographic location.

If the value derived from using the market approach is significantly higher or lower than that from an income-based approach (such as DCF), an available option is to weight both the income and market approaches to determine a final value. Other situations may benefit from using the market approach to place a collar, which represents a high and low value per barrel on the results from the income approach.

Cost approach

Generally, replacement cost and historical cost are not useful for determining the value of proved oil and gas properties. The cost approach generally refers to the replacement cost method. Replacement cost rests on the theory that a knowledgeable buyer would pay no more than the cost of constructing a similar asset of like utility on the valuation date. Asset value is determined by the cost of reproducing or replacing the property as if it were new, less depreciation from physical deterioration, functional obsolescence and economic obsolescence, to the extent they are present and measurable.

Using this method, some appraisers may consider the current owner's historical cost of acquiring the property. If the property was acquired in an arm's-length transaction by the owner shortly before the valuation date, with no interim exploration or development, then the owner's historical acquisition cost may be a strong indicator of the property's value on the valuation date. However, the historical cost of acquiring and exploring a lease generally does not indicate the reserves found or the value of such reserves, especially after further evaluation or development.

Concepts specific to oil and gas properties

Appraisers or others who are valuing assets often consider all three approaches mentioned in this chapter. They may quickly dismiss one or two of them as not applicable or of limited use for a particular valuation. The applicability depends on the nature of the property being valued and the nature and extent of available information. Unlike many businesses for which independent appraisals can be obtained, oil and gas proved reserves are unique assets.

DCF analyses can differ in multiple ways: (1) use of real (constant) or nominal (inflated) dollars, (2) use of pre-tax or post-tax cash flows and (3) risk-adjusting either the cash flows or the discount rate. The industry's widespread use of DCF analysis is demonstrated by the fact that approximately 80 percent of companies prefer to use a DCF analysis when determining the value of property, according to respondents of the 2018 Society of Petroleum Evaluation Engineers survey. Regardless of the form of DCF chosen, consistency is key. If pre-tax cash flows are used, a pre-tax discount rate should be used as well. If the cash flows themselves are risked, the discount rate should exclude significant premiums related to forecast risk.

Most oil and gas valuations are based on a combination of the income approach and market approach. This is common when valuations are prepared for purposes of mergers, acquisitions or regulatory requirements. Although valuations of smaller, less complex or geographically isolated assets may rely on market-based metrics, the larger, more complex or geographically diverse valuations generally lean towards the income approach. Following herein are some specific concepts to consider when using these approaches.

Income approach considerations

In the oil and gas industry, the income approach (DCF) remains the predominant method for determining value, whether for mergers and acquisitions, regulatory requirements or other valuation needs. Appraisers and practitioners should take additional time to develop and document the various assumptions they use in developing cash flows for the DCF. Some considerations include:

Reserves volumes. The source of many DCF models are reserves reports or other internal production or economic models. Reserves reports include volumes, revenues, capital spending, operating costs, production taxes and future AROs. Added to this information are corporate-level general and administrative costs, income taxes and other nonfield-level items, in order to calculate a full cash flow forecast.

When establishing the fair value of acquired oil and gas reserves, the fair value of each category should be established separately since the probability of recovering the estimated hydrocarbons is different for each category (see Chapter 15 for reserve definitions).

According to Reg. S-X Rule 4-10, "proved reserves" can be estimated with reasonable certainty, which is widely regarded as 90 percent probability; "probable" and "possible" reserves have a 50 percent and 10 percent probability, respectively, that the volume recovered will meet or exceed the estimate. In most cases, volumes included in reserve reports are not risked; therefore, accountants must adjust the volumes to reflect the uncertainty of recovery associated with each reserve category. Consistent with these SEC definitions, typical risking is depicted in Figure 33-9.

Figure 33-9

Risking of reserves by volume and cost type

Reserve category	Volume risking		Capex risking*		Opex risking*	
	Conventional	Unconventional	Conventional	Unconventional	Conventional	Unconventional
PDP	100%	100%	100%	100%	100%	100%
PDNP	95% – 100%	95% – 100%	95% – 100%	95% – 100%	95% – 100%	95% – 100%
PUD	80% – 100%	80% – 100%	80% – 100%	80% – 100%	80% – 100%	80% – 100%
Total Proved	**>90%**	**>90%**				
Probable**	40% – 60%	40% – 75%	40% – 70%	40% – 75%	40% – 70%	40% – 75%
Total 2P	**>50%**	**>50%**				
Possible	10% – 25%	10% – 25%	10% – 35%	10% – 25%	10% – 35%	10% – 25%
Total 3P	**>10%**	**>10%**				

* Unconventional resources, especially shale, do not typically pose the same level of dry hole risk as conventional resources. As such, operating and capital expenditure risking will often match volume risking.

** In the event the reserves include technically proven, probable reserves, risking levels between probable and PUD levels may be appropriate.

In addition to risking reserve volumes, risking capital expenditures and operating expenses should be considered. Historically, for conventional wells, there was a significant spread between risking for volumes versus expenses in order to account for the possibility of dry holes. However, with today's unconventional wells, where drilling and production improvements have significantly reduced the risk of dry holes, the spread tends to be minimal or even zero.

Conventional and unconventional reservoirs. Shale and tight reservoir formations have become major sources of oil and natural gas. The existence of shale reserves has been known for many years; however, the technology to economically extract the oil and gas was not available until the advent of horizontal drilling and hydraulic fracturing.

Oil and gas exploration and production faces sizeable geologic risks and commercial uncertainties in terms of well performance, scalability and estimated ultimate recovery (EUR). Currently, practices vary in reflecting these risks and uncertainties in fair value analyses of shale plays.

Typical adjustments may include:

- Adjusting the amount of acreage that ultimately will be productive and applying an expected case for key assumptions, such as well spacing, decline rates and EURs.

- Applying statistical analysis, incorporating the results of actual well performance, including initial production rates and EURs, to develop various probabilistic scenarios.

Pricing. The base price deck selected is the basis for volume and revenue projections in the reserves report. Per ASC 820, a Level 1 input is quoted prices (unadjusted) in active markets for identical assets or liabilities that the reporting entity can access at the measurement date. Quoted prices on the NYMEX for oil or Henry Hub for natural gas are considered Level 1 inputs used for valuing reserves.

NYMEX "strip prices" typically are the most widely used by companies and appraisers. Other quoted price decks lack the support of NYMEX prices, since they are not based on actual market transactions.

Figure 33-10 shows a recent five-year price strip as of December 31, 2019. After determining the price deck, an updated reserves report should be prepared to account for any changes in projected cash flows due to the new pricing.

Figure 33-10
Forward price strip

	2020	2021	2022	2023	2024
WTI Oil	$58.83	$54.38	$52.09	$51.31	$51.44
Henry Hub Natural Gas	$2.29	$2.42	$2.42	$2.46	$2.49

Differentials. After a price deck has been determined, assumptions are made for the price differentials to determine the realized price for oil and gas production. The differential should include reductions (or additions) for transportation costs and product quality. For example, crude oil can be light, light sweet, moderate, heavy and extra heavy (high bitumen). The lighter the oil, the easier the flow; the heavier the oil, the slower the flow, which has a direct correlation with transportation costs.

If the value of an oil property is based on a WTI price deck, and the property produces light WTI oil, the differential should be predictable and generally consistent from year to year. If the oil produced is something other than light WTI, quality basis differentials will apply. Note that the quality differential does not always have a linear relationship with WTI (or whichever crude index is selected as the price deck). Oftentimes, the differential is linear within a range of WTI prices, but in higher commodity price environments, the differential can change disproportionately. In this case, using the differentials implied in a reserves report based on flat pricing may yield an inaccurate answer.

Capital expenditures. Capital expenditures for tax-paying entities should be allocated between tangible and intangible costs. Tangible costs are capitalized and depreciated, while intangible costs typically are expensed immediately, giving the company a larger tax benefit up front. In that case, the percentages allocated to tangibles and intangibles affect the overall valuation. The primary source for allocating these costs should be projections provided by the subject company. If these projections are not available, a view of the subject company's historical split may provide a reasonable estimate. If neither option is available, it is appropriate to use industry guidelines. It should be noted that the information presented in this paragraph is to determine tax-based cash flows used to value the assets, not to determine financial reporting or book-based depreciation.

P&A costs. P&A costs sometimes are overlooked when preparing an oil and gas valuation. Some reserves reports include estimates for P&A costs but others may not, depending on the request of the company commissioning the reserves report. Oil and gas reserves fair-value estimates should reflect, as deductions from the underlying cash flows, the costs of environmental remediation and other costs associated with decommissioning the associated fields and reserves. The fair value of an ARO is estimated according to the requirements of ASC 410 by applying a credit-adjusted risk-free rate to the expected future cash flows.

Corporate G&A expenses. Although reserves reports should include all field or well-level expenses, including any operating overhead expenses for fields, they typically do not include corporate G&A expenses (accounting and finance, human resources, executive management, IT, etc.) that are required to run the business. In purchase price allocations, acquisitions of small assets may not require additional burden from existing corporate G&A resources. However, the valuation of large acquisitions or stand-alone businesses likely would require the inclusion of corporate G&A expenses.

Market approach considerations

In the oil and gas industry, the market approach often is seen as a corroborative tool, rather than the primary value indicator. As previously explained, this is driven by the fact that production profiles are unique to specific properties, making it difficult to accurately employ the market approach for proved properties, especially producing wells. Appraisers and practitioners should take the time to research transactions, confirming that the relevant variables are sufficient. Some factors to consider are discussed in the subsequent sections.

Timing. When commodity prices change, it is no surprise that they influence market prices. Although market prices do not necessarily react to short-term price changes, long periods of higher or lower commodity prices will impact the market. In particular, the dramatic decline of oil and gas prices beginning in late-2014 led to a precipitous decline in valuation multiples for upstream assets as sentiment around future prices declined. A market-based approach requires attention to the timing of the selected sample of comparable transactions.

Location. Oil and gas are commodity products, with values often dictated by the market. However, product quality and location affect valuation. When selecting comparable transactions, consider the location of the assets covered. For example, the value of oil reserves in New Mexico differs from those in Alaska, due to both quality and transportation distinctions, among other variables. In addition, if the subject company operates in multiple locations, single basin comparables may not be the most appropriate.

Product mix. Selecting comparable market transactions based solely on location overlooks an important value driver: the mix of oil and gas in the reserves. Although the thermal energy content of one barrel of oil is approximately six times one Mcf of natural gas, the market prices may vary from a 6-to-1 ratio for many reasons.

The implied value of any transaction is based on expectations for current and future oil and natural gas prices, so to the extent that comparable transactions are weighted more heavily toward oil or gas, they should be selected or removed to make them more comparable to the asset being valued.

Acreage. In a transaction, a company may acquire undeveloped or unevaluated acreage whose development may not be reflected in reserves reports. In this case, a market approach typically establishes the fair value of the acquired acreage.

Using the market approach, recent transactions of nearby acreage are analyzed to establish a benchmark "dollar per acre." The benchmark is then adjusted, by the company or appraiser, to reflect differences in the remaining time to expiration or the result of any recent drilling, either by the company or by other operators on adjacent acreage.

This approach can be limited if recent transaction data is scarce or if the publicly available sources (e.g., state lease sales and data services) are not in a proximate location or close to the valuation date. Typically, a company's internal engineering staff or landmen will be heavily involved in this process, offering insight about drilling results on adjacent properties or knowledge of recent transactions that are not widely available.

Interest type. In a transaction, a company may acquire operating or nonoperating working interests or royalty interests. Each interest exhibits different attributes that likely would lead to different values. Consideration should be given to matching transactions of similar interest types to the subject interest.

Domestic and international properties. Market-based approaches offer insight into the beliefs of independent buyers regarding the true market values of particular assets. In North America, abundant transactions have been completed at many locations; these represent true market values. Elsewhere in the world, transactions may be less frequent. Prices paid also can reflect quasi-governmental intervention by either the buyer or the seller. Thus, it can be difficult to establish a true market price.

Other considerations

The true value of an asset or business can be more or less than the result derived from applying the previously described valuation methods. Further adjustments may include:

Liquidity or marketability. A highly liquid asset or equity investment, such as an oil or gas asset in an active market or an equity investment in a publicly traded company, is worth more than one that is not as liquid. Lack of liquidity arguably produces a delay or higher cost in finding a buyer and the asset or interest may have to be discounted to entice a purchaser. This discount is known as a "liquidity discount" or "marketability discount."

Other assets. In a purchase price allocation, consideration should be given to valuing assets acquired with the reserves, such as undeveloped land and seismic data. Even certain midstream assets may be acquired that are used only for the field or wells in the reserves report.

Fair value measurement under ASC 820 assumes the highest and best use of an asset by market participants. This establishes the valuation premise for each asset acquired, even if the intended use of the asset differs from that of the reporting entity.

SPEE survey of parameters

The Society of Petroleum Evaluation Engineers (SPEE) conducts an annual survey of economic parameters used in property evaluations, reporting to participants, SPEE members and other interested parties. The survey serves as a limited indicator of price and cost escalations, discount rates and risk adjustments employed by E&P companies and their consultants as they determine the fair value or bid price for proved oil and gas properties in general.

Key findings from the 2018 SPEE report[5] were as follows:

- Respondents were 44 percent E&P companies, 40 percent consultants, 10 percent bankers and less than two percent private equity.

- 28 percent of respondents use NYMEX strip as the basis for their future price projections.

- Most respondents believe that cost escalations will not be significant.

- The DCF method was the most useful to determine the value of properties.

- 32 percent determine the discount rate based on company cost of capital and five percent use the company cost of equity, while over 60 percent use some other standard.

Valuation variables by sector

Beyond upstream entities, four additional distinct sectors comprise the energy industry: midstream, downstream, oilfield services and equipment (OFS) and drilling companies. These additional sectors also can be valued using the three approaches previously described. Although commodity prices are the main influence on the operating results of all energy assets and entities, each sector's performance is influenced by unique variables, as illustrated in Figure 33-11.

Downstream entities such as refineries process crude oil delivered by midstream entities into gasoline, fuel oils and other petroleum-based products. Their operating results depend on commodity prices but the relationship often can be inverse. Given that their feedstock is crude oil, and many of their facilities are powered by natural gas, lower commodity prices often can mean improved operating results.

Oilfield service and equipment providers and drilling companies assist upstream producers in many areas, including exploring for reserves, preparing drilling sites, drilling and ultimately producing the reserves.

Although these entities are directly involved in the exploration and production process, valuing them requires few energy-specific variables. Income approaches for these entities should include the effect of working capital requirements, as well as annual capital expenditures. Projections for these entities should consider not only the diversity of the entity's product and service offerings but also its geographic diversity. Less diversified entities may experience large fluctuations in their operating results when specific basins or drilling technologies gain or lose industry favor. These variables should also be considered when identifying comparable companies for the WACC and market approach.

Figure 33-11
Key valuation variables by sector

Upstream	Midstream	Downstream	OFSE	Drilling
Commodity price	Commodity price exposure	Commodity price exposure	Commodity price	Commodity price
Discount rate	Discount rate	Discount rate	Discount rate	Discount rate
Capital expenditures	Tax structure (MLP/Non-MLP)	Capacity	Backlog	Capital requirements
Risking	Long-term contracts	Crack spreads*	Contracts	Contract terms vs. prevailing terms
Drilling data	Dedicated acreage	Processing capability	Noncontractual revenue	Technical specifications
Location	Location	Location	Location of operations	Location of rigs
Operating expenses			Diversity of service offerings	Daily operating expenses
Taxes				Drilling rates
Undeveloped acreage				

* Represents the differential between the price of crude oil and petroleum products extracted from the oil.

Midstream considerations

Midstream businesses are characterized by significant initial capital investment to build a pipeline or other facility, followed by relatively steady contractual cash flows from customers using the pipeline or facility.

Income approach for midstream companies

Given the size of the initial investment, pipelines and associated facilities typically are constructed only when the midstream company has received sufficient volume commitments from customers to earn its desired rate of return for the project. Many of the volume commitments may be "take or pay," meaning the customers must pay the midstream business, regardless of whether they actually use the pipeline.

Given the relatively stable cash flows, as well as sizeable debt in the capital structure, rates of return for midstream entities typically are lower than those of other energy assets or sectors. A few other key considerations for midstream businesses include:

Contract duration. Midstream assets typically are built based on long-term contracts with upstream producers that can continue for decades. Therefore, it is possible to model projected volumes and resulting cash flows for an extended time with reasonable certainty. However, a certain volume, typically between 10 to 50 percent, may remain available or uncommitted. This capacity too must be modeled, based on market expectations.

Discount rate. Discount rate considerations include taxes and "beta" (measures the volatility of a stock's returns compared to the equity returns of the overall market), as shown in Figure 33-12 based on information as of December 31, 2019. Given the non-taxable nature of MLPs, the discount rate should be consistent and not include a tax benefit in the cost of debt.

Concerning beta, midstream companies tend to be relatively stable, even in periods of mild market downturns, although they certainly were affected negatively during the drastic decline in oil prices which began in late-2014. Their relative stability produces betas that are generally lower, and consequently result in lower overall discount rates than those for upstream companies of similar size.

Working capital. Midstream companies typically receive settlement shortly after delivery and do not require significant working capital to operate. Therefore, working capital usually is not included when determining the fair value for these entities when using the income approach.

FERC regulation. Many midstream pipelines are governed by the Federal Energy Regulatory Commission (FERC), which sets the rates for the pipelines under its jurisdiction. When a subject pipeline is under FERC oversight, the latest rate case should be reviewed to understand the current tariff.

Taxes. A significant majority of midstream companies are MLPs, a corporate tax structure that allows companies to avoid paying federal taxes if substantially all of their earnings are distributed to shareholders. Determining the tax status of the subject entity affects the cash flows, as well as the development of the discount rate. See discussion of MLPs in Chapter 29.

Figure 33-12

Illustrative WACCs by market capitalization – Midstream

	Small Cap	Large Cap
Risk-free rate	2.3%	2.3%
Equity risk premium	6.0%	6.0%
Selected re-levered beta	1.6	1.0
Small-stock premium	3.0%	0.0%
Cost of equity	**14.5%**	**8.2%**
Pre-tax cost of debt	9.7%	6.7%
Tax rate	0.0%	0.0%
Post-tax cost of debt	**9.7%**	**6.7%**
Equity weight	85.0%	70.0%
Debt weight	15.0%	30.0%
WACC	**14.0%**	**8.0%**

Market approach for midstream companies

Since the energy industry is a cyclical business, special attention should be paid to the current point in the commodity cycle, as well as the point in the cycle for each transaction observed. Ideally, similar points in the cycle should be used; however, if this is impossible using the available transactions, adjustments for differences can be made or the market approach can be abandoned as an option.

Many of the same market approach considerations for upstream companies also apply to midstream companies, including location, multiple versus single location of operations and commodity mix. Generally speaking, the market approach is more reliable for midstream companies than for upstream companies because their business is relatively stable. It may also be used as a corroborative tool for the income approach. However, the following factors should be considered:

Timing. Midstream operations typically do not rely on one or a few wells; pipelines and facilities usually are built only when there is sufficient demand to consume the majority of the capacity of the new pipeline or facility. Therefore, market approach comparisons among different assets can be more reliable than for other sectors in the industry with respect to the timing, or age, of the assets. In addition, for mature fields the remaining life of the reserves base supporting operations should be considered.

Multiples. Typical market approach multiples include historical or projected EBITDA. Unlike valuation multiples for upstream assets, those for midstream entities typically are not based on reserves or daily production, since neither is associated with midstream assets. Market approaches for downstream entities usually are more appropriate, since those entities often can "diversify away" some of the direct risk of commodity price exposure. Critical considerations for comparisons include size, location, product and service offerings, and feedstocks. With the analysis of each variable, the strength of the market approach improves for similar variables but declines for dissimilar ones.

Other valuation considerations

Asset-intensive entities, such as those in the midstream and downstream segments, also can be valued using a cost approach: determining the replacement cost of each pipeline, facility or downstream plant and adjusting for wear and tear, functionality and utilization. OFSE and oil and gas properties typically are not strong candidates for the cost approach, since their operations are not tangible asset-intensive in nature.

An additional adjustment can be made based on the company's ability to generate cash flow, since no buyer would purchase an entity for more than the cost to create it or the expected value of the cash flows it is expected to generate. This last adjustment (economic obsolescence) should always be part of a robust cost approach.

The following factors should also be considered by companies in the energy industry for valuation purposes:

Intangible assets. Although entities that primarily own oil and gas properties rarely own significant intangible assets, other energy industry entities do; these items should be considered when valuing such entities. Midstream companies may have significant contracts for dedicated acreage that require area producers to use them as their sole transportation source. These contracts also may include minimum volume commitments that further de-risk the entity's cash flows. Downstream entities also may own intangible assets, often highly competitive product formulas or brand names that consumers value, which will result in higher values than for entities producing solely commodity products.

OFSE companies often own many types of intangible assets, from technology that creates a competitive advantage to brand names that assist in sales. Although OFSE companies are less likely to sign long-term contracts, drilling companies typically do, which can mean above- or below-market day rates, especially when commodity prices decline.

Industry cyclicality. This topic has been mentioned multiple times but its importance cannot be overstated. Although windows of three to five years or longer often are appropriate for market approaches in other industries, a time frame of that length in the oil and gas industry could include drastic upward and downward price fluctuations. For that matter, comparison to points within the industry cycle are extremely important.

Lower for longer. During late-2014, commodity prices began a rapid decline as a result of oversupply and under-consumption. U.S. shale production considerably bolstered supply but demand in emerging markets did not meet expectations. For the first 12 to 18 months of the downturn, many expected it to be short-lived and that prices would soon recover to earlier levels. However, as of the publication date of this textbook, a full recovery has not occurred. Many experts are wondering if the price change is permanent due to factors still in place that drove the decline. This serves as a reminder that, for forecasting purposes, a price decline is not always followed by a recovery to previous levels. This possibility must be considered when reviewing any cash flow projections for an oil and gas company.

• • •

1 Tax requirements might affect areas such as: (1) allocation of purchase price among multiple acquired properties, (2) determination of fair value for properties contributed to charity or given as a gift to family member(s) and (3) property tax assessments.

2 In the Matter of Miller Energy Resources, Inc., Paul W. Boyd, CPA, David M. Hall, And Carlton W. Vogt, III, CPA, collectively the Respondents. Order Making Findings And Imposing A Cease-and-Desist Order And Penalties Pursuant To Section 8a Of The Securities Act Of 1933 And Section 21c Of The Securities Exchange Act Of 1934 As To Miller Energy Resources, Inc. File No. 3-16729.

3 Since 1974, editions of *Economic Evaluation and Investment Decisions Methods*, a leading textbook on petroleum economic evaluations, have emphasized that economic analysis should take place after-tax. The editions are authored by Frank J. Stermole, professor emeritus, and his son, John M. Stermole, adjunct professor, Colorado School of Mines and published by Stermole's Investment Evaluations Corp. Additionally, while the 2018 SPEE survey of parameters referenced herein notes that a pre-tax DCF is considered the most useful method by survey respondents, this should not be confused with what is considered the most appropriate method for calculating the fair value of oil and gas properties in accordance with ASC 820, which as discussed herein should typically be performed on an after-tax basis.

4 The formula for derivation and further explanation of the tax shield concept can be found at SPE Paper 19858, *Understanding Minimum Sales Price and Maximum Purchase Price*, by G. C. Daley and D.R. Elmer of ARCO (1989).

5 *2018 Survey of Parameters Used in Property Evaluation* published by the Society of Petroleum Evaluation Engineers. spee.org/2018-parameters-survey.

34

Risk Management Activities

Understanding and addressing the inherent risks in various business environments is critical to strategic leadership. This chapter reviews enterprise-wide risk management, its importance to E&P companies and the consequences for petroleum accounting.

Successful risk management includes an appropriate assessment of the accounting and information needs of a company and its stakeholders; however, risk management involves much more than a simple focus on internal controls. Chapter 3 covers internal control and organizational frameworks for E&P companies.

Risks and uncertainties

Every organization faces some level of uncertainty. Uncertainty creates both risks and opportunities, which can either erode or enhance the company's value. This is especially true for E&P companies that manage a plethora of risks: exploration, competitive, economic, financial, operational, technological, environmental, regulatory, legal and political.

Risk management definition

The development of processes and controls that minimize the negative effect of risks is commonly referred to as risk management. An organization may focus on individual risk elements, such as financial or political risks, or it may take a more holistic approach. Enterprise Risk Management (ERM) is a comprehensive, systematic approach to identifying, measuring and prioritizing risks; it also addresses how entities respond to those risks that could challenge critical objectives and operations.

ERM helps a company decide how much risk it can manage or wants to manage, given the needs and objectives of its stakeholders. ERM also enhances the organization's ability to align its risk appetite with its strategy. By successfully managing risks, an organization can improve its performance and better protect itself from pitfalls. Accordingly, ERM is an integral and essential component of a risk- and value-based management framework.

COSO Framework

In 2004, the Committee of Sponsoring Organizations of the Treadway Commission (COSO) presented an official framework for applying ERM to the accounting profession. COSO's integrated framework describes the essential components, principles and concepts of ERM.

In 2017, COSO released updated guidance given the dynamic changes in industries and the evolution in how organizations view and manage risk. The complexity of business is always changing and new risks continue to emerge at a rapid pace. COSO's updated framework, *Enterprise Risk Management – Integrating with Strategy and Performance*, outlines five components that are intended to align strategy and performance across an organization.

Common industry risks

Risk is inherent in virtually every business action and inaction. It cannot be eliminated entirely and is a natural part of business activity. In fact, a risk-averse organization does not typically survive; new markets, products and responses quickly bypass it. Broad areas of risk exist for every company and its stakeholders.

To be managed effectively, risks first must be recognized and recognition requires an awareness of any affected stakeholders. A company's long-term success depends partly on an intelligent, balanced relationship with its stakeholders.

A stakeholder is defined as any group or individual that affects, or is affected by, the achievement of a company's objectives. Stakeholders include shareholders, creditors, employees, governments, communities in which a company operates – even the world when a company's activities affect general prosperity.

Risks can be categorized in many ways. The most common risks found in petroleum companies include:

- **Strategic.** Arise from corporate decisions about mergers, acquisitions, geographic focus and other strategic actions.

- **Financial.** Relate to capital costs, information systems and fraud.

- **Operational.** Result from property acquisition, exploration, development and production.

- **Compliance.** Driven by the myriad of government laws, regulations and contracts dealing with exploration, production, employees, customers, taxation, anti-trust and environmental safety.

- **Cybersecurity.** Inherent in new customer connections, supply chain integration, new data management models, bulk data and mobility.

The petroleum industry continues to experience significant changes and each change brings new risks that must be identified and addressed. Developments such as globalization have led U.S. companies to seek business in parts of the world where opportunities exist for major discoveries; however, doing business in some of these areas can present major hazards.

Upstream considerations

For an E&P company, risk-taking is a fact of life and, as such, should be managed. Some of the strategies for managing risks while striving to add oil and gas reserves include:

- Acquiring lease rights in identified areas to improve opportunities for exploratory success.

- Using the most suitable exploration technology.

- Spreading risk and gaining expertise via joint ventures.

- Hedging commodity prices in line with management directives.

- Strengthening engineering oversight of production.

- Employing geological, engineering and management personnel with technical, financial and risk management perspectives.

- Financing in strategic ways to provide capital at the lowest cost.

Managing risks is the foundation of the E&P industry. As wells deplete and dry holes occur, new reserves must be found. To survive, E&P companies must focus continuously on adding reserves that are economic to produce. Many business decisions are driven by an assessment of risks. Accordingly, companies strive to discover enough oil and gas to be sold at an adequate profit to meet overall exploration and production goals while minimizing the assessed risks.

For example, leases are purchased on the assumption that opportunities will outweigh hazards. An E&P company enters into many leases expecting to drill successful wells, although a determination may be made that some wells drilled are ultimately dry holes. Entering into several leases and joint venture agreements reduces the risk of little or no success. However, these ventures create exposure to unexpected events, such as a well blowout or a rally of local citizens protesting production from a new discovery.

Given the: (a) core nature of the industry to explore, (b) volatility of commodity prices and exploratory success, (c) industry issues of globalization and climate change and (d) rapid and substantial technological advancements, strong risk management is crucial for E&P companies.

Risk management drives many of the events and transactions that petroleum accountants must address, including:

- Use of joint venture arrangements to manage risk, which can complicate petroleum accounting.

- Globalization to enhance corporate business opportunities, which can necessitate modernized or specialized accounting systems and policies for new foreign locations.

- Strategic financing arrangements, such as conveyances of volumetric production payments, which can necessitate special petroleum accounting treatment.

- Development and use of standardized forms, contracts and joint venture protocols, such as COPAS accounting exhibits, gas balancing agreements, Electronic Data Interchange (EDI) standards, joint venture audits and material transfer accounting procedures.

- Enhanced cybersecurity and data automation for real-time communication of accounting transactions to enable data analytics.

- Hedge accounting for financial and tax reporting.

Petroleum accounting is a key element of risk management for an E&P company. As a company's risk management program increases in importance and sophistication, so should the company's accounting department.

Risk management programs

Derivatives are contracts in which value is derived from the value of an underlying asset, reference rate or index price. Derivatives can be used in various ways depending on the risk they are intended to mitigate. E&P, marketing, pipeline, refining and utility companies, as well as large industrial consumers, use derivatives in their operations despite increased regulations and public scrutiny of the derivatives markets.

Derivative instruments

Companies use derivatives for several reasons: (1) to maintain a desired level of profitability or cash flows during periods of rising or falling prices, (2) to achieve a desired internal rate of return on investments or help secure near term capital budgeting objectives and (3) to obtain additional financing from financial institutions.

Commodity derivatives are widely used to hedge the economic risks associated with the sale ("input price") of relevant commodities. For example, a gas marketing company, which buys gas from producers at spot prices, may offer its customers fixed-price sales contracts. The gas marketing company is exposed to price risk in the event the spot price index increases above the fixed sales contract price, which will produce a loss.

However, the gas marketing company can fix its supply cost by purchasing futures contracts or using other derivative financial instruments. Likewise, pipeline, refining and utility companies, as well as large industrial consumers, can fix their fuel costs by using derivative contracts. It is also common for companies to use derivatives to manage fluctuations in interest rates or credit exposure for counterparties.

Derivatives can be an effective option for managing risk, but they require compliance and oversight. The media and regulators have focused on derivatives in recent years. The financial crisis of 2008 was due, in part, to exponential growth in credit derivatives. Energy companies were not immune to the effect of credit derivatives, combined with their existing open-commodity derivatives, on their perceived and real market liquidity. In recent years, several prominent companies have experienced sizeable losses due to derivatives.

Dodd-Frank Act

The Wall Street Reform and Consumer Protection Act of 2010, also known as the Dodd-Frank Act, was signed into law on July 21, 2010. Dodd-Frank was intended to create increased transparency and additional oversight to address perceived systemic risks posed, in part, by derivatives trading. Although the Dodd-Frank Act is still being implemented, many new rules are now in place, including:

- Rules adopted and interpretative guidance for cross-border security-based swap activities.

- Joint rules with the Commodity Futures Trading Commission (CFTC) regarding the definitions of "swap," "security-based swap dealers," "major swap" and "security-based swap participants," which were further defined and expanded to include the regulation of mixed swaps and security-based swap agreement record-keeping.

- Rules relating to mandatory clearing of security-based swaps, which establish a process for clearing agencies to inform the SEC about the security-based swaps they have accepted.

- Rules that establish new standards for how clearing agencies should manage their operations and risk.

- Rules regarding the registration of security-based swap data repositories.

- Rules regarding the reporting and dissemination of security-based swap information.

A minor roll-back of some regulations on community and regional banks, and nonbank financial institutions in particular that were perceived to be especially burdensome under the original law, was enacted in 2018.

Commonly used derivative instrument types

Derivatives designed specifically for the energy industry have existed for many years. Energy companies use various instrument types, including futures, forwards, swaps and options, in their risk management programs. In general, energy companies enter into derivative contracts with the intent of locking in favorable future prices.

For example, E&P companies may purchase a futures contract to sell oil at the current one-year forward market price, for settlement one year from the contract date, thus attempting to reduce their overall exposure to future declines in oil prices. Typically, E&P companies will seek to hedge a designated percentage of total production, while midstream companies typically hedge based on pipeline capacity.

Depending on the nature of the commodity, derivative instrument and associated risk, derivative contracts typically are settled in three ways:

- **Physical settlement.** The commodity is delivered from the seller and received by the buyer.

- **Financial settlement.** The buyer and seller agree to net settle the value of the contract through a financial or cash transfer.

- **Closing the position.** Generally associated with exchange-traded instruments, a second offsetting contract for the same commodity, volume and delivery period is executed to "close" an open derivative position to further price fluctuation, by offsetting any subsequent market changes in the previously open position until contract expiration.

Futures

A futures contract is an exchange-traded legal contract to buy or sell a standard quantity of a commodity at a specified future date and price. Futures contracts protect against adverse price changes or losses on existing assets, such as inventory, or they can be used to participate in upward and downward price movements of the underlying commodities.

The NYMEX crude oil and natural gas futures contracts have existed since 1983 and 1990, respectively. Both crude oil and natural gas futures contracts are traded on the NYMEX; other exchanges have developed, or are developing, similar contracts. A standard NYMEX crude oil futures contract is for 1,000 barrels for delivery in Cushing, Oklahoma, while a standard NYMEX natural gas futures contract is for 10,000 MMBtu for delivery at Henry Hub in southern Louisiana.

Transactions on an exchange typically are executed through a commodity futures brokerage firm or clearing house. Initial margin deposits of cash or near risk-free securities are required to be posted to begin transacting through the clearing house. On a daily basis, the clearing house will assess the value of the futures contract and require additional "variation" margin to be posted to/from the holder of the individual contract to mitigate losses as a result of adverse price movements or default by a clearing member or end-user. This cash exchange is treated as either: (a) a settlement of an open position, depending on the legal determination under the contract, or (b) a payment of collateral associated with the contract.

This is not an accounting election; it requires a legal assessment of the specific terms of each trade and the legal relationship with the clearing member and clearing house. The clearing house acts as an intermediary between buyers and sellers, guarantees contract performance and assumes all counterparty credit risk. It is relatively easy for buyers and sellers of futures contracts to liquidate their positions by selling or buying an offsetting contract for the same commodity, quantity and delivery month. Most crude oil and natural gas futures contracts are settled in this manner, rather than physically delivering or receiving oil or gas at the exchange delivery points, as is described in Chapter 12.

Forward contracts

A forward contract is a legal agreement between two parties to purchase and sell a specific quantity and quality of a commodity at a specified price, with delivery and settlement at a specified future date. While a forward contract has similar characteristics to a futures contract, a key difference is that forward contracts are not traded on regulated commodity exchanges; the contracts are privately negotiated agreements referred to as over-the-counter (OTC) contracts. Consequently, they lack the liquidity and minimal credit risk exposure offered by exchange-traded futures contracts.

Forward contracts are more flexible than futures contracts because they can be tailored to specific quantities, settlement dates and delivery points. Like futures contracts, forward contracts can be used for both hedging and to create exposure to market price changes.

Swaps

Swaps are contracts between two parties to exchange variable and fixed-rate payment streams based on a specified contract principal (notional amount). Swaps are used primarily for economic hedging purposes or to alter the terms of an existing agreement.

For instance, two companies may enter into a natural gas price swap that requires one company (the fixed-price payer) to pay a fixed price and another company (the variable-price payer) to pay the published gas-index or futures-contract settlement price spanning several settlement periods. The volume of gas (e.g., 1,000 MMBtu per month for six months) used to calculate the variable and fixed-rate payments is the contract principal (notional amount). The settlement amounts of these contracts typically are calculated as the difference between the fixed and variable prices multiplied by the notional volume for the given period. A net payment is received by the company with the realized gain position, from the company with the realized loss.

Swap contracts are also more flexible than futures contracts, for the same reasons as outlined above for forwards. Swap agreements are, for the most part, OTC contracts, but there are now some interest rate swaps that are centrally cleared, similar to futures contracts. Swaps that are OTC contracts expose the parties to counterparty credit risk (i.e., the other party may be unable to pay or honor the contract). Consequently, counterparties to swap agreements may require margin deposits.

As an example, Lockin has several contracts with third parties to sell gas at the average monthly spot price published by a third party. On January 1, 2020, Lockin seeks to lock in the price on its sale of gas to third parties for 2020 and 2021. Skyhigh previously agreed to sell its natural gas production at a fixed price to a cogeneration facility during the next two years; however, it is now optimistic that gas prices will increase substantially.

Accordingly, on January 1, 2020, Lockin and Skyhigh agree to a natural gas swap for 2020 and 2021 with these terms:

- Volume: 10,000 MMBtu per day.

- Fixed price: $2 per MMBtu.

- Variable price: average monthly spot price published by a third party.

- Payments are made at the end of the month after the month of gas sales.

Based on the above terms, Skyhigh will pay cash to Lockin for the excess of the $2 per MMBtu fixed price above the average monthly spot price. Alternatively, Lockin will pay cash to Skyhigh for the excess of the average monthly spot price above the $2 per MMBtu fixed price. On January 31, 2021, the average monthly spot price for the January 2021 production month settled at $2.25, resulting in a settlement amount due from Lockin to Skyhigh as shown below:

Figure 34-1

Swap contract settlement calculation – January 2021

Fixed price per contract	Average monthly spot price	Difference	Settlement amount*
$2.00 per MMBtu	$2.25 per MMBtu	$0.25 per MMBtu	$77,500

* $77,500 = [($2.25 per MMBtu average monthly spot price – $2.00 per MMBtu fixed price) x 10,000 MMBtu per day x 31 days].

Based on the terms of the agreement, Lockin will pay Skyhigh a periodic settlement payment of $77,500 by February 28, 2021. If Lockin sold 10,000 MMBtu at $2.25 per MMBtu to third-parties, the swap would decrease Lockin's effective price to $2 per MMBtu, as follows:

Figure 34-2

Net sales calculation for Lockin – January 2021

Sales to third parties ($2.25 per MMBtu x 10,000 MMBtu x 31 days)	$697,500
Less: settlement payment to Skyhigh	(77,500)
Net sales for Lockin	**$620,000**
Net sales for Lockin per MMBtu ($620,000 ÷ 10,000 MMBtu ÷ 31 days)	$2.00

Alternatively, if Skyhigh sold 10,000 MMBtu at $2 per MMBtu to the cogeneration plant, the swap would increase Skyhigh's effective price to $2.25 per MMBtu, as follows:

Figure 34-3

Net sales calculation for Skyhigh – January 2021

Sale to cogeneration plant ($2 per MMBtu x 10,000 MMBtu x 31 days)	$620,000
Plus: settlement received from Lockin	77,500
Net sales for Skyhigh	**$697,500**
Net sales for Skyhigh per MMBtu ($697,500 ÷ 10,000 MMBtu ÷ 31 days)	$2.25

If on February 28, 2021, the average monthly spot price for the February 2021 production month settled at $1.75, then the settlement amount would be calculated as follows:

Figure 34-4

Swap contract settlement calculation – February 2021

Fixed price per contract	Average monthly spot price	Difference	Settlement amount*
$2.00 per MMBtu	$1.75 per MMBtu	$0.25 per MMBtu	$70,000

* $70,000 = [($1.75 per MMBtu average monthly spot price – $2.00 per MMBtu fixed price) x 10,000 MMBtu per day x 28 days].

Based on the terms of the agreement, Skyhigh will pay Lockin $70,000 to settle the swap by March 31, 2021. If Lockin sold 10,000 MMBtu at $1.75 per MMBtu to third parties, the swap would increase Lockin's effective price to $2 per MMBtu, as follows:

Figure 34-5

Net sales calculation for Lockin – February 2021

Sales to third parties ($1.75 per MMBtu x 10,000 MMBtu x 28 days)	$490,000
Plus: settlement payment from Skyhigh	70,000
Net sales for Lockin	**$560,000**
Net sales for Lockin per MMBtu ($560,000 ÷ 10,000 MMBtu ÷ 28 days)	$2.00

If Skyhigh sold 10,000 MMBtu at $2 per MMBtu to the cogeneration plant, the swap would decrease Skyhigh's effective price to $1.75 per MMBtu as follows:

Figure 34-6

Net sales calculation for Skyhigh – February 2021

Sale to cogeneration plant ($2 per MMBtu x 10,000 MMBtu x 28 days)	$560,000
Less: settlement payment to Lockin	(70,000)
Net sales for Skyhigh	**$490,000**
Net sales for Skyhigh per MMBtu ($490,000 ÷ 10,000 MMBtu ÷ 28 days)	$1.75

The January 2021 net sales calculations are illustrated another way in the flowchart below:

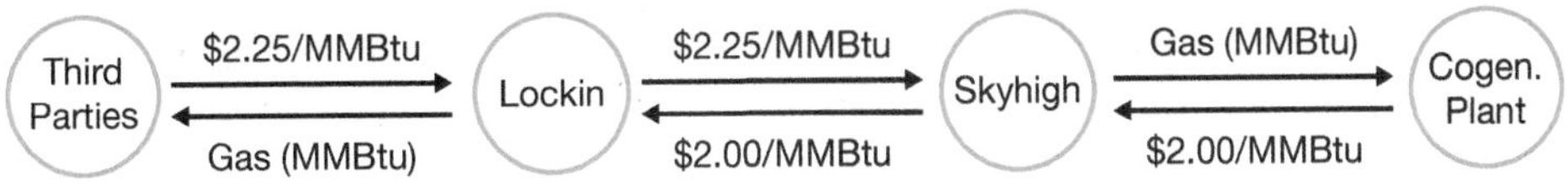

The February 2021 net sales calculations are illustrated another way in the flowchart below:

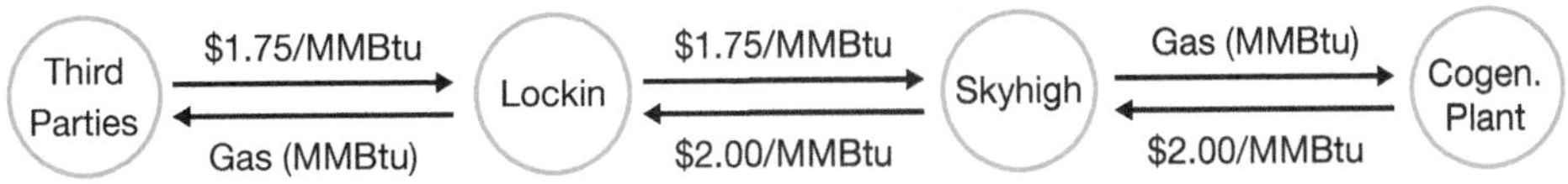

Option contracts

Option contracts give the buyer (holder) a right, but not an obligation, to buy (call) or sell (put) a specified item at a fixed price (exercise or strike price) during a specified exercise period from the seller (writer). The buyer pays a non-refundable fee (premium) to the seller. Options are either exchange traded (such as NYMEX options on the NYMEX crude oil futures contract) or OTC contracts. OTC options expose the holder to counterparty default. Options can be used for both hedging purposes and to create exposure to market price changes.

There are several terms unique to the use of options. Depending on whether a call option's strike price is less than, equal to or greater than the commodity's current price, the call option is considered to be "in-the-money," "at-the-money" or "out-of-the-money," respectively.

In contrast, when a put option's strike price is less than, equal to or greater than the commodity's price, then the put option is considered to be "out-of-the-money," "at-the-money" or "in-the-money," respectively.

The value of an option is derived primarily from its intrinsic value and time value, as well as the underlying commodity's volatility. The extent to which an option is in-the-money is its intrinsic value. Consequently, intrinsic value is never a negative amount. The time value of an option represents the portion of the premium in excess of the option's intrinsic value due to the possibility that the option can move in-the-money during the remaining exercise period.

Volatility refers to the amount a commodity's price fluctuates. More volatile commodities are more likely to move in-the-money during an exercise period. Higher intrinsic values, longer exercise periods and greater price volatility of the underlying commodity result in higher option premiums and risks.

American options can be exercised at any time during the exercise period. European options are exercised only at the end of the exercise period. A payoff for Asian options is linked to the average value of the underlying commodity on a specific set of dates during the life of the option. Burmudan options are similar to American options but may only be exercised on specific periodic dates or at maturity.

Other contract types

As discussed, E&P companies that sell their production at index prices can attempt to protect a portion of their oil and gas reserves from downward price movements by fixing the sales price of their reserves production using futures, forwards and swaps.

Producers create floors by purchasing put options that guarantee minimum oil or gas prices. E&P companies also execute collars by selling a call option and buying a put option on their production. A collar results in a realized price range between the strike prices of the put and call options. When the premium received for the call equals the premium paid for the put, the collar is known as a "zero-cost collar."

Call options. For example, on June 1, 2020, Optimistic Oil Co. (Optimistic) pays Pessimistic Energy Inc. (Pessimistic) a $500 premium for an OTC call option to buy 1,000 barrels of WTI crude oil at $60 per barrel by May 1, 2021. If by May 1, 2021, the spot price of WTI remains less than $60 per barrel, Optimistic's call option is unexercised and expires as worthless.

Alternatively, assume that on April 15, 2021, the spot price is $62 per barrel. Optimistic (the holder) exercises the call option by paying $60,000 to Pessimistic (the writer) in return for the 1,000 barrels worth $62,000. In this case, the call option costing Optimistic $500 would provide, upon exercise, a profit to Optimistic of $1,500 after transaction expenses. Pessimistic loses a net $1,500 from writing the exercised call option. Usually, option contracts are settled on a net cash basis without physical delivery of the commodity.

Put options. Assume GoingUp sold an OTC put option for 1,000 barrels of WTI at $60 per barrel, exercisable on or before May 1, 2021. GoingDown pays a $400 premium to buy the put option, which gives GoingDown the right to sell 1,000 barrels to GoingUp for $60,000. On March 18, 2021, assuming the WTI price has fallen to $58 per barrel, GoingDown exercises the put option by selling 1,000 barrels of WTI to GoingUp for $60,000, for a net profit of $1,600 after the $400 cost of the premium.

The option buyer's risk is limited to the amount of premium paid. Because an option is a right, and not an obligation, the holder can profit from favorable price movements in the commodity underlying the option. The writer of an option bears the risk of an unfavorable change in the price of the commodity underlying the option. Similarly, the writer of a "naked option" (i.e., the writer does not own the commodity underlying the option) is exposed to losses substantially greater than the premium received.

Naked options. In another instance, Paul Pessimistic writes a naked call option on crude oil at a price of $60 per barrel and receives a premium of $1 per barrel. When war breaks out in a key oil-producing region, and the price of crude oil goes up to $70 per barrel, the option is exercised. Paul Pessimistic must buy crude oil at $70 per barrel, sell it for $60 per barrel, and take a loss (after the $1 per barrel premium) of $9 per barrel.

Floor options. Assume Lowrisk buys a put option for $5,000 to sell 10,000 WTI barrels at $58 per barrel; the spot price of WTI is $60 per barrel on the date the option is purchased. If the spot price drops to $56 per barrel, Lowrisk's production would be sold at $56 per barrel, except that Lowrisk can exercise the put option to sell 10,000 barrels for $58 per barrel. After the $5,000 cost of the put ($0.50 per contract barrel), Lowrisk has created a $57.50 net floor price for 10,000 barrels of its production.

Costless collar options. In addition to buying the put option, suppose Lowrisk sold a call option for $5,000, allowing the holder to buy 10,000 barrels at $63 per barrel from Lowrisk. Now Lowrisk receives a $0.50 per barrel call premium, offset by the $0.50 per barrel cost of the put option, and Lowrisk has created a ceiling price of $63 per barrel for 10,000 barrels of production.

If the price rises above $63 per barrel, the call holder exercises the call and pays only $63 per barrel to Lowrisk for the 10,000 barrels. By buying a put for $5,000 and selling a call for $5,000 to create a zero-cost collar, Lowrisk has reduced the price range for 10,000 barrels of production to a range of $58 to $63 per barrel.

Risks of derivative instruments

Although derivatives can protect companies from adverse commodity price movements, they can also expose a company to significant risks.

Price risk

Because oil and gas prices are volatile, producers are exposed to the risk that prices will decline. If a company wishes to use derivatives to hedge this exposure, it should employ knowledgeable risk managers with a good understanding of the company's price risks and the terms of its derivatives and financial instruments. A poor risk management strategy increases exposure to volatile oil and gas prices.

Credit risk

Like other financial instruments, derivatives expose a company to credit risk. Credit risk is the risk that a loss may occur from the failure of another party (counterparty) to perform according to the contract terms. It includes not only the net payable or receivable outstanding but also the cost of replacing a derivative contract if the counterparty defaults.

Counterparty credit risk is further concentrated when companies enter into multiple derivative contracts with the same counterparty or counterparties in the same geographic location or industry. The credit risk is generally lower if the derivative is an exchange-traded contract. Exposure to credit risk can be minimized further by requiring collateral or margin deposits.

Liquidity risk

Exchange-traded derivatives generally are more liquid than OTC derivatives. Liquidity risk results from the inability to easily purchase or sell derivative contracts in required quantities at a fair price. Additionally, fair prices may not be available when there are large discrepancies between the bid price (buyer's price) and the asking price (seller's price).

Correlation risk

The risk that the commodity price in the derivative contract will not move in tandem with the commodity price being hedged is known as correlation risk. Consequently, an increase in the value of a derivative transaction might not fully offset the decrease in value of the hedged commodity, or vice versa. When deciding whether or not to hedge a risk, a key question is whether or not one expects a high correlation between anticipated changes in the market value of the hedging instrument and the market value of the hedged commodity, and whether or not that correlation is likely to continue throughout the hedging period.

Basis difference

Basis is the difference between the spot price of a hedged commodity and the price of the hedging instrument. Basis is sometimes referred to as the "spread." Because the prices received for oil and gas vary by location, quality, local supply and demand conditions and other factors, the commodity price of a hedge contract frequently does not equal the spot price received for the production.

Accounting guidance

ASC 815, *Derivatives and Hedging*, lays out a comprehensive framework of accounting rules that has standardized and created uniform accounting for derivatives.

ASC 815 requires that all derivatives be recognized on the balance sheet at fair value, with an offsetting entry related to unrealized gains and/or losses reflected either:

- As part of current earnings.

- In other comprehensive income, which is a component of stockholders' equity (if hedge accounting is achieved).

The FASB's ultimate goal was to increase the visibility of derivatives and allow hedge accounting only for highly effective hedges. The adoption of ASC 815 resulted in an increase in earnings and equity volatility, as well as an increase in the number of derivative contracts included in the balance sheet accounts for many E&P companies.

For E&P companies, a notable provision in ASC 815 allows certain contracts that would otherwise be accounted for as derivatives at fair value in current earnings to avoid being considered derivatives. Contracts that contain net settlement provisions may qualify for election of the normal purchases and normal sales (NPNS) scope exception if it is probable at inception, and throughout the term of the individual contract, that the contract will not settle net and will result in physical delivery.

In August 2017, the FASB issued ASU 2017-12, *Derivatives and Hedging (Topic 815): Targeted Improvements to Accounting for Hedging Activities*, which is discussed in a subsequent section of this chapter.

Definition of a derivative

ASC 815-10-15-83 defines a derivative as a financial instrument or other contract with all of the following characteristics:

a. Underlying, notional amount, payment provision. The contract has both of the following terms, which determine the amount of the settlement or settlements, and, in some cases, whether or not a settlement is required:

    1. One or more underlyings

    2. One or more notional amounts or payment provisions or both.

b. Initial net investment. The contract requires no initial net investment or an initial net investment that is smaller than would be required for other types of contracts that would be expected to have a similar response to changes in market factors.

c. Net settlement. The contract can be settled net by any of the following means:

    1. Its terms implicitly or explicitly require or permit net settlement.

    2. It can readily be settled net by a means outside the contract.

    3. It provides for delivery of an asset that puts the recipient in a position not substantially different from net settlement.

Understanding the five concepts of: (1) underlying, (2) notional amount, (3) payment provision, (4) initial net investment and (5) net settlement is key to defining a derivative.

Based on these concepts, the definition of a derivative includes not only the typical financial instruments that have been viewed in the past as derivatives but also may include traditional physical-commodity contracts that do not meet the NPNS scope exception in ASC 815 discussed herein. The FASB and Derivative Implementation Group (DIG) have provided additional interpretive guidance pertaining to the net settlement criteria.

Underlying. An underlying in a derivative is a specified commodity price, interest rate, security price or some other variable. It may be a price or a rate of interest but not the asset or liability itself. Generally, the underlying is the referenced index that determines whether or not the derivative has a positive or negative value.

Notional amount. The notional amount is a number representing the determinable amount of barrels of crude oil, MMBtu of natural gas, pounds, bushels, currency units, shares or other units specified in a contract.

Payment provision. In lieu of specifying a notional amount to be applied to the change in an underlying, some derivatives contain a payment provision. A payment provision specifies a fixed or determinable settlement to be made if the underlying behaves in a certain manner.

Initial net investment. Derivative contracts may require an initial payment as compensation for time value or for terms that are more favorable than market conditions (e.g., a premium on an in-the-money option). In order to be considered a derivative, the initial net investment, adjusted for the time value of money, should be "less, by more than a nominal amount" than the initial net investment that would be required to acquire the asset or incur the obligation related to the underlying.

The FASB has not provided a bright line for what constitutes a nominal amount; however, generally an initial net investment that is less than 90 percent of the amount that would be exchanged to acquire the asset or incur the obligation would be considered "less, by more than a nominal amount."

Net settlement. Settlement of a derivative is often determined by the interaction of the notional amount with the value of the underlying. This interaction may consist of simple multiplication, or it may involve a more complex formula. The net settlement requirement can be accomplished in three ways:

- Net settlement explicitly required or permitted by the contract (i.e., symmetrical liquidating damage clause).

- Net settlement of the entire derivative contract by a market mechanism outside the contract (i.e., a futures exchange).

- Delivery of a derivative or an asset related to the underlying that is readily convertible to cash.

Exclusions

Examples of agreements that meet the definition of a derivative and qualify for exclusion from the application of accounting guidance in ASC 815 include:

- NPNS contracts.

- Contracts not traded on an exchange that involve climatic or geological variables, settlement based upon specified volumes of sales or service revenues of a party to the contract or the price or value of a unique non-financial asset.

- Contingent consideration resulting from a business combination.

- Certain insurance contracts.

- Employee compensation arrangements that are indexed to an entity's own stock and classified as part of stockholders' equity.

It is common in the energy industry for physically settled commodity derivatives to qualify for the NPNS exclusion. Under ASC 815, contracts that contain net settlement provisions qualify for the NPNS exclusion if it is probable at inception, and throughout the term of the individual contract, that the contract will not settle net and the quantity delivered will be used in the reporting entity's normal business activities.

NPNS contracts provide for the purchase or sale of something other than a financial instrument or derivative instrument that will be delivered in quantities expected to be used or sold by the company over a reasonable period in the normal course of business. The election of this exclusion results in these derivative contracts not being carried at fair value on the company's balance sheet, instead they follow accrual accounting.

Embedded derivatives

An embedded derivative is a provision in a contract, through its implicit or explicit terms, that contains the characteristics of a free-standing derivative and ultimately affects the cash flows or value of other exchanges required by the contract. The combination of a host contract and an embedded derivative is referred to as a "hybrid instrument." Examples of an embedded derivative include a purchase or sales contract subject to a cap, floor or collar. An embedded derivative should be separated from the host contract and accounted for separately in the financial statements if it meets all of the following criteria:

- The embedded characteristic in the contract meets the definition of a derivative and is otherwise not subject to a scope exception.

- Characteristics and risks of the embedded derivative are not clearly and closely related to the host contract.

- The hybrid instrument is not measured at fair value.

Judgment is required to interpret the phrase "clearly and closely related." It implies that the economic features of an embedded derivative and host contract are somewhat interdependent, and the fair value of the embedded derivative and the host contract are affected by the same variables.

The FASB and DIG have provided interpretive guidance on what is "clearly and closely related;" see DIG Statement 133 Implementation Issues No. B14, B36 and C20, codified as Example 6 at ASC 815-15-55-114, Example 4 at ASC 815-15-55-101 and ASC 815-10-15-22 to 15-51, respectively.

Continued improvements

As mentioned previously, applying the accounting guidance for derivatives and hedging activities continues to be a challenge for entities. In August 2017, the FASB issued ASU 2017-12. The effective date of the amendment for calendar year-end public companies was January 1, 2019, whereas private companies have until January 2021 to adopt the ASU. The objective of the ASU is to better align hedge accounting in the financial statements with an organization's risk management strategy. In addition, the ASU simplifies the application of hedge accounting guidance in areas where practice had been problematic.

The FASB's new guidance makes more financial and nonfinancial hedging strategies eligible for hedge accounting. It also amends presentation and disclosure requirements and changes how companies assess effectiveness. In addition, it eliminates the measurement of hedge ineffectiveness and is intended to more closely align hedge accounting with companies' risk management strategies, simplifying the application of hedge accounting and increasing transparency about the scope and results of hedging programs.

Under the new guidance, more risk management hedging strategies are now eligible for hedge accounting. These include hedges of a contractually specified price component of a commodity purchase or sale, hedges of the benchmark rate component of the contractual coupon cash flows of fixed-rate assets or liabilities, hedges of the portion of a closed portfolio of prepayable assets not expected to prepay, and partial-term hedges of fixed-rate assets or liabilities (e.g., the first and second years of a five-year bond).

Hedge accounting

Transactions that serve to mitigate economic risk do not always meet the accounting criteria for hedge accounting. Transactions that mitigate cash flow or fair value risk but are not designated as hedging transactions for financial reporting purposes often are referred to as "economic hedges."

For transactions that qualify for hedge accounting, the income statement recognition of changes in the fair value of derivatives depends on their intended use. If a derivative does not qualify as a hedging instrument, or it is not designated as such, gain or loss on the derivative, and any periodic settlements, must be recognized in current period earnings together in the same financial statement line item.

To qualify for hedge accounting, the derivative must qualify as a fair value hedge, cash flow hedge or foreign currency hedge, each of which isdiscussed in a subsequent section herein.

Fair value hedge

A fair value hedge represents the hedge of an exposure to changes in the fair value of an asset, liability or an unrecognized firm commitment attributable to a particular risk. An example of a fair value hedge is an interest rate swap contract associated with fixed rate debt.

A derivative designated as a fair value hedge is reflected in the financial statements at market value for each reporting period, and the associated unrealized gain or loss incurred with respect to such an instrument is included in earnings. Changes in the fair value of the corresponding asset/liability being hedged, due to the changes in the designated hedged risk, also are recognized in the financial statements for each reporting period.

As a result, both the income statement and balance sheet of an organization are affected by these transactions. In any given reporting period, the only components that affect net income are any differences between the change in the fair value of the derivative and the calculated change in the fair value of the hedged item, due solely to changes in the designated hedged risk, as well as any periodic settlement payments or receipts on the derivative. ASU 2017-12 eliminated the measurement of ineffectiveness from hedging, so these amounts are now simply referred to as differences affecting earnings, and the new guidance requires that the derivative changes and that of the hedged item are recognized in the same financial statement line item in the income statement. Periodic settlements on derivatives designated in hedge relationships may be recognized in the same financial statement line items as those the hedged item affects or will affect in the future.

Cash flow hedge

This type of hedge addresses variability in cash flows attributable to a recorded asset or liability (e.g., future floating rate interest payments of a debt instrument) or of a forecasted transaction (e.g., future production of crude oil or natural gas). Common examples of hedging instruments include futures, swaps or costless collar arrangements associated with future crude oil and natural gas production, or interest rate swaps associated with variable rate debt.

A derivative designated and effective as a cash flow hedge is shown in the financial statements at fair value for each reporting period, with the associated unrealized gain or loss incurred included in other comprehensive income. The corresponding forecasted transaction or recognized asset or liability is not shown in the financial statements until it occurs. In the period or periods that the forecasted transaction affects earnings, amounts deferred in other comprehensive income are released to the same financial statement line items as the earnings effect of the forecasted transaction in the income statement.

Foreign currency hedge

A foreign currency hedge protects against an unrecognized firm commitment, available-for-sale security, forecasted transaction, interest and/or principal payments on foreign denominated debt, or a net investment in a foreign operation. Foreign currency hedges can exhibit the dynamics of a fair value transaction, cash flow transaction or foreign currency hedge of a net investment in a foreign operation depending on the nature of the underlying physical transaction(s).

The accounting is consistent with the general provisions of a fair value hedge or cash flow hedge previously described. ASC 815 generally retained the FAS 52 hedge accounting provisions, including a narrow scope of transactions for which hedge accounting may be applied to foreign currency/operations and the use of foreign-denominated assets or debt as hedging instruments in certain circumstances.

Documentation considerations

Since the effective date of the standard, the guidance prescribed by ASC 815 has been challenging to apply, in part due to the extensive documentation required to apply hedge accounting. In order to qualify for hedge accounting, an entity must document clearly, at the inception of a hedging relationship, its risk management objective and strategy. It also must assess and document the effectiveness of the hedge, both soon after the outset of the transaction and at least quarterly thereafter. The assessment must also evaluate whether or not the relationship between the hedging instrument and the hedged item is highly effective.

Given the specifics of hedge accounting criteria, it is presumed that without contemporaneous, formal and complete documentation, a hedging instrument does not qualify for hedge accounting. Simply said, the application of hedge accounting is a privilege that is allowed if, and only if, an entity meets the qualifying standards.

The application of hedge accounting is elective. When the current guidance was first issued, many entities believed that applying hedge accounting was the only practical option for their hedging activities, given investor expectations about earnings volatility. Although many entities were able to meet the documentation requirements, some entities lacked the resources to fully comply.

In terms of hedge documentation, ASU 2017-12 amends the timing and required documentation of the initial effectiveness assessment. When designating a derivative under hedge accounting, public business entities, public not-for-profit entities and financial institutions now have until the earliest of: (1) the maturity, termination, non-qualification or de-designation of the derivative, (2) the occurrence of the hedged item, (3) the end of the first quarter or (4) the release of financial statements reflecting the results of the hedge to complete the initial assessment of hedge effectiveness. All other companies, when using the simplified method only, may wait until their financial statements are available.

After an initial quantitative test, or in certain cases a qualitative effectiveness assessment, the new guidance permits the use thereafter of a qualitative effectiveness assessment for certain hedges, instead of a quantitative test (such as a regression analysis) if the company can reasonably support an expectation of high effectiveness throughout the term of the hedge.

Evaluating effectiveness

The FASB declined to quantify the term "highly effective;" however, the DIG provided interpretive guidance on this topic. The effectiveness assessment should be described in the initial documentation. Effectiveness must not only be achieved initially but also over the entirety of the contract term. An assessment of effectiveness should be made at least every three months and whenever financial statements or earnings are reported to the public.

Assessment of hedge effectiveness is prospective (i.e., is there an expectation that the hedge will be highly effective for the upcoming period), as well as retrospective (i.e., was the hedge highly effective for the period just ended). Ordinarily, it is expected that an entity will assess effectiveness for similar hedges in a similar manner, such that the use of different assessment methods for similar hedges must be justified. When performing periodic effectiveness assessments, it is permissible for a reporting entity to use the same analysis for its retrospective test, performed at the end of a reporting period, as it is for the prospective test for the next upcoming reporting period, as long as forward-looking data such as fair values are used in the test.

High effectiveness allows an entity to use hedge accounting; however, high effectiveness is not necessarily perfect effectiveness or offset of the hedged risk.

Items that may generate differences include:

- Different maturity or repricing dates.

- Different underlying (e.g., hedging jet fuel inventory with heating oil futures).

- Location and quality differentials (e.g., San Juan Basin gas versus NYMEX; sweet versus sour barrels).

- Credit differences.

As it relates to cash flow and net investment hedges, if the hedge is highly effective, the amount deferred in other comprehensive income or cumulative translation adjustment (CTA), respectively, is the cumulative gain or loss on the actual derivative instrument. Differences between the actual derivative and the perfect hedge of the exposure from the hedged item are recognized only as the hedged item affects earnings. As mentioned earlier, fair value hedge differences are reflected in current earnings as a result of both the hedge and hedged item being reflected in earnings in the current period.

Any changes an entity makes to its method of assessing effectiveness must be justified and applied prospectively by discontinuing the existing hedge and designating a new one through its use. Changing the effectiveness assessment for a hedged item also changes the assessment for similar hedges.

According to ASC 820, a consideration of credit risk must be included in the fair value measurement of derivative assets and liabilities. Although this credit risk adjustment for counterparty risk (credit valuation adjustment, or "CVA," and debt valuation adjustment for one's own credit, or "DVA") is not technically a source of hedge differences, it could produce increased earnings volatility and affect an entity's ability to continue hedge accounting.

ASC 815-20-25-122 further explains that counterparty credit risk must be considered when determining whether or not a cash flow hedging relationship is expected to be highly effective. Consideration might include counterparty credit ratings and historical default rates or market credit default swap rates.

Discontinuation

The discontinuance of hedge accounting occurs in two situations: (1) if the transaction fails to meet any of the qualifying hedge criteria and (2) if the derivatives expire or are sold, terminated, exercised or simply de-designated as a hedging instrument.

Presentation and disclosure

The disclosure requirements in financial statements for derivatives and hedging activities are quite extensive. Qualitative disclosures should include the objective and strategy, risk management policy and description of hedged items. In addition, the disclosures pertaining to derivatives should include:

- The earnings impact from discontinued hedges.

- The amount of gains and losses included in other comprehensive income to be included in earnings within the next 12 months.

- Measures describing and aggregating the volume of derivatives activity, such as combined notional amounts by derivative types.

- Information concerning the existence and nature of credit risk-related contingent features and how they could be triggered.

- The purpose of derivatives that do not qualify as hedging instruments.

Furthermore, ASU 2017-12 amends the presentation and disclosure requirements for derivatives and hedging activities, and it changes how companies assess effectiveness, by requiring the following:

- Presentation of changes in the value of the hedging instrument in the same income statement line item as the earnings effect of the hedged item.

- Amendments to the previous tabular disclosure of hedging activities, focusing on the effect of hedge accounting on individual income statement line items.

- New disclosure offering more information to investors about basis adjustments in fair value hedges.

Although interpretations aimed at streamlining, and not complicating, existing guidance should increase the clarity and workability of relevant guidance, they are unlikely to eradicate all of the complexities inherent in the accounting for derivative instruments and hedging activities.

Gross versus net presentation

ASC 815-10-25-1 states that, "An entity shall recognize all of its derivative instruments in its statement of financial position as either assets or liabilities depending on the rights or obligations under the contracts." Derivative instruments should be recorded as gross assets or liabilities individually, according to agreed terms.

However, ASC 815-10-45 allows for the netting of transactions with the same counterparty if the entity has the right of setoff according to an enforceable master netting agreement. Netting (or offsetting) of counterparty exposures, when available, is not required; however, the election to offset (or not) must be applied consistently. Entities should disclose the role of master netting agreements in their credit-risk management approach.

An entity that is eligible and elects to present derivative balances on a net basis may also, under certain conditions, net counterparty exposures against collateral paid or received for the instruments presented. Separate gross footnote disclosures are required for collateral amounts that are subject to master netting agreements and have been presented as offsets to derivative balances.

Fair value measurements

ASC 820 offers reporting entities additional guidance and clarification for disclosing and measuring the fair value of derivative assets and liabilities. However, because those items within the scope of ASC 815 must be revalued continually, applying ASC 820's measurements and disclosures still may prove difficult for reporting entities with complex derivative portfolios.

To provide timely and consistent fair value estimates to the users of financial statements, ASC 820 requires reporting entities to consider:

- The "highest and best use" of the derivative asset or liability by market investors.

- The "principal or most advantageous market" for the entity's derivative instruments.

- Appropriate valuation techniques, incorporating assumptions of market participants.

- The most relevant fair value calculation and allocation to each unit of account, using the highest level of input available.

• • •

35

SEC Reporting Considerations

- **Definition of a business**

- **Requirements for an acquired business**

- **Pro forma financial statements**

- **Abbreviated financial statements**

- **Supplemental disclosures**

- **Common control transactions**

Photograph by istock.com/deberrar

This chapter describes certain SEC reporting and financial statement requirements related to acquisitions and capital market transactions, focusing primarily on issues and topics related to the oil and gas industry. However, it also refers to guidance that is not unique to the industry but is integral to oil and gas companies understanding and meeting the necessary requirements. It also includes a general description of other SEC reporting requirements relevant to the industry.

Definition of a business

For reporting purposes, the SEC definition of a business takes into consideration the facts and circumstances involved and whether there is sufficient continuity of the acquired entity's operations prior to and after the transaction, such that disclosure of prior financial information is material to an understanding of future operations. A presumption exists that a separate entity, subsidiary, division or operating segment (as defined within the guidance in GAAP or IFRS, as applicable) is a business. However, a lesser component of an entity may also constitute a business.

The reporting requirements for a significant acquisition per SEC Regulation S-X Rule 3-05 (Reg. S-X Rule 3-05) will depend on the composition of assets acquired. Acquisitions in the oil and gas industry can be structured in many different ways. For example, Company A may acquire all of the operating assets of Company B, a product line, or only certain operating assets, such as a working interest in specific upstream oil and gas properties.

The SEC Financial Reporting Manual (FRM) 2065.11 considers the acquisition of a working interest in an oil and gas property to be the acquisition of a business for which pre-acquisition financial statements are required, if significant. The SEC reporting requirements for significant business acquisitions of oil and gas properties focus on requirements that are specific to acquired upstream properties. These requirements are applicable only to those acquirers that have registered securities in the U.S. or those preparing an initial registration statement to become public (hereinafter referred to as a "registrant"). Additionally, this guidance, while not required, is typically followed in exempt offerings (e.g., Rule 144A offerings).

Requirements for an acquired business

As explained in Chapter 32, if a transaction represents the acquisition of a business, separate financial statements for the acquired business may be required under Reg. S-X Rule 3-05.[1] The first consideration is whether what is acquired meets the SEC definition of a business. If the acquisition meets the SEC definition of a business, the significance of that business relative to the acquirer's existing business will determine whether separate pre-acquisition historical financial statements of the acquired (or to be acquired) business are required and, if so, the historical periods that should be presented. The historical financial statements are typically included within a Form 8-K (Item 9.01), a Form S-1 (Item 11(e)) or a Form 10 (Item 13).

The SEC's pro forma disclosure requirements relating to the businesses acquired and to be acquired, as well as completed or probable dispositions of a significant portion of a business, are contained in Reg. S-X Rule 11-01 and Rule 11-02. Each of these rules leverages the SEC's definition of a significant subsidiary in Reg. S-X Rule 1-02(w) for purposes of evaluating the corresponding disclosure requirements.

Recent SEC amendments

In May 2020, the SEC adopted extensive changes to the financial statement disclosure requirements for business acquisitions and dispositions. The amendments are intended to improve the financial information about acquired or disposed businesses provided to investors, facilitate more timely access to capital, and reduce the complexity and costs to prepare the disclosures.

The changes include the following updates most relevant to companies in the oil and gas industry:

- Updating the tests used to determine significance and expanding the use of pro forma financial information when measuring significance.

- Reducing the maximum number of years for which financial statements under Reg. S-X Rule 3-05 are required to two years.

- Conforming the significance threshold and tests for a disposed business to those used for an acquired business.

- Modifying the disclosure requirements relating to the aggregate effect of acquisitions for which financial statements are not (or not yet) required.

- Revising the pro forma financial information requirements.

- Permitting abbreviated financial statements for certain acquisitions of a component of an entity.[2]

Registrants will be required to apply the new rules no later than the beginning of the registrant's fiscal year beginning after December 31, 2020, with voluntary early compliance generally permitted immediately, provided that the new rules are applied in their entirety from the date of early compliance.

Measuring significance

Registrants are required to measure the significance of an acquired (or to be acquired) business or disposed business using three tests: the asset test, the investment test and the income test. As previously mentioned, the significance tests are determined by reference to Reg. S-X Rule 1-02(w). All three tests must be completed to determine the significance of the business acquired (or to be acquired) or disposed. The tests are completed using the most recent pre-acquisition annual financial statements of the acquired or disposed business as well as the registrant's audited financial statements from the end of the most recently completed fiscal year (unless the registrant uses pro forma financial information to measure significance, as discussed subsequently in this chapter).

The SEC amendments update the investment test and the income test, with no change to the asset test. The three tests from Reg. S-X Rule 1-02(w), as updated, are summarized in Figure 35-1.

Figure 35-1

Significance test calculations

$$\text{Asset test} \quad = \quad \frac{\text{Total assets acquired}}{\text{Registrant's (acquirer's) total assets}}$$

$$\text{Investment test} \quad = \quad \frac{\text{Total purchase price}}{\text{Registrant's aggregate worldwide market value}^*}$$

$$\text{Income test} \text{ (net income component)}^{**} \quad = \quad \frac{\text{Acquired business' income from continuing operations before taxes}}{\text{Registrant's income from continuing operations before taxes}}$$

$$\text{Income test} \text{ (revenue component, if applicable)}^{**} \quad = \quad \frac{\text{Acquired business' consolidated total revenues from continuing operations}^1}{\text{Registrant's consolidated total revenues from continuing operations}^1}$$

[1] After intercompany eliminations.

* In accordance with amended Rule 1-02(w)(1)(i)(A), the registrant's aggregate worldwide market value includes both voting and non-voting common equity and is calculated as the average for the last five trading days of the registrant's most recently completed month prior to the earlier of: (1) the registrant's date of announcement of the acquisition or disposition or (2) the agreement date of the acquisition or disposition.

** In accordance with amended Rule 1-02(w)(1)(iii)(A), the updated income test includes a revenue component. The revenue component does not apply, however, if either the registrant and its subsidiaries consolidated or the acquired business did not have material revenue in each of the two most recently completed fiscal years.

With respect to the investment test, if the registrant does not have an aggregate worldwide market value, such as in an IPO situation or when the registrant's stock is not publicly traded, then the "total purchase price" for the acquired business should be compared to the registrant's consolidated total assets as of the end of the most recently completed fiscal year.

When considering the results of the income test in connection with an acquisition, the registrant should use the lower of the net income component or the revenue component for purposes of evaluating significance in order to determine the number of years of financial statements required to be provided, as discussed in the next section.

If both of the following conditions are met, the amended Rule 11-01(b)(3) permits registrants to measure significance using pro forma amounts that depict significant business acquisitions and dispositions consummated after the latest fiscal year end for which the registrant's financial statements are required to be filed:

- The registrant has filed audited financial statements required by Rule 3-05 for any such acquired business.

- The registrant has filed the pro forma financial information required by Article 11 for any such acquired or disposed business.

The pro forma amounts used may only give effect to significant acquired or disposed businesses and transaction accounting adjustments, as discussed subsequently within this chapter. It should also be noted that if a registrant uses pro forma financial information to determine the significance of an acquisition or disposition, it must continue to do so until its next annual report is filed.

Financial statement periods required

Amended Rule 3-05(b)(2) reduces the maximum number of years for which audited financial statements are required under Rule 3-05 from three years to two years. It also eliminates the requirement to provide financial statements for the comparative interim period when only one year of audited financial statements is required under Rule 3-05.

Based on the highest level of significance calculated in accordance with the three tests prescribed by Reg. S-X Rule 1-02(w), the registrant would be required to file with the SEC the financial statements of the acquired business as outlined in Figure 35-2 below.

Figure 35-2

Financial statements required for an acquired business

Significance threshold	Reg. S-X Rule 3-05 financial statements required
Less than 20%	No financial statements required.
Exceeds 20%, less than 40%	Financial statements for the most recent fiscal year (audited). Latest year-to-date interim period preceding the acquisition (unaudited).
Exceeds 40%	Financial statements for the two most recent fiscal years (audited). Latest year-to-date interim period preceding the acquisition (unaudited). Corresponding interim period of the preceding year (unaudited).

As discussed, the number of years of audited financial statements required to be presented under the amended guidance is summarized in Figure 35-3 below.

Figure 35-3

Number of fiscal years required

Significance threshold	Balance sheet	Statements of income and cash flows
Less than 20%	None	None
Exceeds 20%, less than 40%	1	1
Exceeds 40%	2	2

Amended Rule 3-05(b)(4) permits the omission of separate acquired business financial statements once the business has been included in the registrant's post-acquisition audited annual financial statements for either nine months or a complete fiscal year, depending on significance. This is a significant change as it eliminates certain provisions that required financial statements for older significant acquisitions to be included in filings such as a Form S-1.

Aggregate effect of acquisitions

If the aggregate impact of acquired or to be acquired businesses since the date of the registrant's most recent audited balance sheet for which financial statements are not (or not yet) required to be filed exceeds 50 percent, amended Rule 3-05(b)(2)(iv)(B) requires pre-acquisition financial statements for the most recent fiscal year and the most recent interim period for those acquired or to be acquired businesses that individually exceed 20 percent significance. Additionally, amended Rule 3-05(b)(2)(iv)(A) requires pro forma financial information that depicts the aggregate impact of all acquired or to be acquired businesses, in all material respects. This may require the registrant to disclose pro forma financial information relating to acquired or to be acquired businesses that are individually insignificant.

Consistent with the pre-existing rules, the disclosure requirements relating to the aggregate effect of acquisitions for which financial statements are not (or not yet) required are applicable to certain registration statements and proxy statements. Separate requirements apply to Item 2.01, *Completion of Acquisition or Disposition of Assets*, of Form 8-K.

Pro forma financial statements

SEC Regulation S-X Article 11 requires the presentation of pro forma financial statements if a significant business combination: (1) has occurred in the latest fiscal year or subsequent interim period, (2) has occurred after the date of the most recent balance sheet filed or (3) is "probable" of occurring and, per SEC FRM 3110.3, the transaction is significant at the 50 percent level or higher.

The definition of a "significant business combination" for the purposes of pro forma financial information is identical to the definition in Reg. S-X Rule 3-05 as described earlier in this chapter. The objective of such pro forma financial information is to give investors information about the continuing effect of a particular transaction by showing how the transaction might have affected the registrant's historical financial statements if it had been consummated at an earlier date.

The pro forma financial statements are included within either a Form 8-K (as required by Item 9.02) or in a registration statement (e.g., Form S-4) for existing public companies, or within a Form S-1 for any IPO.

Pro forma requirements

Pro forma financial statements, presented to show the effects of a significant business combination, are derived from historical financial statements of the registrant (acquirer) and of the acquired significant business (or businesses).

These statements consist of historical financial data of the acquirer, retrospectively combined with historical financial data of the acquired (or to be acquired) significant business (or businesses).

Reg. S-X Rule 11-02 generally requires pro forma financial statements to include:

- An introductory paragraph describing the transaction, entities involved, periods presented and the underlying assumptions.

- Condensed pro forma income statement(s).

- Condensed pro forma balance sheet.

- Explanatory notes with sufficient detail to enable a reader to understand the assumptions and calculations.

When pro forma income statements are required, registrants must present them for the most recent annual and interim periods (except for the one exception discussed in the next paragraph). Any interim presentation must cover the period from the most recent fiscal year-end to the date of the latest balance sheet presented. The pro forma income statements should assume that the transaction occurred at the beginning of the earliest fiscal year presented.

One exception to the number of periods presented for the income statement relates to transactions under common control. If the business acquisition is determined to be a transaction under common control, pro forma presentation for all periods is required as set forth in SEC FRM 3230.2.

Pro forma adjustment categories

Amended Rule 11-02(a)(6) and Rule 11-02(a)(7) replace the pre-existing pro forma adjustment criteria with the following three categories of adjustments:

Category	Description
Transaction accounting adjustments	Reflects only the application of required accounting to the transaction, such as purchase accounting.
Autonomous entity adjustments	Reflects the operations and financial position of the registrant as an autonomous entity if the registrant was previously part of another entity, such as a spin-off transaction in which the costs allocated to the entity do not reflect all of the expected costs of operating as a stand-alone public company.
Management's adjustments	Depicts synergies and dis-synergies of an acquisition or disposition for which pro forma effect is given.

Transaction accounting adjustments and autonomous entity adjustments are required when the conditions for their presentation are met. Autonomous entity adjustments must be presented in a separate column from transaction accounting adjustments.

Management's adjustments may be presented only in the notes to the pro forma financial statements at the discretion of management if, in management's opinion, they enhance an understanding of the pro forma effects of the transaction and all of the following conditions are met:

- There is a reasonable basis for each adjustment.

- The pro forma financial information reflects all of management's adjustments that are, in the opinion of management, necessary for a fair statement of the pro forma financial information presented and a statement to that effect is disclosed. When synergies are presented, any related dis-synergies must also be presented.

- The adjustments are limited to the effect of the synergies and dis-synergies on the historical financial statements that form the basis for the pro forma statement of comprehensive income, as if the synergies and dis-synergies existed as of the beginning of the fiscal year presented. If the adjustments reduce expenses, the reduction cannot exceed the amount of the related expense historically incurred during the pro forma period presented.

There are also a number of other presentation requirements, including specified reconciliations and disclosure of the basis for material assumptions or uncertainties. Additionally, amended Rule 11-02(a)(7)(ii)(B) indicates that management's adjustments may need to be updated when included or incorporated by reference in certain registration statements, proxy statements, offering statements or a Form 8-K. Rule 11-02(a)(7) includes an instruction indicating that any forward-looking information supplied is expressly covered by the safe harbor provisions of Securities Act Rule 175 and Exchange Act Rule 3b-6.

Abbreviated financial statements

For an acquisition of net assets that constitutes a business (e.g., an acquired or to be acquired product line), amended Rule 3-05(e) permits registrants to provide abbreviated financials for all required periods if the acquired business meets certain qualifying and presentation conditions as follows:

- The total assets and total revenues (both after intercompany eliminations) of the acquired or to be acquired business constitute 20 percent or less of such corresponding amounts of the seller and its subsidiaries consolidated as of and for the most recently completed fiscal year.

- The acquired business was not a separate entity, subsidiary, division or operating segment (as defined in GAAP or IFRS, as applicable) during the periods for which the acquired business financial statements would be required.

- Separate financial statements for the business have not previously been prepared.

- The seller has not maintained the distinct and separate accounts necessary to present financial statements that include the omitted expenses and it is impracticable to prepare such financial statements.

The SEC did not address acquisitions of businesses that exceed 20 percent of the seller's total assets or total revenues. Additionally, they did not address "carve-out" financial statements, noting that "… because issues relating to carve-out financial statements may require unique judgments that involve the balance between investor protection and capital access, we believe questions relating to carve-out financial statements are best addressed on the basis of their unique facts and circumstances through the staff consultation process."

If the previously outlined conditions are met, Rule 3-05(e)(2) provides various presentation requirements for the statement of revenues and expenses, including which expenses must be included and which may be omitted. The notes to the financial statements must also include additional disclosures, such as:

- A description of the type of omitted expenses and the reason why they are excluded from the financial statements.

- An explanation of the impracticability of preparing financial statements that include the omitted expenses.

- A description of how the financial statements presented are not indicative of the financial condition or results of operations of the acquired business going forward because of the omitted expenses.

- Information about the business' operating, investing and financing cash flows, to the extent available.

Amended Rule 3-05(f)(2) codifies similar provisions for the acquisition of a business which generates substantially all of its revenues from oil and gas producing activities, as defined in Rule 4-10(a)(16). Additionally, amended Rule 3-05(f)(1) requires certain disclosures set forth in ASC 932 for each full year of operations presented for an acquired or to be acquired business that includes significant oil and gas producing activities, as discussed in more detail in the next section. These disclosures may be presented as unaudited supplemental information.

Supplemental disclosures

Chapters 30 and 31 provide a detailed discussion of the supplemental disclosures described in ASC 932. As it relates to the requirements for a business acquisition, there are factors that should be considered by companies with significant oil and gas producing activities with respect to the pro forma financial statements and abbreviated financial statements to be filed by the acquiring company, as detailed below.

Supplemental disclosures in pro forma financial statements

If pro forma financial statements are presented for a significant business combination that includes the acquisition of interest(s) in one or more oil or gas properties (e.g., working interests, net profits interests, etc.), SEC SAB Topic 2.D requires certain supplementary disclosures described in ASC 932 to be presented, giving effect to the acquired properties in notes to the pro forma financial statements.

The registrant should furnish the following pro forma supplementary disclosures for each full year of operations presented for the acquired properties:

- Proved oil and gas reserve quantities and changes therein (ASC 932-235-50-3 through 50-11B).

- Standardized measure of discounted future cash flows (ASC 932-235-50-29 through 50-33).

- Changes in the standardized measure (ASC 932-235-50-34 through 50-36).

The disclosures are derived using historical financial statements of the acquirer, together with historical financial statements of the acquired business, assuming the transaction was consummated at the beginning of the earliest fiscal year presented in the pro forma financial statements.

Supplemental disclosures in abbreviated financial statements

The SEC provides additional relief regarding the supplementary disclosures described in ASC 932 for acquired properties when a registrant presents only the statement of revenues and direct expenses and omits the statement of assets acquired and liabilities assumed. The registrant must furnish the following supplementary disclosures for each full year of operations for the acquired property:

- Proved oil and gas reserve quantities and changes therein (ASC 932-235-50-3 through 50-11B).

- Standardized measure of discounted future cash flows (ASC 932-235-50-29 through 50-33).

- Changes in the standardized measure (ASC 932-235-50-34 through 50-36).

Prior year reserve studies may not be complete for the acquired property (or properties) on a stand-alone basis. As a result, SEC FRM 2065.12 states that it does not object to the computation of reserves for prior years, using only production and new discovery quantities and valuation changes. In this case, there is no revision of prior estimates. Registrants may compute these disclosures based on a reserve study for the most recent year and reflect the changes on a "rollback" basis. When using such methodology, the method of computation should be disclosed in a footnote.

Accordingly, the following supplementary disclosures described in ASC 932 may be omitted when presenting only the statement of revenues and direct expenses for the acquired property:

- Capitalized costs (ASC 932-235-50-12 through 50-16).

- Costs incurred for property acquisition, exploration and development activities (ASC 932-235-50-17 through 50-20).

- Results of operations for oil and gas producing activities (ASC 932-235-50-21 through 50-28).

Common control transactions

Common control transactions are transfers and exchanges between entities under control of the same parent, or transactions in which all of the combining entities are controlled by the same party or parties before and after the transaction and for which control is not transitory. Under GAAP, companies are required to account for these transactions by using the carryover historical cost basis. If the common control transaction is considered to be a business, the company is required to recast prior period financial statements to show the companies on a combined basis for all periods. If the common control transaction is considered to be an asset acquisition, the assets acquired are recorded using the carryover historical cost basis on the acquisition date and accounted for prospectively.

• • •

---

1 Amended Rule 8-04, Rule 8-05 and Rule 8-06 provide corresponding guidance for smaller reporting companies (based on the SEC definition of such companies).

2 While permitting registrants to provide abbreviated financial statements for an acquisition of oil and gas properties is not a new concept under the amended SEC guidance as compared to existing standards, amended Rule 3-05(f)(1) and amended Rule 3-05(f)(2) codify specific provisions for the acquisition of a business which generates substantially all of its revenues from oil and gas producing activities. See further discussion within this chapter.

Regulation S-X Rule 4-10

Reprinted from Electronic Code of Federal Regulations as of December 31, 2019.
https://www.ecfr.gov/cgi-bin/text-idx?amp;node=17:3.0.1.1.8&rgn=div5#se17.3.210_14_610.

Regulation S-X Rule 4-10 prescribes the financial accounting and reporting standards for oil and gas producing activities of Securities and Exchange Commission (SEC) registrants. The subsections are listed below for reference.

§210.4-10 Financial accounting and reporting for oil and gas producing activities pursuant to the Federal securities laws and the Energy Policy and Conservation Act of 1975.

This section prescribes financial accounting and reporting standards for registrants with the Commission engaged in oil and gas producing activities in filings under the Federal securities laws and for the preparation of accounts by persons engaged, in whole or in part, in the production of crude oil or natural gas in the United States, pursuant to section 503 of the Energy Policy and Conservation Act of 1975 (42 U.S.C. 6383) (*EPCA*) and section 11(c) of the Energy Supply and Environmental Coordination Act of 1974 (15 U.S.C. 796) (*ESECA*), as amended by section 505 of EPCA. The application of this section to those oil and gas producing operations of companies regulated for ratemaking purposes on an individual-company-cost-of-service basis may, however, give appropriate recognition to differences arising because of the effect of the ratemaking process.

Exemption. Any person exempted by the Department of Energy from any record-keeping or reporting requirements pursuant to section 11(c) of ESECA, as amended, is similarly exempted from the related provisions of this section in the preparation of accounts pursuant to EPCA. This exemption does not affect the applicability of this section to filings pursuant to the Federal securities laws.

DEFINITIONS

(a) *Definitions.* The following definitions apply to the terms listed below as they are used in this section:

    (1) *Acquisition of properties.* Costs incurred to purchase, lease or otherwise acquire a property, including costs of lease bonuses and options to purchase or lease properties, the portion of costs applicable to minerals when land including mineral rights is purchased in fee, brokers' fees, recording fees, legal costs, and other costs incurred in acquiring properties.

    (2) *Analogous reservoir.* Analogous reservoirs, as used in resources assessments, have similar rock and fluid properties, reservoir conditions (depth, temperature, and pressure) and drive mechanisms, but are typically at a more advanced stage of development than the reservoir of interest and thus may provide concepts to assist in the interpretation of more limited data and estimation of recovery. When used to support proved reserves, an "analogous reservoir" refers to a reservoir that shares the following characteristics with the reservoir of interest:

        (i) Same geological formation (but not necessarily in pressure communication with the reservoir of interest);

        (ii) Same environment of deposition;

        (iii) Similar geological structure; and

        (iv) Same drive mechanism.

Instruction to paragraph (a)(2): Reservoir properties must, in the aggregate, be no more favorable in the analog than in the reservoir of interest.

(3) *Bitumen.* Bitumen, sometimes referred to as natural bitumen, is petroleum in a solid or semi-solid state in natural deposits with a viscosity greater than 10,000 centipoise measured at original temperature in the deposit and atmospheric pressure, on a gas free basis. In its natural state it usually contains sulfur, metals, and other non-hydrocarbons.

(4) *Condensate.* Condensate is a mixture of hydrocarbons that exists in the gaseous phase at original reservoir temperature and pressure, but that, when produced, is in the liquid phase at surface pressure and temperature.

(5) *Deterministic estimate.* The method of estimating reserves or resources is called deterministic when a single value for each parameter (from the geoscience, engineering, or economic data) in the reserves calculation is used in the reserves estimation procedure.

(6) *Developed oil and gas reserves.* Developed oil and gas reserves are reserves of any category that can be expected to be recovered:

    (i) Through existing wells with existing equipment and operating methods or in which the cost of the required equipment is relatively minor compared to the cost of a new well; and

    (ii) Through installed extraction equipment and infrastructure operational at the time of the reserves estimate if the extraction is by means not involving a well.

(7) *Development costs.* Costs incurred to obtain access to proved reserves and to provide facilities for extracting, treating, gathering and storing the oil and gas. More specifically, development costs, including depreciation and applicable operating costs of support equipment and facilities and other costs of development activities, are costs incurred to:

    (i) For each cost center for each year that a statement of comprehensive income is required, disclose the total amount of amortization expense (per equivalent physical unit of production if amortization is computed on the basis of physical units or per dollar of gross revenue from production if amortization is computed on the basis of gross revenue).

    (ii) Drill and equip development wells, development-type stratigraphic test wells, and service wells, including the costs of platforms and of well equipment such as casing, tubing, pumping equipment, and the wellhead assembly.

    (iii) Acquire, construct, and install production facilities such as lease flow lines, separators, treaters, heaters, manifolds, measuring devices, and production storage tanks, natural gas cycling and processing plants, and central utility and waste disposal systems.

    (iv) Provide improved recovery systems.

(8) *Development project.* A development project is the means by which petroleum resources are brought to the status of economically producible. As examples, the development of a single reservoir or field, an incremental development in a producing field, or the integrated development of a group of several fields and associated facilities with a common ownership may constitute a development project.

(9) *Development well.* A well drilled within the proved area of an oil or gas reservoir to the depth of a stratigraphic horizon known to be productive.

(10) *Economically producible.* The term economically producible, as it relates to a resource, means a resource which generates revenue that exceeds, or is reasonably expected to exceed, the costs of the operation. The value of the products that generate revenue shall be determined at the terminal point of oil and gas producing activities as defined in paragraph (a)(16) of this section.

(11) *Estimated ultimate recovery (EUR).* Estimated ultimate recovery is the sum of reserves remaining as of a given date and cumulative production as of that date.

(12) *Exploration costs.* Costs incurred in identifying areas that may warrant examination and in examining specific areas that are considered to have prospects of containing oil and gas reserves, including costs of drilling exploratory wells and exploratory-type stratigraphic test wells. Exploration costs may be incurred both before acquiring the related property (sometimes referred to in part as prospecting costs) and after acquiring the property. Principal types of exploration costs, which include depreciation and applicable operating costs of support equipment and facilities and other costs of exploration activities, are:

    (i)   Costs of topographical, geographical and geophysical studies, rights of access to properties to conduct those studies, and salaries and other expenses of geologists, geophysical crews, and others conducting those studies. Collectively, these are sometimes referred to as geological and geophysical or G&G costs.

    (ii)   Costs of carrying and retaining undeveloped properties, such as delay rentals, ad valorem taxes on properties, legal costs for title defense, and the maintenance of land and lease records.

    (iii)   Dry hole contributions and bottom hole contributions.

    (iv)   Costs of drilling and equipping exploratory wells.

    (v)   Costs of drilling exploratory-type stratigraphic test wells.

(13) *Exploratory well.* An exploratory well is a well drilled to find a new field or to find a new reservoir in a field previously found to be productive of oil or gas in another reservoir. Generally, an exploratory well is any well that is not a development well, an extension well, a service well, or a stratigraphic test well as those items are defined in this section.

(14) *Extension well.* An extension well is a well drilled to extend the limits of a known reservoir.

(15) *Field.* An area consisting of a single reservoir or multiple reservoirs all grouped on or related to the same individual geological structural feature and/or stratigraphic condition. There may be two or more reservoirs in a field that are separated vertically by intervening impervious, strata, or laterally by local geologic barriers, or by both. Reservoirs that are associated by being in overlapping or adjacent fields may be treated as a single or common operational field. The geological terms structural feature and stratigraphic condition are intended to identify localized geological features as opposed to the broader terms of basins, trends, provinces, plays, areas-of-interest, etc.

(16) *Oil and gas producing activities.*

   (i)   Oil and gas producing activities include:

      (A)   The search for crude oil, including condensate and natural gas liquids, or natural gas ("oil and gas") in their natural states and original locations;

      (B)   The acquisition of property rights or properties for the purpose of further exploration or for the purpose of removing the oil or gas from such properties;

      (C)   The construction, drilling, and production activities necessary to retrieve oil and gas from their natural reservoirs, including the acquisition, construction, installation, and maintenance of field gathering and storage systems, such as:

         (1)   Lifting the oil and gas to the surface; and

         (2)   Gathering, treating, and field processing (as in the case of processing gas to extract liquid hydrocarbons); and

      (D)   Extraction of saleable hydrocarbons, in the solid, liquid, or gaseous state, from oil sands, shale, coalbeds, or other nonrenewable natural resources which are intended to be upgraded into synthetic oil or gas, and activities undertaken with a view to such extraction.

   Instruction 1 to paragraph (a)(16)(i): The oil and gas production function shall be regarded as ending at a "terminal point", which is the outlet valve on the lease or field storage tank. If unusual physical or operational circumstances exist, it may be appropriate to regard the terminal point for the production function as:

      a.   The first point at which oil, gas, or gas liquids, natural or synthetic, are delivered to a main pipeline, a common carrier, a refinery, or a marine terminal; and

      b.   In the case of natural resources that are intended to be upgraded into synthetic oil or gas, if those natural resources are delivered to a purchaser prior to upgrading, the first point at which the natural resources are delivered to a main pipeline, a common carrier, a refinery, a marine terminal, or a facility which upgrades such natural resources into synthetic oil or gas.

   Instruction 2 to paragraph (a)(16)(i): For purposes of this paragraph (a)(16), the term saleable hydrocarbons means hydrocarbons that are saleable in the state in which the hydrocarbons are delivered.

(ii) Oil and gas producing activities do not include:

   (A) Transporting, refining, or marketing oil and gas;

   (B) Processing of produced oil, gas or natural resources that can be upgraded into synthetic oil or gas by a registrant that does not have the legal right to produce or a revenue interest in such production;

   (C) Activities relating to the production of natural resources other than oil, gas, or natural resources from which synthetic oil and gas can be extracted; or

   (D) Production of geothermal steam.

(17) *Possible reserves.* Possible reserves are those additional reserves that are less certain to be recovered than probable reserves.

   (i) When deterministic methods are used, the total quantities ultimately recovered from a project have a low probability of exceeding proved plus probable plus possible reserves. When probabilistic methods are used, there should be at least a 10% probability that the total quantities ultimately recovered will equal or exceed the proved plus probable plus possible reserves estimates.

   (ii) Possible reserves may be assigned to areas of a reservoir adjacent to probable reserves where data control and interpretations of available data are progressively less certain. Frequently, this will be in areas where geoscience and engineering data are unable to define clearly the area and vertical limits of commercial production from the reservoir by a defined project.

   (iii) Possible reserves also include incremental quantities associated with a greater percentage recovery of the hydrocarbons in place than the recovery quantities assumed for probable reserves.

   (iv) The proved plus probable and proved plus probable plus possible reserves estimates must be based on reasonable alternative technical and commercial interpretations within the reservoir or subject project that are clearly documented, including comparisons to results in successful similar projects.

   (v) Possible reserves may be assigned where geoscience and engineering data identify directly adjacent portions of a reservoir within the same accumulation that may be separated from proved areas by faults with displacement less than formation thickness or other geological discontinuities and that have not been penetrated by a wellbore, and the registrant believes that such adjacent portions are in communication with the known (proved) reservoir. Possible reserves may be assigned to areas that are structurally higher or lower than the proved area if these areas are in communication with the proved reservoir.

(vi) (Pursuant to paragraph (a)(22)(iii) of this section, where direct observation has defined a highest known oil (HKO) elevation and the potential exists for an associated gas cap, proved oil reserves should be assigned in the structurally higher portions of the reservoir above the HKO only if the higher contact can be established with reasonable certainty through reliable technology. Portions of the reservoir that do not meet this reasonable certainty criterion may be assigned as probable and possible oil or gas based on reservoir fluid properties and pressure gradient interpretations.

(18) *Probable reserves.* Probable reserves are those additional reserves that are less certain to be recovered than proved reserves but which, together with proved reserves, are as likely as not to be recovered.

    (i)   When deterministic methods are used, it is as likely as not that actual remaining quantities recovered will exceed the sum of estimated proved plus probable reserves. When probabilistic methods are used, there should be at least a 50% probability that the actual quantities recovered will equal or exceed the proved plus probable reserves estimates.

    (ii)   Probable reserves may be assigned to areas of a reservoir adjacent to proved reserves where data control or interpretations of available data are less certain, even if the interpreted reservoir continuity of structure or productivity does not meet the reasonable certainty criterion. Probable reserves may be assigned to areas that are structurally higher than the proved area if these areas are in communication with the proved reservoir.

    (iii)   Probable reserves estimates also include potential incremental quantities associated with a greater percentage recovery of the hydrocarbons in place than assumed for proved reserves.

    (iv)   See also guidelines in paragraphs (a)(17)(iv) and (a)(17)(vi) of this section.

(19) *Probabilistic estimate.* The method of estimation of reserves or resources is called probabilistic when the full range of values that could reasonably occur for each unknown parameter (from the geoscience and engineering data) is used to generate a full range of possible outcomes and their associated probabilities of occurrence.

(20) *Production costs.*

    (i)   Costs incurred to operate and maintain wells and related equipment and facilities, including depreciation and applicable operating costs of support equipment and facilities and other costs of operating and maintaining those wells and related equipment and facilities. They become part of the cost of oil and gas produced. Examples of production costs (sometimes called lifting costs) are:

        (A)   Costs of labor to operate the wells and related equipment and facilities.

        (B)   Repairs and maintenance.

        (C)   Materials, supplies, and fuel consumed and supplies utilized in operating the wells and related equipment and facilities.

(D) Property taxes and insurance applicable to proved properties and wells and related equipment and facilities.

(E) Severance taxes.

(ii) Some support equipment or facilities may serve two or more oil and gas producing activities and may also serve transportation, refining, and marketing activities. To the extent that the support equipment and facilities are used in oil and gas producing activities, their depreciation and applicable operating costs become exploration, development or production costs, as appropriate. Depreciation, depletion, and amortization of capitalized acquisition, exploration, and development costs are not production costs but also become part of the cost of oil and gas produced along with production (lifting) costs identified above.

(21) *Proved area.* The part of a property to which proved reserves have been specifically attributed.

(22) *Proved oil and gas reserves.* Proved oil and gas reserves are those quantities of oil and gas, which, by analysis of geoscience and engineering data, can be estimated with reasonable certainty to be economically producible – from a given date forward, from known reservoirs, and under existing economic conditions, operating methods, and government regulations – prior to the time at which contracts providing the right to operate expire, unless evidence indicates that renewal is reasonably certain, regardless of whether deterministic or probabilistic methods are used for the estimation. The project to extract the hydrocarbons must have commenced or the operator must be reasonably certain that it will commence the project within a reasonable time.

(i) The area of the reservoir considered as proved includes:

(A) The area identified by drilling and limited by fluid contacts, if any, and

(B) Adjacent undrilled portions of the reservoir that can, with reasonable certainty, be judged to be continuous with it and to contain economically producible oil or gas on the basis of available geoscience and engineering data.

(ii) In the absence of data on fluid contacts, proved quantities in a reservoir are limited by the lowest known hydrocarbons (LKH) as seen in a well penetration unless geoscience, engineering, or performance data and reliable technology establishes a lower contact with reasonable certainty.

(iii) Where direct observation from well penetrations has defined a highest known oil (HKO) elevation and the potential exists for an associated gas cap, proved oil reserves may be assigned in the structurally higher portions of the reservoir only if geoscience, engineering, or performance data and reliable technology establish the higher contact with reasonable certainty.

(iv) Reserves which can be produced economically through application of improved recovery techniques (including, but not limited to, fluid injection) are included in the proved classification when:

(A) Successful testing by a pilot project in an area of the reservoir with properties no more favorable than in the reservoir as a whole, the operation of an installed program in the reservoir or an analogous reservoir, or other evidence using reliable technology establishes the reasonable certainty of the engineering analysis on which the project or program was based; and

(B) The project has been approved for development by all necessary parties and entities, including governmental entities.

(v) Existing economic conditions include prices and costs at which economic producibility from a reservoir is to be determined. The price shall be the average price during the 12-month period prior to the ending date of the period covered by the report, determined as an unweighted arithmetic average of the first-day-of-the-month price for each month within such period, unless prices are defined by contractual arrangements, excluding escalations based upon future conditions.

(23) *Proved properties.* Properties with proved reserves.

(24) *Reasonable certainty.* If deterministic methods are used, reasonable certainty means a high degree of confidence that the quantities will be recovered. If probabilistic methods are used, there should be at least a 90% probability that the quantities actually recovered will equal or exceed the estimate. A high degree of confidence exists if the quantity is much more likely to be achieved than not, and, as changes due to increased availability of geoscience (geological, geophysical, and geochemical), engineering, and economic data are made to estimated ultimate recovery (EUR) with time, reasonably certain EUR is much more likely to increase or remain constant than to decrease.

(25) *Reliable technology.* Reliable technology is a grouping of one or more technologies (including computational methods) that has been field tested and has been demonstrated to provide reasonably certain results with consistency and repeatability in the formation being evaluated or in an analogous formation.

(26) *Reserves.* Reserves are estimated remaining quantities of oil and gas and related substances anticipated to be economically producible, as of a given date, by application of development projects to known accumulations. In addition, there must exist, or there must be a reasonable expectation that there will exist, the legal right to produce or a revenue interest in the production, installed means of delivering oil and gas or related substances to market, and all permits and financing required to implement the project.

NOTE TO PARAGRAPH (a)(26): Reserves should not be assigned to adjacent reservoirs isolated by major, potentially sealing, faults until those reservoirs are penetrated and evaluated as economically producible. Reserves should not be assigned to areas that are clearly separated from a known accumulation by a non-productive reservoir (i.e., absence of reservoir, structurally low reservoir, or negative test results). Such areas may contain prospective resources (i.e., potentially recoverable resources from undiscovered accumulations).

(27) *Reservoir.* A porous and permeable underground formation containing a natural accumulation of producible oil and/or gas that is confined by impermeable rock or water barriers and is individual and separate from other reservoirs.

(28) *Resources.* Resources are quantities of oil and gas estimated to exist in naturally occurring accumulations. A portion of the resources may be estimated to be recoverable, and another portion may be considered to be unrecoverable. Resources include both discovered and undiscovered accumulations.

(29) *Service well.* A well drilled or completed for the purpose of supporting production in an existing field. Specific purposes of service wells include gas injection, water injection, steam injection, air injection, salt-water disposal, water supply for injection, observation, or injection for in-situ combustion.

(30) *Stratigraphic test well.* A stratigraphic test well is a drilling effort, geologically directed, to obtain information pertaining to a specific geologic condition. Such wells customarily are drilled without the intent of being completed for hydrocarbon production. The classification also includes tests identified as core tests and all types of expendable holes related to hydrocarbon exploration. Stratigraphic tests are classified as "exploratory type" if not drilled in a known area or "development type" if drilled in a known area.

(31) *Undeveloped oil and gas reserves.* Undeveloped oil and gas reserves are reserves of any category that are expected to be recovered from new wells on undrilled acreage, or from existing wells where a relatively major expenditure is required for recompletion.

   (i)   Reserves on undrilled acreage shall be limited to those directly offsetting development spacing areas that are reasonably certain of production when drilled, unless evidence using reliable technology exists that establishes reasonable certainty of economic producibility at greater distances.

   (ii) Undrilled locations can be classified as having undeveloped reserves only if a development plan has been adopted indicating that they are scheduled to be drilled within five years, unless the specific circumstances, justify a longer time.

   (iii) Under no circumstances shall estimates for undeveloped reserves be attributable to any acreage for which an application of fluid injection or other improved recovery technique is contemplated, unless such techniques have been proved effective by actual projects in the same reservoir or an analogous reservoir, as defined in paragraph (a)(2) of this section, or by other evidence using reliable technology establishing reasonable certainty.

(32) *Unproved properties.* Properties with no proved reserves.

Successful efforts method

(b) A reporting entity that follows the successful efforts method shall comply with the accounting and financial reporting disclosure requirements of FASB ASC Topic 932, *Extractive Activities – Oil and Gas.*

Full cost method

(c) *Application of the full cost method of accounting.* A reporting entity that follows the full cost method shall apply that method to all of its operations and to the operations of its subsidiaries, as follows:

(1) *Determination of cost centers.* Cost centers shall be established on a country-by-country basis.

(2) *Costs to be capitalized.* All costs associated with property acquisition, exploration, and development activities (as defined in paragraph (a) of this section) shall be capitalized within the appropriate cost center. Any internal costs that are capitalized shall be limited to those costs that can be directly identified with acquisition, exploration, and development activities undertaken by the reporting entity for its own account, and shall not include any costs related to production, general corporate overhead, or similar activities.

(3) *Amortization of capitalized costs.* Capitalized costs within a cost center shall be amortized on the unit-of-production basis using proved oil and gas reserves, as follows:

   (i) Costs to be amortized shall include (A) all capitalized costs, less accumulated amortization, other than the cost of properties described in paragraph (ii) below; (B) the estimated future expenditures (based on current costs) to be incurred in developing proved reserves; and (C) estimated dismantlement and abandonment costs, net of estimated salvage values.

   (ii) The cost of investments in unproved properties and major development projects may be excluded from capitalized costs to be amortized, subject to the following:

      (A) All costs directly associated with the acquisition and evaluation of unproved properties may be excluded from the amortization computation until it is determined whether or not proved reserves can be assigned to the properties, subject to the following conditions:

         (1) Until such a determination is made, the properties shall be assessed at least annually to ascertain whether impairment has occurred. Unevaluated properties whose costs are individually significant shall be assessed individually. Where it is not practicable to individually assess the amount of impairment of properties for which costs are not individually significant, such properties may be grouped for purposes of assessing impairment. Impairment may be estimated by applying factors based on historical experience and other data such as primary lease terms of the properties, average holding periods of unproved properties, and geographic and geologic data to groupings of individually insignificant properties and projects. The amount of impairment assessed under either of these methods shall be added to the costs to be amortized.

         (2) The costs of drilling exploratory dry holes shall be included in the amortization base immediately upon determination that the well is dry.

(3)   If geological and geophysical costs cannot be directly associated with specific unevaluated properties, they shall be included in the amortization base as incurred. Upon complete evaluation of a property, the total remaining excluded cost (net of any impairment) shall be included in the full cost amortization base.

(B)   Certain costs may be excluded from amortization when incurred in connection with major development projects expected to entail significant costs to ascertain the quantities of proved reserves attributable to the properties under development (e.g., the installation of an offshore drilling platform from which development wells are to be drilled, the installation of improved recovery programs, and similar major projects undertaken in the expectation of significant additions to proved reserves). The amounts which may be excluded are applicable portions of (1) the costs that relate to the major development project and have not previously been included in the amortization base, and (2) the estimated future expenditures associated with the development project. The excluded portion of any common costs associated with the development project should be based, as is most appropriate in the circumstances, on a comparison of either (i) existing proved reserves to total proved reserves expected to be established upon completion of the project, or (ii) the number of wells to which proved reserves have been assigned and total number of wells expected to be drilled. Such costs may be excluded from costs to be amortized until the earlier determination of whether additional reserves are proved or impairment occurs.

(C)   Excluded costs and the proved reserves related to such costs shall be transferred into the amortization base on an ongoing (well-by-well or property-by-property) basis as the project is evaluated and proved reserves established or impairment determined. Once proved reserves are established, there is no further justification for continued exclusion from the full cost amortization base even if other factors prevent immediate production or marketing.

(iii)   Amortization shall be computed on the basis of physical units, with oil and gas converted to a common unit of measure on the basis of their approximate relative energy content, unless economic circumstances (related to the effects of regulated prices) indicate that use of units of revenue is a more appropriate basis of computing amortization. In the latter case, amortization shall be computed on the basis of current gross revenues (excluding royalty payments and net profits disbursements) from production in relation to future gross revenues, based on current prices (including consideration of changes in existing prices provided only by contractual arrangements), from estimated production of proved oil and gas reserves. The effect of a significant price increase during the year on estimated future gross revenues shall be reflected in the amortization provision only for the period after the price increase occurs.

(iv)   In some cases it may be more appropriate to depreciate natural gas cycling and processing plants by a method other than the unit-of-production method.

(v)   Amortization computations shall be made on a consolidated basis, including investees accounted for on a proportionate consolidation basis. Investees accounted for on the equity method shall be treated separately.

(4)   *Limitation on capitalized costs.*

     (i)   For each cost center, capitalized costs, less accumulated amortization and related deferred income taxes, shall not exceed an amount (the cost center ceiling) equal to the sum of:

         (A)   The present value of estimated future net revenues computed by applying current prices of oil and gas reserves (with consideration of price changes only to the extent provided by contractual arrangements) to estimated future production of proved oil and gas reserves as of the date of the latest balance sheet presented, less estimated future expenditures (based on current costs) to be incurred in developing and producing the proved reserves computed using a discount factor of ten percent and assuming continuation of existing economic conditions; plus

         (B)   the cost of properties not being amortized pursuant to paragraph (i)(3)(ii) of this section; plus

         (C)   the lower of cost or estimated fair value of unproven properties included in the costs being amortized; less

         (D)   income tax effects related to differences between the book and tax basis of the properties referred to in paragraphs (i)(4)(i) (B) and (C) of this section.

     (ii)   If unamortized costs capitalized within a cost center, less related deferred income taxes, exceed the cost center ceiling, the excess shall be charged to expense and separately disclosed during the period in which the excess occurs. Amounts thus required to be written off shall not be reinstated for any subsequent increase in the cost center ceiling.

(5)   *Production costs.* All costs relating to production activities, including workover costs incurred solely to maintain or increase levels of production from an existing completion interval, shall be charged to expense as incurred.

(6)   *Other transactions.* The provisions of paragraph (h) of this section, "Mineral property conveyances and related transactions if the successful efforts method of accounting is followed," shall apply also to those reporting entities following the full cost method except as follows:

(i)   *Sales and abandonments of oil and gas properties.* Sales of oil and gas properties, whether or not being amortized currently, shall be accounted for as adjustments of capitalized costs, with no gain or loss recognized, unless such adjustments would significantly alter the relationship between capitalized costs and proved reserves of oil and gas attributable to a cost center. For instance, a significant alteration would not ordinarily be expected to occur for sales involving less than 25 percent of the reserve quantities of a given cost center. If gain or loss is recognized on such a sale, total capitalization costs within the cost center shall be allocated between the reserves sold and reserves retained on the same basis used to compute amortization, unless there are substantial economic differences between the properties sold and those retained, in which case capitalized costs shall be allocated on the basis of the relative fair values of the properties. Abandonments of oil and gas properties shall be accounted for as adjustments of capitalized costs; that is, the cost of abandoned properties shall be charged to the full cost center and amortized (subject to the limitation on capitalized costs in paragraph (b) of this section).

(ii) *Purchases of reserves.* Purchases of oil and gas reserves in place ordinarily shall be accounted for as additional capitalized costs within the applicable cost center; however, significant purchases of production payments or properties with lives substantially shorter than the composite productive life of the cost center shall be accounted for separately.

(iii) *Partnerships, joint ventures and drilling arrangements.*

  (A)   Except as provided in paragraph (i)(6)(i) of this section, all consideration received from sales or transfers of properties in connection with partnerships, joint venture operations, or various other forms of drilling arrangements involving oil and gas exploration and development activities (e.g., carried interest, turnkey wells, management fees, etc.) shall be credited to the full cost account, except to the extent of amounts that represent reimbursement of organization, offering, general and administrative expenses, etc., that are identifiable with the transaction, if such amounts are currently incurred and charged to expense.

  (B)   Where a registrant organizes and manages a limited partnership involved only in the purchase of proved developed properties and subsequent distribution of income from such properties, management fee income may be recognized provided the properties involved do not require aggregate development expenditures in connection with production of existing proved reserves in excess of 10% of the partnership's recorded cost of such properties. Any income not recognized as a result of this limitation would be credited to the full cost account and recognized through a lower amortization provision as reserves are produced.

(iv)   *Other services.* No income shall be recognized in connection with contractual services performed (e.g., drilling, well service, or equipment supply services, etc.) in connection with properties in which the registrant or an affiliate (as defined in §210.1-02(b)) holds an ownership or other economic interest, except as follows:

    (A)   Where the registrant acquires an interest in the properties in connection with the service contract, income may be recognized to the extent the cash consideration received exceeds the related contract costs plus the registrant's share of costs incurred and estimated to be incurred in connection with the properties. Ownership interests acquired within one year of the date of such a contract are considered to be acquired in connection with the service for purposes of applying this rule. The amount of any guarantees or similar arrangements undertaken as part of this contract should be considered as part of the costs related to the properties for purposes of applying this rule.

    (B)   Where the registrant acquired an interest in the properties at least one year before the date of the service contract through transactions unrelated to the service contract, and that interest is unaffected by the service contract, income from such contract may be recognized subject to the general provisions for elimination of inter-company profit under generally accepted accounting principles.

    (C)   Notwithstanding the provisions of paragraphs (i)(6)(iv) (A) and (B) of this section, no income may be recognized for contractual services performed on behalf of investors in oil and gas producing activities managed by the registrant or an affiliate. Furthermore, no income may be recognized for contractual services to the extent that the consideration received for such services represents an interest in the underlying property.

    (D)   Any income not recognized as a result of these rules would be credited to the full cost account and recognized through a lower amortization provision as reserves are produced.

(7)   *Disclosures.* Reporting entities that follow the full cost method of accounting shall disclose all of the information required by paragraph (k) of this section, with each cost center considered as a separate geographic area, except that reasonable groupings may be made of cost centers that are not significant in the aggregate. In addition:

    (i)   For each cost center for each year that an income statement is required, disclose the total amount of amortization expense (per equivalent physical unit of production if amortization is computed on the basis of physical units or per dollar of gross revenue from production if amortization is computed on the basis of gross revenue).

    (ii)   State separately on the face of the balance sheet the aggregate of the capitalized costs of unproved properties and major development projects that are excluded, in accordance with paragraph (i)(3) of this section, from the capitalized costs being amortized. Provide a description in the notes to the financial statements of the current status of the significant properties or projects involved, including the anticipated timing of the inclusion of the costs in the amortization computation. Present a table that shows, by category of cost, (A) the total costs excluded as of the most recent fiscal year; and (B) the amounts of such excluded costs, incurred (1) in each of the three most recent fiscal years and (2) in the aggregate for any earlier fiscal years in which the costs were incurred. Categories of cost to be disclosed include acquisition costs, exploration costs, development costs in the case of significant development projects and capitalized interest.

(8)   For purposes of this paragraph (c), the term "current price" shall mean the average price during the 12-month period prior to the ending date of the period covered by the report, determined as an unweighted arithmetic average of the first-day-of-the-month price for each month within such period, unless prices are defined by contractual arrangements, excluding escalations based upon future conditions.

INCOME TAXES

(d)   *Income taxes.* Comprehensive interperiod income tax allocation by a method which complies with generally accepted accounting principles shall be followed for intangible drilling and development costs and other costs incurred that enter into the determination of taxable income and pretax accounting income in different periods.

● ● ●

Disclosure by Registrants Engaged in Oil and Gas Producing Activities

Reprinted from Electronic Code of Federal Regulations as of December 31, 2019.
https://www.ecfr.gov/cgi-bin/text-idx?amp;node=17:3.0.1.1.11&rgn=div5#sp17.3.229.229_11200.

§229.1201 (Item 1201) General instructions to oil and gas industry-specific disclosures.

(a)   If oil and gas producing activities are material to the registrant's or its subsidiaries' business operations or financial position, the disclosure specified in this Subpart 229.1200 should be included under appropriate captions (with cross references, where applicable, to related information disclosed in financial statements). However, limited partnerships and joint ventures that conduct, operate, manage, or report upon oil and gas drilling or income programs, that acquire properties either for drilling and production, or for production of oil, gas, or geothermal steam or water, need not include such disclosure.

(b)   To the extent that Items 1202 through 1208 (§§229.1202-229.1208) call for disclosures in tabular format, as specified in the particular Item, a registrant may modify such format for ease of presentation, to add information or to combine two or more required tables.

(c)   The definitions in Rule 4-10(a) of Regulation S-X (17 CFR 210.4-10(a)) shall apply for purposes of this Subpart 229.1200.

(d)   For purposes of this Subpart 229.1200, the term by geographic area means, as appropriate for meaningful disclosure in the circumstances:

   (1)   By individual country;

   (2)   By groups of countries within a continent; or

   (3)   By continent.

§229.1202 (Item 1202) Disclosure of reserves.

(e)   *Summary of oil and gas reserves at fiscal year end*

   (1)   Provide the information specified in paragraph (a)(2) of this Item in tabular format as provided below:

Summary of Oil and Gas Reserves as of Fiscal-Year End Based on Average Fiscal-ear Prices

Reserves category	Reserves				
	Oil (mbbls)	Natural gas (mmcf)	Synthetic oil (mbbls)	Synthetic gas (mmcf)	Product A (measure)
PROVED					
Developed:					
Continent A					
Continent B					
Country A					
Country B					
Other Countries in Continent B					
Undeveloped:					
Continent A					
Continent B					
Country A					
Country B					
Other Countries in Continent B					
TOTAL PROVED					
PROBABLE					
Developed					
Undeveloped					
POSSIBLE					
Developed					
Undeveloped					

(2)   Disclose, in the aggregate and by geographic area and for each country containing 15% or more of the registrant's proved reserves, expressed on an oil-equivalent-barrels basis, reserves estimated using prices and costs under existing economic conditions, for the product types listed in paragraph (a)(4) of this Item, in the following categories:

(i)   Proved developed reserves;

(ii)   Proved undeveloped reserves;

(iii)   Total proved reserves;

(iv)   Probable developed reserves (optional);

(v)   Probable undeveloped reserves (optional);

(vi)   Possible developed reserves (optional); and

(vii)   Possible undeveloped reserves (optional).

Instruction 1 to paragraph (a)(2): Disclose updated reserves tables as of the close of each fiscal year.

Instruction 2 to paragraph (a)(2): The registrant is permitted, but not required, to disclose probable or possible reserves pursuant to paragraphs (a)(2)(iv) through (a)(2)(vii) of this Item.

Instruction 3 to paragraph (a)(2): If the registrant discloses amounts of a product in barrels of oil equivalent, disclose the basis for such equivalency.

Instruction 4 to paragraph (a)(2): A registrant need not provide disclosure of the reserves in a country containing 15% or more of the registrant's proved reserves if that country's government prohibits disclosure of reserves in that country. In addition, a registrant need not provide disclosure of the reserves in a country containing 15% or more of the registrant's proved reserves if that country's government prohibits disclosure in a particular field and disclosure of reserves in that country would have the effect of disclosing reserves in particular fields.

(3)　Reported total reserves shall be simple arithmetic sums of all estimates for individual properties or fields within each reserves category. When probabilistic methods are used, reserves should not be aggregated probabilistically beyond the field or property level; instead, they should be aggregated by simple arithmetic summation.

(4)　Disclose separately material reserves of the following product types:

(i)　Oil;

(ii)　Natural gas;

(iii)　Synthetic oil;

(iv)　Synthetic gas; and

(v)　Sales products of other non-renewable natural resources that are intended to be upgraded into synthetic oil and gas.

(5)　If the registrant discloses probable or possible reserves, discuss the uncertainty related to such reserves estimates.

(6)　If the registrant has not previously disclosed reserves estimates in a filing with the Commission or is disclosing material additions to its reserves estimates, the registrant shall provide a general discussion of the technologies used to establish the appropriate level of certainty for reserves estimates from material properties included in the total reserves disclosed. The particular properties do not need to be identified.

(7)　*Preparation of reserves estimates or reserves audit.* Disclose and describe the internal controls the registrant uses in its reserves estimation effort. In addition, disclose the qualifications of the technical person primarily responsible for overseeing the preparation of the reserves estimates and, if the registrant represents that a third party conducted a reserves audit, disclose the qualifications of the technical person primarily responsible for overseeing such reserves audit.

(8)　*Third party reports.* If the registrant represents that a third party prepared, or conducted a reserves audit of, the registrant's reserves estimates, or any estimated valuation thereof, or conducted a process review, the registrant shall file a report of the third party as an exhibit to the relevant registration statement or other Commission filing. If the report relates to the preparation of, or a reserves audit of, the registrant's reserves estimates, it must include the following disclosure, if applicable to the type of filing:

(i) The purpose for which the report was prepared and for whom it was prepared;

(ii) The effective date of the report and the date on which the report was completed;

(iii) The proportion of the registrant's total reserves covered by the report and the geographic area in which the covered reserves are located;

(iv) The assumptions, data, methods, and procedures used, including the percentage of the registrant's total reserves reviewed in connection with the preparation of the report, and a statement that such assumptions, data, methods, and procedures are appropriate for the purpose served by the report;

(v) A discussion of primary economic assumptions;

(vi) A discussion of the possible effects of regulation on the ability of the registrant to recover the estimated reserves;

(vii) A discussion regarding the inherent uncertainties of reserves estimates;

(viii) A statement that the third party has used all methods and procedures as it considered necessary under the circumstances to prepare the report;

(ix) A brief summary of the third party's conclusions with respect to the reserves estimates; and

(x) The signature of the third party.

(9) For purposes of this Item 1202, the term reserves audit means the process of reviewing certain of the pertinent facts interpreted and assumptions underlying a reserves estimate prepared by another party and the rendering of an opinion about the appropriateness of the methodologies employed, the adequacy and quality of the data relied upon, the depth and thoroughness of the reserves estimation process, the classification of reserves appropriate to the relevant definitions used, and the reasonableness of the estimated reserves quantities.

(f) *Reserves sensitivity analysis (optional).*

(1) The registrant may, but is not required to, provide the information specified in paragraph (b)(2) of this Item in tabular format as provided below:

Sensitivity of Reserves to Prices by Principal Product Type and Price Scenario

	Proved reserves					Probable reserves					Possible reserves				
	Oil	Gas	Syn. oil	Syn. gas	Product A	Oil	Gas	Syn. oil	Syn. gas	Product A	Oil	Gas	Syn. oil	Syn. gas	Product A
Price case	mbbls	mmcf	mbbls	mmcf	measure	mbbls	mmcf	mbbls	mmcf	measure	mbbls	mmcf	mbbls	mmcf	measure
Scenario 1															
Scenario 2															

(2) The registrant may, but is not required to, disclose, in the aggregate, an estimate of reserves estimated for each product type based on different price and cost criteria, such as a range of prices and costs that may reasonably be achieved, including standardized futures prices or management's own forecasts.

(3)   If the registrant provides disclosure under this paragraph (b), disclose the price and cost schedules and assumptions on which the disclosed values are based.

Instruction to Item 1202: Estimates of oil or gas resources other than reserves, and any estimated values of such resources, shall not be disclosed in any document publicly filed with the Commission, unless such information is required to be disclosed in the document by foreign or state law; provided, however, that where such estimates previously have been provided to a person (or any of its affiliates) that is offering to acquire, merge, or consolidate with the registrant or otherwise to acquire the registrant's securities, such estimate may be included in documents related to such acquisition.

§229.1203 (Item 1203) Proved undeveloped reserves.

(a)   Disclose the total quantity of proved undeveloped reserves at year end.

(b)   Disclose material changes in proved undeveloped reserves that occurred during the year, including proved undeveloped reserves converted into proved developed reserves.

(c)   Discuss investments and progress made during the year to convert proved undeveloped reserves to proved developed reserves, including, but not limited to, capital expenditures.

(d)   Explain the reasons why material amounts of proved undeveloped reserves in individual fields or countries remain undeveloped for five years or more after disclosure as proved undeveloped reserves.

§229.1204 (Item 1204) Oil and gas production, production prices and production costs.

(a)   For each of the last three fiscal years disclose production, by final product sold, of oil, gas, and other products. Disclosure shall be made by geographical area and for each country and field that contains 15% or more of the registrant's total proved reserves expressed on an oil-equivalent-barrels basis unless prohibited by the country in which the reserves are located.

(b)   For each of the last three fiscal years disclose, by geographical area:

(1)   The average sales price (including transfers) per unit of oil, gas and other products produced; and

(2)   The average production cost, not including ad valorem and severance taxes, per unit of production.

Instruction 1 to Item 1204: Generally, net production should include only production that is owned by the registrant and produced to its interest, less royalties and production due others. However, in special situations (e.g., foreign production) net production before any royalties may be provided, if more appropriate. If "net before royalty" production figures are furnished, the change from the usage of "net production" should be noted.

Instruction 2 to Item 1204: Production of natural gas should include only marketable production of natural gas on an "as sold" basis. Production will include dry, residue, and wet gas, depending on whether liquids have been extracted before the registrant transfers title. Flared gas, injected gas, and gas consumed in operations should be omitted. Recovered gas-lift gas and reproduced gas should not be included until sold. Synthetic gas, when marketed as such, should be included in natural gas sales.

Instruction 3 to Item 1204: If any product, such as bitumen, is sold or custody is transferred prior to conversion to synthetic oil or gas, the product's production, transfer prices, and production costs should be disclosed separately from all other products.

Instruction 4 to Item 1204: The transfer price of oil and gas (natural and synthetic) produced should be determined in accordance with FASB ASC paragraph 932-235-50-24 (Extractive Activities – Oil and Gas Topic).

Instruction 5 to Item 1204: The average production cost, not including ad valorem and severance taxes, per unit of production should be computed using production costs disclosed pursuant to FASB ASC Topic 932, Extractive Activities – Oil and Gas. Units of production should be expressed in common units of production with oil, gas, and other products converted to a common unit of measure on the basis used in computing amortization.

[74 FR 2193, Jan. 14, 2009, as amended at 76 FR 50121, Aug. 12, 2011]

§229.1205 (Item 1205) Drilling and other exploratory and development activities.

(a)   For each of the last three fiscal years, by geographical area, disclose:

   (1)   The number of net productive and dry exploratory wells drilled; and

   (2)   The number of net productive and dry development wells drilled.

(b)   *Definitions.* For purposes of this Item 1205, the following terms shall be defined as follows:

   (1)   A *dry well* is an exploratory, development, or extension well that proves to be incapable of producing either oil or gas in sufficient quantities to justify completion as an oil or gas well.

   (2)   A *productive well* is an exploratory, development, or extension well that is not a dry well.

   (3)   *Completion* refers to installation of permanent equipment for production of oil or gas, or, in the case of a dry well, to reporting to the appropriate authority that the well has been abandoned.

   (4)   The *number of wells drilled* refers to the number of wells completed at any time during the fiscal year, regardless of when drilling was initiated.

(c)   Disclose, by geographic area, for each of the last three years, any other exploratory or development activities conducted, including implementation of mining methods for purposes of oil and gas producing activities.

§229.1206 (Item 1206) Present activities.

(a)   Disclose, by geographical area, the registrant's present activities, such as the number of wells in the process of being drilled (including wells temporarily suspended), waterfloods in process of being installed, pressure maintenance operations, and any other related activities of material importance.

(b)   Provide the description of present activities as of a date at the end of the most recent fiscal year or as close to the date that the registrant files the document as reasonably possible.

(c)   Include only those wells in the process of being drilled at the "as of" date and express them in terms of both gross and net wells.

(d)   Do not include wells that the registrant plans to drill, but has not commenced drilling unless there are factors that make such information material.

§229.1207 (Item 1207) Delivery commitments.

(a) If the registrant is committed to provide a fixed and determinable quantity of oil or gas in the near future under existing contracts or agreements, disclose material information concerning the estimated availability of oil and gas from any principal sources, including the following:

   (1) The principal sources of oil and gas that the registrant will rely upon and the total amounts that the registrant expects to receive from each principal source and from all sources combined;

   (2) The total quantities of oil and gas that are subject to delivery commitments; and

   (3) The steps that the registrant has taken to ensure that available reserves and supplies are sufficient to meet such commitments for the next one to three years.

(b) Disclose the information required by this Item:

   (1) In a form understandable to investors; and

   (2) Based upon the facts and circumstances of the particular situation, including, but not limited to:

      (i)   Disclosure by geographic area;

      (ii) Significant supplies dedicated or contracted to the registrant;

      (iii) Any significant reserves or supplies subject to priorities or curtailments which may affect quantities delivered to certain classes of customers, such as customers receiving services under low priority and interruptible contracts;

      (iv) Any priority allocations or price limitations imposed by Federal or State regulatory agencies, as well as other factors beyond the registrant's control that may affect the registrant's ability to meet its contractual obligations (the registrant need not provide detailed discussions of price regulation);

      (v)   Any other factors beyond the registrant's control, such as other parties having control over drilling new wells, competition for the acquisition of reserves and supplies, and the availability of foreign reserves and supplies, which may affect the registrant's ability to acquire additional reserves and supplies or to maintain or increase the availability of reserves and supplies; and

      (vi) Any impact on the registrant's earnings and financing needs resulting from its inability to meet short-term or long-term contractual obligations. (See Items 303 and 1209 of Regulation S-K (§§229.303 and 229.1209).)

(c) If the registrant has been unable to meet any significant delivery commitments in the last three years, describe the circumstances concerning such events and their impact on the registrant.

(d) For purposes of this Item, *available reserves* are estimates of the amounts of oil and gas which the registrant can produce from current proved developed reserves using presently installed equipment under existing economic and operating conditions and an estimate of amounts that others can deliver to the registrant under long-term contracts or agreements on a per-day, per-month, or per-year basis.

§229.1208 (Item 1208) Oil and gas properties, wells, operations, and acreage.

(a)   Disclose, as of a reasonably current date or as of the end of the fiscal year, the total gross and net productive wells, expressed separately for oil and gas (including synthetic oil and gas produced through wells) and the total gross and net developed acreage (i.e., acreage assignable to productive wells) by geographic area.

(b)   Disclose, as of a reasonably current date or as of the end of the fiscal year, the amount of undeveloped acreage, both leases and concessions, if any, expressed in both gross and net acres by geographic area, together with an indication of acreage concentrations, and, if material, the minimum remaining terms of leases and concessions.

(c)   *Definitions.* For purposes of this Item 1208, the following terms shall be defined as indicated:

   (1)   A *gross well or acre* is a well or acre in which the registrant owns a working interest. The number of gross wells is the total number of wells in which the registrant owns a working interest. Count one or more completions in the same bore hole as one well. In a footnote, disclose the number of wells with multiple completions. If one of the multiple completions in a well is an oil completion, classify the well as an oil well.

   (2)   A *net well or acre* is deemed to exist when the sum of fractional ownership working interests in gross wells or acres equals one. The number of net wells or acres is the sum of the fractional working interests owned in gross wells or acres expressed as whole numbers and fractions of whole numbers.

   (3)   *Productive wells* include producing wells and wells mechanically capable of production.

   (4)   *Undeveloped acreage* encompasses those leased acres on which wells have not been drilled or completed to a point that would permit the production of economic quantities of oil or gas regardless of whether such acreage contains proved reserves. Do not confuse undeveloped acreage with undrilled acreage held by production under the terms of the lease.

● ● ●

Excerpts from Accounting Standards Codification Section 932-10

Overview and Background

05-1 The Codification contains two Topics for the extractive industry due to the differing accounting treatment for various subindustries. The Topics include:

    a. This Topic, Extractive Activities – Oil and Gas

    b. Topic 930, Extractive Activities – Mining.

05-2 Paragraph superseded by Accounting Standards Update No. 2010-03.

05-3 This Topic provides guidance specific to oil- and gas-producing activities. It contains several Subtopics that interact with other Topics in the Codification. Guidance in these Subtopics rather than the more general guidance in the other Topics shall be applied to the specific issues addressed. These Subtopics are:

    a. Overall

    b. Income Statement

    c. Notes to Financial Statements

    d. Interim Reporting

    e. Segment Reporting

    f. Investments – Equity Method and Joint Ventures

    g. Inventory

    h. Intangibles – Goodwill and Other

    i. Property, Plant, and Equipment

    j. Debt

    k. Revenue Recognition

    l. Other Expenses

    m. Income Taxes

    n. Consolidation

    o. Derivatives and Hedging

    p. Interest.

Pending Content:

Transition Date: *(P) December 16, 2017; (N) December 16, 2018*

Transition Guidance: 606-10-65-1

This Topic provides guidance specific to oil- and gas-producing activities. It contains several Subtopics that interact with other Topics in the Codification. Guidance in these Subtopics rather than the more general guidance in the other Topics shall be applied to the specific issues addressed. These Subtopics are:

  a.   Overall

  b.   Income Statement

  c.   Notes to Financial Statements

  d.   Interim Reporting

  e.   Segment Reporting

  f.   Investments – Equity Method and Joint Ventures

  g.   Inventory

  h.   Intangibles – Goodwill and Other

  i.   Property, Plant, and Equipment

  j.   Debt

  k.   Subparagraph superseded by Accounting Standards Update No. 2014-09

  l.   Other Expenses

  m.   Income Taxes

  n.   Consolidation

  o.   Derivatives and Hedging

  p.   Interest.

05-4   This Subtopic provides overall guidance for extractive activities in the oil and gas industry, including identification of entities that fall within the scope of this Topic and common definitions of industry terms. The other Subtopics address unique requirements for the industry.

Scope and Scope Exceptions

Overall Guidance

05-1   The Subtopics within the Extractive Activities – Oil and Gas Topic provide incremental industry-specific guidance for the entities defined in this Scope Section. Entities within the scope of this Topic shall also comply with the applicable guidance not included in this Topic.

Entities

05-2   This Topic applies to all entities with oil- and gas-producing activities.

05-2A Oil- and gas-producing activities include the following:

   a.   The search for crude oil, including condensate and natural gas liquids, or natural gas in their natural states and original locations

   b.   The acquisition of property rights or properties for the purpose of further exploration or for the purpose of removing the oil or gas from such properties

   c.   The construction, drilling, and production activities necessary to retrieve oil and gas from their natural reservoirs, including the acquisition, construction, installation, and maintenance of field gathering and storage systems, such as:

   1.   Lifting the oil and gas to the surface

   2.   Gathering, treating, and field processing (as in the case of processing gas to extract liquid hydrocarbons).

   d.   Extraction of saleable hydrocarbons, in the solid, liquid, or gaseous state, from oil sands, shale, coalbeds, or other nonrenewable natural resources that are intended to be upgraded into synthetic oil or gas, and activities undertaken with a view to such extraction.

Transactions

05-3   The guidance in this Topic does not apply to the following transactions and activities:

   a.   Transporting, refining, and marketing of oil and gas

   b.   Processing of produced oil, gas, or natural resources that can be upgraded into synthetic oil or gas by an entity that does not serve as a producer of such natural resources

   bb. Activities relating to the production of natural resources other than oil, gas, or natural resources from which synthetic oil and gas can be extracted

   c.   The production of geothermal steam

   d.   Subparagraph superseded by Accounting Standards Update No. 2010-03

   e.   Accounting for interest on funds borrowed to finance an entity's oil- and gas-producing activities (for general guidance, see Topic 835).

05-4   This Topic does not prohibit an entity from applying the full-cost method of accounting.

Glossary

Condensate

Condensate is a mixture of hydrocarbons that exists in the gaseous phase at original reservoir temperature and pressure but that when produced is in the liquid phase at surface pressure and temperature.

Development project

A development project is the means by which petroleum resources are brought to the status of economically producible. As examples, the development of a single reservoir or field, an incremental development in a producing field, or the integrated development of a group of several fields and associated facilities with a common ownership may constitute a development project.

Economically producible

The term *economically producible*, as it relates to a resource, means a resource that generates revenue that exceeds, or is reasonably expected to exceed, the costs of the operation. The value of the products that generate revenue shall be determined at the terminal point of oil- and gas-producing activities.

Exploration

Exploration involves both of the following:

a. Identifying areas that may warrant examination

b. Examining specific areas that are considered to have prospects of containing oil and gas reserves, including drilling exploratory wells and exploratory-type stratigraphic test wells.

Oil- and gas-producing activities

Paragraph 932-10-15-2A defines the term oil- and gas-producing activities.

Production

Production involves lifting the crude oil and natural gas to the surface, extracting saleable hydrocarbons, in the solid, liquid, or gaseous state from oil sands, shale, coalbeds, or other nonrenewable natural resources that are intended to be upgraded into synthetic oil or gas, gathering, treating, field processing (as in the case of processing gas to extract liquid hydrocarbons), and field storage.

The oil and gas production function shall be regarded as ending at a terminal point, which is the outlet valve on the lease or field storage tank. If unusual physical or operational circumstances exist, it may be appropriate to regard the terminal point for the production function as:

a. The first point at which oil, gas, or gas liquids, natural or synthetic, are delivered to a main pipeline, a common carrier, a refinery, or a marine terminal

b. In the case of natural resources that are intended to be upgraded into synthetic oil or gas, if those natural resources are delivered to a purchaser before upgrading, the first point at which the natural resources are delivered to a main pipeline, a common carrier, a refinery, a marine terminal, or a facility that upgrades such natural resources into synthetic oil or gas.

Properties

Mineral interests in properties (hereinafter referred to as properties), which include all of the following:

a. Fee ownership or a lease

b. Concession

c. Other interest representing the legal right to produce or a revenue interest in the production of oil or gas subject to such terms as may be imposed by the conveyance of that interest.

Properties also include:

a. Royalty interests

b. Production payments payable in oil or gas

c. Other nonoperating interests in properties operated by others.

Properties include those agreements with foreign governments or authorities under which an entity participates in the operation of the related properties or otherwise serves as producer of the underlying reserves (see paragraph 932-235-50-7); but properties do not include other supply agreements or contracts that represent the right to purchase (as opposed to extract) oil and gas.

Properties are classified as proved properties or unproved properties.

Proved properties

Proved properties are properties with proved reserves.

Reserves

Reserves are estimated remaining quantities of oil and gas and related substances anticipated to be economically producible, as of a given date, by application of development projects to known accumulations. In addition, there must exist, or there must be a reasonable expectation that there will exist, the legal right to produce or a revenue interest in the production, installed means of delivering oil and gas or related substances to market, and all permits and financing required to implement the project.

Reserves should not be assigned to adjacent reservoirs isolated by major, potentially sealing, faults until those reservoirs are penetrated and evaluated as economically producible. Reserves should not be assigned to areas that are clearly separated from a known accumulation by a nonproductive reservoir (that is, absence of reservoir, structurally low reservoir, or negative test results). Such areas may contain prospective resources (that is, potentially recoverable resources from undiscovered accumulations).

Resources

Resources are quantities of oil and gas estimated to exist in naturally occurring accumulations. A portion of the resources may be estimated to be recoverable, and another portion may be considered to be unrecoverable. Resources include both discovered accumulations and undiscovered accumulations.

Saleable hydrocarbons

Hydrocarbons that are saleable in the state in which the hydrocarbons are delivered.

Unproved properties

Unproved properties are properties with no proved reserves.

General Note: The Master Glossary contains all terms identified as glossary terms throughout the Codification... The Master Glossary may contain identical terms with different definitions, some of which may not be appropriate for a particular Subtopic. For any particular Subtopic, users should only use the glossary terms included in the particular Subtopic Glossary Section (Section 20).

Acquisition of properties

See paragraph 932-10-S99-1, Regulation S-X Rule 4-10(a)(1), for the definition of acquisition of properties as used within that Rule.

Developed oil and gas reserves

See paragraph 932-10-S99-1, Regulation S-X Rule 4-10(a)(6) for the definition of developed oil and gas reserves as used within that Rule.

Development costs

See paragraph 932-10-S99-1, Regulation S-X Rule 4-10(a)(7), for the definition of development costs as used within that Rule.

Exploration costs

See paragraph 932-10-S99-1, Regulation S-X Rule 4-10(a)(12), for the definition of exploration costs as used within that Rule.

Production costs

See paragraph 932-10-S99-1, Regulation S-X Rule 4-10(a)(20), for the definition of production costs as used within that Rule.

Undeveloped oil and gas reserves

See paragraph 932-10-S99-1, Regulation S-X Rule 4-10(a)(31), for the definition of undeveloped oil and gas reserves as used within that Rule.

Transition and Open Effective Date Information

65-1   Paragraph superseded on 07/14/2011 after the end of the transition period stated in Accounting Standards Update No. 2010-03, *Extractive Activities – Oil and Gas(Topic 932): Oil and Gas Reserve Estimation and Disclosures.*

• • •

Other Reference Sources

Sources of Petroleum Accounting Information

2019 PricewaterhouseCoopers Survey of U.S. Petroleum Accounting Practices. The Survey collects information on industry accounting practices, especially those not typically disclosed in annual reports. Respondents are categorized in two ways: (1) successful efforts and full cost and (2) public companies and private companies. For copies of the latest survey, order from the Institute of Petroleum Accounting.

Council of Petroleum Accountants Societies. The Council of Petroleum Accountants Societies (COPAS) publishes COPAS Accounting Guidelines (AG), the COPAS Computerized Equipment Pricing System (CEPS), ePublications, Model Form (MF) Accounting Procedures and related interpretations and modifications, as well as other educational resources including training and reference materials. Ordering information is available on the COPAS website.

Entities with Oil and Gas Producing Activities – Audit and Accounting Guide. Published by the American Institute of Certified Public Accountants (AICPA), the guide summarizes applicable practices and delivers advice for handling most types of financial statements. It describes relevant matters, conditions and procedures unique to the oil and gas industry. Financial statements and reports are illustrated in order to caution auditors and accountants about unusual problems. Paperback, eBook and online subscription versions are available online at the AICPA store website.

International Accounting Standards Board. The International Accounting Standards Board (IASB) commenced its research project on extractive activities in 2018. At the time of publication, the IASB is gathering evidence to help it decide whether to start a project to develop proposals on accounting requirements that would replace or amend International Financial Reporting Standard (IFRS) 6, *Exploration for and Evaluation of Mineral Resources*, which was issued by the IASB in 2004 with the intention that it would be a temporary standard. This recent research project is not a continuation of the previous research that the IASB conducted, the findings of which were published in a discussion paper in 2010. Education sessions are being planned for early 2020 to provide the IASB with further explanation of the key features of extractive activities along with the main accounting issues that are associated with these key features. The IASB will then decide on the scope of the research project. The current stage of the project can be found on the IASB website.

Accounting Regulations

Financial Accounting Standards Board. The Financial Accounting Standards Board (FASB) establishes standards for financial accounting and reporting. Its work is considered authoritative by the Securities and Exchange Commission (SEC) and AICPA. Stakeholders, such as investors, creditors, auditors and the general public, rely on financial information prepared in accordance with FASB standards.

Other Industry Sources

American Petroleum Institute. The American Petroleum Institute (API) is the primary trade association of the oil and gas industry in the U.S. Founded on March 20, 1919, it is one of the largest national trade associations in the U.S., with more than 625 corporate members and offices in 21 state capitals. API's mission is to promote safety across the industry globally and to influence public policy in support of a strong, viable U.S. oil and gas industry.

Independent Petroleum Association of America. The Independent Petroleum Association of America (IPAA) was founded in the summer of 1929 by a small group of determined independents and has grown to an organization that today represents over 9,000 independent oil and natural gas producers in the U.S. For over 90 years, IPAA's volunteer leaders have skillfully aligned business savvy with political skills to keep the independent oil and natural gas industry alive and thriving. As a national trade association, its stated mission is to put a face on America's oil and natural gas industry. IPAA represents independent oil and natural gas producers across the U.S. that develop 91 percent of the nation's oil and natural gas wells.

Energy Information Administration. The U.S. Department of Energy's Energy Information Administration (EIA) is the government source for industry statistics and information. Prices, production, trade and sector overviews are available on a monthly or annual basis.

● ● ●

Glossary

Glossary words noted with an asterisk (*) are informational terms and may not be found in chapter material.

ABANDONED. Ceased attempts to produce oil or gas from a well or lease, plugged the RESERVOIR in accordance with regulatory requirements and recovered equipment.

ABSORBER.* Field equipment, usually a tower, that removes oil or water from a gas stream using absorption (as opposed to adsorption explained below). In absorption, the removed liquid changes by mixing with another liquid. For example, a triethylene glycol (TEG or triglycol) absorber removes water from a gas stream in a process where wet gas enters at the bottom of the unit, passes through a TEG stream and exits dry at the top. The resulting wet glycol is dried in a reboiler to remove the water.

ACIDIZE.* To increase the flow of oil from a well by introducing acid into a carbonate FORMATION, such as limestone, to open passages through which oil can flow into the WELLBORE. Acidizing may also be called an acid job.

ACQUISITION COSTS. Direct and indirect costs incurred to acquire rights to natural resources.

ACQUISITION WELL.* A well drilled in exchange for a mineral interest in a property. Also can be called an obligation well.

ACRE-FOOT. RESERVOIR analysis measure of volume equalling 43,560 cubic feet or 7,758 barrels. One acre-foot represents the volume that would cover one acre to a depth of one foot.

ACT SYSTEM.* See LEASE AUTOMATIC CUSTODY TRANSFER (LACT) UNIT.

AD VALOREM TAXES. Local taxes, such as county and school district taxes, based on the individual property value.

ADSORPTION PLANT.* Field equipment for removing liquid from a gas stream by adsorption (as opposed to absorption as explained above). In adsorption, the removed liquid is unchanged but clings to the surface of a solid absorbent such as activated charcoal.

ADVANCE ROYALTY (ADVANCED ROYALTY).* Generally, a royalty that must be paid regardless of production and revenue levels, such as a MINIMUM ROYALTY or a SHUT-IN ROYALTY, for which future production royalties may or may not be reduced.

AFE. See AUTHORIZATION FOR EXPENDITURE.

AIR DRILLING.* Use of compressed air as a substitute for drilling MUD in rotary drilling.

AIR/GAS LIFT.* Method of raising oil from a FORMATION by injecting air or gas directly into the fluid in the casing.

ALLOWABLE. Amount of oil or gas that a well or lease can produce during a given time period according to government regulations.

AMERICAN ASSOCIATION OF PETROLEUM GEOLOGISTS (AAPG). Founded in 1917, AAPG is a professional association comprised of approximately 40,000 members in 129 countries focused on the science of petroleum geology in the upstream sector of the energy industry.

AMERICAN ASSOCIATION OF PROFESSIONAL LANDMEN (AAPL). Founded in 1955 as the American Association of Petroleum Landmen, the organization changed its name in 1992 to what is now known as the American Association of Professional Landmen with more than 16,000 landmen and land professionals through 41 affiliated local associations across North America.

AMERICAN OPTIONS. A type of option contract which may be exercised at any time before or on the expiration date.

AMERICAN PETROLEUM INSTITUTE (API). Founded on March 20, 1919, it is one of the largest national trade associations in the U.S., with more than 625 corporate members and offices in 21 state capitals. API's mission is to promote safety across the industry globally and to influence public policy in support of a strong, viable U.S. oil and gas industry.

AMI. See AREA OF MUTUAL INTEREST.

ANGLE OF DEFLECTION.* In directional drilling, the angle expressed in degrees at which a well is deflected from the vertical by means of a whipstock or other deflecting tool.

ANNULAR SPACE (ANNULUS). Space between an object which is inserted into another circular object. For example, the space around a pipe suspended in a WELLBORE is often termed the annulus, and its outer wall may be either the wall of the borehole or the casing.

ANTICLINE. Underground mountain-shaped strata covered with a cap rock or an impervious rock layer.

API GRAVITY. Established by the AMERICAN PETROLEUM INSTITUTE (API), it is the standard industry measure of gravity (i.e., density) of a liquid petroleum product, expressed in degrees (o API). The formula for API gravity in terms of specific gravity (g) is: [(141.5 ÷ g at 60oF) – 131.5]. Very light crude oils and gasoline have an API gravity in the range of 50o to 60o API. The API gravity for light crude oils ranges from about 35o to 45o API. Heavy (dense) crude oils have an API gravity range from about 6o to 25o API. In comparison, water has an API gravity of 10o API and a specific gravity of 1.

API WELL NUMBER.* Distinct 12 digit number assigned to a U.S. well. Digits 1 and 2 are state codes, digits 3 through 5 are county/parish or offshore codes, digits 6 through 10 identify the well and digits 11 and 12 identify special well conditions such as a sidetracking.

APO. After payout. See PAYOUT.

ARAB LIGHT (ARL).* A medium-gravity, high sulfur crude oil produced by Saudi Arabia, it is the major export grade for Saudi Arabia and a global BENCHMARK CRUDE.

AREA OF INTEREST. Federal income tax term used in allocating geological and geophysical costs to certain properties. A large-scale geophysical survey may indicate several areas of interest. Costs of the survey must be allocated to each area of interest and, when leases are obtained, the geophysical costs become part of the basis of the property. See GEOLOGICAL AND GEOPHYSICAL (G&G) COSTS.

AREA OF MUTUAL INTEREST (AMI). A term found in joint venture agreements designating a geographic area around the joint venture's leases. The agreement provides that any joint venture participant obtaining new property rights within the AMI must offer such rights to the joint venture.

ASIAN OPTIONS. A type of option contract for which the payoff is determined by the average underlying price over a pre-set period of time.

ASSIGNEE. In oil and gas law, the term commonly means, but is not limited to, the transferee of an oil and gas lease.

ASSIGNMENT. In oil and gas law, usually a transfer of a property interest or a contract. The most common usage refers to the assignment of an oil and gas lease.

ASSIGNOR. In oil and gas law, the term commonly means, but is not limited to, the conveyor of an oil and gas lease. In law, generally a transferor; the party who conveys a right, title or interest in a property or a contract.

ASSOCIATED GAS. Natural gas occurring in the form of a gas cap overlying an oil zone (as opposed to NONASSOCIATED GAS from a gas RESERVOIR with no oil and CASINGHEAD GAS from an oil reservoir without processing).

AUTHORIZATION FOR EXPENDITURE (AFE). Budgeting and approval form used during the planning process for a well about to be drilled and for other projects. It includes an estimate of costs to be incurred in the intangible drilling costs (IDC) category and in the tangible equipment category. Costs are shown in total with accompanying breakdowns. The AFE form represents: (1) a budget for the project against which actual expenditures are compared and (2) a joint venture form for evidencing agreement by joint interest owners to participate in the budgeted project. May also be called an Authority for Expenditure.

BACK-IN INTEREST.* OVERRIDING ROYALTY INTEREST (ORRI) or CARRIED INTEREST which converts to a WORKING INTEREST (WI) at a specific time or event, such as one year from well completion or completion of a PAYOUT provision (e.g., 300 percent payout).

BACKWARDATION. A market condition wherein commodity prices are expected to decrease in the future.

BAFFLE.* Device which changes the direction of flow of fluids.

BAKKEN SHALE. An area of geological interest located in the Williston Basin in Eastern Montana and Western North Dakota, as well as parts of Saskatchewan and Manitoba, that is estimated to hold up to 4.3 billion barrels of recoverable oil.

BALANCING SHIPPER. Normally the largest shipper of a pipeline who absorbs the imbalance along a pipe and determines the source of imbalance and remediates all counterparties.

BARNETT SHALE. An area of geological interest in North Texas that is one of the largest onshore natural gas fields in the U.S. with an estimated 40 trillion cubic feet of natural gas.

BARREL (BBL). Standard measure of volume for crude oil and liquid petroleum products. One barrel is equivalent to 42 U.S. gallons.

BASIC SEDIMENT & WATER (BS&W). Impurities contained in produced oil. Purchasing companies will ordinarily not accept oil having more than 1 percent of BS&W. If the fluid as produced contains more than this proportion of foreign matter, some of the impurities such as sand and water may be removed from the crude after settling in the bottom of the lease storage tank.

BATTERY. See TANK BATTERY.

BBL. See BARREL (BBL).

BBLD. Barrels per day.

BCF. One billion cubic feet.

BEAM WELL.* A well from which oil is lifted by use of a walking beam pump unit.

BEHIND-PIPE RESERVES. Oil or gas reserves that cannot be produced until future perforation of casing at the depth of that RESERVOIR. Often, these are reserves in reservoirs above currently producing zones.

BENCHMARK CRUDE. A price quote for a crude grade that is used as a reference for pricing other crudes. Typically, benchmarks are for a highly traded commodity, with a quality and location similar to other commodities. See ARAB LIGHT (ARL), BRENT CRUDE and WEST TEXAS INTERMEDIATE (WTI).

BENCHMARK PRICING.* An agreement between parties to buy and sell oil or gas in the future at a percentage or function of a future published oil or gas price routinely determined by another party. The benchmark might be another party's posted price for crude oil (or a published average spot gas price) at a specified location on the date of sale. One of four methods is used to price gas while one of five methods is used to price oil for Federal royalty purposes. Furthermore, benchmark pricing generally is used in processed gas sales.

BERMUDAN OPTIONS. A type of option contract similar to AMERICAN OPTIONS, but which may only be exercised on specific periodic dates or on the expiration date.

BIT. Located on the bottom of the DRILLSTRING, the bit is a tool used to crush or cut rock that works by scraping or crushing the rock, or both, usually as part of a rotational motion. Everything on a DRILLING RIG directly or indirectly assists the bit in crushing or cutting the rock, which must be changed when it becomes excessively dull or stops making progress.

BLEED.* To drain off liquid or gas slowly through a valve called a bleeder.

BLOW BY.* Escape of gas with the liquid from a separator.

BLOWOUT. Sudden, violent expulsion of water, oil and gas from a well followed by an uncontrolled flow of formation fluids from the WELLBORE. Possible during all types of well activities, not just drilling operations, a blowout occurs when high pressure gas is encountered in the hole, and sufficient precautions, such as increasing the weight of the MUD, have not been taken.

BLOWOUT PREVENTER (BOP). A large valve at the top of a well that is usually operated remotely and may be closed if the drilling crew loses control of formation fluids. By closing the valve, the drilling crew attempts to regain control of the RESERVOIR and perform procedures to increase the MUD density until it is possible to re-open the BOP and retain pressure control of the FORMATION. Some BOPs can effectively close over an open WELLBORE, some are designed to seal around tubular components in the well and others are fitted with hardened steel shearing surfaces that can actually cut through DRILLPIPE.

BOBTAIL PLANT. A gas plant that removes NGLs as a single stream, which then gets sent to a fractionation facility.

BOE. Amount of energy resource equal to one barrel of oil converted on an energy basis. One barrel is equivalent to 42 U.S. gallons or 6 MCF.

BOED. Barrels of oil equivalent per day.

BOREHOLE. The WELLBORE itself, including the open hole or uncased portion of the well.

BOTTOM HOLE CONTRIBUTIONS. Money or property transferred to an OPERATOR for use in drilling a well on property in which the payer has no property interest. The contributions are payable when the well reaches a predetermined depth, regardless of whether the well is productive or nonproductive. The payer may receive proprietary information on the well's potential productivity.

BOTTOM HOLE LETTER (BOTTOM HOLE CONTRACT).* An agreement by which an OPERATOR contemplating the drilling of a well on its own property secures the promise of another to contribute to the cost of the well, usually in return for proprietary information on the well's potential productivity. In contrast to a dry hole letter, a bottom hole letter requires payment upon drilling and testing the well at a specified depth or FORMATION even if the well does not produce.

BOTTOM HOLE PRESSURE (BHP). RESERVOIR or rock pressure at the bottom of the hole, whether measured under flowing conditions or not, and usually measured in pounds per square inch. If measured under flowing conditions, pressure readings are usually taken at different rates of flow in order to compute a theoretical value for maximum productivity. In some reservoirs, decline in pressure furnishes a guide to the amount of depletion from the RESERVOIR and the amount of remaining proved reserves.

BPO. Before PAYOUT. Used with working interests and net revenue interests to indicate ownership BPO versus APO.

BRENT CRUDE. A light sweet grade of crude oil produced in the North Sea, it plays an important role in the global oil industry by acting as a BENCHMARK CRUDE against which most other crude grades are priced.

BRITISH THERMAL UNITS (BTU). Measure of the amount of heat required to raise the temperature of one pound of water by one degree Fahrenheit (°F). The energy values of petroleum products are approximately as follows (on an MBtu to Bbl basis): average U.S. crude petroleum is 5.8; residual fuel oil is 6.29; distillate fuel oil is 5.83; gasoline is 5.35; jet fuel (kerosene type) is 5.67; jet fuel (naphtha type) is 5.36; kerosene is 5.67. The energy values of natural gas are approximately as follows (on an MMBtu to Mcf basis): dry gas averages 1.03; wet natural gas is 1.110; natural gas in pipelines ranges from 0.95 to 1.05. Approximately 5.6 Mcf of dry gas has the same energy content (approximately 5.8 MMBtu) as one BBL of oil.

BS&W. See BASIC SEDIMENT AND WATER.

BTU. See BRITISH THERMAL UNITS.

BULLET PERFORATOR.* Perforator that fires projectiles through the casing in order to provide holes through which the well fluids may enter.

BUTANE. A HYDROCARBON gas (C_4H_{10}) extracted as a NATURAL GAS LIQUID (NGL) from NATURAL GAS. It is used as a gasoline ingredient increasing volatility and improving cold engine starts.

CABLE-TOOL RIG. Equipment used to drill a well by pounding a chisel-shaped BIT up and down to pulverize the rock. This original well drilling method has now largely been replaced by rotary drilling where the drill bit rotates to grind, rather than pulverize, the rock.

CAPACITY. Maximum volume a well is capable of producing in a unit of time. Generally expressed as an amount per hour. Capacity may also refer to a maximum volume of fluid for a given container or RESERVOIR.

CARRIED INTEREST. See CARRIED INTEREST ARRANGEMENT (AGREEMENT).

CARRIED INTEREST ARRANGEMENT (AGREEMENT).* An arrangement under which one party (CARRYING PARTY) agrees to pay for a specified portion or for all of the development and operating costs of another party (CARRIED PARTY) on a property in which both own a portion of the WORKING INTEREST (WI). The carrying party may be able to recover a specified amount of costs from the carried party's share of the revenues from the production of petroleum, if any, from the property.

CARRIED PARTY. Party for whom funds are advanced in a CARRIED INTEREST ARRANGEMENT.

CARRYING PARTY. Party advancing funds in a CARRIED INTEREST ARRANGEMENT.

CARVED-OUT. Scenario in which a NONOPERATING INTEREST is carved-out of a WORKING INTEREST (WI). It is often an OVERRIDING ROYALTY INTEREST (ORRI) and sometimes can be a production payment. For example, the owner of a 20 percent WI, with a 15 percent NET REVENUE INTEREST (NRI), may carve-out and convey to a key employee an ORRI with one percent NRI. This leaves the WI owner with a 20 percent share of well costs and a 14 percent share of revenues.

CASH BALANCING. Method of paying cash, in lieu of delivering gas, to eliminate a gas imbalance. Terms for cash balancing may be set out in a separate GAS BALANCING AGREEMENT or in the JOINT OPERATING AGREEMENT.

CASING. Steel pipe placed in an oil or gas well as drilling and completion progresses. The function of casing is to prevent the wall of the hole from caving in during drilling and to facilitate safe oil and gas production if the well is productive.

CASING POINT. Point in a drilling project when drilling operations cease and the well owners must decide whether well COMPLETION should begin or whether the well should be plugged and abandoned. Casing point may also refer to the depth to which CASING is set in a well.

CASINGHEAD. The top of the well's CASING between the first casing string and either the BLOWOUT PREVENTER (BOP) stack during the drilling phase or the WELLHEAD after the well is completed.

CASINGHEAD GAS. Wet gas produced along with crude oil from oil wells. The DISSOLVED GAS is dissolved in the reservoir's crude oil but bubbles out of the oil when exposed to normal atmospheric pressures.

CEMENTING. To prepare and pump cement down the WELLBORE to fill the space created between the rock walls and the casing. Various types of cementing jobs include primary, secondary, squeeze, plug-back or multi-stage.

CENTRIFUGE. Machine in which samples of oil are placed and spun at high speed to break out sediment.

CHECKERBOARD ACREAGE.* Mineral interests situated in a checkerboard pattern.

CHRISTMAS TREE. A descriptive term applied to the WELLHEAD which refers to the valves, spools and fittings assembled at the top of a well to control the flow of production.

CLEAN-OUT COSTS.* Costs incurred to clean-out a well in order to maintain its productive capacity or restore it to original capacity.

CLEARING ACCOUNTS. Accounts used to accumulate expenses during a period. Any clearing account balances are allocated to other accounts on a predetermined basis at period-end.

COALBED METHANE. High-methane natural gas adsorbed to underground coal. It was not substantially produced until the late 1980s when available IRC Section 29 tax credits sparked a drilling boom. See METHANE.

COLLAR. Financial position created when a company sells a call option and buys a put option on its production. A collar effectively fixes the realized price between the strike prices of the put and call options. When the premium received for the call equals the premium paid for the put, the collar is known as a zero-cost collar.

COMMINGLED PRODUCTION.* Production from multiple producing horizons into a single tank or meter that must be allocated due to different ownership percentages.

COMMON CONTROL TRANSACTION. Transfers and exchanges between entities under the control of the same parent.

COMPLIANT TOWER.* An offshore rig in which the legs are designed to move with the current in order to prevent breakage.

COMPRESSOR. Equipment on a gas pipeline to raise gas pressure to keep gas flowing.

CONCESSION. A mineral rights arrangement with a government that allows a company to drill for and extract oil, gas or minerals for a specific period of time from government-owned lands or lands in which the government owns the rights to produce oil, gas or minerals.

CONDENSATE. A light HYDROCARBON liquid (generally NATURAL GASOLINES C5 to C10) that condenses to a liquid as the WET GAS is sent through a mechanical SEPARATOR near the well.

CONTIGUOUS LEASES.* Leases which have a common boundary line.

CONTINUING INTEREST.* Any interest in a mineral property that lasts for the entire period of the lease contract with which it is associated.

CONVENTIONAL RESOURCES. Oil and natural gas produced using traditional recovery methods. See UNCONVENTIONAL RESOURCES.

CONVEYANCE. Assignment or transfer of mineral rights to another person.

CONTANGO. A market condition wherein commodity prices are expected to increase in the future.

CORE. Cylindrical sample of rock taken from a FORMATION during drilling for purposes of determining the formation's permeability, porosity, HYDROCARBON saturation and other characteristics of petroleum productivity

CORE ANALYSIS. Study of the CORE in a laboratory to determine the following properties of the FORMATION from which the core was taken: porosity, permeability, fluid content, angle of dip, geological age, lithology and probable productivity.

CORRELATIVE RIGHTS.* The rights of the mineral estate owner to develop and enjoy his/her minerals.

COST CENTER. Geological, geographical or legal unit by which revenues and costs are identified and accumulated. Examples may be the lease, the field or the country.

COST CENTER CEILING. Limit placed on the carrying value of oil and gas properties in a COST CENTER pursuant to rules established by the Securities and Exchange Commission (SEC).

COST DEPLETION. Under cost depletion, units-of-production from each property during the year are divided by proved, probable and prospective RESERVES attributable to the property at the beginning of the year to calculate a cost factor. This factor is multiplied by net leasehold costs of the property (capitalized minerals costs less depletion previously taken) to arrive at a cost depletion amount.

COUNCIL OF PETROLEUM ACCOUNTANTS SOCIETIES (COPAS). Established in 1961, COPAS provides expertise for the oil and gas industry through the development of Accounting Guidelines (AG), Model Form (MF) Accounting Procedures, Model Form Interpretations (MFI), Model Form Modifications (MFM) as well as other various publications. COPAS also provides training and reference materials for industry professionals.

CROSS-SECTION MAPPING.* Maps of cross-section of underground formations.

CRUDE OIL. Liquid petroleum as it comes out of the ground, as distinguished from oil which has been processed in a refinery. Crude oil may also be referred to simply as crude. It varies radically in its properties, including specific gravity and viscosity. Depending on the chemical nature of its chief constituents, crude oil is classified as paraffin base, asphaltic base or mixed base.

CYCLING. PRIMARY RECOVERY method by which CONDENSATE is recovered from gas produced from a condensate gas RESERVOIR. The RESIDUE GAS is compressed and returned to the reservoir from which it was originally produced. The return of the residue gas serves to maintain the reservoir pressure so that the condensate remains in a gaseous state in the reservoir. If reservoir pressure drops low enough for the condensate to liquefy in the reservoir, substantially less condensate may be recovered.

DAILY DRILLING REPORT.* 24 hour on-site report indicating all important events which occurred in drilling a well.

DAMAGE PAYMENTS. Payments made to the surface landowner by the OPERATOR for damages to the land, growing crops, streams or other assets of the landowner.

DAY RATE CONTRACT. Agreement between a DRILLING RIG contractor and an OPERATOR wherein an agreed upon amount of money per day will be paid to the drilling contractor until a well is drilled to an agreed upon depth.

DEAD MAN.* Buried anchor to which guy wires are tied to steady the DERRICK, boiler stacks, or other equipment.

DECLINE CURVE. Graph of oil and/or gas production plotted over a period of time and used to extrapolate the expected future production of a well for estimating proved reserves.

DEFERRED BONUS. Rental payments made in instalments and distinguishable from a DELAY RENTAL in that a deferred bonus payment is due even if the LEASE is dropped whereas a delay rental is not.

DEHYDRATION. Process of removing water content from a gas stream to reduce the formation of hydrates, which is usually performed at the well site by use of a dehydrator which may treat commingled gas from several wells. Hydrates refer to solid, crystalline compounds that can disrupt natural gas movement and which may be 90% water and 10% hydrocarbons.

DELAY RENTAL. An amount paid to a LESSOR, subsequent to the payment of any LEASE BONUS, for the privilege of deferring the commencement of a well or commercial production on the LEASE. Normally, delay rentals are paid prospectively on an annual basis.

DELINEATION WELL.* See FIELD EXPLORATORY WELL.

DELIVERY. Flow of oil or gas through a meter.

DELIVERY PRESSURE.* Pressure of the gas from a well to be delivered into a pipeline. This amount is set out in the sales contract and stated in terms of pounds per square inch.

DEPLETION. Federal income tax term regarding allowable income tax deduction related to exhaustion of mineral reserves or the portion of the carrying value prorated in each accounting period as an element of amortization. Two methods exist for computing a depletion allowance: COST DEPLETION and PERCENTAGE DEPLETION.

DEPRECIATION. Financial accounting principle that recognizes the expense of a capital asset over its estimated useful life. Depreciation also can be an income tax deduction for a tangible cost whereby part of the purchase price is deducted every year over the asset's assigned useful life. E&P company support facilities such as trucks, field units, warehouses and equipment, among others, may be subject to depreciation.

DERIVATIVE. A financial instrument used by oil and gas companies to help manage the risk of price fluctuations in the market. The types of derivatives utilized include futures contracts, forward contracts, swaps and options. Accounting Standards Codification (ASC) 815 provides authoritative guidance on accounting for derivatives.

DERRICK. The structure used to support the crown blocks and the DRILLSTRING of a DRILLING RIG.

DETAILED SURVEY.* Intensive geological and geophysical exploration of an area of interest.

DEVELOPED PROPERTY. Property where wells have been drilled and production equipment has been installed.

DEVELOPMENT COSTS. Costs incurred to obtain access to PROVED RESERVES and to construct facilities for producing, treating and storing the hydrocarbons.

DEVELOPMENT WELL. A well drilled within the proved area of an oil and gas RESERVOIR to the depth of a stratigraphic horizon known to be productive.

DEVIATED WELL.* A well drilled at an angle from the vertical. See DEVIATION WELL.

DIRECTIONAL DRILLING. Technique for drilling a well at an angle from the vertical to access a specific part of the RESEROIR.

DISCOVERY WELL. Exploratory well which discovers a new oil field.

DISMANTLEMENT, RESTORATION AND ABANDONMENT (DR&A). See PLUGGING AND ABANDONMENT (P&A).

DISPOSAL WELLS. Wells used for the disposal of waste fluids or salt water that were produced along with the oil and gas. Disposal wells are commonly subject to regulatory requirements to avoid ground water contamination.

DISSOLVED GAS. Natural gas mixed with crude oil in a producing FORMATION.

DIVISION ORDER. A contract between the owners of an oil and gas property and the company purchasing production from the property. The division order sets forth the interest of each owner and serves as the basis for payment of each owner's respective share of oil and gas proceeds.

DOGHOUSE.* Small structure on the rig floor used for records, storage and other functions.

DOME. Geological FORMATION associated with the accumulation of oil where a portion of the underground strata has been thrust upward and has deformed the overlying layers of rock. A dome can trap oil above the ANTICLINE formed, alongside it and even below the FORMATION.

DOUBLE.* Two lengths or joints of drill or other pipe joined together.

DRILLING PERMIT. A permit issued by a governmental body which gives permission to drill on a specified location to a specified depth and which commits the OPERATOR to conform to all other regulatory drilling requirements.

DRILLING RIG. The machine used to drill a WELLBORE. Major components of the drilling rig include the MUD tanks, the mud pumps, the DERRICK or mast, the drawworks, the rotary table or topdrive, the DRILLSTRING, the power generation equipment and auxiliary equipment.

DRILLCO.* Short for drilling participation arrangement, in a drillco transaction, an investor and E&P company enter into a drilling JOINT VENTURE where the investor funds all or a significant portion of the E&P's drilling costs of a certain number of wells in exchange for a WORKING INTEREST (WI) in each of the wells.

DRILLPIPE. Tubular steel conduit fitted with special threaded ends called tool joints, it connects the rig surface equipment with the bottom hole assembly and the BIT, both to pump drilling fluid to the bit and to be able to raise, lower and rotate the bottom hole assembly and bit.

DRILLSTRING. The combination of the DRILLPIPE, the bottom hole assembly and any other tools used to make the drill BIT turn at the bottom of the WELLBORE.

DRILLSHIP. Seagoing vessel that serves as a platform for exploratory drilling offshore.

DRY GAS. Natural gas composed of over 90 percent METHANE and suitable for use by customers of local gas distribution companies. In the U.S., dry gases are defined as those that contain less than 0.1 gallon of condensables per 1 Mcf of produced gas.

DRY HOLE. Exploratory or development well that does not produce oil or gas in commercial quantities.

DRY HOLE CONTRIBUTION. Money or property transferred by a property owner to an OPERATOR drilling a well on adjacent property in which the payer has no property interest. Such contributions are payable only in the event the well reaches an agreed depth and is found to be dry. The payer may be entitled to proprietary information on the well.

DUAL COMPLETION. A well that simultaneously drains two reservoirs of oil or gas at different depths with the production from each zone separated by tubing.

E&P. Exploration and production.

ECONOMIC INTEREST. An interest in minerals in-place which the owner has acquired by investment and which secures income derived from the extraction of such minerals.

EFFECTIVE DATE. Initial date a LEASE, acquisition or assignment is in-force. May also be used to refer to the balance sheet date for which a reserves estimate or COST CENTER CEILING test is applied.

EIA. U.S. Energy Information Administration.

EAGLE FORD SHALE. Located in South Texas, the play produces from various depths between 4,000 and 14,000 feet. It takes its name from the town of Eagle Ford, Texas where the shale outcrops at the surface in clay form.

EMBEDDED DERIVATIVE. Element of a contract (excluding certain scope exceptions in ASC 815) that meets the definition of a DERIVATIVE per ASC 815, even though the host contract does not, in its entirety, meet the definition of a derivative per ASC 815.

ENHANCED RECOVERY. Any method used to drive hydrocarbons from reservoirs into a well in excess of that which could be produced through natural RESERVOIR pressure, energy or drive through PRIMARY RECOVERY methods. See SECONDARY RECOVERY and TERTIARY RECOVERY.

EQUAL DAILY QUANTITIES (EDQ).* An average daily volume used for pricing CRUDE OIL by allocating volumes from multiple run tickets in a month.

EQUALIZATION. Adjustment clause within a UNITIZATION agreement providing that participants with undeveloped leases will pay cash to participants with fully or partially developed leases in order to make the capital contributions for wells and equipment equivalent.

ETHANE. HYDROCARBON gas (C_2H_6) extracted as a natural gas liquid from NATURAL GAS. Ethane can be used as a fuel and as a refrigerant.

EUROPEAN OPTIONS. A type of option which may be exercised only on the expiration date.

EXEMPT OWNERS. Any owner, typically a government agency, whose interest is exempt when calculating production, severance or AD VALOREM TAXES.

EXPLORATION COSTS. Costs incurred in identifying areas that may warrant examination and in examining specific areas for oil and gas resources. These costs include drilling exploratory-type wells and stratigraphic test wells.

EXPLORATION RIGHTS. Permission granted by landowners allowing others to enter their property to conduct geological and geophysical surveys.

EXPLORATORY WELL. A well drilled to find and produce oil or gas in an unproved area, to find a new RESERVOIR in a field previously found to be productive in another reservoir or to extend a known reservoir.

EXTENSIBLE BUSINESS REPORTING LANGUAGE (XBRL).* An XML-based markup language used for standardized reporting of business information, especially that relating to a company's financial performance.

FARMIN. One party contributes property to the venture and the other party agrees to contribute a certain amount of capital to explore or develop the property in exchange for a vested interest in the venture.

FARMOUT. Transfer of all or part of the operating rights from a WORKING INTEREST (WI) owner to an assignee, who assumes all or some of the burden of development in return for an interest in the property. The assignor usually retains an OVERRIDING ROYALTY INTEREST (ORRI) but may retain any type of interest.

FASB. The Financial Accounting Standards Board, established in 1973, is the independent, private-sector, not-for-profit organization that establishes financial accounting and reporting standards for public and private companies and not-for-profit organizations that follow generally accepted accounting principles (GAAP). The FASB is recognized by the SEC as the designated accounting standard setter for public companies.

FAULT. Oil and gas trap formed by the breaking and shearing of strata resulting from significant moving or shifting of the Earth's surface.

FEE INTEREST. Ownership of both the surface and mineral rights in a property.

FERC. The Federal Energy Regulatory Commission is an independent agency that regulates the interstate transmission of natural gas, oil and electricity. FERC also regulates natural gas and hydropower projects.

FIELD. Area consisting of a single RESERVOIR or multiple reservoirs all grouped on or related to the same individual geologic structural feature and/or stratigraphic feature.

FIELD EXPLORATORY WELL. A well drilled just outside the proved limits of a RESERVOIR. May also be called a DELINEATION WELL.

FIELD FACILITY.* Oil and gas production equipment serving more than one LEASE, for example a SEPARATOR or extraction unit.

FIELD PROCESSING. Treatment of oil or gas before it is delivered to a gas plant or refinery.

FIRE WALL.* Earthen dike built around an oil tank to contain the petroleum in the event of a tank rupture.

FISH.* Any object accidentally dropped or stuck in the WELLBORE during drilling, completion or workover operations. Activities to recover the object are called fishing.

FLARE. To burn unmarketable gas from a LEASE.

FLASH GAS. High BTU content gas which is vented from a low-pressure SEPARATOR.

FLOW CHART.* Used to refer to either: (1) a circular paper chart that records metered gas differential pressure and static pressure and is used to determine gas volume flowing through the meter or (2) a schematic of how gas flows from point to point.

FLOW LINES. Pipes carrying produced emulsion (oil, gas, or water) from wells to lease treatment and storage facilities.

FLOW TANKS. Tanks for storing oil after it has been produced.

FLOW TREATER.* Equipment that separates oil and gas, heats oil and treats oil and water.

FLOWING WELL.* A well that lifts oil and gas to the surface using natural RESERVOIR pressure.

FLUE GASES. Gas generated by burning hydrocarbons with air, sometimes used as an enhanced oil recovery (EOR) injectant. The composition consists mainly of nitrogen, carbon dioxide, water vapor and excess oxygen with some impurities, such as carbon monoxide, nitrogen oxides and sulfur oxides. Generally, more carbon dioxide in the flue gas results in a better recovery factor for EOR. By contrast, using more nitrogen results in a lower recovery factor for EOR. However, high concentration of impurities, such as oxygen, nitrous oxides and carbon monoxide, can cause corrosion in production tubulars and surface equipment.

FLUSH PRODUCTION.* Large flow of production from a well immediately after being drilled.

FOOTAGE RATE CONTRACT. Drilling contract providing for payment of a specified price per foot for drilling a well to a certain depth.

FORCE MAJEURE. Provision of a LEASE or contract whereby a LESSEE is not in violation of the agreement in the event the lessee is incapable of fulfilling the terms due to conditions or events beyond the lessee's control.

FORMATION. A body of rock composed predominantly of the same type(s) of strata throughout. A tight formation may be used to describe a rock formation in which there are small, densely packed particles.

FORMATION PRESSURE. The pressure of fluids within the pores of a RESERVOIR, usually HYDROSTATIC PRESSURE, or the pressure exerted by a column of water from the formation's depth to sea level.

FORMATION TESTING.* Procedures to determine potential productivity before installing CASING in a well.

FORMULA PRICING.* Methodology that ties a particular CRUDE OIL stream to one or more widely traded crude oil streams for determining a trade price. Adjustments are made for quality and market differentials.

FORWARD CONTRACT. Financial instrument which provides for two parties to purchase and sell a specific quantity and quality of oil or gas at a set price with delivery and settlement at a selected future date. Forward contracts are over-the-counter (OTC) products used by a company to manage pricing risks.

FRACKING (FRACING). See HYDRAULIC FRACTURING.

FRACTIONATION PLANT. Receives NATURAL GAS LIQUIDS (NGLs) from one or more gas processing plants and separates the NGLs into separate products.

FREE WELL. Sharing arrangement in which one party drills one or more wells completely free of costs to a second party in return for some type of ECONOMIC INTEREST in the property.

FULL COST. One of two methods of accounting for oil and gas properties and related activities which can be elected by an E&P company. As described in Reg. S-X Rule 4-10(c), a full cost company capitalizes all costs incurred in property acquisition, exploration and development. See SUCCESSFUL EFFORTS.

FUTURES CONTRACT. Financial instrument that is an exchange-traded legal contract to buy or sell a standard quantity and quality of a commodity at a specified date and price. Futures contracts are used by a company to manage pricing risks.

GAS BALANCING AGREEMENT (GBA). Contract between two or more parties to account for any differences between measured volumes and confirmed nominations of gas deliveries at a particular date, such as monthly. The GBA provides for the rights and obligations of the joint venture's WORKING INTEREST (WI) owners regarding producer gas imbalances and generally forms a part of the JOINT OPERATING AGREEMENT.

GAS CAP. Free gas overlying an oil zone and occurring within the same producing FORMATION as oil. It can provide the primary drive mechanism for the recovery of oil in the reservoir.

GAS CHROMATOGRAPH. Analytical instrument that separates gases from each other. The gases are carried by a carrier, an inert gas that is usually nitrogen or helium, through a column filled with either a solid or liquid that is called the stationary phase or packing. This separates the gases into individual components depending on their affinity for the stationary phase. More volatile, lighter and less polar compounds pass through the column the fastest. A gas chromatograph is composed of a sample preparation, sample valve, column, detector and signal recorder. The sample is introduced into the gas chromatograph with a syringe where it is immediately vaporized by heat. The separated compounds are identified by flame ionization or by a thermal conductivity detector and are recorded on the gas chromatogram.

GAS LIFT. Artificial means of extracting oil whereby gas is injected down the hole between the CASING and production tubing. The injected gas aerates the liquid and floats up the tubing to the surface. Gas lifts are commonly used on offshore wells.

GAS MAKE-UP. Gas taken in a later period that was paid for previously under a TAKE-OR-PAY CONTRACT.

GAS-OIL RATIO.* Measure of the volume of gas produced along with oil from the same well.

GAS PAYMENT.* Production payment payable out of gas produced.

GAS PLANT. A plant where NATURAL GASOLINES are removed from the gas.

GAS PLANT PRODUCTS.* NATURAL GAS LIQUIDS (NGL) removed from NATURAL GAS in refineries or field facilities.

GAS SETTLEMENT STATEMENT. Record of the amount of gas transferred from a well to a pipeline that provides details for the gas producers' and buyers' accounting departments to record product sales.

GAS WELL. A well primarily producing NATURAL GAS.

GATHERING SYSTEM. Group of small pipelines which moves the oil or gas from several wells into a TANK BATTERY (in the case of oil) or major pipeline.

GAUGE TICKET.* Form on which the measurement of oil in lease tanks is recorded.

GAUGER. Individual responsible for the measurement of quantity and quality of oil and gas on a LEASE.

GENERAL PARTNERSHIP (GP). Legal form of organization in which all of the partners are general partners (GPs), have the right to participate in management and have unlimited liability.

GEOLOGICAL AND GEOPHYSICAL (G&G) COSTS. Exploratory costs of topographical, geological and geophysical surveys along with costs incurred to obtain the rights to make such surveys. Salaries and other expenses of the personnel required to carry out the surveys are also included.

GEOLOGICAL AND GEOPHYSICAL STUDIES. Processes which seek surface or subterranean indications of the Earth's structure or formations where experience has shown mineral deposits may exist.

GEOLOGICAL SURVEY.* Exploratory program directed to the examination of rocks and sediments obtained by boring or drilling or by inspection of surface outcroppings.

GEOLOGY. Science of the history, development and structure of the Earth, especially the Earth's crust.

GEOPHYSICAL SURVEY.* Study of the configuration of the Earth's crust in a given area as determined by the use of seismic, gravity, magnetic and geochemical procedures.

GEOPHYSICS. A subject of natural science concerned with the physical processes and physical properties of the Earth and its surrounding space environment, and the use of quantitative methods for their analysis.

GPM. Measure used to express the volume of NATURAL GAS LIQUIDS (NGLs) in gallons per MCF. May also be used as an abbreviation for gallons per minute.

GRAVITY. The Earth's gravitational field, or the attractive force produced by the mass of the Earth. Variations in the gravitational field can be used to map changes in the density of formations in the Earth. Gravity surveys can be used to map the extent or depth of sedimentary basins or even individual HYDROCARBON prospects.

GRAVITY METER.* An instrument used for measuring variations in the gravitational pull of the Earth.

GROSS WELLS.* Total number of wells participated in, regardless of the ownership percentage in each well. For example, a company owning a 10 percent interest in each of 20 wells is said to have 20 gross wells or two net wells, calculated as 20 wells x 10% = 2 net wells. See NET WELLS.

HAYNESVILLE/BOSSIER SHALE. A large shale gas FORMATION located in East Texas and Western Louisiana. There has been some confusion in whether the formation is the Haynesville Shale and/or the Bossier Shale because of different geological naming conventions in Texas and Louisiana. It is generally recognized that the shale interval in East Texas is the Lower Bossier that correlates with the Haynesville of Louisiana.

HENRY HUB. A terminal and trading hub in Louisiana where NATURAL GAS prices are quoted and trades are settled.

HORIZON. Underground geological FORMATION which is a portion of the larger formation possessing sufficient POROSITY and PERMIABILITY to constitute a RESERVOIR.

HORIZONTAL ASSIGNMENT.* Assignment of an interest in the minerals above, below or between specified depths or in a given stratum or HORIZON.

HORIZONTAL DRILLING. Deviation drilling that becomes horizontal or near horizontal to increase the length of the WELLBORE penetrating the target FORMATION.

HYDRAULIC FRACTURING. Procedure to stimulate production by forcing a mixture of fluid and proppant into the FORMATION under high pressure. Interchangeably referred to as hydrofracturing, FRACKING or fracing, it creates artificial fractures in the RESERVOIR rock to increase POROSITY and PERMIABILITY.

HYDROCARBON. A naturally occurring organic compound of hydrogen and carbon.

HYDROSTATIC PRESSURE.* The normal, predicted pressure for a given depth, or the pressure exerted per unit area by a column of freshwater from sea level to a given depth.

IGNEOUS ROCKS. Rocks that are formed directly from the molten state.

IN-SITU COMBUSTION. Process of setting fire to some oil in the RESERVOIR and creating a burning front of gases intended to drive oil ahead of it to the WELLBORE.

INDEPENDENT PETROLEUM ASSOCIATION OF AMERICA (IPAA). An organization that represents the thousands of independent oil and gas producers and service companies across the U.S. See INDEPENDENT PRODUCERS.

INDEPENDENT PRODUCERS. Oil companies that engage in exploration, drilling and/or production but do not engage in transportation, refining or retail sales. Independent producers may process and market NATURAL GAS to gas consumers by using third party pipelines to transport it. See INDEPENDENT PETROLEUM ASSOCIATION OF AMERICA (IPAA).

INITIAL PRODUCTION (IP).* Figure given to a well indicating its capability to produce, it may be the first full day's production, or a fraction thereof, multiplied to the equivalent of a day.

INJECTION WELLS. Wells used to inject gas, water or LIQUEFIED PETROLEUM GAS (LPG) under high pressure into producing formations to maintain sufficient pressure to produce the recoverable RESERVES.

INSTALLMENT BONUS. See DEFERRED BONUS.

INTANGIBLE DRILLING COSTS (IDC). Federal income tax term that refers to any cost which in itself has no salvage value but is necessary for and incident to the drilling of wells and getting them ready for production. IDC can also occur when deepening or plugging back a previously drilled oil or gas well, or an abandoned well, to a different FORMATION. Examples of IDC are labor, fuel, repairs, transportation and supplies.

INTEGRATED OIL COMPANIES. Companies that engage in exploration, drilling and production as well as significant refining, transportation or retail operations in the petroleum industry.

INTERMEDIATE CASING STRING.* String of CASING set in a well after the surface casing and before the production casing. It serves to protect the WELLBORE as the well is deepened and to seal off problem formations such as high pressure areas.

INTERMEDIATE CRUDE. Crude oil with an API gravity greater than 18 degrees and less than 36 degrees and located in the spectrum between sour and sweet crude. See WEST TEXAS INTERMEDIATE (WTI).

INTERRUPTIBLE GAS.* Gas sold or transported without a pipeline's prior guarantee to move the gas.

ISOPACH MAPS.* Maps showing variations in the thickness of a particular sedimentary bed and the interval between one sedimentary bed and another.

JACKUP RIG. An offshore rig in which the rig is floated into position and the legs are mechanically levered to the ocean floor.

JOINT. Single length of DRILLPIPE or casing that is usually 20 to 30 feet in length.

JOINT INTEREST (JOINT VENTURE). Association of two or more persons or companies to drill, develop and operate jointly owned properties. Each owner has an undivided interest in the properties.

JOINT OPERATING AGREEMENT. Contractual agreement between two or more owners in a lease that provides for the operation of the lease. One owner typically operates the lease with all other WORKING INTEREST (WI) owners sharing in the costs. The 2005 Accounting Procedure Joint Operations issued by the COUNCIL OF PETROLEUM ACCOUNTANTS SOCIETIES (COPAS) as Model Form 6 (MF-6) provides an operating agreement exhibit that establishes joint venture accounting practices using one of several standard forms typically employed by joint interest parties in the industry.

KEEP-WHOLE ARRANGEMENTS. Processing agreements where the producer receives 100 percent of the attributable RESIDUE GAS and consideration for the attributable PLANT-VOLUME REDUCTION (PVR). Payment for the PVR either can be equivalent BTUs of additional residue gas or a cash payment. The processor generally keeps 100 percent of the liquids extracted as payment for processing.

KELLY. Heavy square or hexagonal steel member that turns the DRILLSTRING. It is suspended from a swivel through the rotary table and is connected to the DRILLPIPE.

KILL.* Industry term meaning to stop formation fluids, which are usually under dangerous high pressure, from coming up a well. The stopping process uses MUD or water to halt production rather than closing WELLHEAD valves.

LACT SYSTEM.* See LEASE AUTOMATIC CUSTODY TRANSFER (LACT) UNIT.

LANDMAN. Person employed by an E&P company responsible for identifying, negotiating, acquiring, retaining or disposing of oil and gas leases. A landman may also manage the company's internal land department. The term also refers to an independent broker for identifying, negotiating and acquiring leases. Landman, whether referring to a male or female, continues to be more commonly used than the term landperson. See American Association of Professional Landmen (AAPL).

LEAN-OIL ABSORPTION. A chemical process to extract NATURAL GAS LIQUIDS (NGLs) from a gas stream as they pass through a series of special, oil-bearing contactor towers. They are inefficient in extracting lighter NGL components but use minimal fuel for compression and have flexibility in how much gas can be processed efficiently.

LEASE. An agreement in which the owner of a mineral interest (LESSOR) assigns all or a part of the operating rights to another party (LESSEE) but retains a continuing nonoperating interest in production from the property. Commonly, the LESSEE is an E&P company that obtains temporary and limited rights to explore for, develop and produce minerals from the property subject to the terms of the lease agreement.

LEASE AND WELL EQUIPMENT. Capital investment in equipment used in a well or on a LEASE and having a potential salvage value. Such items can include the cost of casing, tubing, WELLHEAD assemblies, pumping units, lease tanks, treaters and separators.

LEASE AUTOMATIC CUSTODY TRANSFER (LACT) UNIT. Automatic device for moving and measuring oil from lease storage to the pipeline. The process also requires a pump, an oil meter and a BS&W measuring device. May also be called a LACT or ACT system.

LEASE BONUS. Consideration paid by the lessee to the lessor upon execution of an oil and gas LEASE.

LEASE CONDENSATE. See CONDENSATE.

LEASE OPERATING EXPENSE (LOE). Costs of operating the wells and equipment on a producing lease, many of which are recurring and may be variable or fixed in nature.

LEASE USE. NATURAL GAS or NATURAL GASOLINE used at a well site to operate production equipment.

LEASEHOLD INTEREST. See WORKING INTEREST (WI).

LESSEE. Individual or company entitled to exploit the mineral deposits per the terms of an oil and gas LEASE executed with a LESSOR.

LESSOR. Owner of the mineral rights of a property.

LIFTING COSTS. See PRODUCTION COSTS.

LIMITED PARTNERSHIP (LP). Legal form of organization of a business that involves one or more general partners (GPs) with unlimited liability and at least one or more limited partners (LPs) who have limited liability. E&P limited partnerships may adopt either the successful efforts or full cost method of accounting.

LINEFILL. The amount of crude oil required to fill a new line before deliveries can be made at take-off points or at the end of the line.

LINEPACK. A method used to manage pressure within a pipeline, which may sometimes involve increasing pressure by "packing" more gas into the pipeline to facilitate movement of product.

LIQUEFIED NATURAL GAS (LNG). NATURAL GAS that has been condensed to a liquid, typically by cryogenically cooling the gas to (327.2) degrees Fahrenheit (F) and applying pressure.

LIQUEFIED PETROLEUM GAS (LPG). Liquefied petroleum gas which may contain some butane but generally consists of PROPANE, the fuel used in portable gas grills.

LOCATION. Site for a well to be drilled or at which a well has been drilled.

LOGGING. Process of taking and recording physical measurements about formations being drilled.

MAKING A TRIP. Act of hoisting the DRILLSTRING out of and returning it into a WELLBORE.

MANAGING PARTNER. Partner in a GENERAL PARTNERSHIP (GP) that performs overall management duties, including maintaining business records, filing tax returns and providing an accounting to partners.

MARCELLUS SHALE. Gas-producing geological FORMATION that extends in the subsurface from Southern New York to Northeastern Kentucky and Tennessee. It is the most prolific NATURAL GAS producing formation in the Appalachian basin, covering about 95,000 square miles with a prospective area of about 72,000 square miles.

MARGINAL WELL.* A well with limited production that has become barely profitable to operate.

MASS SPECTROMETER.* Instrument used to determine molecular weights and relative abundances of isotopes in a substance. The molecular components are ionized and disassociated by electronic bombardment. Positive ions are then accelerated in an electric field and separated magnetically by mass. A mass spectrometer is often used for gas analysis because it is fast and accurate. It can determine the amount of METHANE, ETHANE, PROPANE, isobutane, N-butane, pentanes, hexanes, heptanes, and heavier hydrocarbons along with carbon dioxide, hydrogen sulfide, nitrogen and helium content. A mass spectrometer also can calculate the BTU content of gas.

MCF. Standard measure of volume for NATURAL GAS equal to one thousand cubic feet.

METAMORPHIC ROCKS. Rocks developed as a result of SEDIMENTARY ROCKS subjected to heat and pressure.

METHANE. The lightest and most abundant of the HYDROCARBON gases (CH_4) and the principal component of NATURAL GAS. Methane is a colorless, odorless gas that is stable under a wide range of pressure and temperature conditions in the absence of other compounds.

MINERAL INTEREST. Economic interest in underground minerals, such as a MINERAL RIGHT, WORKING INTEREST (WI) or OVERRIDING ROYALTY INTEREST (ORRI).

MINERAL RIGHTS. The rights of ownership of oil, gas or other minerals beneath the surface which can be conveyed by deed.

MINIMUM ROYALTY. Obligation of a LESSEE to pay a LESSOR a periodic sum of money after production occurs, regardless of the amount of production. Such minimum royalty may or may not be recoverable under the terms of the LEASE.

MISCIBLE SOLVENT. TERTIARY RECOVERY process similar to a water flood but involving the injection of a solvent that mixes with CRUDE OIL.

MMBTU. One million BRITISH THERMAL UNITS (BTU); also, a measurement of the energy released when NATURAL GAS is burned.

MMCF. One million cubic feet.

MOBILE DRILLING RIGS. A type of DRILLING RIG consisting of either: (1) a small onshore rig mounted on a truck used for shallow wells or (2) an offshore rig that can be floated from one drill site to another. See DRILLSHIP, JACKUP RIG and SEMI-SUBMERSIBLE RIG.

MOUSE HOLE.* Hole drilled under the DERRICK floor, which is temporarily cased, where a length of DRILLPIPE is temporarily suspended for later connection to the DRILLSTRING.

MUD. Drilling fluid circulated through the DRILLPIPE and back to the surface during rotary drilling and workovers.

MULTIPLE COMPLETIONS. A well that is producing oil and/or gas from different zones at different depths in the same WELLBORE with separate tubing strings for each zone. This type of well differs from a commingled well which uses just one tubing string.

NATIONAL OIL COMPANIES. Oil companies solely owned by the government of the country of origination.

NATURAL GAS. Light hydrocarbons existing in a gaseous state in the Earth's crust under certain atmospheric and temperature conditions. Natural gas often is found in association with oil.

NATURAL GAS LIQUIDS (NGLs). Hydrocarbons which can be extracted from wet natural gas and become liquid under various combinations of increasing pressure and lower temperature. NGLs consist primarily of ETHANE, PROPANE, BUTANE and NATURAL GASOLINES.

NATURAL GASOLINES. Hydrocarbons found in natural gas and consisting of PROPANE, BUTANE, pentane, hexane and heptane. Natural gasolines (C_5H_{12} to $C_{10}H_{22}$) are recovered from the natural gas stream in refineries primarily by means of absorption or compression technologies.

NET PROFITS INTEREST (NPI). Interest in production created from the WORKING INTEREST (WI) and measured by a certain percentage of the net profits from the operation of the property as defined in the contract.

NET REVENUE INTEREST. A share of production after all burdens, such as royalty and overriding royalty, have been deducted from the WORKING INTEREST (WI). It is the percentage of production that each party actually receives.

NET REVENUES. The proceeds of oil and gas sales less any royalties and overriding royalties, production and severance taxes, marketing and transportation costs and operating expenses.

NET WELLS.* Aggregate of fractional interests an owner has in more than one well. See GROSS WELLS.

NEW FIELD WILDCAT.* A well drilled in an area where there had been no previous production of oil or gas.

NEW YORK MERCANTILE EXCHANGE (NYMEX). A commodities exchange with highly active trade in oil commodities and derivatives.

NOMINATION. Anticipated volume a producer expects to deliver into a pipeline in the next month, which may be changed and confirmed as necessary, as communicated to the pipeline company for confirmation.

NONASSOCIATED GAS. Natural gas (usually dry) not in contact with crude oil in a RESERVOIR.

NONCONSENT. Common provision in a JOINT OPERATING AGREEMENT that allows certain WORKING INTEREST (WI) owners to not participate in the drilling, reworking or completion of a well (also referred to as "going nonconsent"). The parties interested in participating must absorb all costs of the drilling operation, including any dry hole costs, and are permitted to recoup a percentage of those costs out of the future production attributable to the interests of the nonconsenting parties. The percentage recovery is specified in the joint operating agreement and may range from 100 to 800 percent.

NONCONTINUING INTEREST.* An interest in a mineral property whose life is limited in terms of dollars, units of product or time.

NONOPERATING INTEREST. An interest in minerals for which the holder does not have the responsibility to bear the costs of developing and producing the minerals. Examples include royalties, overriding royalties and volumetric production payments.

NONOPERATOR. An entity that is a joint venture participant that is not the OPERATOR managing the joint venture.

OFFSET WELL. Type of well drilled on a well spacing unit adjacent to a producing well spacing unit. May also refer to a well drilled on a lease to minimize drainage of reserves by wells on an adjacent lease.

OIL POOL.* Underground RESERVOIR containing oil in SEDIMENTARY ROCKS.

OIL SANDS. Any porous RESERVOIR, generally sandstone, containing oil. The term oil sands may refer to formations close to the surface containing heavy hydrocarbons whereby the sands are mined and processed to produce synthetic CRUDE OIL.

OIL SEEP.* Area where tiny amounts of petroleum have migrated to the Earth's surface.

OIL WELL. A well which can and does produce CRUDE OIL with minimal natural gas. Most state regulations classify a well as an oil well, as opposed to a GAS WELL, if it produces less than 15 MCF of gas per BARREL (BBL) of oil.

OPERATING AGREEMENT. See JOINT OPERATING AGREEMENT.

OPERATOR. An entity that is a joint venture participant that is responsible for managing the joint venture, paying joint venture expenses and billing the nonoperators for their respective shares of joint venture costs.

OPTION CONTRACTS. A financial instrument that gives the buyer (holder) a right, but not an obligation, to buy (call) or sell (put) a specified item at a fixed price (exercise price or strike price) during a specified exercise period from or to the seller (writer). The buyer pays a non-refundable fee (premium) to the seller. Option contracts are either exchange traded (such as NYMEX options on the NYMEX crude oil futures contract) or over-the-counter (OTC) contracts. OTC contracts expose the holder to counterparty default. Option contracts can be used for both hedging purposes and to create exposure to market price changes.

OUTPOST WELL (STEP-OUT WELL). A well drilled outside well locations offsetting a producing well but within the possible or probable extent of the RESERVOIR.

OVERRIDING ROYALTY INTEREST (ORRI). Royalty interest which is created out of the operating or WORKING INTEREST. Its term is co-extensive with that of the operating interest.

PARTICIPATION FACTORS. Set of undivided interests in the total area covered by a UNITIZATION agreement. Factors may be classified as either operating or nonoperating depending on the type of property contributed. Also, percentages could be revised as more information about the contributed RESERVES becomes available.

PAY. Oil- or gas-saturated rock that is capable of producing oil or gas.

PAYOUT. A condition that occurs when revenues to a given interest in a well equal all land, acquisition, drilling, completing and operating costs allocated to that interest. Used with working interests and net revenue interests to indicate ownership before payout (see BPO) versus after payout (see APO).

PCAOB. Public Company Accounting Oversight Board.

PERCENTAGE DEPLETION. Federal income tax term referring to a deduction based on the gross income from mineral properties. Percentage depletion is computed on a property-by-property basis and is subject to certain limitations. It is also known as statutory depletion.

PERCENTAGE OF INDEX (POI). Contracts priced at: (1) a percentage discount to a specified index price, (2) a specified index price less a fixed amount or (3) a percentage discount to a specified index price less an additional fixed amount.

PERMEABILITY. Measure of the relative ease that oil can move through a RESERVOIR.

PETROLEUM. Oil or gas obtained from the rocks of the Earth, usually by drilling down into a RESERVOIR and producing the hydrocarbons to the surface.

PIG.* A scraping instrument for cleaning a pipeline. The pressure of the oil stream pushes the pig along the pipeline to clean out rust, wax, scale and debris.

PIPELINE GAS IMBALANCE. An imbalance that occurs when a WORKING INTEREST (WI) owner nominates and sells to a customer (or customers), and the pipeline delivers to that customer, a gas volume that differs from the WI owner's share of gas in the pipeline. See PRODUCER GAS IMBALANCE.

PLANT-THERMAL REDUCTION (PTR). The BTU equivalent of the liquid products extracted from NATURAL GAS by a processing plant, plus the natural gas used as plant fuel to extract those liquids, plant flare and other losses. When expressed as a volume in MCF, PTR is referred to as PLANT-VOLUME REDUCTION (PVR).

PLANT-VOLUME REDUCTION (PVR). See PLANT-THERMAL REDUCTION.

PLUG-BACK. Act of sealing off a lower FORMATION in a WELLBORE in order to produce from a higher FORMATION.

PLUGGING AND ABANDONMENT (P&A). Activities performed and costs incurred to plug and seal a well below the surface and remove surface equipment after the well has reached its economic limit. May also be referred to as DISMANTLEMENT, RESTORATION AND ABANDONMENT (DR&A).

POOL. Underground RESERVOIR having a common accumulation of oil or gas.

POOLING. Provision in an oil and gas LEASE that permits the OPERATOR to combine the leased property with properties owned by others. The separate tracts are joined to form a drilling unit which can result in cost savings. Ownership shares are issued according to the acreage contributed or by the production capabilities of each producing well for fields in later stages of development. See UNITIZATION.

POROSITY. Relative volume of the pore space in a RESERVOIR compared to its total bulk volume.

POSSIBLE RESERVES. The SEC defines the term to include those additional reserves that are less certain to be recovered than probable reserves. When deterministic methods are used, the total quantities ultimately recovered from a project have a low probability to exceed the sum of proved, probable and possible reserves. When probabilistic methods are used, there must be at least a 10 percent probability that the actual quantities recovered will equal or exceed the sum of proved, probable and possible estimates.

POSTED FIELD PRICE.* Published price a CRUDE OIL purchaser will pay for a specific grade of crude at the point it is delivered by the seller and accepted by the purchaser on or after a stated date.

PRESSURE MAINTENANCE. Injection of gas, water or other material to re-pressure an oil field.

PRESSURE REGULATOR.* Instrument for maintaining pressure in a pipeline downstream from the VALVE.

PRICE BULLETIN. Posting of the price per BARREL (BBL) a purchaser will pay for each grade of CRUDE OIL in a geographic area.

PRIMARY RECOVERY. The first stage of HYDROCARBON production in which natural RESERVOIR energy, such as gas drive, water drive or gravity drainage, displaces hydrocarbons from the reservoir, into the WELLBORE and up to the surface.

PROBABLE RESERVES. The SEC defines the term as those additional reserves that are less certain to be recovered than proved reserves but which, in sum with proved reserves, are as likely as not to be recovered. When deterministic methods are used, it is as likely as not that actual remaining quantities recovered will equal or exceed the sum of estimated proved plus probable reserves. Similarly, when probabilistic methods are used, there must be at least a 50 percent probability that the actual quantities recovered will equal or exceed the proved plus probable reserves estimates.

PRODUCER GAS IMBALANCE. An imbalance that occurs when one or more producers sells or utilizes an amount of NATURAL GAS that differs from its respective ownership share of the volumes.

PRODUCT LOSS ALLOWANCE (PLA). Clause in some crude transportation contracts that offsets losses due to evaporation, measurement interface losses and other losses in transit.

PRODUCTION COSTS. Costs of activities that involve lifting oil and gas to the surface (see LIFTING COSTS) and operating and maintaining wells and related equipment and facilities.

PRODUCTION PAYMENT. Obligation to pay or receive a specified portion of production proceeds or to deliver a specified portion of certain production volumes before the production is expected to cease.

PRODUCTION SHARING CONTRACT (PSC). An arrangement where the host government owns the reserves and contracts with an E&P company to perform or manage specified activities. Investments made by a participating E&P company (or companies) are reimbursed through assignment of future HYDROCARBON production. The E&P company typically is also entitled to a share of production, which represents its return on investment. See SERVICE CONTRACT.

PRODUCTION STRING. Last and deepest string of CASING set in a well through which oil or gas will be produced.

PRODUCTION TAXES. Statutory amounts levied by state governments on mineral production based on the value and/or quantity of production volumes. One type of production tax includes severance taxes.

PRODUCTIVITY TEST.* Test of the maximum or other rates at which a well can produce.

PROJECT AREA.* Large territory a taxpayer determines can be explored advantageously in a single integrated operation.

PROPANE. A HYDROCARBON gas (C_3H_8) extracted as a natural gas liquid from NATURAL GAS. Propane, also called LPG, is stored in a liquid state under pressure.

PROPERTY. Aggregate economic interest owned through a LEASE or acquisition of a MINERAL INTEREST, as defined for financial accounting purposes. For income tax purposes, property refers to each separate interest owned by a taxpayer in each mineral deposit in each separate tract or parcel of land. Certain interests for tax purposes may be combined to form a property.

PROVED DEVELOPED RESERVES. Reserves which can be expected to be recovered through existing wells with existing equipment and operating methods.

PROVED PROPERTY. For financial accounting purposes, a property containing PROVED RESERVES. For income tax purposes, a property whose principal value has been demonstrated by exploration, discovery or development.

PROVED RESERVES. Quantities of reserves that appear with reasonable certainty to be recoverable in the future from known oil and gas reserves based on geologic and engineering data and under existing economic and operating conditions.

PROVED UNDEVELOPED RESERVES. Reserves expected to be recovered from new wells on undrilled proved acreage or from existing wells where a relatively major expenditure is required for completion.

PSIA. Pounds per square inch absolute.

PUMPER. Individual responsible for all equipment contained on the lease.

QUARTER SECTION.* A one-fourth section of land, it measures one-half square mile per side, or 160 acres. A full section is 1 square mile or 640 acres.

RABBIT.* Line cleaning instrument consisting of a small plug which is run through a line.

RAT HOLE*. A hole from 30 to 35 feet deep with CASING that projects above the DERRICK floor, where the KELLY is placed when hoisting operations are in progress.

RECOMPLETION. As defined in the AMERICAN ASSOCIATION OF PETROLEUM LANDMEN (AAPL) Model Form Operating Agreement, "an operation whereby a completion in one zone is abandoned in order to attempt a completion in a different zone within the existing wellbore." See WORKOVER.

RESERVES. See PROVED RESERVES, PROVED DEVELOPED RESERVES and PROVED UNDEVELOPED RESERVES.

RESERVOIR. Porous and permeable underground FORMATION that contains natural accumulations of producible oil or NATURAL GAS. Formations are confined by impermeable rock or water barriers and are individual and separate from other reservoirs.

RESIDUE GAS. Gas produced at the tailgate of a gas processing plant after all NATURAL GAS LIQUIDS (NGLs) and natural gas liquids products have been removed.

RETAINED INTEREST. Interest kept by the grantor when selling or assigning an interest to another party.

REVERSIONARY INTEREST. Portion of an ECONOMIC INTEREST that will be returned to its former owner after a predetermined amount of production or income has been produced.

RING-FENCING. A concept that restricts all cost recovery and/or deductions to production from a discrete license or field.

ROYALTY INTEREST. The landowner's (lessor's) share of oil or gas production, typically in increments of one-eighth (1/8), one-sixth (1/6) or one-fourth (1/4) and free of costs, but subject to severance taxes unless the lessor is a government agency.

RUN TICKET. Record of the quantity of oil removed from a stock tank into a pipeline or tank truck. A run ticket will generally have opening and closing volumes, observed gravity and temperature, BS&W and date and time of delivery. It is usually made in triplicate and filled out by the GAUGER employed by the purchaser. Sometimes the entries will be witnessed by the PUMPER as a subcontractor or an employee of the E&P company operating the well.

SEC. The Securities and Exchange Commission was created by the Securities Exchange Act of 1934. Its primary responsibilities consist of: interpreting and enforcing federal securities laws; issuing new rules and amending existing rules; overseeing the inspection of securities firms, brokers, investment advisers and ratings agencies; overseeing private regulatory organizations in the securities, accounting and auditing fields; and coordinating U.S. securities regulation with federal, state and foreign authorities.

SECONDARY RECOVERY. The second stage of producing hydrocarbons during which an external fluid such as water or gas is injected into the RESERVOIR through injection wells located in rock that has fluid communication with production wells. The purpose of secondary recovery is to maintain reservoir pressure and to displace hydrocarbons toward the WELLBORE. The most common secondary recovery techniques are gas injection and WATERFLOODING.

SEDIMENTARY ROCKS. Rocks formed by the accumulation of sediment at the bottom of a body of water that is compressed over time.

SEISMIC. Exploration method of sending energy waves or sound waves into the Earth and recording the wave reflections to indicate the type, size, shape and depth of subsurface rock formations. 2D seismic provides two dimensional information and 3D seismic provides three dimensional pictures. 4D seismic produces 3-D pictures over time and is used to indicate fluid movement in producing reservoirs.

SEISMOGRAPH.* Device for detecting vibrations in the Earth used in prospecting for probable oil-bearing structures.

SEMI-SUBMERSIBLE RIG. Mobile DRILLING RIG structure that is commonly used in deepwater offshore drilling or in hazardous offshore drilling conditions.

SEPARATOR. Cylindrical or spherical device located at the well site to separate commingled oil and gas by means of gravity and centrifugal force. In the process, the oil drops out of the mix and the gas rises and escapes through separate outlets.

SERVICE WELL. A well drilled or completed for the purpose of supporting production in an existing field. Wells in this class are drilled for the following specific purposes: gas injection (NATURAL GAS, PROPANE, BUTANE or FLUE GAS), water injection, steam injection, air injection, salt-water disposal, water supply for injection, observation or injection for in-situ combustion.

SERVICE CONTRACT. An agreement where the host government owns the reserves and contracts with an E&P company to perform specific activities. Fees for service contracts are paid in cash rather than as a share of production. See PRODUCTION SHARING CONTRACTS (PSCs).

SHALE. A type of SEDIMENTARY ROCK from which oil and gas can be produced by utilizing different extraction techniques.

SHALE SHAKER. A vibrating screen that separates cuttings from drilling MUD before the mud is returned to the well.

SHOOTING RIGHTS. Limited rights obtained through agreement with the landowner which gives theoperator the right to enter onto the property and conduct exploration activities, but grants no drilling or production rights.

SHUT-IN ROYALTY. A payment received by a royalty owner in lieu of actual production when a well is shut-in due to the lack of a suitable market, a lack of facilities to produce the product or other scenarios defined within the shut-in royalty provisions contained in the LEASE.

SMOG. Acronym for the supplemental oil and gas disclosures required by ASC 932 of the standardized measure of discounted future net cash flows relating to proved oil and gas reserves.

SONDE. Any of various devices for testing physical conditions, often for remote or underwater locations.

SOUR CRUDE OIL. Oil with a high sulfur content.

SOUR GAS. Gas with a high sulfur content.

SPACING. Regulation concerning the number of wells which can be drilled on a given area of land. Depending on the depth of the RESERVOIR, one well may be allowed on a small area of five acres or on an area up to 640 acres. Typical spacing is 40 acres for oil wells and 640 acres for gas wells. However, spacing for tight-sands FORMATIONS may be 20 acres.

SPLIT CONNECTION.* One gas well that is connected to more than one pipeline that occurs when two or more WORKING INTEREST (WI) owners use different pipeline companies.

SPOT PRICE. A transaction price concluded on a one-time basis for a transaction that usually only involves one specific quantity of product. This contrasts with a term contract sale price which obligates the seller to deliver a product at an agreed-upon frequency and price over an extended period.

SPUD. Commencement of actual drilling operations.

STEAMFLOODING. Process whereby steam is injected to improve oil recovery by heating oil and decreasing its VISCOCITY and employing physical displacement similar to WATERFLOODING.

STIMULATION. Mechanical or chemical process designed to increase production by changing the characteristics of the portion of the RESERVOIR near a well. See ACIDIZE, HYDRAULIC FRACTURING and WORKOVER.

STRADDLE PLANT. A plant situated on a transmission pipeline system as opposed to between the field gas GATHERING SYSTEM and the pipeline.

STRATIGRAPHIC TEST WELLS. Wells drilled to obtain information about geologic conditions.

STRIPPER WELL. A well with marginally economic production.

STRIPPING A WELL.* The act of pulling both the rods and tubing from a well simultaneously.

STRUCTURAL MAPS.* Maps that indicate the contours of the subsurface.

SUCCESSFUL EFFORTS. One of two methods of accounting for oil and gas properties and related activities which can be elected by an E&P company. As required by ASC 932, costs incurred in searching for, acquiring and developing oil and gas RESERVES are capitalized only if they result directly in acquiring, finding or developing PROVED RESERVES. All other costs are expensed as incurred. See FULL COST.

SWAB. Device that fits tightly inside the tubing of a well and, when pulled through the tubing, lifts out fluid.

SWAP. Financial instrument that enables two parties to exchange variable and fixed-rate payment streams based on a specified contract principal or notional amount. For example, one company may pay a fixed price and the other company may pay based on a published price index or futures contract settlement price spanning several settlement periods.

SWEET CRUDE OIL. Oil with a relatively low sulfur content.

SWEET GAS.* Gas with a relatively low sulfur content.

TAKE-OR-PAY CONTRACTS. Agreements where the purchaser of gas agrees to take a minimum quantity of gas per year, if it is not prevented from doing so by circumstances beyond its control and if the gas is available for delivery. If the purchaser does not take the minimum quantity, it is required to pay for that minimum quantity at the contract price. The purchaser may make up deficiency amounts in future years if it purchases in excess of minimum amounts.

TANGIBLE COSTS. Costs of assets that, in themselves, have salvage value.

TANK BATTERY. Group of storage tanks that are connected to receive crude oil production from a well or a producing lease and in which the oil volume is measured and tested before pumping the oil into the pipeline system.

TANK STRAPPER. Individual who measures a tank and prepares the tank table.

TANK TABLE. Table showing the volume of a tank at various levels based on one-fourth-inch intervals.

TCF. Trillion cubic feet.

TD. Total depth to the bottom of a well.

TEMPORARILY ABANDONED WELL. A well, which is deemed nonproductive, but which is not permanently plugged. An intent exists to use it for some other purpose or to re-establish production if economics improve.

TERTIARY RECOVERY. Traditionally, the third stage of HYDROCARBON production, comprising recovery methods that follow WATERFLOODING or pressure maintenance. The principal tertiary recovery techniques used are thermal methods, gas injection and chemical flooding. The term is sometimes used as a synonym for enhanced oil recovery (EOR), but because EOR methods today may be applied at any stage of reservoir development, the term tertiary recovery is less commonly used than in the past.

THIEF. Device for extracting oil samples from a tank.

TIGHT HOLE. A drilling or completed well for which the OPERATOR refuses to release information to interested parties.

TOP LEASE. Lease provision granting a new oil and gas LEASE to be executed prior to the termination of an existing one. The new lease becomes effective upon expiration of the old lease.

TUBING. Small diameter pipe suspended in a well through which gas or oil is produced.

TURNKEY WELL. Completed, producing well which is drilled and equipped by a contractor for a fixed price.

UNCONVENTIONAL RESOURCES. Oil and natural gas produced using methods other than conventional methods, frequently recovered from heavy oil and tar sands, tight-gas sands, oil and gas shales and coalbed methane. See CONVENTIONAL RESOURCES.

UNDEVELOPED PROPERTY. Property that has not been drilled or equipped for production.

UNITIZATION. A contractual or legal consolidation of multiple areas or blocks to permit the field or a pool to be efficiently developed. See POOLING.

UNIT-OF-PRODUCTION (UOP) AMORTIZATION. Method of computing depreciation or depletion provisions based on quantities produced in relation to reserves.

VALVE. Device used to control the flow rate in a line, open or shut off a line completely or serve as an automatic or semi-automatic safety device.

VISCOSITY. Ability of a fluid to flow as a result of its physical characteristics.

VOLUMETRIC PRODUCTION PAYMENT (VPP). A financing method where the owner receives cash in exchange for a production payment payable in oil and gas volumes to be produced from the well(s) subject to the VPP.

WATERFLOODING. A SECONDARY RECOVERY method in which water is forced down injection wells laid out in various patterns around the producing wells. The injected water displaces the oil and forces it to the producing wells.

WATER INJECTION. See WATERFLOODING.

WATER WELL.* A well drilled to obtain a supply of water for drilling or operating use.

WEIGHTED AVERAGE COST OF CAPITAL (WACC). The average a company is expected to pay its security holders to acquire financing through debt or equity.

WELL. Hole drilled in the ground to obtain geological information, find and produce oil or gas or provide service to the operation of an oil or gas property.

WELLBORE. The drilled hole or BOREHOLE, including the open hole or uncased portion of the well.

WELLHEAD. Equipment located at the top of a well CASING that is used to maintain surface control of a well.

WEST TEXAS INTERMEDIATE (WTI). A light sweet crude oil produced in the interior of the U.S., it is a well-known BENCHMARK CRUDE in oil pricing and the underlying index of oil futures contracts on the NEW YORK MERCANTILE EXCHANGE (NYMEX). There are three major locations where WTI prices are quoted: (1) Cushing, Oklahoma, (2) Houston, Texas and (3) Midland, Texas, the price point closest to the actual production of WTI crude oil.

WET GAS. Gas that contains a large quantity of liquids.

WILDCAT.* EXPLORATORY WELL that is particularly risky due to a lack of available information from seismic data or nearby producing fields to support the prospect.

WORKING INTEREST. Ownership interest in the oil and gas in-place with responsibility for the cost of development and operation of the property. May also be referred to as an operating interest.

WORKOVER. Major remedial operations on a completed well to restore, maintain or improve the well's production. Workovers use workover rigs and can take many forms such as acidizing or fracking the well or removal of sand or paraffin build-up. The term workover is also used for deepening an existing well or plugging back to produce from a shallower FORMATION. Costs to explore to an unproved formation are EXPLORATION COSTS. Costs to access a proved FORMATION are DEVELOPMENT COSTS. The term workover excludes minor repairs or well servicing such as repair or replacement of downhole equipment.

ZONE. Stratigraphic interval containing one or more reservoirs.

• • •

Index

F

M

N

O

U

V